Wednesday's Child

MARGARET ARBORE BERG

Wednesday's Child

a tale of love and courage

Muhlenberg Press   Philadelphia

8135.4
B45W

40164
Oct '60

Wednesday's child is full of woe,
Thursday's child has far to go.

From an old nursery rhyme

DEDICATION

For the thousands and thousands of fathers and mothers whose hearts are in bondage to a brain-damaged child this little book has been especially written. It is a dipping of colors in greeting; it is a cracking of cannon in salute. I greet you because I know your grief. I salute you because I know your courage. I know your patience and ingenuity and have felt a need of them. I know your philosophy and have been sustained by it.

Yours is an army which is serving with honor. I am proud to belong to it too.

M. A. B.

Before All

I'd like to give you this about Mama and Rose so you'll see how it was. Yet, if you did not have a sister like mine, will you know how pain and joy can be so closely woven that the finished texture looks much like joy? And if the mother you had was not like the mother we had, can you be kind in judgment of ours? And if you would do less and more where she did more and less, is it that you have never been scraped by a grief that was like her grief? Though it was Rose who was at the center of it all. I think you must know Mama first to see how it was with us.

She wasn't a person to draw crisply in black and white with India ink and a fine steel pen, though you might say "And why not?" She was precise, of course, our mama, and permitted no witting mistake in her own living and thinking. For that you might want to put ink onto Bristol board, but if you do not draw you would never know that ink can be bladed out or whited over. Our mama was never like that. Mama was a subject for water color, in ripe plum-and-

1

apple hues, grading from deep to dainty and from blaze to bleach, with all the values there but the lines, just the lines, not sharp.

If you don't know water colors as Mama did, or as we who watched her knew them, you might think this a sort of splash-and-splotch art, with cribby-crabby shading to grub out your mistakes and give yourself another chance, but there too you would be wrong because with water color, once the color is there, it's there. Mistaken or not, it's all there. Look . . . can you picture a little how Mama was, and how she'd fool you with her gentleness so that you'd never guess the thrust that lay beneath? Or how sometimes anyone could see the clear-colored purpose of her reasons and rulings, only to watch them blend softly out into nothingness?

It wasn't a thing she'd been given by nature. Mama by herself loved perfection. Rose loved it, too. She wanted rules and rightness, pattern, plan, and program; but in Rose's life there could be little that was perfect, complete, and whole. It was this that had so qualified Mama that you might say first with your knowing part, "Mama did thus or thus or this way," and then your feeling part would always add, "Or rather, it was Mama and Rose."

Living a little for another one—that is the way we have always lived whose homes are the homes of star-crossed children. We live first a life for ourselves and then half-again a span for that frailer one. We live in a charged atmosphere. Just there we stand where the flaming nebulae wheel and whirl, where meteors leap and galaxies of other worlds flash past. We do our one small pirouette, but we cannot see the cosmic ballet. We feel only the aching toe.

2

Ours is a different rhythm. We long for wholeness as the broken do, yet as the broken do we see only in part. We suffer in such little ways, and in little ways we find our solace. Our earth rocks; knowledge burns brightly out of the bodies of the crushed. We weep for the fallen sparrow. We are comforted by Grandma's jelly bread.

We are a curious blend, and you cannot know us truly unless you would weigh us two and two. Mama's life pivoted not on the true center of joy but on the off-center of pain, and the course it followed was not always the well-ordered one her thought decreed.

No, I cannot put Mama alone on paper. Mama who loved perfection—I cannot trace her removed from Rose, or even removed from the rest of us.

Long Ago at Our House

The minute the wall telephone rang I felt in my bones what it was—and my heart thudded under my gingham apron. Mrs. Klemmerer telling on Harold. About the slop pail in Opal Tenn's yard and the sunflower stalk and Mary Margaret's flag dress. Was it the sort of thing they could put you in reform school for?

I stopped feeding Jud his Egg-O-See and closed the Dowagiac Dream Book that I'd been looking at on the high-chair tray, and though I was past seven years and old as old, I waited, sick and scared. Once Harold did a mustache on Martin Luther and I got Mama's art gum and erased it quick so he wouldn't go to hell, but I couldn't do a thing about Mary Margaret's flag dress or what was coming over that telephone.

Mama stopped singing. Her cake-making song was "Here I raise mine Ebenezer," the way "Jesus, Saviour, pilot me" went with pushing the Bissell. Carefully she laid down her batter spoon and the pan of melted chocolate she was getting ready to pour into a big bowl for devil's food. She glanced expectantly toward the telephone.

"All right! All right! I'm coming!" Mama called out. Then she smoothed her bungalow apron and patted her brown hair as though company were at our door.

"Fred Hanneman's residence. Mrs. Hanneman speaking," Mama sang into the transmitter. Her voice waited, and behind their gold-rimmed glasses her blue eyes smiled.

Oh, Mama! Poor Mama! I thought. To have to stand there and listen while Mrs. Klemmerer shrieks and shouts about Monica and Veronica and Mary Margaret, and Harold chasing them with a sunflower stalk! And about the slop pail in Opal Tenn's yard, when all Mama wants in the world is to have children that everybody likes and admires! Poor, poor Mama!

Jud opened his mouth like a little wren, and I popped in three spoonfuls of Egg-O-See in a row and then stopped to listen. Mama's voice was shocked.

"No. No. Oh, no! But that's very dreadful," said Mama, her pointed patent-leather shoe beating a tattoo on the gray painted floor. "You know that I don't want my children doing things like that, and I do thank you for telling me."

A big bluebottle fly settled on the Tanglefoot on the woodbox top, and I watched him lift his legs one after one in a helpless march. He zizzed horribly then and was still. I spooned some more cereal into Jud and gave him a *Schluck* of milk, and all of a sudden Mama's voice was different and she was talking about how nice our new peas were, and now she was saying that Klemmerers must have some and she would send a panful over by the children. That was Mama always, being nice even to the awful people like Mary Margaret's mother. Our good new peas! I stopped feeding Jud entirely and tried to figure it out.

Mama came back to the work table then with her mouth in a straight line. She was so angry that even her apron crackled, but her voice was still all flutes and fiddle strings.

"What next!" Mama sighed, picking up the chocolate that had got too thick to pour and taking it back to the range in the summer kitchen. "Mrs. Klemmerer, and Mary Margaret's flag dress getting dirty in all this heat, and two cakes to finish and ice for the Aid Society before your father gets home! If you youngsters must play with the Dompatrick Street children, why can't you manage to behave?" asked Mama, starting to scold me, since Harold wasn't handy. "Just you wait until Mister Harold comes in looking for some jelly bread," Mama said, and she gave the chocolate a good stir and the little blue pan a thump. "Just you wait!"

"Mama," I said, watching her go back to the table and pour out the chocolate in a thick, dark stream, "don't send Harold to reform school. He didn't do it to be bad. I know he didn't." I left Jud sitting there with his cereal and went and stood next to her and slid my head under her arm almost on a line with the devil's food bowl. The batter was a beautiful yellow, streaked with brown where the chocolate hadn't mixed yet.

"He wasn't bad, Mama," I said. "It was about Rose again."

Mama pushed me aside, but it was a gentle push. She stopped stirring batter and looked off across the room

6

toward the coal company calendar shining against the pink Alabastined wall. It was a beautiful calendar this year, embossed and covered with sparkle stuff, with doves carrying a scroll that said "1913" and this verse:

> On the balmy winds of morning
> Comes the sound of Easter bells.

Mama looked but didn't seem to see.

"Yes?" Mama said. "Yes, Ivy?"

"Well, we were out by the back fence, just minding our business and squashing potato bugs with a Fourth-of-July cap stick, and the Klemmerers and Opal Tenn came over to buy some pieplant from Grandma." I rushed on, looking out the door to be sure that Rose, tied into her gocart, was still sitting under the catalpa tree. I needn't have worried. She looked busy and happy. With both hands Rose gripped the toy broom Papa had gotten for her from the blind broom man. She leaned far forward against the muslin binder that held her and swept the ground in wild, broken circles. Rose's head bobbled and her feet thrashed. It wasn't right, but it was the way she was. I turned back to Mama.

"Grandma went in to get her big knife," I said, "and we all sat on the pump platform, and Mary Margaret had her very best flag dress on just to play in because they went to the program yesterday and it wasn't dirty enough to wash. I showed the kids where I dropped the lighted punk on my toe when Harold and I were making a sizz out of the no-good firecrackers, and so Opal Tenn started to show everybody her gumboil. Of course I knew that Rose would want to see too. It was all swole up and just *horrible*, Mama, and

7

I said I'd get Rose, and do you know what those kids did, Mary Margaret and Monica and Veronica, and Opal Tenn too? They touched their foreheads and laughed."

"There, you see," Mama said. "It would be far better to leave her in the house when other children come."

"Harold couldn't stand it, Mama," I said, "and do you know what he did? Harold pulled up a sunflower stalk and chased them and hit them over the head just as hard as he could and got their hair all dirty, and they yelled and ran, and he followed, and it served them good and right, Mama. For doing that about Rose. Rose is my own twin sister and she isn't dumb. They make me mad when they say she is, and they make Harold mad too, and he chased them. Then they all jumped the fence into Opal Tenn's yard, and Opal Tenn's Aunt Eeny had just set the slop pail out . . ."

"Set it out?" gasped Mama.

"Oh, for just a minute, Mama. She came out the door, and Mrs. Noteboom called her over because the coffee lady had just been and she had a new prenium . . ."

"Premium," Mama said.

"Premium," I said. "A hand-painted plate with 'Give us this day our daily' and then a picture of a loaf of bread under it. And Eeny went over and . . ."

"We don't call big people by their first names."

"I mean Opal Tenn's Aunt Eeny went over, and she said they were saving for the button-and-bell pattern sugar and creamer, and she didn't notice she'd left the slop pail standing next to the wash-bench, and Harold kept yelling, 'Here's old Teddy at San Juan Hill!' and the kids came running just as fast as they could and they all tripped over it and . . ."

8

"I think I get the general idea, Ivy," Mama said quietly. Then she yipped, "Look out for Jud!"

"Don't you want to hear about the three buttons coming off of Opal Tenn's sprigged mull guimpe?" I asked, but Mama just said "Jud!" and pointed.

I got back to him as fast as I could, but he had already tipped his dish over his head, and the Egg-O-See was coming down his forehead and into his eyes.

"Oh, you terrible little boy!" I snapped and took the dish away and got a rag and started to clean him up. Jud's hair was in a sort of baby's Buster Brown cut, and his long blond bangs were plastered to his head. I poured a little water from the teakettle and cooled it from the drinking bucket. When I leaned over to wash his face, Jud gave me a big, wet kiss and got Egg-O-See on me too. It took quite a while to make us both clean, but I was glad because I didn't have to look at Mama.

"Obby? Obby? Obby-obby-obby!" Jud said, smiling wetly between his shining cheeks.

Mama was stirring batter again and sifting flour into it with a *kip-kip* sound. Sunshine came in by the west window and sparkled on the paper-covered glasses of currant jelly that Grandma had just made. It poured like a waterfall over the pot of saxifrage swinging in its three chains above the bamboo paper-stand, and a narrow ray of it came from between the starched white curtain and the sash and slanted down to the maple rocker where Peezitch napped and purred. Mama had named him Psyche when we thought we were going to have a girl-cat, but Papa and Harold always called him Peezitch and so I called him Peezitch too.

9

I looked at the little walnut house with the clock in its gable ticking, ticking, on the shelf. Time in our kitchen moved slowly for a little bit, with no sounds but gentle ones, purring, ticking, and sifting, and the funny gurgling noises a baby makes. Fourth of July was over and my toe hurt and now about Harold.

Harold *couldn't* go to reform school! If he did, we all might just as well be dead and buried, Rose and I and Mutzi-Putzi the poodle and even Peezitch, and the clock could go right on ticking on the shelf.

Finally I could say something. "Mama, don't send Harold to reform school," I pleaded. "Give him Hail Columbia or take away his Boy Scout Signal Sender (or, When Wig-Wag Knowledge Paid) or don't let him try the root beer until next week. Only don't send him to reform school. Harold didn't mean to be bad, Mama."

"Didn't mean! Didn't mean! Mrs. O'Leary's cow didn't mean to kick over the lantern either! Oh, such children! I'm almost ashamed to face my . . ."

But just then Harold himself came in the door, slipped across the kitchen like an Indian, tiptoed behind Mama, untied her careful apron bow, and gave her a big bear hug around her neat, round waist.

"'We're going to have hodgepodge for dinner!' quoth Elder Brewster," Harold said.

Mama unpinned his arms and whirled around. "I'll Elder Brewster you in a moment!" Mama said. "The things I have to hear! I have to be ashamed to face my neighbors."

Harold backed off a little and made field glasses with his two hands. He looked hard at Mama through them. "*Gibt's*

Prügel, Mama?" Harold asked in a funny voice, expecting to be spanked.

Mama took a deep breath and began again. "Well! Don't you think you deserve *something*? Quarreling with those Dompatrick Street children. You know I don't want any trouble with the Klemmerers. And on a hot day, with two cakes to make and ice for Aid before your father comes."

"Here I stand. I cannot do otherwise," Harold said. "Mama, they had it coming. Those guineas are all mean, and besides, they're dumb. They're awful dumb. Even their mother is dumb."

"*Har*-uld!" Mama said.

"Well, she is," Harold insisted. "Mama, you know how dumb those Klemmerers are? When Tudyman sent up the Fourth-of-July balloon, Mrs. Klemmerer waved at it and said, 'Bye-bye, pitty sing!' Good nightshirt, Mama, you'd think their think-tank had sprung a leak. Mama, they had it coming."

"Shame on you, Harold," Mama said. "You're a sassy, impertinent boy," and she pointed her mixing spoon at him. "How can I face my neighbors? Now you'll march right into the bedroom and get your catechism and stay there until you've learned every bit of the 'He Says Thus' with the 'What Does This Mean?' March!" Mama said.

Harold looked at her in wonder, and his eyebrows climbed up almost to his hair. Memory work! Why, he could learn whole pages as easily as look at them. He pranced toward the door of the sitting room, holding high a make-believe lance, and the Japanese windbells tinkled as he passed. He crossed the red carpet in two leaps, hurling a pretend-javelin,

11

and the cornflowers in their cut-glass vase danced and jiggled. "Charge, Chester, charge! On, Stanley, on!" bellowed Harold.

One knickerbocker leg was unbuckled and hanging to his ankle, the other was neatly fastened above a bare and terribly dirty leg. Harold's hair stuck up like a bluejay's crest, his elbows were barked and dirty, but from the back he always looked like a small copy of Papa. Dark, wiry, and businesslike, he went into the bedroom to tackle the "What Does This Mean?"

Mama watched him go, and she bit her lower lip. "I'm going to have to take that boy in hand," Mama said.

Then, all of a sudden, her eyes met mine and she started to laugh. A laugh like the ripple of water. A laugh like the chiming of bells. "That dress must have been a sight!" Mama said.

I laughed too and stopped thinking about reform school.

"Oh, it was, Mama! It was the worst worst *worst!*" I gave Jud the rest of his milk, and then all three of us laughed together. Mama's laugh was good to hear, but under it all I knew that the Terrible Pain was there again. I was past seven years and old as old, and so I knew all about that pain. It wasn't anything I could do anything about, but it was there all right, a pain that came back every day for nearly seven years because Rose couldn't walk.

"It's so hard to see her just sitting there, year after year," Mama would grieve. "If only she could walk, like everyone else!"

12

"Now, Louise," Grandma Hanneman would answer, "our Rose will be all right. Rose learns from the *Kinder*."

Mama didn't think so at all, but she never contradicted Papa's mother. How could she when the very roof over our heads was Grandma's?

When Mama and Papa and Harold and the loaf-shaped tin trunk and the mission furniture came back from California after the San Francisco fire, Grandma said they had better move in with her and her fat poodle, Mutzi-Putzi, while they looked for a place to live. Years later they were still looking and still living in the little blue house with hollyhocks on the east wall and tiger lilies in the garden.

Papa wanted to build, but his watchmaker's wages were only so much, and with babies and bills he couldn't think of anything else, so the little blue house kept on being home. Rose and I and Jud were all born there.

Rose and I are twins and Jud is six years younger. We twins were born in a time of flowers and bird song and school-free barefoot children. They named us garden names because it was summer. *Ganz schön*. Rose and Ivy Hanneman. Quite beautiful.

Harold was there first, of course, a big boy four years old; and Papa always told us how our brother had sat on the front step and bellowed his pride to passing strangers, "Man! Lady! We've got two babies!" while Mama lay in her high brass bed, too weak to care. Later she laughed about it, and we laughed too. See, we needed to laugh.

I was the lucky twin, large and healthy as a burdock bush, a Thursday's child by the grace of twenty minutes that followed the midnight hour, but Rose was Wednesday-born, and she inherited the Wednesday's child's full share of woe with her first wispy breath.

After our second year Mama no longer dressed us alike, and when I was already in school plaids Rose wore sheer, white baby frocks. When we were five Harold could still lug her about with him, her tense arms clutching his neck and her legs in their long white stockings hanging over his arm like sticks. With a bit of squinching she fitted into my tiny rocker, a pillow behind her head and a dish towel to tie her in.

Rose could not walk, or even sit well alone, and all during her early years she had no real speech, but with me she did not need it. Is there some secret channel of thought between twins, or did I only divine her wants by knowing what I myself would think? Her likes and dislikes, her wants and want-nots—I felt them as surely as I did my own. And for the rest of it, there was her code: a smile, a yawn, a crow, a sigh; a wild waving of arms; a long, steady, meaningful look, or only an insistent flutter of her tiny, twisting hands. There were "yes" and "no"—nod or shake—oh, you could learn a lot by that! We had days, of course, when Rose lay flushed and panting in Mama's room with its dresser of bird's-eye maple and its *vernis Martin* bed, for little illnesses were big to her, but most of the time she had a strength you wouldn't suspect, and she would shriek with joy at the games that Harold and I invented for her.

Once we plumped her into a clothes-filled wash basket and gave her a wild, bumpy ride over the orchard grass. Mrs. Pulse, our neighbor, saw us and was horrified. She said Rose belonged in bed. She said we should be reported, but

14

Grandma Hanneman just laughed and said, "Iss goot! Rose learns from the *Kinder*."

Mama didn't like us to play so hard with Rose either, but when Grandma was around she didn't say too much about it. The blue house was, after all, Grandma's, and even though Mama had fixed it up with some of her things like prints of "Cupid Asleep" and "Cupid Awake" and the green, marbleized parlor clock, she always felt like a visitor there and showed Grandma the politeness that a visitor would.

The only way we could tell that she was ever mad at Grandma was that she'd make a fancy salad straight out of the *Delineator* or pile her hair some newer way and put on an extra-ruffly shirtwaist. It was her way of saying, "So there, too!"

I always loved those shirtwaists and all of Mama's clothes. They were so special and ladified; not at all like the things the other Henning Street mothers wore. Wrappers until noon! Boudoir caps over kid curlers! You never saw Mama in them.

Nothing about Mama, for that matter, was like the other Henning Street mothers. Where they were fat, Mama was only round. She was tall; they were dumpy. They complained of tiredness after a little cleaning. Mama was up before the sun, working in Grandma's garden, flying like a whirlwind through the little blue house, keeping the tag ends of everything in her mind—the day for Papa's white shirts to go to the Chinese hand laundry, the deviled eggs and scalloped corn for *Missionsfest*, Aunt Lyd's birthday, and the name of the lady in church who wanted three little

15

girls' princess slips, size eight, reserved at the annual sale and supper.

Remembering now, I think there must have been times when she was bone-weary with it all. Think of the not knowing, the crumpled hopes, the endless trying, and all of that work for all of us! Yet, long ago at our house, it seemed that Mama could go on forever.

Mama could clean the henhouse, take off her dusting cap and gloves and walk through the garden, smiling through her glasses like a lady at a lawn party. Mama loved perfection, but with it all, she could still laugh. A good joke? Well, that was a perfect thing too, and in and around the little blue house Mama's laughter rippled and rang.

Everything in Mama's world had to run smoothly. Square corners must be rounded, straight lines made fluid and graceful. We were to put our best foot forward, be kind to animals, scatter sunshine, never say "Sheeny" or "Hunyock," do well in school, and brighten the corner where we were. For Harold and me it was too large an order; for Mama it was the simple and beautiful way to live. Oh, the little daisies embroidered on small petticoats! Oh, the thin, thin sandwiches for *Kaffee Klatsch* and the perfect hang of the parlor curtains!

Can you see then how it hurt Mama to have a child like Rose? A beautiful, sweet, lovable child with a Something Wrong that no one could identify or help? Can you see now why Mama laughed so much? It was her safety valve. She laughed because she had to.

Papa laughed too, but his laughter was of another kind. A happy, bubbling little man with button-black eyes and the

16

narrow look of a fox in a fable, whose happiness could be scored by grief but never cracked. Papa took Rose's trouble as the work of the hand of God, covered up his hurt, and went on fixing watches at Judson Beckwith's Jewelry Store, reading *McClure's Magazine*, and getting his weekly workouts at the Turners' Hall. For Mama there was no such happy road open. Rose must be made whole. Rose must be completely healed if that could be, but most of all, Rose must walk as we did. Mama's daughter? She *must* walk.

It was so long before I realized her tragedy. To me Rose had never been different. She was every child's dream come true—a doll who lived and breathed. I would spend endless time fussing over her—swinging her useless legs as Mama did, trying to awaken them, or brushing her thick, black bob. Harold and I both loved her with the fiercest love, and whenever we fought with other children we fought for Rose. The alley boys used to watch us playing and say, "What's the matter with Rose? Is she a dummy?" and Harold and I would have to paste them. It was almost all we could do for Rose. We *had* to paste them.

Rose wasn't a dummy, though. It was just that her body wouldn't obey her. There was weakness in her lower back and motion that she couldn't control. She couldn't sit up alone or talk at all when we were seven or go to school like the rest of us. For all of that, I know that she knew the name of everything in her limited world; the things of the house, of the chicken yard, and of Grandma's garden. What she couldn't reach to touch, we brought her. Flowers or twigs or angleworms; baby chicks, stones and garden earth, her fingers had handled them and her eyes had seen them. Rose

17

loved to learn and she seldom forgot anything. She even remembered the night Kenneth was born.

Kenneth lived only three days, but Jud, the next baby, was fine. Jud was pretty much a Grandma's boy, Harold and I were as independent as tadpoles, and that gave Mama extra time to spend with Rose. With Rose and for Rose.

The first years Mama went from doctor to doctor, and when they all shook their heads she began trying skunk oil and electric waters. Once a peddler told Mama to bathe Rose's legs in brandy, and once she paid a hermit a silver dollar for a prayer to put under Rose's pillow. You put the prayer there every night for a year and then you brought the hermit another silver dollar, and the person was well. Mama said she'd try anything, and she put the prayer under Rose's pillow every night for a week, but then Grandma put Jud on the bed to change him and he found the prayer and ate it up. Grandma Hanneman gave him some camomile tea, and Mama said, "Oh, pshaw! It's just a superstition, anyhow. God doesn't work that way." She forgot about the hermit then and went back to giving Rose exercises and massage and trying to teach her to walk.

Rose improved in fits and flashes, in dashes and darts; and in between these good times lay the long, discouraging, bad ones when all that Mama or any of us could do was wait, wait, wait. It was during these times of waiting that new things had to be found and different treatments tried. It was during these long waiting periods that Mama dreamed of a wonderful cure—a pill, a potion, or perhaps a person who knew something more, something which might help and hadn't been tried.

18

Nowadays they have clinics and schools for the lucky ones, and physical therapy and speech classes, but Rose was born too soon for that. More than anything in the world, Mama wanted Rose to be like everyone else, but there was no rule to follow in making her so. Long ago at our house, with whatever means might come to hand, Mama had to work it out for herself.

Even today there's no flower-strewn path for those whose destinies are tied to a brain-injured child. It's a cruel road at best, with steep miles outnumbering smooth ones, but here and there today's searcher finds hands not only willing but with the skill to help. For Mama there were no expert hands, no chart or plan or knowledge. She broke her own path through the wilderness and steered by a goal that arched ahead, a rainbow gayer and brighter than any laughter.

A Wonderful Dress for Rose

Late August is always a time of waiting. Jars and glasses in the cellar say that berry time is over. Peas and beans are long since picked and packed, and now they sit companionably on loaded shelves shining under glass. Choke-cherries have been paired with sugar, their sour character all subdued. In Grandma Hanneman's garden summer has budded and blown, but the gifts of fall are not yet ready. Placid squash sits fat with promise, and plums hang thick upon the trees, not yet full enough, not yet sweet enough. August's breath comes hot and slow. August sighs and says, "Soon! Soon! Soon!"

In the little blue house we wait too. School starts in another week, and Mama has been getting our things ready. Harold's last year's Sunday suit, a trifle tighter, a trifle shorter, has been cleaned and pressed to serve for school, and Harold has some new calico blouses and a brand-new suit for Sunday.

I have a dark blue Peter Thompson dress, and my let-out

jumper has a challis guimpe patterned with tiny blue roses. Harold's lace-boots have been at the shoemaker's, and copper tips have been added to the toes. My button shoes are patent leather. With cloth tops. With tassels. Mama plans it all so well!

And then the school supplies. Mama has already studied the lists and has bought us what we need. Writing folios and drawing folios. All You Can Carry tablets. For Harold's paint box a new cake of red; a replaced charcoal gray for mine. Dixon high school pencils. Eberhart Faber erasers. Esterbrook pens. Mama has seen that all are on hand. I have a new Wheeler's *Reader*, and I have written on the flyleaf, "Don't take this bok from your fiend," but this has passed unnoticed.

Harold has not fared so well. He has scratched something across the ends of the pages of his new Tarr and McMurray *Geography*. "In case of fire, throw this in," it says. Mama has been angry about it, and even Harold's punishment has been taken care of. Harold has been made to sit and cut inch-wide strips of material for Grandma's braided rug, and he has spent a closely timed hour at this art.

I have new plaid ribbons for my hair, and both Harold and I own bright wool sweaters which Papa has bought for us at the Canada Store. And so, in 1913, August waits. What more is there to do just now? What more?

Mama knows what more. It is something she has known for long. It is something that is always at the forefront of her mind, but it is something that cries louder each succeeding year as she sees us start back to school leaving Rose behind.

Five, six, seven, the birthdays pass. Each time the Terrible Pain cuts deeper, and in Mama's eyes is a look that says, "August is nearly over and school is about to begin, and two are ready, but what of the third? What of the child with the eager eyes and the asking mind? What of the child who is carried like a doll? What of the child with the twisting limbs?"

But this is 1913. No one answers, and August only waits.

It began like any other noon of the year, that noon of the night of the wonderful dress. Rose was tied into the big rocker with fat pillows all around her. In her lap she held a handful of pictures from magazines and illustrated papers, a half dozen or so in all; much loved and *versudelt*, their edges softly frayed. The Jell-O girl, the Ceresota boy, Maude Adams as Peter Pan, the little Tsarevitch of all the Russias—all children like ourselves, cut out by Aunt 'Melia's careful scissors, the friends of a lonely child.

"I'll put these in your box for you," Harold said, and he laid them nicely away in a yellow Athena underwear box in just the order that Rose liked.

Lunch was almost ready. We were going to have only fried potatoes and some warmed-up meat because it was Saturday, and Grandma was at the stove in the summer kitchen chopping the food fine with a baking powder can. Harold and I set the table. It was hot in the kitchen, and we didn't fight much. Jud sat on the floor, playing with Bocka-Bocka, my broken old doll that had a magnesia bottle for a body. I had to step over him every time I came to the end place where Mama always sat, but Jud didn't mind. He just liked to be where we were, and he liked the noise you could make with Bocka-Bocka. Panting with the heat, Mutzi-Putzi lay spread out like a little white rug in the doorway. Only Mama looked cool and relaxed. In her green voile dress, Mama sat beside the table filling these last few minutes before lunch by crocheting on something pink and small.

We heard a whistle like a bobwhite's from the street and the clicking of the front gate, and then in his shirtsleeves and Panama hat, here was Papa home. He opened the screen door, stepped over Mutzi-Putzi, bent to kiss Jud, straightened to kiss Mama, and when he saw the small pink something he gave a low gasp. "Why, Mama Louise!" Papa said and kissed her another big smack. Then he went over to the rocker, untied Rose, and sat down with her in his lap. "Why, Mama Louise!" Papa said.

"Fred!" Mama scolded in the voice she usually used for Harold. "Fred, you know it isn't. I'm not . . . I mean, this is for Frau Pastor Schwinn." Frau Pastor Schwinn with her graying hair was whisper-whisper, Mama said, and she found out when they two were buying the Sunday meat at Heimbach's Market over on Alice Avenue.

"She had Edith with her," Mama said, "and they had been waiting a long time." Frau Pastor Schwinn, who laced too tight anyway, had been about to faint, Mama said, and so she took her arm and led her outside, and then while Edith was buying the horse-radish and liverwurst and a five-pound roast and, Mama thought, a little Liederkranz, Frau Pastor Schwinn told her that she was whisper-whisper again.

Edith was Pastor Schwinn's oldest girl, and she was 15. They had one boy, Waldemar, who was in Harold's class, and white-banged Anna Marie in mine. Papa always called them Firstly, Secondly, and Thirdly, and now he broke into a big laugh, and Rose looked at him and bubbled with laughter too.

"Fourthly!" Papa roared. "Well, I never knew a preacher to stop at thirdly! Will Fourthly be lastly, do you think?" But Mama just said, "Fred! The children!" and then she told him how Frau Pastor Schwinn was going to a new doctor, and when Papa wanted to know why, Mama said, for a very good reason. Mama said it was because when Thirdly was born Dr. Utecht hadn't got there soon enough, and when he came Thirdly was already there. Frau Pastor Schwinn was lying back among the pillows, and Dr. Utecht took one look and said, "How the mighty are fallen!" Mama said that Frau Pastor Schwinn wasn't going to listen to any how-the-mighty-are-fallen talk from Dr. Utecht or anyone else, and then Grandma Hanneman came in and said the meal was ready, so I plopped Jud into his high chair. Papa put Rose back into her rocker and pulled her close to the table, and after he had washed his hands and Harold and I had said, "Heavenly Father, bless this food," we all sat down to eat.

After a while, Mama said, "Fred, it's a Dr. McRae that Frau Pastor Schwinn goes to. She says he's fine." Papa buttered a piece of bread for Rose and helped Jud to drink his milk, Harold poured about half a bottle of catsup on his fried potatoes, and Grandma said, "Geh' mal!" to Mutzi-Putzi when he came under the table to beg, before Papa

24

answered; and then he said, "When do you want to go?" because he had a soft and gentle spirit, and people's minds wrote their wishes on it without too much asking.

Mama helped Rose hold her cup and guided her spoon hand for her, and then she said, "You aren't working this afternoon, Fred?" and Papa said, "No, this is that fool Ambler's Saturday." So Mama said that she didn't think Noteboom were going any place and that we could probably borrow Mr. Noteboom's Favorite Horse.

And that's the way it happened. Harold wore one of his new school blouses; I put on my Peter Thompson dress although the heat was unbearable; Papa hitched up Mr. Noteboom's Favorite Horse, which happened to be his only one; and with Rose on Mama's lap we drove downtown that very afternoon to see if Dr. McRae could fix Rose so she'd walk like everyone else.

The first place we stopped was Tudyman's, just around the corner on Dompatrick Street. Tudyman had the tinshop there, with his house fastened on the back, and guess what we brought him—a gooseberry pie.

Tudyman's was a wonderful house to go to, although Grandma had her private opinion of the way he kept it. We loved to go there and have him tell us how *die alte* Trudchen, his housekeeper, scolded him for his beer drinking, his pipe smoking, and his almost endless games of skat. Trudchen was a big fat toad who lived under the steps leading into Tudyman's tiny garden, and her opinions somewhat reflected Grandma's own. Grandma's friendship with Tudyman was a squabbling, scornful, sneering, loving, and enduring one that had seen them through at least fifty years.

25

No names hard enough for Tudyman were known to Grandma, but we noticed that hot fresh bread, currant jelly, and rosy Whitney crab apples made a sort of continuous trail between Grandma's trim kitchen and Tudyman's *unmenschlich* one. And so, on a sweltering August Saturday, this juicy gooseberry pie!

Harold carried it in, and I followed him through the woodshed into the dark little kitchen. Harold put the pie down on the table, and now I could see what nettled Grandma. Down went the crimped, brown, beautiful pie on the greeny-gray, cracked oilcloth. There were other things on that table! A loaf of pumpernickel lay open to the air, and beside it butter melted foolishly in an ironstone dish. Here was Tudyman's Tuxedo can, a stiff Sunday collar, a *Police Gazette*, fishhooks, and a cork bob, and all among them the pine shavings from Tudyman's whittling.

From a distance his voice billowed into the room:

> "I'll do the cooking, Honey,
> I'll pay the rent.
> I know I done you wrong!
> 'Member that rainy evening
> When I threw you out . . ."

A wall motto reading "The Book of Deeds—Is Your Name in It?" shivered on the wall. The Dutch shelf where the chunky brown steins sat looked as if it might come down—but I felt lulled and soothed. "I love Tudyman the most in the world," I said, "and Rose loves him too."

There was a tiny, whirring sound, and Frau Schultz, the little green hen canary, fluttered down and picked at the end of the pumpernickel loaf. I put my finger out and Frau Schultz pecked it. She wasn't a bit afraid.

Tudyman came in from the shop, his immense gray head lowering to go through the doorway. He thanked us for the pie, and then he said it was too bad we were just a bit too late to hear the sneezing sunflowers. They had been at it all night, Tudyman said, and naturally neither he nor Frau Schultz had got a wink of sleep. But just ten minutes ago, Tudyman said, he had been playing his zither out on the back step and the music had charmed them into quietness. I ran to the window, wanting to believe, and sure enough, there in the sunshine were the sunflowers nodding in a drowsy row.

"Guess what! We're going to a new doctor!" I said. "To see if he can help Rose."

"Mama thinks maybe he'll fix it so she'll walk," Harold explained.

"Dr. McRae," I said. "Mama thinks he's real real real real good."

Tudyman held out his hand, and Frau Schultz flew up and perched on one knobby fingertip. He watched her awhile and sighed and shook his head.

"Tell your mama we don't always get what we want in this world," he said. "Tell your mama lots of times we have to go on without getting what we want. All of us can't be lucky like little Frau Schultz. Frau Schultz here hasn't got a thing to . . . No. Don't tell your mama any of that. I just now remembered something. Your mama is a woman. It's no use to tell her any of that."

"Frau Schultz is a woman too," I said.

27

"Yah, sure," Tudyman said. "Frau Schultz is a woman, but she doesn't get notions."

I looked out of the window. Under a pink mosquito netting Blucher, Tudyman's horse, was tied beside the house. He came over when he saw me and put his head through the unscreened opening. He was wearing his straw hat, and Tudyman had poked a spray of butter-and-eggs through an ear hole. I scratched his wiggling nose.

"Can we give Blucher some sugar, Tudyman?" I asked, and when Tudyman said yes, Harold and I each fed him a lump. We had almost forgotten Papa and Mama and Rose out in the buggy, but here came Papa's "bobwhite" whistle, and so we hurried out.

Harold and I hurried, that is, but Tudyman came in his own way, his short leg in its ugly built-up shoe dragging across the floor. When he came to the short flight of steps at the front of his shop, he went down like a baby just learning how, two feet to a tread.

Harold and I climbed into the buggy, and Tudyman stood by the hitching post shaped into the head of a little silver horse and visited with Papa and Mama. To say thank you once more for the pie. To tell Rose about the sunflowers. And then, while Harold and Rose and I waved and waved, Papa clucked to Noteboom's Favorite Horse, and we clattered off toward Alice Avenue, downtown, and Dr. McRae who might help Rose.

Harold said, "Hey. Pud Pokorny's cousin's father cut off his thumb splitting kindling, and his mother . . ."

"Pud Pokorny's cousin's father's mother?" Papa asked.

"No," Harold said, "Pud Pokorny's cousin's mother

picked it up and put it in a spoon glass and kep' it until the doctor came."

"*Kept* it, dear," Mama said, without quivering a muscle.

"Kept it," Harold said, although he liked "kep" better because Woody Hecht, the new druggist at Porcher's, always said "kep." "So when the doc saw it, he said, 'We can't use this, Ma'am. You're welcome to save it for a souvenir!' "

"*Har*-uld!" Papa and Mama said it at exactly the same time.

"Well, criminy!" Harold said. "We're not at the table or anything!"

Heat folded around us like a blanket, and Noteboom's Favorite Horse went right on walking. When we got to Five Corners, we tied him to the hitching post; and after Papa carried Rose into the doctor's varnish-bright waiting room, he and Harold left us to pick up a Green Stamp premium from the Our Word Is Our Bond Store. They chose an eight-sided taboret that Grandma would think was *ganz schön* with a Boston fern on it and that Mama would like well enough too. But I didn't go to the Our Word Is Our Bond Store. Mama always liked to have me to go to the doctor's with her and Rose to open doors and carry her pocketbook and, I suppose, as a sort of medical record to show how healthy and strong she wanted Rose to be too.

I was clammy with worry. Two worries—one for Rose and one for Mama. Sometimes the doctors were snippy and sometimes the doctors were grim, but always I was afraid of them and their beards and touched-together fingertips.

Rose didn't fear them, though. For her the doctors were

29

a big adventure and almost the only place she ever went. There were new faces then, new places, and a being-important for a while over the rest of us.

When the doctor examined her I held on to her hand, but it wasn't courage I gave to Rose but something for myself that I looked for and found.

Rose wasn't frightened at all, and after a few minutes none of us were, not Mama or anyone, for Dr. McRae wasn't like any of the other doctors, neither in the way he looked at Rose nor the way he talked nor the way he found red cinnamon sticks for both of us. Dr. McRae was different, and Dr. McRae was kind, but even he, like the others before him, shook his head.

So the answer was no. Not no-absolutely but rather a sort of no-maybe. It was better than the other times. Not much better, but some. A little. Better, anyway. I looked at Mama to see if she was glad, and I saw the light fade from her face as she sat and clasped and unclasped her hands. For her a no-maybe wasn't half good enough.

But then Dr. McRae did a different thing. He took both of Mama's hands in one of his square ones, and he looked her straight in the eye, and this is what he said. I was seven years old then, but I'd never heard anyone talk that way before, and I think I've remembered almost every word.

"You are a person who loves success," Dr. McRae said. "You are so used to succeeding that you cannot bear the thought of failure, but this is one time when you cannot and will not succeed. Not in the way you are thinking of. Take her home, Mother, and do the best you can for her. You have a lovely little girl here, but you cannot make a normal child of her, and I cannot either. Do for her the things which seem sensible to you. Work with her. Pray for her. Teach her what she is ready to learn. You cannot hurry her. A child like this is a closed book. You must open it page by page. Doctors call this Little's disease. I do not call it a disease so much as a challenge."

Mama shook her head, and her eyes said "No!" but Dr. McRae didn't notice.

"Rose will improve slowly," he said. "She may improve a great deal, but whether you accomplish much or little, if you try you will make something of yourself in the process." Then he let go of her hands so that she could dab at her eyes with the tatting-edged handkerchief Aunt 'Melia had made her.

"Oh, if she could somehow walk!" Mama said. "If she could only walk, we'd manage the rest!"

Dr. McRae took a knobby-looking pipe from his desk and filled it with tobacco from a green suède pouch.

"Did you ever hear a jenny wren scolding you from the clothes post?" he asked. "That's the way you sound to the Almighty right now. Walk or not, that's his business. Yours is to go home and help her. Teach her to walk if you can. Teach her to bear it if you can't. I like gingery women and I hate to make them cry, but what I've told you is the truth. In dealing with a child like this, we must learn to see what is left, never what is gone.

"Treat her as much like a normal child as you can, and she will respond as normally as she is able. And remember this. If in the end we fail, we can at least fail with honor."

Mama managed a smile, and as she thanked him her

voice was light, and I couldn't tell what she thought. I couldn't tell in the least.

Rose and I licked our cinnamon sticks; a man with three broken fingers came in and Rose, Mama, and I went out to the row of varnished chairs to wait for Papa and Harold.

Well, it was that fool Ambler's Saturday to work and Papa's Saturday off, but just the same there was one thing more that Papa had to do for Mr. Judson Beckwith before his time was all his own, and that was to wind the courthouse clock.

We put Mama and Rose in the buggy down at Five Corners. Papa got us each a bottle of strawberry pop and gave Noteboom's Favorite Horse a drink of water. Mama had Rose lie down with her head on Mama's lap so that people wouldn't see how very much was wrong, and Harold, Papa, and I went off to the courthouse.

First, up four floors in the elevator, then through a door that Papa unlocked into a stuffy little room. Now on a straight iron ladder, up, up, into the tower. Part of the way we were closed in by walls and part of the way we were out in the open air with just four stone posts around us. Now into a little room again, and here suddenly, large and inside-out, was the clock.

Oh, the hands were longer than any of us! They moved with a jump and a grinding sound. Light came dimly through the dusty glass of the clock face, and blue-gray pigeons gurgled and waddled about and whirred and whizzed through broken panes.

I looked through a hole in the glass near six o'clock. Far below us, wagons were hitched in rows, with here and there an automobile. Ladies walked slowly in the dusty street, their skirts flowing around them like big pink and blue and white mushrooms, and I could see kids down there like tiny, scurrying ants. Far, far out there was the old winding river carrying houseboats and barges and bits of hot August sky. Smoke hung in the distance; a train crossed a bridge, and its smoke ribboned out to join the rest.

Harold went to look into a pigeon's nest, and the mother bird came swooping down to protect her two babies. She dared Harold to hurt them. We listened closely to her bubbling, boiling kind of talk; she went on and on, but the only words we recognized were "Dr. McRae!" "Dr. McRae!"

Papa had inspected and adjusted the clock now and was hard at work winding it, pulling down on the winding-crank at least a hundred times. Then Harold and I both had a try at it. Papa took out his shining gold watch and studied the scurrying second hand. He always had the exact time in his own pocket, and now, far up in the air, he moved the giant hands of the clock so that north, south, east, or west, the whole city could look up and set its time by ours.

When my mind takes out its pictures and I think of the way it was, I see Mama making things pretty. When I see Papa, I see him making things right. It's a thing about Papa I like to remember.

"There!" Papa said, brushing his palms, and Harold added, "We fixed her all right!"

I ran to the break in the clock face and took one last look at the faraway river, and then we all went through the narrow doorway and began our downward way to the street.

My neck itched and prickled with the heat, and the sleeves of my Peter Thompson dress clung damply to my arms, but I wouldn't have missed the tower trip for anything in the world. Back we went to the buggy, to Mama and to Rose.

"The pigeons all said 'Dr. McRae!'" I said, and Rose laughed, but Mama didn't seem to hear.

"He's the strangest man, Fred," Mama was saying. "He almost talks as though tragedy were of no importance at all. Just something you can live with, like . . . well, like red hair or an aversion to cabbage."

"He may be right," Papa said. "Steinmetz is a hunchback, Edison is deaf, Milton was blind, and I, myself . . ."

"But there's nothing wrong with you, Papa," Harold protested.

"Don't interrupt me, son," Papa said. "I was about to remind you that I myself have two left feet."

Mama flashed him that special smile that she never used on the rest of us. "O fudge, Fred!" Mama said. She hugged Rose. "Your Papa's a simp'!" she told her.

Papa headed Noteboom's Favorite Horse toward home. Harold and I began to sing:

> "We're fifty miles from home,
> We're fifty miles from home,
> We walk a mile, we rest awhile,
> We're forty-nine miles from home."

Rose beat time with us. Mama noticed a lady in a pink etamine dress, and she said, "I believe they're wearing sleeves a little fuller." Suddenly, though, her mind slipped

34

away to that far-off thinking place where it used to go, and for quite a few blocks it was as if she was with us but not with us, and because of the Terrible Pain this was an often thing. Then, quite as suddenly, she was back again and spoke to Papa.

"Stop at Mrs. Dween's Dry Goods when you get to Alice Avenue, Fred," she told him. "I want to get a Lady May package."

Mama went into the little shop that was run by Mrs. Dween and Miss Elvy Bonta, and as quickly as she went in she came out again, because she had often looked them all over and knew exactly which Lady May Stamped Embroidery package she wanted: "Child's party frock, Number 217B, sizes four to six."

Well, that's how it was that Mama sat up late that Saturday night doing cross-stitch on a wonderful dress for Rose. It was of soft green linen with little boys and girls and windmills and tulips in colors to be worked all across the yoke.

Remember that I was seven too and that I had never had a dress like that. Never. But do you think I yammered? Look, now. Long ago at our house, kids didn't have to ask about every little thing. I knew well enough that Rose hadn't climbed the tower or heard the pigeons or even seen Tudyman's sneezing sunflowers, and I thought then that was why she got the dress.

It wasn't until much later that I really understood. The dress was Mama's way of saying that if they failed they would do it with honor together, Mama and Rose and the wonderful dress.

The Fair

———

"But Mama," I said for the twentieth time, "I want to wear my new shoes. Why can't I wear my new shoes?" And Mama said, "Do have sense, Ivy. You'll wear your old shoes."

Then she gave the cover of the straw telescope with our lunch in it a whack that said in its own way, "And another one for you if you don't stop pesticating."

"All that walking in the dust," Mama said, "and you and Harold always having to slosh through every last one of the cattle and swine barns. Your papa isn't made of shoe money. If you don't stop plaguing me you can't go at all."

"But Mama, I have to go!" I said. "Because Feather Tibble a girl-in-my-room-in-school's mother's London Pride quilt is there and I promised Feather Tibble that I'd go to see her mother's London Pride quilt, and she got a bird whistle too."

"Heather Thibeau," Mama said calmly. "Don't make that child's name any odder than it is. Now run and tell Rose goodbye like a good sister."

I swallowed something that was hurting me worse than having to wear my old shoes, and dashed into the sitting room where Grandma was making a cat's cradle for Rose. Rose couldn't pick up the strands right, but she always would try, and Grandma would say, "Some day, Rosie, we do it good!"

"Goodbye, Grandma and Jud," I said, "and goodbye, Rose. We'll bring you lots of samples and a bird whistle like Feather Tibble got and a teeny little can of molasses and a fan from the Up-to-Date-Home booth, and Harold and I will both tell you about the horses . . ." I tumbled it all out fast because I ached over Rose having to stay home.

Mama came into the sitting room then, and by the little mirror in the oak secretary she tied on the pale blue hair bandeau that she always wore with her picnic middy and white duck skirt. Then I stood and watched her rub her shammy over her face, and I was scared at what I knew I was going to do. I was scared but I had to do it. Sometimes there are things that you can step around, and sometimes there are things that you have to plow right through. This was a plow-through thing. I had to do it or never be happy again. Quick! While Mama tied the bandeau and pasted a tiny court-plaster beauty spot high on her cheek.

"Mama," my voice came out of my flannel-dry mouth, "why can't she go too? Rose?"

Mama's lips made a straight line and she got the look on her face that said, "Now you've said too much. You've said one thing too much!"

I had seen this look on Mama's face before when neighbor ladies like Opal Tenn's Aunt Eeny told Mama things they thought she should know about Rose. I hated them when they made her look like that, and I never meant to do it myself. Only now I had. I felt hot under my braids. I couldn't look anywhere. Then I found my voice again.

"Rose," I said, "Grandma and you and Jud are going to have fun too, and I won't forget the bird whistle."

Mama still didn't say a single word, but she kissed them all. Papa came out of the kitchen wearing a white linen cap and carrying the telescope. Harold joined us at the front gate, and away we hurried to catch the Alice Avenue-South Harvey Street car to go to the fair.

You hear people talking about the fair—this fair or that fair and how they have been there and what they have seen, but more likely than not it wasn't THE FAIR. Our fair was THE FAIR, the best and the most of everything gathered together under a September sky. Everything did its utmost there; hogs were their heaviest, seams their finest, and loaves their lightest, until even the air about you seemed to shout "Best!" and "Most!"

Our fair came at you from all sides and found you in a thousand ways. It came through your eyes with silver balloons and flag-bright quilts, with the gleaming metal of farm machinery and the light that glinted from a horse's burnished rump. It found your nose with church-tent coffee and stink of pig and the winey, wonderful smell of cider-making in the sunshine. It found your tongue with red bananas and cotton candy, and it gave your ears a symphony formed of the yelling men, the ebb and flow of merry-go-round music, and the tiny *squee-ee-ee* of many metal bird-whistles.

38

Our fair touched you in the chill of the fish building and in the sweaty press of too many people. It got you and held you and filled you brimful. It filled you with pictures and sounds and memories to hold forever. It gave you the best, our fair did, and it gave you the most, in overflowing, bountiful, lavish abundance. It gave you the best and it gave you the most, and where was Rose the whole living time of it but at home with Grandma?

Rose was at home because once long ago when I'd had her out in the gocart a lady stopped me and said, "Is she just sort of drying up?" Mama found that hard to forget, and she found it even harder to forget the time a man in Dr. Utecht's waiting room looked at Rose and said, "I suppose you get to like them almost as much as you do a regular kid."

Hearing such things was what Mama wanted to spare Rose, and the price for that was staying home. The thing that Mama didn't seem to understand, though, was that inside of her body with its bobbing head and waving arms Rose was just a regular kid who would like to do anything that Harold or I did. And the main thing that Mama didn't understand was that if people were mean to Rose, I'd be right there to make faces and call names back at them.

After I bought the bird whistle, though, I began to feel better. We went in by the main gate and started with Agriculture. It was in front of the Hewitt County booth with the wheat bundles in it that Mama started to laugh.

Papa raised his eyebrows and said, "Was ist los?"

Mama said, "Oh. I forgot to tell you my dream, is all. I dreamed we were all out here last night, Lydia and the

39

Schwinns and Mr. Beckwith and everybody, and instead of tramping around, we rolled. Everyone rolled."

Harold said, "That's a nifty idea."

Papa said, "Rolling! I can imagine Becky!"

I tugged Mama's arm. "Tell some more, Mama. Was my teacher there? Was Mrs. Pulse? How could we see into the booths? Did everybody just sort of roll around?"

"The booths were low," Mama said, "and I was waving a pennant."

"What kind of a pennant, Mama?"

"Just a pennant," Mama said. As we talked, we walked along and looked into the Gower County booth and the Indian Lake booth. There was wheat in them too.

Harold said, "The Ladies' Orchestra is going to play in ten minutes." But Papa thought we'd better not wait.

"I know what Mama Louise wants to do," Papa said. "Mama wants to go to the Women's Building and see how many ribbons she's won. She needs only one more to finish that sofa pillow she's making for the papa to nap on."

And Mama said, "No, Fred, you know I'm not in any hurry. This is mostly for the children anyway."

"Such an unemotional attitude," Papa said, "can only stem from the positive knowledge that she is going to win. Her husband, however, does not have her calm certainty and is therefore curious. He is expecting her to buy him at least a new necktie with that prize money. On to the Women's Building, men! Forward the Light Brigade!"

"Charge, Chester, charge!" yelled Harold, and I finished for him, "On, Stanley, on!"

Mama said, "Honestly, they act like crazy Ikes!"

40

Then Papa bought us all some cotton candy, and passing up everything else we crossed the grounds to the Women's Building. It stood under the morning sun, gleaming white in its new coat of paint, with red salvias blooming along the wall like little lead soldiers. Beside the door an untidy man was shouting, "Go to the polls and vote! Go to the polls and vote!"

"Oh, but I can't," said Mama.

Harold asked, "Mama, are you a suffragette?"

Mama just laughed her silver-bell laugh and didn't answer, but Papa started to sing,

> "I should worry, I should fret,
> I should marry a suffragette."

"You're a crazy Ike too!" Mama said. "You're all of you crazy Ikes."

It was the same way every single year, the way we did the Women's Building. First a quick once-over-all to see who had won what. Then, while Papa and Harold wandered off to Machinery Hall or the Pike, Mama and I would go over it all again, slowly and carefully, and sometimes Mama would make notes of a color, pattern, or style in a five-cent notebook. It seemed as if this year would be the same as the others, but it wasn't.

This year was the most different from anything that had ever happened to us. We finished our cotton candy, wiped the last of the hot sugar taste from our lips and took a quick look around. Sure enough. Mama had won a prize for pyrographic work, and not only a blue first but a purple sweepstakes as well. The hunting dog! The grapes and grape leaves! The Gibson girl head! The Lord's Prayer in a border of lilies! Why on earth *wouldn't* she win?

She got a red on "nightgown yoke" (crochet), another red on "boy's muffler" (wool-knit), and a blue on "spiced peaches." Aunt Lyd won a first on "monkey lace," another on "child's toque" (crochet), and Aunt 'Melia had a blue on "watermelon pickles" and I don't know how many more. Sacques, toques, boudoir caps, camisoles, pickles, novelty bags, and pastries—no matter what they entered, Mama and Aunt 'Melia and Aunt Lyd always won something.

In the hobby booth we found Tudyman's carved doll cradle, and that had won a first too. "Oh, I just love-love-love that little cradle of Tudyman's!" I said. Harold agreed that it was nifty all right and said maybe he could make me one. I thought so too, but I knew he never finished anything like that, and I said so.

Harold said, "Well, I like *you!*" and we were just having this out when who puffed in, in a tan and red sailor dress, but Aunt Lyd with a basket. "I knew I'd find you all in here," Aunt Lyd said, setting the basket down and straightening her Panama.

Then Papa checked the basket and our telescope at the service booth, and we were trying to decide where we'd meet for lunch when into the Women's Building came someone else.

Through the door on the opposite side of the Hall came someone who made us all stop dead as though we were in a witch's spell. He was a boy about nine years old, being pushed in a little wicker wheelchair. He wore a white sailor suit which had once been starched and clean but was now rumpled and mussed. He had white-topped patent leather shoes, and over his Buster Brown haircut sat a little yellow straw hat held under his chin by elastic. Pillows wedged him in, and straps across his chest and around his legs kept him from falling forward. He had eyeglasses, but except for that he was so much like Rose that he could have been her twin. Not Rose's brother but Rose's twin. Rose's true twin!

I grabbed Mama's arm. "Look, Mama, look!" I said. But she didn't need to be told, or Papa either. Both of them were just eating up the little boy with their eyes.

"I've got to know them," Mama said. "Fred, I wonder, would they think it strange . . . ?"

But Papa was already on his way toward the boy and his big, red-faced father and little, gray-haired mother. We saw them talking together for a bit, and my heart raced and I suppose Mama's did too. Then we saw them all looking toward us, and Papa motioned for us to come.

All the grownups shook hands, and Mama and Aunt Lyd reached out theirs to the boy. His name was Ronnie, and his father and mother were Mr. and Mrs. Carman Hartzell of Mhatawan. They came to the fair every year. Mr. Hartzell was in the plumbing business and had a shop in Mhatawan. Mama said she had two children at home besides these two, and Mrs. Hartzell told Mama that she had a married son and a grown daughter and then Ronnie. Mr. Hartzell said there were lots of headaches in the plumbing business, and Papa said that watch-repairing was no bed of roses either.

Mrs. Hartzell said, "Brenda—that's my daughter—works at the Handy Store, but she's home lots and helps me with

43

Ronald. I give her all the credit for Ronald," Mrs. Hartzell said. "You know what she does when she gets home from work, Brenda? She puts on a pair of b-l-o-o-m-you-know's, and then she gets down on the floor and fights with Ronald. She gets him to fight her and it makes him strong. She's a case, Brenda, but I give her the credit."

Harold said, "Ronnie, have you been on the Streets of Venice yet? We always go on the Streets of Venice."

Mr. Hartzell drew a bill out of his pocket and said, "Here, you kids go and take it in. All go. You can check the chair with the ticket taker. Ask him to lift Ronnie."

"Just see he's tied in good after," Mrs. Hartzell reminded.

I looked at Mama and she seemed doubtful, but Mr. Hartzell said, "Oh, let them have fun. They're only young once."

Mama still seemed worried about letting us go alone, but then Aunt Lyd spoke up and said she'd go too and watch the chair and so on.

Mr. Hartzell turned to Papa. "Now, take a South Bend watch, for instance . . ."

Mrs. Hartzell turned to Mama. "They told us that too. The mind of an idiot, one doctor said, but look at him! Knows the name of everything Carman has in the shop. Carman lets him fool around down there, and is he happy! Knows the entire town. If there was a way he could set at a desk, I'd send him to the parochial school. The public wouldn't take him, of course, but those nuns are real good!"

Mama said she couldn't even begin to think about school for Rose yet because she couldn't walk or even talk, but she was teaching her to read at home, using cards and pictures.

44

Mrs. Hartzell said, "Read! Just think!"

Aunt Lyd pushed Ronnie's wheelchair; Harold and I each took hold of one of his hands, and we headed for the Streets of Venice. We went to the Streets of Venice every year, but this year was the most fun we'd ever had. Aunt Lyd kept Ronnie's chair out by the gate, and the man helped Ronnie into the little boat. Harold and I held him up between us, and then the machinery started to grind, and over the waves we went.

From time to time we would round a corner and a little stage would appear out of the dark—the Doge's Palace that Harold always called the Dog's Place, the Rialto, St. Mark's with the pigeons. We had seen them all so often but they were always wonderful, and, with Ronnie, it was like seeing them for the first time all over again.

Then we noticed that in the boat ahead of us there were a dude and a girl, and we smacked the back of our hands real hard to make people think he had kissed her in the dark.

Harold said, "Mama would murdelize us!" and Ronnie laughed and said, "My mama would murdelize me too!" He could talk but you had to listen closely to be sure what he was saying.

We went around twice and wanted to go a third time, but Aunt Lyd protested, "You don't have to spend the whole dollar. Goodness, we have to bring Mr. Hartzell some of the dollar back!"

So we strapped Ronnie into his wheelchair once more and went back toward the Women's Building. Only this time we went through some other buildings on the way. At one booth a man was showing the damage that rats can do.

45

He had big planks to show how a rat gnaws his way even through thick pieces of lumber. And there were rats in cages. One rat was labeled "Rattus-Rattus-Rattus," and another rat was labeled "Rattus-Norvegicus." Harold read the names out loud and Ronnie laughed. That was all Harold needed.

When we got to the door he ran ahead and said to Aunt Lyd, "I'll open the door for you, Rattus-Rattus-Rattus." Aunt Lyd let him and then she answered politely, "Thank you, Rattus-Norvegicus."

Ronnie laughed and jerked and kicked his feet and we were all glad that his papa had put straps on the wheelchair. When we got to the next building and came to the door, Ronnie yelled to Harold, "Open the door, Rattus-Norvegicus!" and Harold and I both raced to do it and yelled back, "I'll do it, Rattus-Rattus-Rattus!"

The fair. THE FAIR. The big State Fair! Never in all the world was it so much fun as with Ronnie. He laughed so hard and enjoyed it so much. Sometimes people stopped and stared at him and his little straw hat tied on over his wheat-colored bangs. Once we heard a man say, "Hey, look at the crippled kid!" Once a couple of ladies came up to Aunt Lyd and whispered loudly behind their hands, "What's the matter with the boy?" But before Aunt Lyd could answer, Ronnie himself said, "They say I got Little's disease." The ladies couldn't get over it, nor Aunt Lyd either.

At the Jell-O booth they gave us each a big Jell-O box with strings to carry them around our necks, and we really began to work to fill them up. Pieces of roofing material, pamphlets saying "Swat That Fly!" or telling how to make a fireless cooker, pamphlets about cattle diseases, pamphlets about fowl brood, pamphlets about roup. Buick pennants, six-inch rulers reading, "Abstinence, a good rule to follow." Cookbooks with testimonials: "So tired I couldn't do my work until I tried Cardui." Blotters scented with cologne, fans with Indian chieftains and fans with flowers, flour caps, tape measures, pin trays, and jumping frogs with rubber binders to make them go. Little cans and bottles and jars—and pamphlets, pamphlets, pamphlets. We took them all for Ronnie and for Rose.

Back at the Women's Building Papa and Mama and Mr. and Mrs. Hartzell were still talking. Mama was telling about the Montessori method.

"We read in *McClure's* about this famous Italian school," Mama said, "and so Mr. Hanneman brought me a copy of the teaching manual as soon as it was available. We've made the buttoning and lacing frames to help train Rose's fingers, and we'll try making some of the other materials later on."

"Now that's a real idea!" Mr. Hartzell said.

"The book even shows blocks for teaching arithmetic," Mama said.

Mrs. Hartzell looked hard into Mama's face and said, "Well, I never heard the like!"

Then Harold said he wanted to go to Machinery Hall, and Mr. Hartzell said, "Let's go!"

Aunt Lyd said she'd go along with them as far as the Bee Building. I offered to stay with Ronnie, and Mama said we'd all meet here at twelve for lunch. When the others had gone I took Ronnie riding through the Women's Building. I showed him all of our things and told him about Rose and Jud and Mutzi-Putzi, and he told me about Mhatawan and the plumbing shop.

Sometimes we'd go back to Mama and Mrs. Hartzell, but they were talking so hard they hardly noticed that we were there. Once I heard Mama say, "Well, I always live five minutes at a time. If you get through that you can live through the next. People say to me, 'Well, how will you ever manage when she's older?' but I try not to think. Five minutes at a time, that's all."

Ronnie wanted a drink then, and I took him to the fountain and got him some water in a little cup his mother had in her bag. I took a drink myself, and it tasted like iron. Then Ronnie tried to imitate a chicken drinking, and I took another *Schluck* and held my head like a chicken too. Ronnie kicked his feet and laughed and laughed. Then he suddenly remembered something. "Rattus-Norvegicus!" Ronnie said. "Rattus-Rattus-Rattus!" I said. We both doubled up laughing.

Back we went giggling to our mothers, but they were talking still. "What bothers me so much," Mrs. Hartzell was saying, "is the toys. Nothing is worn out. Nothing is broken. He gets so many, and my land! we just pass them on to someone else. It's hard."

Mama said, "Well, Jud takes care of that department pretty well at our house. But what I find difficult to bear is the way her shoes are never worn out. When they're outgrown the bottoms are all brand new as though they'd just come from the store. It's things like that that hurt." Mrs. Hartzell nodded. She understood perfectly well about new little old little shoes.

After lunch Aunt Lyd said she wanted to buy a souvenir. When she came back she had a red glass toothpick holder that said "Mother" on it. Mrs. Hartzell said that Ronnie had to lie down and she'd just take him over to the Rest Cottage but Mama said, "Why not out here on the grass? It's so pleasant and cool. And then we can still visit." Mrs. Hartzell thought that was a good idea. She spread out the blanket and pillow from Ronnie's wheelchair while his father held him. Then Mama opened her *Schirm* and set it up to shade the pillows. Mrs. Hartzell said, "I'll get my bumbershoot too," and she opened it and set it next to Mama's. Mr. Hartzell laid Ronnie down on the bed then between the two parasols, and they made a cozy little house for him. Harold and I crawled in and out under the parasols and said, "Hello, Rattus-Norvegicus," and Ronnie would shriek happily, "Goodbye, Rattus-Rattus-Rattus!" It was wonderful fun.

But then here came Mrs. Hartzell, flapping an Indian chieftain fan. "Here now, you hooligans!" Mrs. Hartzell said. "You get out of there now and let him sleep or I'll dust your backsides."

So Harold and I scooted. While Ronnie napped we went with the men to see the stock exhibits. We stopped for a glass of apple cider in front of the horse barns, and here there was a preacher shouting, "Watchman, what of the night? Watchman, what of the night?"

We stopped at the Industrial Building to watch the Chinamel man making plain varnished wood look like quarter-sawed oak or curly maple by swirling and twisting his hands. We went into the Northern Counties Building and saw miniature woods and beaver dams and smelled the fir and cedar trees. Then Mr. Hartzell took us to the Pike and paid for Harold and me to go on almost every ride while he and Papa smoked cigars and talked. "Wilson makes a good President," Mr. Hartzell said. He bought Harold and me each a whip and one for Ronnie and one for Rose. As we turned to leave the Pike he turned to Papa, winked, and said, "How about it, Fred, shall we do a hootchy-kootchy show?"

Harold said, "Mama'd murdelize him!" Papa laughed and said, "I believe Harold has a point."

Well, the evening was when to watch the fireworks, and we all sat on the hill to see the rockets and Roman candles. Ronnie and Harold and I recited Sapolio poems like this:

"This is the Spotter of Spotless Town
Who spotted a spot on the butcher's gown . . ."

Over the fair grounds soft September dusk sank down. Weary little knots of people settled down on grassy hills; shoes came off, and the last remnants of lunches were unpacked and eaten. Babies sagged against their mothers.

Papa and Mr. Hartzell lit cigars. Mrs. Hartzell breathed in appreciatively. "I love the smell of a good cigar!" she said.

"We're planning on hearing Fiske O'Hara sing tomorrow," Mr. Hartzell said.

"He's good," Papa agreed, "but he'll never take the place of Olcott with me."

Stars like tiny pinpricks pierced a plush velvet sky, and beneath them, and outblazing them, the colored balls burst in showers of fiery arrows.

50

"Looka! Oh looka!" Blue flame and gold flame; lightning flash and ember glow; and the wonder of the set pieces, two clasped hands, the flag, the rose. We yelled until we were hoarse, but Mama and Mrs. Hartzell sat quietly and talked.

"Rose has Beef Wine and Iron right along," Mama said, "and, through the winter, Scott's Emulsion."

"Mister thinks King of the Blood is such a good tonic," from Mrs. Hartzell. Peacock-blue comets trailed coppery tails, and a last set piece was lighted. Gasps greeted the showing of "The Spirit of Seventy-Six," and when three bands burst into the anthem, even the smallest knew that it was time to leave.

Harold said, "Ronnie, I'll make you a terribly funny comic valentine." Mama said, "Now keep in touch!" Mrs. Hartzell said, "Ta! Ta!" Papa said, "So long!" Mrs. Hartzell said, "We'll surely write," and then, while Ronnie called, "Goodbye, goodbye," and Harold hollered, "Rattus-Rattus-Rattus, what of the night?" we hurried away to catch the streetcar, with Harold carrying the straw telescope all full of our samples. We couldn't bring Rose any cotton candy, but I guess we had almost everything else.

Harold said, "I've never had so much fun at a fair."

I said, "I've never had so much fun either."

Papa said, "They're fine people."

Mama said, "Hartzell's a real case!"

I skipped ahead and caught hold of Mama's hand. "Mama," I asked, "did you have fun?"

Mama squeezed my fingers. "Darling," she said, "I hope you never have to know how much fun I've had. How much fun I've really had!"

'I Am Lolo'

Death tapped so often at our door that he should not have seemed wholly strange, yet there in the little blue house we thought of him in quite different ways. To Mama his very name was frightening.

I know why, of course. Once with never a word he slipped in and took precisely what he came for, Kenneth, our small pink brother, not yet having a strong living habit. A tap on the pane, a whisk over the threshold, and then, quite soon after, the order to Mr. Vollhaber for the white marble lamb with "The Lord Is My Shepherd" carved under the too-close-together dates.

Quick. Rude. Shocking. It's no wonder that Mama always froze when the cold shape neared, though he worked quickly only once.

Usually it was Rose for whom the ice-blue fingers groped. Rose, who you might think had no real purpose in life, whose highest hopes could never be a rounded happiness but only a smaller-than-expected measure of grief. Rose, whose life seemed to hang by a spider-spun thread but who fought as hard as any tiger against the hand that sought to snap it. Rose, who willed to live for no better reason than the best reason of all—that we needed her.

There was something else. Another hand, bigger and stronger than the hand of bone, fending, feinting, guarding, and warding off, and guiding this greater hand, a mind that said, "Not yet! Not yet! Fall back, eager Death. She has work to do. She is loved. She is needed."

How lucky I was when I was seven! For then I understood as never since about this mighty mind, this mighty hand. They belonged to the white-bearded man named The Lord. He looked like the color enlargement of Grandpa Hanneman that Grandma kept hanging over the sitting-room lounge, and except for the threat of hell which he held over us just as Mama held the spanking slipper we called the Swatter, he was thoughtful and he was kind. I knew that he would be good to a little kid like Rose. Poor Mama was not so lucky as I. She said and she said, but she did not know. She did not know and she could not make herself know; and so, with the tapping of the icy fingers, for her came fear.

This happened once in October when a day was kissed with the warmth of Indian summer and everyone knew that Rose was dying. Everyone except me. I knew that she wasn't, only why, when it was all so plain, didn't the big people know it?

Grandma didn't know it. Mama didn't know it, and when I was in the room with them I didn't know it either. When I was with Grandma and Mama I could see that they were right. Rose made no more of a heap in Mama's big bed than a linden leaf might. The Irish Chain quilt, with the sheet tucked down over it, was neat and straight under her chin, and you scarcely saw a rise beneath it where knees or toes might be. Dry as rattling paper, her breath scraped in and out, yet the quilt lifted and fell only a little. Rose's face looked strange, as strange as this room where shades were drawn and the air was sweet with medicine and brittle with fear.

I teetered at the edge of the bed and looked down at the smoldering eyes of my unhappy little twin, and I felt fury and resentment wash over me because, of course, Mama was right. Death was already in this room.

Away from Mama it was better, though. Away from Mama, and out in the sunshine, I could think about The Lord and Rose. I could think him not letting her die. I could know him not letting her die. I could push the thinking and the knowing through my head, into my blood and into me. I could think it and know it so hard that at last I believed, and when I believed it was easy to go right on believing in spite of knowing how right Mama was.

I was sitting in the rope swing with Jud in my lap, and Harold was high above us in the biggest crab apple tree.

"I don't believe it," I said. "Mama thinks Rose is dying, but she isn't, of course."

"No," Harold said, but his voice wasn't certain. "Of course she isn't. She can't be dying."

"Grandma thinks she's dying," I said.

"How do you know?" Harold asked, throwing down a shriveled crab apple that the bluejays had somehow missed. Peezitch saw it roll and scurried after it, daintily tapping it with one soft paw.

"She walks around the house stiff-legged," I said. "She walks as if she's afraid to have her feet touch the floor. Look. There's Pastor Schwinn. That shows you that Mama and Grandma are scared."

Pastor Schwinn climbed from his buggy and, holding his black book behind him with both hands, walked solemnly up our walk.

"Dr. McRae didn't say she was dying," I said. "He said he'd be back this evening. He wouldn't say he'd be back if you-know."

"No," Harold said, but it sounded gloomy and not much like Harold. Maybe it was because he'd just been sick himself. We'd all been sick, Harold, Jud, Mama, and I, and the Vapo-Cresoline lamp burned for days at our house. Dr. McRae called it *la grippe*. Our noses ran and we ached all over, but finally, one after another, we got well and could take the wool stockings off our throats.

Next it was Rose's turn, and whenever Rose was sick she was the sickest of any of us. Her temperature went up and stayed there. Grandma gave her some sweet spirits of niter, but it didn't help at all. Her eyes stayed hot and bright, and big gray circles crept down over her cheeks. Mama looked at her and swallowed, and even Grandma shook her head. Death waited. He knew how to wait.

In the morning when Mama first called Dr. McRae, everyone began to walk about the house on tiptoe and talk

55

in whispers. It got worse when Mama tried to reach Papa and have him come home. Then, when she couldn't talk to him, the walls of our house seemed to shrink and grow tight.

Mr. Beckwith said Papa'd gone out on a grandfather's-clock job and couldn't be reached by phone. He said he'd have him call as soon as he located him. Then Mama called Aunt Lyd, and Aunt Lyd said she'd be over as soon after the roofing men came as she could.

But Pastor Schwinn was already in the house. "I wonder what *he* thinks about it?" I said. Back of his pince-nez and toothbrush moustache, who could ever tell what Pastor Schwinn was thinking?

Harold didn't answer. He was looking hard at the little blue house and the window of Papa's and Mama's room where Rose was lying on the *vernis Martin* bed.

Harold is scared, too, I thought. *He's enough like big people to be scared.*

Peezitch curled his long tail around my ankles.

"You know there's something going on, don't you, Peezitch, dear?" I asked.

"Rowr!" Peezitch said, and Jud laughed.

"Here's Aunt Lyd now," Harold called down. Her black Ground Grippers came firmly up our walk, and she was holding her hat with both hands.

"Aunt Lyd looks scared, too," I said. Everyone was scared but me. Everyone in our whole world. I tried to think of reasons to tell Harold. There were none.

"She's too young," I thought, but I knew that was wrong. Our brother Kenneth had lived only three days.

"She's too pretty to die." That wasn't an argument. Opal

56

Tenn's pretty little mother had died the year before when Tenns' Toddy was born. Mama was pretty and had her baby and lived. Opal Tenn's pretty little mother had her baby and died. You couldn't make a rule out of that.

From the window of the little blue house came Pastor Schwinn's crisp voice, "The Lord is my light and my salvation . . ." Harold swung down out of the tree, and he looked as if he were going to cry. I had to think of something, quick.

"Harold," I said, "Rose can't die because she's a twin."

"She can too!" Harold sniffed. "I mean she won't, of course, but one twin can die without the other. Look at Little Lily."

Little Lily was Papa's sister. "Lily never lived at all," I said, making up a rule to suit myself, "and that's why her twin Walter could live to grow up, but if she had of lived . . ."

"It doesn't make a bit of difference," Harold said. Reaching his arms to Jud, he lifted him from my lap, and off they went for a horsey-ride all around the garden. A had-to-do-it thing. A so-I-wouldn't-see-him thing.

While they were gone, I sat in the swing and twisted the ropes round and round. Purple asters nodded beside the pump platform and a fat bee tasted and tried them. A sparrow came to drink at the butter crock that Grandma always filled with water for the birds. On the ground behind him an acorn landed with a little *plop!* and he flew away, frightened.

"The sky is falling!" I yelled after him. "A piece of it fell on your tail!"

From the house Pastor Schwinn's voice knifed through the air, cutting the sentences sharp.

"And now shall mine head be lifted up above mine enemies round about me: therefore will I offer in his tabernacle sacrifices of joy; I will sing, yea, I will sing praises unto the Lord."

Harold came back and slid Jud onto my knees. Tears had made two dirty roadways down his cheeks, and there was sadness in the way he lifted his feet. It made my throat hurt.

"Look," I said, "I'm Rose's twin, and if she was dying wouldn't I at least be bleeding some place? Well, I'm not."

"If there was only something we could do!" Harold said, because, like Mama, he was a doer.

"Mrs. Powers says we're supposed to pray for sick people," I said.

Harold sat down on an upturned pail that Mama used for gathering cut flowers. Mutzi-Putzi came to him to get his stomach rubbed, but Harold didn't notice. "Well," he said, "do you know how?"

"Heavenly Father, bless this food."

"Don't be a simp'!" Harold said.

"*Ich bin klein, mein Herz ist rein . . .*"

"That's no good either."

"That's all I know. You say one, Harold."

"I'll climb up here first." Harold climbed back into the Whitney crab apple tree.

"Go ahead then."

"I can say the long prayer," Harold said.

"All right. Say it."

From the branches above Harold's voice floated down.

". . . We give Thee thanks for all Thy goodness and tender mercies, especially for the gift of Thy dear Son, and for the revelation of Thy will and grace; and we beseech Thee so to implant Thy Word in us, that, in good and honest hearts, we may keep it and bring forth fruit by patient continuance in well doing."

I began to swing softly. Down the alley came the rag man's call, "Raigs! Raigs!" His wagon's wheels squeaked, and the horse's hooves clumped gently in the dust.

"Obby?" Jud said.

". . . so to rule and govern Thy Church universal, that it may be preserved in the pure doctrine of Thy saving Word, whereby faith . . ."

From Dompatrick Street came the whine of the scissors sharpener's cart and the ting of his little bell. A door slammed, and there were running feet. The Klemmerers must have had something to be sharpened. I kicked the dirt as I swung, and Peezitch chased the tassels of my shoes. They were old shoes and the tassels were raggy, but I couldn't bear to have Mama cut them off.

"Obby-obby?" Jud said.

I kissed him and smoothed his bangs. Out of the tree Harold's voice drifted down.

". . . especially to the President of the United States, the Governor of this Commonwealth, and to all our Judges and Magistrates; and endue them with grace to rule after Thy good pleasure, to the maintenance of righteousness, and to the hinderance and punishment of wickedness . . ."

Papa came hurrying up the walk and waved at us.

"Papa's home," I said, looking up into the tree.

Harold glared at me and went right on.

"All who are in trouble, want, sickness, anguish of labor, peril of death, or any other adversity, especially those who are suffering for Thy Name and for Thy truth's sake . . ."

Mr. Hafner was working over at Schermerhorns' today, cutting the winter wood. Through the clear air you could hear the chatter of his gasoline engine and the hum of the saw. *Bap-bap-bap-bap shish! Bap-bap-bap-bap shish!* Over and over and over again. *Bap-bap-*

And above me, Harold. "Preserve us from false and pernicious doctrine, from war and bloodshed, from plague and pestilence, from all calamity by fire and water . . ."

A bicycle bell rang, and 'way over on Alice Avenue a streetcar clanged. Somewhere a little kid started to cry, and a woman's voice shouted, "Come here, Annie. I'll lick you right away!" I wondered what Annie had done. Then I wondered about oleander leaves and if you could get poisoned from eating one. I thought about the alley boys, the Pokornys and Lou Tietz, and wondered why they always said "mushmelons" and "mushrat." I thought about a picture that was nailed up in the "Mrs. Jones" of a soldier with a wooden leg looking at a scornful girl in a pink ruffled dress. Under the picture was a rhyme that went,

> O, Nelly Gray! O, Nelly Gray!
> For all your jeering speeches,
> At duty's call I left my leg
> In Badajose's breeches.

I asked Mama once what it meant, and she said, "Oh, that. That's by a poet, Thomas Hood. That's been hanging out there for ages."

I thought about the ways of counting out and how the Klemmerers said, "Ocka bocka stona crocka," but we always said, "Inty minty dibbity figs." Then I remembered how a girl in Harold's room at school taught us "Ink pink penny wink," and Mama said we'd better not let her hear us counting out *that* way if we knew what was good for us. I tried to keep my mind on what Harold was saying, but it was hard to follow.

"Cause also the needful fruits of the earth to prosper, . . . to all lawful occupations . . . all pure arts and useful knowledge . . ."

Up on Mrs. Beikel's roof I could see the chimney sweep. I watched to see if he had his bugle with him and wondered if he would play it.

Harold's voice said, ". . . who liveth and reigneth with Thee and the Holy Ghost, ever One God, world without end, Amen," and then he was back on the ground.

"Was that all about Rose?" I asked.

"Well, no. That was general. That was the General Prayer."

"Rose isn't a general."

"Don't be a nut. Are you guineas always so dumb?" Harold sounded more like Harold.

"How can you remember all that?" I asked. "I don't even know what it means."

"Oh, I know lots more," Harold said. "I know collects, and antiphons, and versicles, and all sorts of stuff. I always read them in the hymnbook when I get tired of listening to Schwinn."

Harold looked toward the house. "She never saw the

61

circus," he said. "She never even saw the Dog and Pony Show. She never saw Buffalo Bill."

"Harold," I said, "you know what? We could have a circus for Rose. We could practice and have it real good and then give a show when she gets well."

"We'll do it," he said, but it showed how scared Harold was that he wasn't the one to think of it first instead of me.

So we went into the barn, Harold carrying Jud, and Mutzi-Putzi and Peezitch tagging after.

Out of the golden medley of the outdoors into the silvery quiet of the barn. Ours wasn't a busy barn; ours was a resting one, a place of cobwebs and shavings and cans half full of paint. There was the smell of old harnesses there and a feeling of peace.

Peezitch found a warm spot for himself and settled down in it with one wide-open yellow eye watching a late and lazy wasp. Mutzi-Putzi spread himself out in the doorway to gnaw on a kohlrabi he'd been saving. Harold found some blocks of wood and an old kettle for Jud to play with.

Jud took them and gave us both a wide grin. "Howda," Jud said. "Howda howda."

Harold looked at all three of them. He seemed far away and not like Harold at all, but suddenly he had an idea. "I could make a cage for Peezitch," he said, "and he could be the only genuine fierce chewed-off-ear tomcat in captivity. I'll put the cage on my express wagon."

"And we'll get Mama to make a little yama-yama suit for Mutzi-Putzi."

"And have him sit on the box as if he's the driver."

"Then we can put Jud in the doll buggy, and he can be

62

the little midget. We'll give him a little drum to play and put one of Papa's old hats on him."

"And a vest."

"And a watch and chain."

"The box Pud Pokorny's gamecock came in is out by the fence," Harold said. "I could make that into a cage. I could do it easy."

Harold went to get the box, and I took a stubbed-off broom and swept a ring clear in the center of the floor. I knew exactly what I wanted to be.

When the ring was clean I galloped around it, singing march music, making horse noises, and waving a sweater behind me for a tail.

On the west side of the barn there was a long crack. Sunshine streamed through it in a wide, bright bar. Tiny dust fairies danced in it along all its length, and it looked like a picture in a lesson leaflet. I galloped toward the shimmering light.

Harold came back with the box and started to saw laths for the cage bars.

"Harold," I said, "I'm going to be the gracious and beautiful Lolo, the bareback toe dancer. This is my horse, Crystal Flake. I ride Crystal Flake 'round and 'round the ring, and then . . ."

"I bonies to be the ringleader," Harold said. "And I'll have my high hat on and use my whip from the fair, and when I crack that old fair whip, believe me, all you animals had better perform!"

"Howda! Howda! Howda!" said Jud, grabbing the bars that Harold had just sawed.

"Here," Harold said. "Those are Harold's. These ones are Jud's."

"And now Crystal Flake is galloping galloping galloping . . ." I had an idea. I took the ribbons off my hair and opened my braids. My hair was all wavy. It fell down over my shoulders like a waterfall, and when Crystal Flake galloped hard, it flowed out behind us. Now I was Lolo. I really was Lolo! Lolo with her spangles! Lolo with her tarlatan skirts! Lolo with her flying hair!

"I stand on tiptoe on my horse's back," I said, "and I dance and wave my hands and bow to the people. They all clap and wave back, and Crystal Flake gallops harder and harder and faster and faster. And at this end of the ring there's a hoop of fire." I pointed toward the bar of light.

Harold stopped working and watched me. Surely this was a different Harold today, or he wouldn't have stood for any of it. Anna Marie and I often played this way, but when Harold and I were together the rules and the ideas were his. Today, though, he was sitting on the gamecock's box and watching me, the saw held loosely in his hand.

"Crystal Flake gallops under the fiery hoop," I said, "but I jump straight through. Lolo, the gracious and beautiful Lolo, jumps through the hoop and jumps through the fire."

"You're gonna go to hell for that." The voice was not accusing. It only stated what it thought was a fact.

From the snowy back of Crystal Flake, Lolo the dancer twirled on her toes and looked at the sawdust ring far beneath her. I looked too, of course. In the doorway was Erma Pulse. Erma was the daughter of our neighbor Mrs. Pulse. She was nearly a grown lady, about fifteen years old, and going to business school. Erma could type "The quick brown fox jumped over the lazy dog," and she liked to talk in a knowing way about Pitman and Gregg, so you can see how it was for me just then. If she had been younger, or if it had been Opal or Veronica, I could have grabbed a stick and chased her or put my hand under my chin and said, "Baa-baa-baa-baa!" But Erma, in her plaid shirtwaist and with a flat bow on her pinned-up braid, was so nearly a lady that I had to watch myself.

"I don't know what you're talking about," I said.

"You're going straight to hell," Erma repeated, staring hard down her narrow nose.

"See anything green?" Harold said, but Erma didn't pay any attention to that. She went right on, "You're going straight to hell, Miss Ivy Hanneman, careening around here like a wild Indian, and your own twin sister about to die. Ma was in there this morning, and she said it'd be a real blessing . . ."

"I don't care what your mother said," I told her. "Rose is not going to die."

"And you can't make her, or your mother either," Harold said, "so shinny on your own side."

"I'm Lolo, the gracious and beautiful bareback dancer," I said, "and this is my horse, Crystal Flake. We're going to be in a circus for Rose when she gets well because she's never even seen the Dog and Pony Show. This is the way Crystal Flake goes galloping galloping galloping around the ring! Then when she gets to the fiery hoop, what does Crystal Flake do but run right under it, and Lolo jumps through the fire and lands on the horse's back again on the

65

other side. I jump right through the fire, and I'm not the least bit afraid. Then round and round we go . . ." Off I galloped. It was as though Erma wasn't there, I was Lolo. I *was* Lolo! I was Lolo, and I wasn't a bit afraid.

"Well!" Erma said. "I never seen such a wild Indian! You're going through the fire, all right. You're going straight to hell. Straight-gate-snate-bait-wait-straight to hell!" And off she flounced.

"Think you're cute with a pimple on your snoot!" Harold yelled. "Rose is not going to die and Ivy is not going to hell. Hell-gell-smell-bell-yell! You and your Pioneer Business School!"

Then he picked up Jud, and we both did some stunts with him. "He'll be the little acrobat boy," I said. And Harold said, "Rubber-limbed Robert! Rubber-limbed Robert who can turn himself inside out."

Rubber-limbed Robert! It was the best idea of all. We laughed and laughed.

"We'll make signs!" I said. "Maybe Mama'll let us use some of her good drawing paper."

"We'll ask the other kids too, but first we'll have a show just for Rose. She'll laugh at Rubber-limbed Robert."

Harold was Harold again. About then Jud began to get fussy, though, so Harold picked him up and gave him a horsey-ride back to the house.

A strange house. A quiet house. But here came Aunt Lyd, wearing one of Grandma's long blue cross-stitched aprons.

"I was coming out to look for you," Aunt Lyd said.

"Jud wants dry p-a-n-t-s," I spelled, but Harold asked, "How is she?"

66

"Right as rain," Aunt Lyd said. "They're all three sleeping on the big bed, holding hands like paper dolls—your Mama, Papa, and Rose. It was just all that phlegm. Couldn't get it up or down. No wonder she felt sick. A double handful. Just sat there and rattled. I finally put my finger down her throat and made her gag. She coughed it up then, all right. A double handful. I'll take the baby, Harold. Was he a fussy boy, was he then?"

Inside the kitchen, supper was cooking and the table set. Grandma was sitting down grinding the coffee. She finished and emptied the little drawer into the blue coffeepot. Then she pulled me over to the washstand and wet-combed and braided my hair for supper.

"Strudelkopf!" Grandma laughed. "Mop-head!"

Supper was a happy meal, almost like someone's birthday. Aunt Lyd made apple dumplings, and Mama wore her new waist. Tudyman came in to ask about Rose, and Grandma asked him to stay "so the poor fellow will get a decent meal for once," she said. Tudyman threw back his big lion's head and roared, but he stayed.

After supper Mama said that Rose could be on the sitting-room lounge if we'd all be good. Good? Why wouldn't we be, that evening? Right after the dishes were done, we went into the sitting room and Tudyman started to tell us a story. Rose was on the lounge, propped up with pillows, and Papa was feeding her a little dish of sauce. Tudyman held me on his lap. Harold lay on the floor with his feet up on the platform rocker and Peezitch across his stomach.

"Have you heard of the Fiddle Bush?" Tudyman asked.

Then the door opened. From the side porch Mama and

Aunt Lyd came in with Dr. McRae, and all three of them had dancing eyes.

"It's things like this that make you feel humble," Dr. McRae was saying. "You study for seven years and practice for twenty-five, and then a woman with a crooked little finger makes a monkey out of you."

Then he took Rose's temperature and counted her pulse, and Grandma Hanneman came in and said that this would be a good chance to try the dandelion wine and if it was all right with the doctor she'd give the *Kinder* a taste too.

Out came the little cut-glass cups, and even Harold and I had a *Schluck*. Mutzi-Putzi found the Swatter and took it behind the Radiant Home heater to chew it. The clock struck eight, and Dr. McRae hurried off in his Hupmobile to see another patient way out on Henning Street.

Tudyman began his story again. "Have you ever heard of the Fiddle Bush? Now, Peter hadn't either . . ."

I looked around the room. How different it seemed from that morning, and yet it was just the same. The same worn red carpet. The same table and chairs. The very same people, and from the wall above the lounge Grandpa Hanneman's picture looking down on all of us, just the same as always.

The Lady Who Brought
the Boughten Pie

———◆———

"Well, anyway," I said, "she smells good, like men's shaving, and she brought Rose and I both a teeny Turkish rug from her husband's tobacco. I hope she really knows how to teach Rose to walk."

Harold and I were sitting in Tudyman's crowded kitchen, feeding some ground-up meat to Izzy, the robin who stayed too long. We found him in our yard one afternoon, drooping with the November cold. We couldn't figure out if he'd lost his timetable or why he didn't go south with the other birds, but when Mama examined him she found his poor, broken wing. So we put him in a shoe box with a little hay and took him straight to Tudyman to take care of because Peezitch looked at him evilly out of his golden eyes. Tudyman named him Izzy and kept him until the wing healed and then until spring, and he ground up meat for him and let Harold and me feed it to him like worms.

Usually we had to beg a little to get to go to Tudyman's after school, but this time Mama actually sent us so we'd be out of the way when Mrs. Pahousek came. We got only a quick look at her and her pompadour and her shape in its tight-fitting, tailored suit. She gave us each a big smile, I got my rug, and then, whisk! away Harold and I both had to go to Tudyman's so we wouldn't bother Rose.

I felt cold in my neck and excited in my stomach to think of Rose maybe learning to walk and making Mama happy at last, but there was something Mama said about Mrs. Pahousek that I didn't understand, and so I had to ask Harold.

Harold made a face as though he were going to be awfully sick in about half a minute, the way he often did when I asked him something.

"A beard!" Harold said. "What do you mean, a beard? Guineas never have any sense about anything and you seem to have less sense than most. Mrs. Pahousek doesn't have to be barefoot or bearded or Catholic or dead to come to our house and teach Rose how to walk."

"But Mama said she was a saint!" I said.

"Oh, what a prune!" Harold said. "Mama only means that she's good. She means that Mrs. Pahousek is a real good person because she wants to come and help Mama teach Rose how to walk, and she doesn't have to be Catholic or barefoot to do that. Why do girls always have to act as if their think-tank had sprung a leak?"

I dribbled a little more meat in front of Izzy and watched him pick it up. Frau Schultz fluttered down and sat on my hand, but she didn't want any ground meat. Maybe I didn't

70

know whether Mrs. Pahousek was a saint or not, but I was glad she was at our house now, trying to help Mama; and I did know, because of what I'd heard Mama telling Papa the night before, that if the other ladies of St. John's Aid Society had all acted like saints, Mama might never have found out about Mrs. Pahousek and Rose might never have had any special exercises at all. That happened the day before at the annual sale and supper.

Rose and Jud were at home with Grandma as usual. Harold and I and Papa and Mama were all at the church at six o'clock. We left our coats and hats in a chilly pew upstairs and then found places at the long white tables in the basement. Mama wasn't in on the serving part so she could sit with us.

Papa sat down, closed his eyes, and began to mutter under his breath.

"For pity's sake, Fred," Mama whispered, "you don't say grace here. Pastor Schwinn always does that." But Papa said, "I wasn't, Mama Louise. I am quite familiar with the customs of this place. I was only closing my eyes and betting what was going to be on that plate. Veal loaf, mashed potatoes, peas and carrots, chunk pickles, cole slaw, with a choice of chocolate cake or apple pie. Right?"

"It's corn salad, you ninny," Mama laughed, but Papa said, "I was eighty-five per cent right, anyway."

Coffee!

Do you know how coffee always smelled at a church supper? It's sort of like a personality—much more than just

71

something steaming in a pot. And the chunk pickles and the chocolate cake? Do you know the way a church supper always sounded, with the clattering of dishes and silver and the drone and buzz and *abadabadaba* of people talking, and sometimes a baby crying or a big man laughing *huf-huf-huf*? That's the way it always was at St. John's. And another way it was at St. John's is kids running and sliding on the long floor, and boys Harold's age sneaking off to the choir loft for foolishness, and girls hanging around the doll booth and squealing which doll is the prettiest and which one they'd simply die to own.

But another way it always was is for Pastor Schwinn to get up after the supper is over and make a few gentle jokes and then to light a cigar, and after that the men all know that it's all right for them to smoke. Then Mrs. Theodore Mahler, who has been president of the Aid Society for ever and ever, gets up and makes a few remarks.

This time, Mrs. Theodore Mahler's few remarks went like this: first a word of welcome to one and all who had come to this annual sale and supper at this time; then a remark about the Pilgrim Fathers and Mothers who had come to this bare land of ours and made it teem with life and industry, who shot the deer and the wild turkeys in the woods and made overalls to cover their nakedness and built towns and cities and fine churches like St. John's Lutheran. The next remark was what a fine pastor we had in Pastor Schwinn and how lucky we were to have him and his good wife and how we should patronize the wonders of the bazaar which the ladies had toiled to make, where there was something for every purse and a fish pond for the youngsters. All of us, Mrs. Mahler knew, were in for an interesting evening of fun and fellowship. But toward the last Mrs. Theodore Mahler got sort of winded. Her words came faster and faster, and she finally wound up, ". . . and as a church we are blessly riched at this time."

Well, Waldemar Schwinn was sitting next to Harold, and the way those two were, what made one of them snicker made the other laugh even harder. Across the table from us Papa's eyes began to dance, although he didn't laugh out loud, and even our Mama took out her tatting-edged handkerchief and pretended to wipe her nose so that no one would notice that she was laughing too.

Oh, the annual sale and supper! Long ago at St. John's Lutheran, that's the way it always was.

Anna Marie Schwinn and I and the Yaegers helped the ladies clear the tables and then we went around to the booths and bought some divinity fudge. The Yaegers always called it "angel spit," but Anna Marie and I didn't because we had a good, clear idea of what Mama and Frau Pastor Schwinn would do to us if we started any of that "angel spit" talk around them.

Mama went to work in the Baked Goods booth. Do you know how the Baked Goods sale worked? Ladies work all morning making pies and cakes and then in the evening they look at them hard and see who made the best. Then, after they've looked them all over and talked about them a lot, they buy somebody else's pie or cake. This was called "fund-raising," and it brought in lots of money for St. John's and paid for tuning the organ or buying new hymnbooks or the white muslin for making cottas for the choir.

73

Mama always worked hard at fund-raising, not only in the Baked Goods booth, but by stocking up on aprons and embroidered underpants and other things like that, so I knew she would be having a busy evening.

I was having a busy evening too, chasing kids and sliding on the long floor and watching Miss Pauline Page cut out silhouettes of children freehand and watching Mrs. Omar Horton embroider names for ten cents on the autograph quilt, and so I didn't see much of Mama until everything was over and it was time to go home.

Papa and Harold took the big packages and Mama carried one little flat one. "I'll carry this one myself," Mama said. "It might crush."

Well, after we got home again and I'd got into a pair of Dr. Denton's with the feet cut off because I grew so fast, I slipped into my trundle bed beside Rose's crib. I lay awake a long time and listened to Mama and Papa talking. Our little room opened off theirs, and through the open door in the lamplight I could see Papa as he loosened his tie and took off his stiff collar. I couldn't see Mama at all, but I knew that she was sitting by the dresser, brushing and braiding her long, brown hair.

Mama sounded as if she was holding her tortoise-shell comb in her teeth and talking around it, but then she put it down and I could understand her better.

"I should think," she said, "that sometimes God would lose his mind. I should think he'd completely lose his mind when he looks down and sees St. John's Aid Society and the way some of those ladies behave. They warm a pew every single Sunday and get all set up over what they give to Missions, and yet when a stranger comes into the Aid and wants to do what she can to help, they have to cluster together like a bunch of silly schoolgirls and talk about her in hissing whispers behind their hands. That poor woman knew they were talking about her, and I nearly died of embarrassment. I've never seen anything so disgraceful," Mama said. " 'The boughten pie! The boughten pie!' I should think God would lose his mind."

Papa bent over and began slowly to unlace his shoes. "You are several steps ahead of me, Mama Louise," Papa said. "Tell me slower. What really did happen?"

Mama laid the brush down, and you could hear the clink of her rings against the cover of the hair receiver. Then she began rummaging in her little drawer for the Pompeian Massage Cream. "You know how they are," Mama said, "about their pies. Mrs. Oscar Schoeneman and her famous crisscross cranberry, and Mrs. Herman Lothmann and her lemon pie with the three-inch meringue, and Mrs. Roth's blue-ribbon apple with the one extra ingredient in it that she won't disclose even to a relative. Mrs. Diehl's bitter-black chocolate, and all the rest of it. Well, they were standing around, looking at all these creations and each one simply wallowing in glory over what she'd done . . ."

"Did you wallow a little too?" Papa wanted to know.

"Ninny!" Mama laughed. "I never wallow, but if I do say it, my pies can always measure up to any of theirs. Then suddenly this lady came up to the booth with her contribution. She was new in the Aid. I know I've never seen her before. Well, what does she bring in and hand over the counter to Mrs. Roth but a cherry pie in a box from Oehler's

Big White Bakery! I thought Mrs. Roth's eyes would pop out of her head, but at least she did have the grace to thank her. Next minute, though, when they'd opened the box and all had a look, the simpering and whispering began. Mrs. Roth didn't even want to set it up on the shelf with the others, but I marched right over there . . ."

"Like a Valkyrie, with a cry of 'Ho-yo-to-ho!' " said Papa.

"Not exactly," Mama said, "But I did march over there and set it right on the shelf with the rest. Think how that poor soul would feel if she'd walked by and not seen it. Nobody dislikes those leathery things from Oehler's worse than I do, but that woman wanted to help, and I thought the ladies should have taken that pie the way it was meant. Instead, one after another would edge up and whisper, 'Who ever brought a boughten pie?' 'Imagine bringing a boughten pie!' Boughten pie! Boughten pie! I kept thinking about that poor woman, and finally I asked Mrs. Helmuth Holtz to take my place and I went out on the floor and found her sitting off there by herself. Papa, she's a Mrs. Pahousek. She and her husband have the little tailor shop out on Alice Avenue. She works in the shop all day long, pressing and so on. How could a poor soul like that find time to do any baking for the sale? We got to talking, and she's the loveliest person, really. I told her about the children, and she was so interested in Rose. She said she had studied Swedish massage before she was married, and maybe she could show me some things to do that would help Rose. You know Rose hasn't had a cold in weeks. It would be a good time to try something.

"Then do you know what she said? (Harold or Ivy must

76

have been into my Pompeian Cream again. I'm going to have to do something!) She said if I wanted, she'd come at four tomorrow when she leaves the shop and see what she could think of that would help Rose. Just think of it! To want to do something like that for a complete stranger! I was so happy to meet her, Fred. She's a perfect saint, and to think of the shabby way those ladies treated her. 'Boughten pie! Boughten pie!' I get so furious at them sometimes."

"And you look so pretty when you do," Papa said. "She comes tomorrow? That's fine."

Then he dropped his shoe on the floor, and I must have gone to sleep, because I never did hear the other one drop.

Well, the next day was Thursday and it happened the way I said. We went to Tudyman's to play with Izzy and Frau Schultz. Then Tudyman finished soldering the downspout for Tegmeiers' house, and he came into the kitchen and started to make his supper.

The paper boy threw the *Courier* on the side porch, the lamplighter came by on his bike and lighted the gas lamp on the corner, and we decided it was late enough maybe for us to go home and without disturbing Rose.

Rose was in her rocker when we came in. We asked her if the walking exercise was fun, and she showed how very much she had liked Mrs. Pahousek and the lessons.

"What did you learn?" I asked. Rose got very excited and waved her arms, and Harold got her out of the rocker and down on the lounge in the sitting room. She managed to get over on her stomach and tried to lift her head.

"Is that walking?" Harold asked. "It looks more like some kind of circus stunt." But Mama said, "You don't understand, dear. Rose has to learn to lift her head first before we can even begin to think of standing and walking. I had never thought of it before, but it does seem logical. Mrs. Pahousek taught her to try to lift her head and look for a big spider on the wall."

"In your house?" Harold said.

Mama laughed. "You goose, it's just pretend, of course. She has to learn to lift her head that way and when she's on her back. When she can do that, we'll go on to something else. Mrs. Pahousek showed me how to rub her, too, and so we'll have massage and exercise every single day."

Rose was very excited. She caroled and crowed and waved her arms, and several times she made a sound that meant "walk." Then I got out our little dolls and put the new Turkish rugs in the doll house. I liked the rugs to lie kitty-cross, but Rose wasn't happy unless they were straight. I fixed them the way she wanted, and we let the dolls walk on them until supper time.

What was for supper was *Sauerbraten* that Grandma had been fixing all the time Mrs. Pahousek was there. Mama had got the last of the fresh tomatoes up from the cellar and had taken them out of the newspapers, and they were nice and ripe. There were hot poppy-seed rolls right out of the oven; Papa let Harold and Rose and me drink a little tea like the big people. Rose had to have hers in the apple-blossom cup because she'd had it that way before. Everything seemed all right until dessert time.

Then, what of all the strange things in the world did Mama bring in but the boughten pie from St. John's annual sale and supper.

If you don't know what it was like long ago at our house, you can't imagine how strange that pie looked on our table—greasy-shiny and crackly brown on its paper plate, and the edges sort of too brown and too crisp, not like any relation to the beautiful golden pies Grandma and Mama turned out so easily.

Harold and Papa and I all looked at it in wonder, and when Mama started to serve it Papa said, "It's all right, Mama Louise, about expecting us to eat this product, but do we have any real way of knowing when we get through the crust and begin to nibble on the paper plate?"

Harold and Rose and I all thought this was very funny, and even Grandma laughed, but our Mama didn't think it was funny at all. To know why you'll have to remember what was in the very front of Mama's mind. Rose. Always Rose.

If the pie had been made of nightgown flannel Mama would have eaten it that night, and she quickly made it plain that we must too. Mama cut a wedge of pie for every single one of us, and she was very firm about the way she handed the plates around, and she was firm too in what she said.

"This pie," Mama said, "was given by Mrs. Pahousek to the honor and glory of Him who moves in mysterious ways His wonders to perform. I don't want to hear another silly word out of any of you."

Under his breath Harold said, "We are blessly riched

at this time," but it was a lucky thing for him that right then Mama was busy with both Rose and Jud so she didn't hear.

"Mama Louise," Papa said, "I'll bet you were a perfect terror to your pupils when you taught fifth grade."

But even Papa cleaned up his plate; and long ago at our house the boughten pie from Oehler's Big White Bakery was never mentioned again.

'The Cattle are Lowing'

It wasn't that Grandma Hanneman needed a cuckoo clock. She had her walnut house clock in the kitchen and an alarm clock with a fat bell on top standing on the spraddle-legged table beside her bed. Mama's pillared parlor clock sat on the sectional bookcase in that room. But these weren't cuckoo clocks.

If you are German, you will understand right away why Grandma wanted one, and if you are not German, what use is there for me to explain? Grandma wanted a genuine Black Forest cuckoo clock. Papa loved Grandma and he also loved clocks. This year things had gone well for us, and so he had Judson Beckwith order one for her.

It came in a wooden box the day before Christmas, and at noon, because Papa couldn't wait any longer, the clock was hung on the sitting-room wall, across from the picture of Grandpa Hanneman and between the sepia print of "The Horse Fair" and the milk-glass plate with a scarlet ribbon running through its lacy border.

Papa checked to see that it hung level; he pulled the chains with the heavy pine cones on them to wind it; the hour came, and then the half-hour, and we saw that it wasn't only a cuckoo clock but a cuckoo-and-quail clock, with the birds taking turns calling "Cuckoo!" and "Bob-white!"

Grandma Hanneman dabbed at her eyes with a blue-checked apron corner and said, "Ach, Fred!" Rose squealed, and Jud said, "My clock!" and so in a wonderful way that year Christmas came to the little blue house.

Mama cut circles of cardboard and dripped a blob of wax on each of them to hold the window candles; Harold and I strung the tree chains, and I slipped off to our little bedroom for the thirty-eighth time to wrap Papa's calendar and, most wonderful of all, the Pritchard that Rose and I had made for Mama. Harold sneered at it and said, "There isn't any such thing. You can't give Mama a Pritchard because there aren't any Pritchards!" But I knew better.

I knew Mama, and I knew that when she saw this Pritchard, and we told her what it was, she'd say, "Why, girls, it's just what I wanted!" and she'd hang it on the arm of her bird's-eye maple dresser.

You may want to know how a Pritchard is made. Ours didn't have a "how." It just grew. We didn't have any money, and I didn't know how to make anything for mothers except horse reins and hairpin holders and we had already given her several of those.

This year we were seven, and we wanted to make something special like the yellow and blue and pink things on the "Handwork Makes the Gift" pages in the ladies' magazines.

I asked Mama if Rose and I could borrow the piece bag and the millinery box, and Mama said, "Go ahead, dear, only don't use the beaded butterfly or any of the Cluny lace."

What could we make? Corset covers and nightgown cases took bigger pieces of goods than we would have, and our mama never wore boudoir caps. We had to make up something.

So with Rose's help I did. Rose helped by holding scissors and trying to keep her unsteady fingers on bowknots while I tied them. Cardboard from a Cream of Wheat box came first, rolled into a short tube and tied with string. Over that went cotton batting to pad it nicely, Alice-blue satin left from a hat to cover that, and ecru fringe to edge it. Now a spray of lily of the valley tacked to one side, a bow of black illusion on the other. "Here's a bare spot, Rose." Four gold sequins filled it, tacked in place with purple silk. Rose showed that it needed something to hang it up by. Blue baby ribbon then, tacked to the tube in four places; a long silk tassel below, and where the ribbons met on top, another little puff of illusion, with a pink button to cap it all.

We looked and looked at it. It was done. It was beautiful. It was almost unbelievable. And then here came Harold to ask in a practical way, "What is it?" and I answered with the first thing that came into my mind.

"Well, it's a sort of a Pritchard," I said.

When I showed it to Papa, he was kinder than Harold, but even he had some misgivings and asked, "Will Mama know what it is for?"

83

Mama knew. Our mama did, and, exquisite in its ribbons, the Pritchard swung on the dresser arm for three years or maybe more.

So Christmas came to our house long ago, with the company dishes to be washed and made ready, with pieces to run through again before The Program, with stockings to hang near the Radiant Home heater, and with the Pritchard and the calendar to wrap and tie just one more time.

So, to the ticking of the cuckoo clock and the fluting of its marvelous birds; with the embossed card the Hartzells of Mhatawan sent to say, "Hope Santa will be good to you"; with smells of cardamom and candles and spruce and shellac, Christmas came again.

There was no commandment about fighting, and certainly none about fighting on Christmas. In all the Small Catechism not one; yet to Mama this was an offense surely as bad as coveting your neighbor's ox or his manservant or his maidservant. How could Harold do it?

Somehow, though, he did, and his explanation of what had happened in the Intermediate Department of Sunday school was satisfactory to no one but Harold.

Up in church Mama heard about it from Mrs. Herman Lothmann, whose way of breaking the news to her was, "They're fighting like crazy down there. I think at least one of them is dead."

Frightened and breathless, Mama hurried down the stairs toward the Sunday school rooms and met Harold coming up. And when she saw him she said, "Have you been *fighting*?" although anyone could see the blood and the rips.

Harold had to explain. "A kid as big as a cow picked on me," Harold said, pulling on his striped stocking cap and buttoning up his reefer. "I was just minding my business and this kid had to pick on me, and I slugged him and he smashed me in the moosh."

"But why?" Mama wanted to know, fretted by the awfulness of a fight on Christmas and in the Sunday school at that, although she didn't know, then or ever, that a table was upset and duplex envelopes and a stack of memory cards with "The Office of the Keys" on them had been sent every which way.

"Why on earth did you do it?" Mama kept asking, but Papa tushed her to silence, saying, "Later is soon enough," and the four of us walked home through the winter dusk. Tapioca snow had fallen while we were in church, and it crunched beneath our feet.

Harold went ahead. I walked between Papa and Mama and tried to explain, as I so often did. "Harold wasn't bad," I said. "It was because . . . It was because . . ." It was about what? I knew, all right, but how could I make the big people see? How tell, how show a thing that hadn't been touched but only felt?

The fight didn't happen until after The Program. The Program! The big, important, spine-tingling event of Christmas afternoon. Long ago at our house Christmas came in acts like a well-written play. Christmas Eve was stocking-and-candle time, with Mama doing some last-minute stitch-and-tack flurrying, and all of us going to sleep with ears that strained for sounds of little hooves above us. Christmas morning was the time of the lighted tree, the screaming over new dolls, the trying out of sets, the poring over rules books, the cutting of tabs and slits, the winding of keys, and the long, nonstop gorge. Dinner, the meal we didn't need, was served at two o'clock, and Tudyman and Aunt 'Melia and Aunt Lyd were always there. By three-thirty the new blouse and tie, the shining shoes, the important dress were on and the Colgate's Imperial Lilac had been poured into the new handkerchief. At four o'clock, our offerings tightly held, Harold and I were in our places, beginning the long slow march up the stairs and into the sanctuary of St. John's Lutheran.

The Program lasted while the daylight paled; then somewhere a bulb went on, and light streamed through the Good Shepherd window and turned the dress that Jesus wore the color of cranberry sauce beside the whiteness of his lamb.

On and on The Program went. Between her pink hair ribbons Anna Marie recited "Among Judean Hills" with expression, while I squirmed with embarrassment because she had broken the unwritten code which said that you did it in a flat monotone. Harold's class sang "While Shepherds Watched" and Alfred Picha did "That Mizzable Mouse Et Santy's Cake." The Pichas always did that. The year before Orrin had done it, and for two years before that, Dosia. It was something we always had at St. John's like "Wonderful! Counsellor!" or Luther's Cradle Hymn yelled by the infant class. Then, when we were all drowsy and conscious of sitting too long, the giving of the gifts.

Anna Marie and I sat together, of course, and we had barely ripped the holly paper from our candy boxes when

Harold was beside me in the aisle whispering, "Quick, Ivy, yours and mine!"

I pulled the remaining scraps of paper from the box and handed it unwrapped to him, and my book too. Then I saw his purpose. The Mullers were there again, and the gift committee had forgotten that they would be, for Christmas was the only time they ever came.

One Muller was bigger than the other Muller, but they both had thin, whitish pigtails, long, no-colored dresses, and boys' shoes.

Where were the Mullers the rest of the year? We didn't know, but Harold had seen them just in time and had done something about it while other people were sitting there thinking, "Now who are those odd-looking children?"

Pastor Schwinn had lifted his hand for the Benediction. Then Harold came forward. "Here are two extras, Rev'rund," Harold called, handing our gifts up to him. Harold, who could torture our dolls until our very sawdust ran cold, he could be this way too!

The older Muller got Harold's box and *A Day of Fate.* The younger Muller smiled to receive mine and *Uncle Seth's Bible Stories.* Quickly she opened the box and sat sucking a strip of ribbon candy as a far-off dreamy look gentled her pale eyes. The older Muller didn't open her box at all but clutched it and the book close to her thin chest.

She's saving them, I thought. *She's saving them for somebody at home.* Her mother? A little baby? A sister like Rose?

My heart pounded sickeningly as I thought of what a narrow escape it had been, and I heard Pastor Schwinn finish, "The Lord lift up His countenance upon thee, and give thee peace." He asked all the papas and mamas to remain seated while the boys and girls marched out. And, to the tune of "Joy to the World," we did.

That should have been the end of it, with all of us finding our coats and plush bonnets and stocking caps, and scrambling for our rubbers from the piles in the Sunday school rooms; but it didn't turn out that way. Not this year.

When Harold got down into the Intermediate Department, a crowd of boys was waiting for him. I saw it all. Two of them, Tyler Tepp and Bubber Schoeneman, were pushed forward in his path. Bubber was the one we dreaded. He teased and he teased and there was always enough truth in what he said to make you squirm. Now he came forward with a mincing step.

"Oh, Miss Mullah! Deah Miss Mullah!" Bubber said in a foolish, prissy voice. "May I see you home from ze cantay-tuh this evening? Take my ahm, Miss Mullah deah!" With fingers curling, Bubber sidled past us.

Tyler, a long, thin boy with a head shaped like a Vienna loaf, tweaked the sides of his knickerbockers between fingers and thumbs and curtsied low. "Thank yaw indeed, Hay-rold," he drawled. "I would luh-hike to go with you to ze can-tay-tuh, but I would luh-huv to go with you to ze Elite Ballroom and dance ze turkey trot, Hay-rold deah!"

"Oh, Miss Mullah," Bubber giggled, "I do like ze rag-time! We will dance ze bunny hug to ze old ragtime band, and I will buy you another box of dee-licious candy and maybe a genuine two-cent diamond ring." He extended his arms toward Tyler. "Kiss me, my fool!" Bubber said.

But Harold had had enough. Lowering his head like a bull, he charged straight at them. Head and belly met with a hollow sound, and down all three went, with Harold under. It didn't last long, but kids screamed, and chairs and a little folding table went over, and there were grunts and tearing cloth and a little blood.

I chewed my bonnet strings and couldn't yell or make a sound. In Sunday school! Then I heard running feet, and Mr. Tepp was there, angrily pulling his son out of the heap, and Woody Hecht was tugging at Harold and Bubber.

"Out of here fast, you young apes," Woody said, and because they liked him so much they obeyed. Harold always used to say about him, "That Woody Hecht is a nifty fellow. He bent a dime once. He drives a Velie car."

"Get!" Woody ordered.

While they scrambled to their feet, Millie and Tina Obst came running. Their hands, which always fluttered like sparrows, now darted like frightened ones. Miss Tina's gray feather boa, usually gentle as a baby's powder puff, swung about like an awakened serpent. Maribou quivered on Miss Millie's hat. Their mouths showed shock.

"Why, they're regular little vagabonds!" Miss Millie screamed, but Miss Tina said only the one word, "Dreadful!" After a few gasps they got control of themselves and started to straighten up the chairs and pick up the envelopes and the "Rally Day—We're Going Forward!" banner.

"And that's every bit the way it happened," I told Papa and Mama. "Harold couldn't help it at all."

89

"The defense rests?" Papa asked, and I knew that he at least was satisfied, but Mama was still full of questions.

"Does he *like* that Muller girl?" Mama wanted to know.

"*Like* her!" I said. "He probably hates her. He probably hates her like anything. He just gave her our gifts, that's all." You could tell our mama anything, and if she saw, she saw, but if she did not, how could you make her see? "Please don't give him Hail Columbia," I said. "His nose hurts him real bad already."

"That's not the end she usually operates on," Papa objected, and Mama said, "Why, Fred!" But she laughed at last, and I knew that Harold was safe.

I ran along the piles of snow, hummocky-bummocky up and down until I caught up with him.

"They were glad to get them," I said.

"Dumb old girls!" Harold sneered.

"They were real glad, Harold," I said. "The little one started to eat her candy right away, and I was glad she had it. The big one didn't open hers."

"She was glad to get it, though," Harold said. "She was saving it for somebody. I notice she always does."

We walked awhile, not talking or sliding. Then Harold exploded, "I'd like to murdelize those kids for saying that I go with her," he said. "Dumb old girls! Both of them look like sour milk smells. But I had to do something. Rose can't even walk, and she gets to wear pretty shoes for Christmas. Did you see what those Mullers wear? Did you see the clodhoppers?"

"They had hooks on them," I remembered. "Boys' shoes with hooks. They always wear boys' shoes."

90

"They wore their white stockings," Harold said, and then he gulped and put his arm up over his face. I thought that his nose was hurting worse, but thinking back now and knowing the path he later chose, I know that it wasn't his nose at all. What was hurting Harold was differences, and his tears were from knowing that there were in our world many things that would never weigh the same.

Mama gave Harold a witch hazel rag for his face, and after supper he felt better. He and Papa sat on the floor and began fooling with the insides of a wind-up train. Tudyman held Rose on his lap; Jud lay asleep in Grandma's. Mama's lap didn't have anybody, so I got up there and began to think about the Inchies. I pointed over to the tree and said, "Inchies, Rose." I didn't know if Rose could do Inchies by herself, but she smiled back, so I guessed she was trying to do them.

Inchies were the people, no bigger than your thumb, who lived in our Christmas tree. They ate *Lebkuchen* and cinnamon sticks, and little Inchies hated horehound.

Inchie babies curled in the walnut baskets that Papa had carved and Harold had gilded; Inchie kids slid down the popcorn strings. An Inchie woodman felled tiny great-oaks with the tiny George Washington hatchet. Inchie aunties warned about candle flames. Inchie mamas feared dripping wax.

Brave Inchies rode the sky-blue airship that was shaped like a sweet potato, or soared with the glossy paper cupid in the pink glass balloon. Bird-riding and bell-swinging were

Inchie sports; one brave explorer Inchie who had traveled to the topmost branch had seen the tinsel star.

Deeper and deeper into the Inchie world my eyes bored, and as Mama rocked my head grew heavy. A corset stay made a stiff place under my back, so I moved a little as my mind walked with a little girl Inchie into the beckoning spruce wood beside a blue glass ball.

Step-step-step went the little girl Inchie, farther and farther into the forest. Up she climbed and down she jumped, and (wouldn't you know it, and wasn't it sad?) she was lost. Lost! Lost!

This was the best part of doing Inchies; the scary part where Little Girl Inchie was frightened and lost and alone. Needles pricked my elbows; my neck was cold, and it was black as black in the Christmas tree's heart with never a candle lighted to show the way to poor little, lost little Little Girl Inchie.

And then all at once, through the dark unending forest she saw a light! She saw! She *saw!* In a lumpy golden tear-drop mirrored in a silver bell, a single ray of lamplight gleamed, and out of the darkness and out of the fear Little Girl Inchie went step-step-stepping toward it.

Well, there it was, our Christmas—or rather, it was a part of all Christmas. Change the names a little, let the goose be duck, the Pritchard a marvel in thumb-printed clay. Have an uncle bring the pull-toy, an aunt the tatted yoke. Have my doll a blond in blue. Eat *Julekake* or mince pie under roofs in Michigan or Maine; let the Sunday school

92

be Baptist and the tree a balsam, and you have your long-ago Christmas instead of mine.

Your slice and my slice, they were all part of the whole—a shimmering-sparkling-ringing-singing-red-and-green-melodious something that seeped in with the morning's light, blew in on the frosty air, danced upon eager, snowy feet, warmed us and quickened us and looked down tenderly upon us all. Upon Mary Elizabeth Genevieve Eloise as she lay dreaming her porcelain dreams in her varnished cradle; upon Rose's dangling feet; upon Harold's swollen nose; and upon the little Lord Jesus asleep on the hay.

Your Christmas. Mine.

Tuberoses are Too Sweet to Bear

From towers everywhere the bells rang out. New Year's came and January blew across the world. The air was filled with powder-dry flakes and the smoke from the burning of Christmas trash.

There were the jokes. "Hey, Mama, I'm hungry. I haven't had anything to eat since last year. Hello! I haven't seen you since last year. Mama, Harold hasn't had a bath since last year."

Bellies flopped atop sleds on every hill we knew, and over the surfaces of the ponds the bright blades flashed; but for the few in years, for the short of limb, there was the level, straight-legged ride with up-pointed toe and the long, strong pull by taller folk. Steam rose from the nostrils of heavy-haunched teams as they tugged to pull sleighs heavy with coal. Mittens dried in warming ovens, and grandmothers rubbed tallow into children's shoes.

Neighbor nodded to neighbor now before counters where staples changed hands, and all agreed that the cold had begun to strengthen. Calendars were hung and meticulous entries made in briefly-to-be-kept diaries. Young Mrs. Zaumweber put on an Empire dress. In the little blue house the hand-painted plates that had held our stocking candies were returned to the china cupboard; the shimmering birds and balls from Germany were tucked into their flimsy strawboard boxes and lifted once more to the highest shelf; the last hard *Pfeffernuss* was dunked and eaten.

January—and such as Miss Poznanski and Miss Bennet urged such as Harold and me to buckle down and strive for stars on charts and records.

Grade Twos recited:

> "January brings the snow,
> Makes the toes and fingers glow."

Grade Sixes learned that

> "Every pine and fir and hemlock
> Wore ermine too dear for an earl."

January blew over the world, and in the newness of the year—the looking forward, the beginning again—the screws were tightened, the knife was turned, the brand thrust forward. For Mama the year's opening meant a sharper-than-ever renewal of the Terrible Pain.

Happy New Year! The same to you! Oh, what shall I do for Rose!

If Mr. Omlie's tuberoses had come at any other time, Mama would have been better able to stand them, and she might not have traded the ostrich plume she almost had for a course of health lectures by Herbert Trumpeter, but they did and she did, because it was January and a time for doing rather than enduring.

While he lived, old Mr. Omlie wouldn't have harmed a hair of Mama's head. He liked the way she walked with her shoulders back, and he liked the way she laughed at his thin old jokes.

"I got a admiration for you," Mr. Omlie used to say, enjoying the thick bean soup that Mama brought or the garden flowers she arranged for him with a little bit of asparagus fern to make them artistic.

"Good!" Mr. Omlie used to say, or "Pretty!" and he'd motion her to take a stool beside the Morris chair that held him by day and by night because the rheumatism couldn't hold off long enough to give him a few hours straight in bed like other people.

Sometimes Mama used to have us pick pennyroyal to make tea for Mr. Omlie, and she always sent him our *McClure's Magazine* when Papa was done with it. For all of these things Mr. Omlie had his admiration for Mama, but he never would have thought of showing it by sending to our house the tuberoses that were meant to brighten his grave. Not for anything in or out of this world would Mr. Omlie have done a thing like that.

We guessed who did, of course. Thrifty Mrs. Schermerhorn. You could almost see the way her mind worked. "It's snowing and blowing like fury out there to the cemetery, and with him going into the vault, these flowers won't be seen at all. Why not send them where they'll do some good? That little invalid girl of Fred's can enjoy them. They'll cheer her up!" Thrifty Mrs. Schermerhorn!

And so, not a half-hour after Mama returned from the service at the Methodist Church, here was a pull at our front bell and Mama's heels going to answer it, *tappety-clickety* down the narrow hall. And this was a part of her pain, the eager way she'd go to answer the phone or the door or to peer into our mailbox. Always seeking, searching, hoping. It was a wistful little way she had. Hope. Now maybe? Run! She wasn't prepared to see the hearse before the gate and Mr. Kile, the undertaker, on our front step.

"Flowers," Mr. Kile was saying. "Flowers for the little sick girl, Ma'am."

And what was Mama making herself thank him for but a bouquet of tuberoses. Flowers that filled the air with an overpowering sweetness. Flowers smelling of death. Flowers from beside an old man's coffin, in our front hall and meant for Rose, who was resting now after three painful days of swollen glands.

Can you see how Mama couldn't stand it, and how she crumpled onto the next-to-the-bottom step right there in the hallway and cried and cried?

We so seldom saw her that way that I was frightened. I ran and got Grandma.

"*Was ist los?*" Grandma wanted to know. Mama pointed to the bouquet, still wrapped in stiff brown paper.

"They sent these!" Mama said, wiping tears with the heel of her hand like a child who's too miserable to find a hand-kerchief. "They sent them for Rose!" and she began to cry again.

"Well, out with them," said Grandma, who was practical about almost anything. "Into the ash barrel!"

"Oh, but we can't!" Mama wailed. "They're expensive. They meant well. What will Mr. Omlie think?"

"That one is dead now and has other things on his mind," Grandma said; and she took the bouquet and walked briskly to the summer kitchen with it.

"Calf of Moses!" Grandma said.

Mama dried her eyes and came back into the kitchen; and then, because she was so very sad, she was suddenly very gay. Her voice was quick and brittle, and her laughter was a laughter of the lips and not of the eyes. Then, with New Year and the tuberoses hurting her so much, she got out the ironing things. As she set up the board she began to sing,

> "If a hen should lay an orange,
> What would all the chickens say?
> 'Look at the orange Mama laid!' "

I wondered if Mr. Omlie knew where the tuberoses were, now that he was just a soul and no longer smelled of Omega Oil, and if he floated around heaven and understood. Poor Mr. Omlie! Poor Mama!

The storm had blown all day, and now at four o'clock the snow still whirled outside. Shining frost ferns decorated our windows; there was a roaring at the keyholes; house boards snapped with the cold. Rubbers were piled up on an old braided rug beside the door, and chunks of maple wood dried in the oven. I liked the look and feel of our kitchen on such a day, but I liked even better the clean, frozen washing smell from the grotesquely bent union suits thawing over a little line.

Grandma took down her eyeglasses from the wall pocket

that said, "Where's my specs?" and began to read her *Zeitung*. No one cared to be out in the weather; even Harold was inside. He stood in the open pantry making himself a slice of jelly bread. Peezitch came and rubbed against his knees, begging.

"Go to Mama," Harold said. "Ask Mama for some *Wurst* or something. You know you don't like currant jelly. Go to Mama, Peezitch." So Peezitch did.

"Har-old!" Mama said in a chirpy, bright voice. "I've told you and told you that I won't be Mama to a cat."

"What's he supposed to call you then?" Harold wanted to know, smearing jelly over his buttered slice of bread. "Louise?"

"I hardly think so," Mama said. "He's ever so much younger. It doesn't sound quite proper, do you think? And Mrs. Hanneman is so formal!"

"How would 'Mrs. H' be?" Harold asked.

"Why, nice and friendly," Mama said. "Not so pert as Louise and yet nice and friendly."

"Rowr!" Peezitch said.

"He knows we're talking about him!" Mama laughed. Then she went to the range to test the iron. It answered her moistened finger with a satisfying *Tsst!* so she snapped it into the wooden handle and went back to the board. Now she reached for one of my Sunday aprons from the pile of rolls in the willow basket and started to press out the lace edging. Mama loved to iron, and even after a long day of it she was happy when she could make tiny tucking smooth and narrow laces stand out smartly. My school aprons were plain blue-and-white checked gingham, but the Sunday ones were white. This one was of dimity with a pink cross-stitched initial on the pocket. Mama's fingers caressed it—it's a thing I like to remember, the way her hands looked as she worked.

Harold and I settled down to teaching Peezitch Mama's new name. "Mrs. H! Go to Mrs. H! Go to Mrs. H, Peezitch!" we ordered. Rose, in the big rocker, waved and pointed.

"She's saying 'Mrs. H' too," I said.

Jud came into the kitchen. He could walk now, so he no longer wore baby dresses, and in his red Russian blouse he looked like a round holly berry.

"Cookie!" Jud demanded, so I found him a Zu Zu.

Mama finished with my apron, and I began to fold away Harold's blouses and all the underwaists and petticoats that Grandma had ironed.

"I still have the large holiday cloth to do," Mama said. "Ivy, run and get me some papers to cover the floor."

I hurried to find the Courier and spread the sheets where Mama wanted them. Mama hung my finished apron over a chair back. Then something in the Courier caught her eye, and she bent over to read it. It was a quarter-page ad:

HEAR HIM! HEAR HIM! HEAR HIM!
Hear him and find health!
Herbert Trumpeter tells you the truth!

Down on the floor went Mama to read the smaller type:

Herbert Trumpeter has for many years operated the famed Natura Health Farms. He is an authority on the Kneip Cure and creator of the Wate-Away Diet. He has performed veritable miracles upon the human body through correcting wrong food habits. Herbert Trumpeter will be heard in this city in a series of five lectures:

Nature's Way	Starving in the Midst of Plenty
Ills the Flesh is Heir to	Fountain of Youth

Take Up Thy Bed and Walk

Admission—$5.00 for the single lecture
$20.00 for the course

Enroll for all and save!

HEAR HIM! HEAR HIM! HEAR HIM!

There was an address and a telephone number.

It was lecture five that caught Mama's eye, and there, because of the Terrible Pain, went Mama's ostrich plume, full-curling and sable black.

If there was one thing that Mama had dreamed of for herself it was that plume. She had smaller plumes and bits of plumes, bird breasts and a variety of feathers and quills, but now she wanted a plume like those that Mrs. Fiske and Mrs. Leslie Carter wore. Remembering now, I see that for Mama there were symbols for everything. A brick house meant wealth, an auto modest success, a good black dress a good woman, a red dress a flighty one. A leather-bound set of The Poets meant a home of taste; when you saw *Shepherd of the Hills*, *Graustark*, or *The Four Million* on the bookshelf, it became a home not only of taste but of livability, and when you found Maeterlinck's *Life of the Bee*, *Sartor Resartus*, and *The Making of an American*, that home was turned into a home of culture. (Ours was a home of culture as nearly as Mama could make it one.) A spit curl

101

to Mama meant brazenness, a wheelchair despair. Later an ostrich plume was added to these symbols. It meant the utmost in elegance, the height of charm, a woman cherished, a woman adored. I know that now. But when I was seven I only knew that Mama wanted that plume almost as much as I wanted dancing lessons.

The stores at home didn't have the kind she had in mind, so Papa said she should send to Florida for one, and for Christmas he gave her twenty dollars for a plume. Twenty dollars for Mama to spend just on herself! It was such a happy thing to think about that Mama lingered to taste a little longer the feeling of being able to do it. Then New Year's came, and Mama waited a week more. Another week passed. Mama wrote the letter to the Floradora Ostrich Farms, enclosed a check, and put the envelope up against the parlor clock for Papa to mail. But Papa forgot.

"HEAR HIM! HEAR HIM! HEAR HIM!"

Mama read the ad from beginning to end. Then she called the number on the telephone and made a reservation for the entire series of lectures. She took the envelope from beside the clock and tore up the letter and the check to Florida. She had to do it.

Outside the snow flew, and what was left on earth of Mr. Omlie, straight at last, lay in the vault in Hillside Cemetery waiting for spring. Inside our kitchen it was cozy and warm. Grandma's amaryllis made ready to bloom. Mama's iron thudded rhythmically as she finished up the holiday tablecloth, and as she worked she sang,

"In the valley where the bluebirds sing!
In the valley where the church bells ring!"

102

The brittle note was gone from her voice. Mama put away the ironing things and started to fix our supper.

Kids were admitted free to *Nature's Way* and the other lectures, so Mama thought I should go. "It will be educational," Mama argued.

Papa nodded. "Who knows? Someday Ivy may be a nurse," he said.

"Dancer!" I whispered it under my breath. It was too soon to let Papa know that the nurse idea was out.

"Or a teacher," Mama said.

"No, dancer!" I whispered again, but I whispered it low. I didn't want to spoil her teacher dream either. I knew I could dance if they'd let me. I could dance enough for both Rose and me. *Dancer! Dancer!* I thought, but anyway they sent me to *Nature's Way*.

The lectures were held in Workingmen's Hall, and Mama and I went in and took our places on collapsible chairs. Mine collapsed right away. The man behind me said, "Oopsadaisy!" and picked me up and straightened the chair. He leaned far over me with his Sen Sen breath and began to tell Mama about his stomach. "Ain't et a square meal in years!" the man said proudly.

Then a lady in front of us turned around and wanted to tell about her digestion. "Nothing wrong with *it!*"

"Ain't had a square meal in years," the man insisted.

On the other side of Mama a tiny little lady with a black transformation that kept sliding to one side spoke up. "I went to the rubber doctor," the lady said, "and do you know what he told me? 'There isn't two of your vertimins in a straight line!' That's just what he told me!"

Other voices said, "Got me an electric belt!" "Threw away my rheumatism ring!" "She was so sick that she had to use the galvanic battery!" "My daughter went as high in nursing as anyone could go—higher than a doctor even—and here's what she thinks . . ." Like crickets in the night, the voices crackled around us. Mama looked a little troubled by them, but she managed to smile and say "Well!" and "The idea!" and such things, and so keep everyone near her happy until the lights flashed and there was the sudden beating of a gong.

Then onto the stage, with a fancy heel-and-toe step, came Herbert Trumpeter.

"He doesn't look so very healthy," I whispered to Mama.

Music played. It was the "Husk and Peel" song.

One last voice spoke: "I was in bed with what four doctors called 'nervous prostration.'"

Herbert Trumpeter started to sing:

> "Husk and Peel, Husk and Peel,
> Lots of lukewarm water,
> From head to heel, makes you feel
> GOOD, the way you oughter!"

He grabbed a handful of raisins from a table in the middle of the stage and chewed awhile. Then he winked and jerked his head at us.

"'At's the stuff!" Herbert Trumpeter said. "Lots of nourishment in 'ese!"

"He talked with his mouth full, Mama," I whispered, and Mama said, "Hush, Ivy!"

"Let's see the hands of all who had an adequate breakfast this morning," Herbert Trumpeter suggested. Hands went up all over the hall. He asked a lady in a purple suit to come forward. "All right, ma'am, tell us what you ate."

The woman looked pleased at being chosen, the way Gladys Yaeger always did in school when Miss Bennet asked her to recite. "Well," the woman said with a broad smile, "I've always been a hearty eater. Like to eat real hearty. This morning I eat two boiled eggs, buttered toast, a slice of bacon, and then I eat my fill of Toasty Kinks with plenty of whole milk and sugar on it. I believe in a good breakfast." She smiled again, like Gladys expecting to get at least a ninety-five on her recitation. But Miss Bennet fooled her. I mean, Herbert Trumpeter did.

"Pah!" said Herbert Trumpeter. "You've insulted the gut! Boiled eggs! Pah! Fried bacon! Glah! *Patent* breakfast food! Toasty Kinks! You've insulted the gut!"

Red-faced, the woman went back to her seat, breathing hard. Then Herbert Trumpeter began to tell what we should eat. Oranges with the rind left on, sliced thin and covered with honey, coconut, or raisins. Eight glasses a day of luke-warm water, and a dish of Herbert Trumpeter's own Crackin' Good All-Around Food. And lots of buttermilk.

"No coffee?" asked the man next to me.

"Coffee!" yelled Herbert Trumpeter. "Builds bile! That's what's the matter with this famed twentieth century. We read books and let an old goat name Frood tell us that our wives are having evil dreams. We wear crippling shoes. We try to correct disease by the inhuman practice of punching germs into the blood stream. We scour our insides with

105

physic. We swig booze by the gallon, and if not booze, then that other invention of the Old Scratch, coffee. The amount of agony that I see in this world by reason of ignorance calling itself sense cannot be measured. Wake up, men and women of America! Wake up and live!

"We go out in society, thinking ourself one of the elite, and dance the bunny hug. We let our young men smoke and live unpure lives . . ."

"It's the Gawd's truth!" said the man behind me.

"We let our young fellows smoke cigareets. Turkish Trophies! Sweet Caporals! Pah! We lace up our daughters into straight-front corsets and let them live unpure lives. Why, one day, walking down the streets of Gotham . . ."

"Ivy, dear," Mama whispered, "it's so warm in here. Wouldn't you like to go out to the bubbler in the hall and get a nice drink?"

I slipped out, and when I got back Herbert Trumpeter was no longer talking about sin. He was talking about bran. He saw me coming down the aisle toward Mama and asked if I would come forward. I looked at Mama and she nodded. Mama was always afraid of hurting someone's feelings— even Herbert Trumpeter's.

He asked me to sit at a little table, and a lady in a white dress came in with a tray. She put it in front of me, and Herbert Trumpeter said I should try Nature's own delicious health meal. I tried; I really did, while Herbert Trumpeter talked about chemicals and minerals and chewing enough. I knew we were doing this for Rose, and I did my best. The orange slices were all right, and the honey and coconut, but I never could stand buttermilk, and the Crackin' Good All-

Around Food looked like something to give Noteboom's Favorite Horse. I tried a little and then I said, "Thank you, Mr. Trumpeter, I'm afraid I'm full."

The audience laughed at this, but Herbert Trumpeter looked mad.

"We stuff our little folks with ultra-sanitary, refined foods from which the vital goodness has been ground out," he yelled. "We pamper 'em, fill 'em with luxuries, and then, like this little lady here, they cannot eat the natural food that their Creator in his beneficence has provided for putting the life essence into their bodily cells. You may take your seat, little lady, and I hope that from now on you will change your manner of eating. Feed your cells or they will bring you grief." He handed me a box. "Tell your mummy that you want Trumpeter's Crackin' Good All-Around Food for optimum health. Get vim!"

"Thank you," I muttered, and scrambled down from the stage. Mama didn't look terribly happy, but still she didn't say that we should leave. We stayed until the end of the lecture, and everybody sang the "Husk and Peel" song at least three times, holding hands around the hall and smiling.

"Get vim!" Herbert Trumpeter yelled, and then he left the stage with his fancy heel-and-toe step. Chairs slammed, and we put on our coats.

"It can't be over," the man next to me said. "I haven't heard a Ford joke yet."

Outside the wind was blowing and I was glad that I was wearing my kitty hood. "Glah! but I hate buttermilk," I said.

The next evening we went again. Mama asked Harold if

107

he'd like to come too, but he said that he and Papa were going to try out the Magic Lantern that Papa was fixing for Judson Beckwith, so Mama and I went alone to *The Ills the Flesh is Heir To.*

One ill that Herbert Trumpeter was heir to was leaving town when he had his pockets lined with money. A sorry-sounding notice tacked up on Workingmen's Hall told us what had happened. In the street were a dozen angry people. The hearty breakfast woman was madder than any of them. "They say he left for Omaha," she kept saying.

Mama bit her lip. She looked as if someone had slapped her. Then she took my hand, and we hurried to the Alice Avenue streetcar. I tried to cheer her up.

"*I'm* glad," I said. "You know why I'm glad? I'm glad because my own twin sister won't have to do Nature's Way. Herbert Trumpeter's Crackin' Good Food looks like pencil shavings. Mama, Rose wouldn't have liked it at all."

Mama didn't say a word. The car filled, and we headed toward home. I sat and looked at a sign which said,

> Please do not spit on floor.
> Forbidden by law.

"Mama," I asked, "why does it say 'please' if it's forbidden by law?"

Mama didn't answer. I don't think she heard me. I tried something else.

"Glah! but Rose hates buttermilk," I said. "Glah! and Pah!"

When we reached home Mama went straight into the big bedroom to take off her hat and coat and the fur collar with

ae mink tails. Papa raised his eyebrows when he saw us
ack so early, but he didn't ask a question. He looked into
ne reservoir on the kitchen range and saw that it needed
water. I kept my coat and kitty hood on and followed him
s he picked up the pails and went outside.

I watched Papa pump. "Nature's Way isn't any good," I
told him.

"I know," Papa said, "but just when did Mama Louise
nd out?"

"Herbert Trumpeter went to Omaha. He never came
onight."

Papa gave a long whistle. "Worse than I expected. I
thought she'd get let down slow and easy. This is kerplunk!"

"Papa," I worried, "Mama can't get the plume she wanted
now, can she? Nature's Way isn't going to work, and she
can't get the plume either. It's awful."

"I'm sorry about Nature's Way not working," Papa said,
"but don't let the plume worry you. Mama Louise didn't
really want one at all."

I jumped to keep warm. "Oh, but she did, Papa. She
wanted it the worst worst worst."

"Not really," Papa said. "Chicken, what Mama Louise
wanted was only to want that plume, not really to have it.
Now she can start wanting it all over again."

One pail was full. Papa set it aside and started to fill the
other one.

"Glah! but Rose and I hate Herbert Trumpeter," I said.

109

The White Elephant Sale

Long ago at our house there were early morning sounds just as there probably were at yours, and the sounds of winter mornings were different from the summer ones. Harder sounds. Sharper sounds. Not the voices of the early birds or the gentle *tuf-tuf* of muslin curtains blowing against the screens or the occasional *clup!* of a breeze-stirred window shade. The winter sounds were different sounds, born of cold weather and the season's needs, but at both times, summertime or wintertime, the breakfast sounds were always there.

Rose and I would lie in our beds, side by side, holding hands across the narrow space between us, and we'd make a game of naming each sound as it came.

First Papa's alarm clock with the very gentlest *ting!* for he was always awake beforehand and grabbed for it as soon as the alarm began. Then the sounds of Mama's dressing. This always took a long time because when she was dressed our Mama was dressed—no curl papers or slip-slap slippers, early on a winter's morning or ever. Next came the wood sounds, with Papa starting the fire in the kitchen range and stirring the coals in the Radiant Home heater in the sitting room. Now the teakettle's song, and after it the *clomp-clomp* of feet going through the summer kitchen and the opening and closing of doors as Papa went outside to thaw the frozen pump.

Now Mama would start to grind the coffee, and if it was summer I wouldn't stay in bed a second longer, but in winter, of course, we both waited until the house was warm. So we'd lie there, hand in hand, and play a game.

There'd be a heavy sound of iron grating on iron, followed by a *flump!*

"That was Papa putting a big chunk of wood into the range," I'd say. Then a liquid pouring sound, and it would be Rose's turn to guess. "Was it Mama pouring Peezitch's milk?" I'd ask, and Rose would shake her head for no.

"Was it Papa filling the stove reservoir?"

At "reservoir," Rose would start to laugh and tug at my hand. It was her special way of saying yes.

Then there'd be a dullish sort of crockery sound, and I'd say, "Mama getting butter out of the jar," and Rose would tug my hand in agreement. Those hands were a sort of telephone system between us, and for the longest time we used them to exchange ideas. Papa used to say that was one reason why Rose didn't talk, because I understood her so well that she didn't need words. But the main reason, Papa always said, was because we did too much for her. "She never gets to want or to want not," Papa would complain.

111

But how could we stop the hand-talking when it was so much fun for both of us?

When there was a sort of *bup!* sound, *bup!* and *bup!* and *bup!* again, I'd ask Rose, "Was that Grandma slicing bacon?" and she'd know it was and laugh and tug yes. By that time, the house would be warmer and full of golden-brown smells, coffee and toast and bacon smells, which drew us out of bed.

That's the way it usually happened in winter. But one Saturday in February, morning came in quite a different way. Or rather, it was a different day all through, so that the strange beginning of it was perhaps only the normal beginning of a day that was strange.

It started simply enough with Papa's alarm, and the stove sounds, and the dressing sounds, and then, quite suddenly, before she had time to set out a single plate, here was Mama calling us all—Rose from her crib, me from my trundle bed, and Harold from his bed on the sitting-room lounge.

"Children, wake up! Everybody, wake up!" and by the hurry in her voice you'd think the house afire, but by the gladness in it you'd know it was something else.

"Everyone up! Everyone up quickly!" Mama called. "There's a pure white squirrel in the garden!"

I pulled on my sheep-shoes and fumbled into my kimono. Harold dressed fast, and Mama bundled Rose into two blankets so she wouldn't catch cold. Outside we all went, and oh, the squirrel! The little white squirrel!

Snowy as a polar bear, he sat upon an oak branch, chewing and crunching something and showering the shell bits down.

He was so lovely and unbelievable that for a little while we couldn't say a single word. Squirrels were common in our yard because of the acorns, big fat gray squirrels, but never a white one until today.

It was a fairy-tale morning. New snow had fallen and everything was sparkling with it. Every fence post had a fur hat, and the lilacs and apple trees wore lacy collars and aprons. Beside the house the lawn stretched away like a velvet carpet, broken only by the frolicking footprints of the squirrel and here and there the lacy tracks the sparrows and chickadees had made. The whole yard was a fairy tale, and Harold and Rose and I were all part of it.

We watched the squirrel eat his acorn. He frisked his tail and scurried up a branch. Then with lightning swiftness he reversed his path and jumped to the branch beneath.

"But Mama," Harold said in a wondering voice, "he plays just like any other squirrel."

"That's because underneath he is just an ordinary squirrel," Mama answered. "He's what is called an albino. By nature he's a gray squirrel, gray in every way. It's just the color of his fur and eyes that's different."

Papa picked up a broom and swept a spot clear on the pump platform, and he and Harold sprinkled crumbs and sunflower seeds to feed the birds. They flew down almost at once, for they were used to feeding there, but nearly as soon as they came, Peezitch saw them with his hungry yellow eyes and snake-wiggled his body toward them.

"Velvet paws, Peezitch!" I screamed. "Velvet paws!" But Peezitch ignored me and stealthily crept nearer. Harold was a doer, though, and he didn't waste time on screaming.

Harold scooped up Peezitch in his arms and carried him into the summer kitchen. I watched them go and, when I looked back for the squirrel, he was gone.

From the corner the Catholic bells chimed the half-hour; the sun was higher now, the breeze loosened the snow from the trees, and little chunks of it fell plopping to the ground.

Mama took Rose into the house and I followed. I dressed by the kitchen range and took particular pains to get my long underwear rolled smoothly before I pulled up my black ribbed stockings.

Harold helped Rose with her breakfast, and Mama dished up ours. Papa said he would have the afternoon off after all, and if Mama wanted to go to the schoolhouse to help at the sale, that would be all right.

Grandma said that she would be needing a little more black Zephyr yarn to finish the chest protector she was making and wondered if Papa would pick it up on his way home at noon. Mama let us put brown sugar on our oatmeal, and in every way you'd think this was just another Saturday. Only how could it be when it started with a white squirrel and ended with a White Elephant sale? And how could it be, when for Mama it marked a sort of a beginning?

The White Elephant sale at James Monroe School was where people used to get rid of whatever they didn't need. One thing we got rid of was something nice made of buffalo horns and red plush. Nobody knew what it was for, but it surely was a wonder. We got rid of a comb pocket to be put on a kitchen wall, a pair of button oxfords that pinched

Mama, a yard-of-roses picture and a hand-painted spoon glass. But there were other things.

Because I'd cleaned the kitchen knives with brick dust and folded away all the baby's wash, Mama let me go with her. We went into the schoolhouse, and a girl was pushing another girl across the floor in a wheelchair.

Mama said that wasn't nice. A well child shouldn't even sit in a wheelchair and certainly shouldn't use it for fun, but these kids didn't mind. They rolled around corners as fast as anything and nearly knocked down a plaster statue of the Winged Victory of Samothrace. Mama said that didn't show good rearing. Harold and I had good rearing, I think. We would have known without being told how it is about a wheelchair. This chair had been put in the White Elephant sale to be sold, and not for kids to be acting like *Heu-ochsen* over. Like overgrown calves.

The sale was in the big middle hall where two stairways met and long tables had been set up under the brown pictures of *Song of the Lark* and *Angelus*.

Mama got right to work pricing, and I helped by putting things where the ladies said I should. I kept my rubbers on at first, but Mrs. McCabe said, "Take them off, girlie, or you'll get sore eyes."

"Yes'm," I said, and I took them off and put them under a chair because anybody knew that Mrs. McCabe was right about that.

Mrs. Elmer Narr set down a box. It was full of china dishes, pretty and hardly nicked at all, and the ladies began reaching for them almost as fast as we got them out.

Then Mama asked if I would go down to the girls' basement and get a cloth wet to wipe off a Rogers group that looked a little dusty. When I got back, more boxes had been brought in and more ladies were coming to help and to buy. All of them were talking at the same time, and there was that happy hum in the room that you always hear when ladies are busy together. I listened to the hum awhile, and then it turned into voices, and loudest was Mrs. Latta's.

"Mrs. Hobelsperger won't be here," Mrs. Latta was saying. "She irons today at my dodder's house. Gladys, my dodder, her feet's swole so fierce she can't stand. Nineteen years old and two boys already, and she has to get in the family way. Whine, whine, whine, that's all she does, she can't lift the sad-irons, Gladys. 'So you would get married and no bigger than a snot-nose,' I said, but just the same, Mrs. Hobelsperger comes to iron."

"Mama, what's family way?" I asked. Someone chuckled, and all the ladies raised their eyebrows.

Mama handed me a bean pot pasted all over with cigar bands. "Little pitchers!" Mama said, and I knew I had made a mistake. You see, long ago at our house, life wasn't fed to you drop by drop but hoarded and saved. You learned what you could when you could, but the rest was poured out in a rush. A cold bath for you then and a sharp awakening. But this came later. Now I was seven, and I asked, but how I wished I hadn't!

Making my own logic, I began to hate Mrs. Hobelsperger. I hated Gladys, and most of all I hated Mrs. Latta who had brought this all on and made me feel stupid and too big in the mouth.

Logical? Of course I wasn't, but what was at the White

116

Elephant sale? Was it sensible for me to be running around between the ladies' skirts, pulling the boxes open and laying things out for Mama to price? Were the things themselves sensible?

What about the wooden picture of the bulldog with a real chain tacked on and a sign that read, "All I did was growl a little"? Or the ostrich egg, painted with palm trees and "Souvenir of Florida"? What about a table heaped high with corset covers, hobble skirts, and the poems of Ella Wheeler Wilcox? What about gravy boats set beside wool petticoat lace, and black jersey tights next to abalone shells? What about the leather hanging with two Dutch children on it that said, "Liff, Laff, and Luff!" in burnt-in printing? What about those two girls tearing about in that wheelchair like crazy? And what, when you got right down to it, about Mama working side by side with Mrs. Latta (whose husband owned a saloon with "Buffet" over the door in white electric bulbs), and little Mrs. Marko who was black as a licorice Teddy bear?

Sensible or not, the things came streaming in and the people kept on buying. Someone set out Tickie Wing's outgrown dancing shoes with the crisscross pink ribbons, and I felt a wave of jealousy because of course Mama would never buy them for me so I could get my picture in the Courier the way Tickie did, with "Little Miss Entertains at Elks' Party" over it. Tickie was the only person I ever envied, though Mama didn't think much of her and her cloud of tarlatan skirts that just barely covered her behinder. But now, for ten cents Mrs. Sol Mednikoff had bought her shoes and there was no use thinking about them.

I went back to the pricing table, and Mrs. Chodie was asking Mrs. Latta how it was that Mrs. Hobelsperger could go out doing Martha-by-the-day work like that. "What does she do with Ruthie?" Mrs. Chodie wanted to know.

"Oh, Ruthie she goes on crutches now," Mrs. Latta explained, twirling a silver candleshade to fluff out the fringe. "Ruthie she's back in school and she gets around real good. The doctor says she does real good. Mrs. Hobelsperger give the wheelchair to the sale. You noticed," Mrs. Latta said.

"Oh," Mama said, "that's where it came from," and she went on pricing.

Then Mrs. Latta asked, "How about you, Mrs. Hanneman, couldn't you use that nice little chair for your little crippled child? Couldn't she use that chair? It'd be a good buy. Four dollars is all they want."

Mama stiffened the way she always did when people she didn't know well talked about Rose. I knew she was mad, but from her voice you couldn't tell. Mama could be simply furious and still her voice would ripple on like water over cool stones.

"Oh, thank you. No, I think not," Mama said. "Rose isn't crippled, you know. It's only that she hasn't yet learned to walk. Rose won't be needing a wheelchair."

"It'd be just a nice size for her," Mrs. Latta insisted. "You know, she's growing and she'd soon grow right into it. She isn't going to be a baby forever."

Mama had had enough, and she just wasn't going to take any advice from Mrs. Latta. "Thank you, no!" Mama said, and she wrote a hard, black "79¢" on a chamber set in Blue Gentian design.

Mrs. Latta tossed her head and bustled off, and Mama worked for a while without saying a word. After a few minutes, little Mrs. Marko looked up timidly and said, "I heard what you ladies was saying. You got a little child can't walk? I got a little child can't walk too."

Mama always told Harold and me that we shouldn't be nose-pokey and stand around listening to grown folks' talk, but this time I couldn't help myself. I knew about some of Mrs. Marko's children: Osmand, who was the noisiest boy in my room, smiling Vina in Harold's grade; big, big Booker W. who was way up in B-Eight and who could rumble in such a deep voice when they had the programs, boom-boom, sailor beware! Of course, I knew all about those three, but how in the wide world would I know a thing about tiny black Land of the Leal who was only two years old and had an injured spine so he couldn't move his legs or even wiggle so much as one toe?

"I looked at the wheelchair for him," Mrs. Marko said, "but it's much too big. What's your child's trouble?"

Mama said, "Rose has what they call Little's disease, but it isn't any kind of disease, really. It's just something about her nerves, and so she hasn't learned to walk yet."

"Lord love her!" Mrs. Marko shook her head so that the cherries on her black hat bobbed.

Then Mama told her about Mrs. Pahousek and the exercises, and the way Rose could lift her head alone now, and how the massage was making her stronger, and that someday we all hoped that she'd be able to walk and go to school like other children.

"Lord love her!" Mrs. Marko said again.

119

Next Mama had to tell about Rose and me and how we talked with our hands, and how she had taught Rose to read, holding up a card and having her show by no or yes or some other way what the card said.

"You surely have studied that child!" Mrs. Marko said. Some of the other ladies had stopped working now and were listening too, but once she had started to tell about Rose it was as though Mama had drawn a little magic ring around herself and Mrs. Marko, and there wasn't a soul left in the world but just the two of them.

"It's a wonder the way you figured it out!" Mrs. Marko sighed, and then timidly she added, "Now, I wish you could see that little child of mine. I do wish you could see that little Landy!" From the waist down he would always be paralyzed, Mrs. Marko said. "But I wish you could see him!" She looked up into Mama's eyes, and her anxious little face was like a waiting basket where you could drop a rock or a rose.

Mama fiddled with a work bag made of striped pompadour ribbon, and her knowing fingers that always seemed to be at home with different materials smoothed and fluted the lace edging, but her voice was kind.

"Why, I'd like to," Mama said. "Someday I will come to see him. Ivy and I will both come."

On Mrs. Marko's hat the wooden cherries bobbed and clicked, and under them she smiled. "I do hope."

Mrs. Chodie came up then and announced that both the Axminster rug and the hall tree had been sold, and so the ladies decided that the sale was over.

Mrs. Marko bought the framed motto that said "Blessed

120

are the Poor in Spirit," and Mama got a little garden trowel that was a bargain at eight cents. We boxed everything else and piled the boxes and a green glass lamp with prisms into the wheelchair. Then we pushed it all into a storeroom to wait until the next White Elephant sale.

By the time the school hall was cleaned, it was late and the streets were already dark. When we reached Henning Street and home, Papa had made the coffee, but nothing else was ready because Grandma had gone to have birthday cake with Aunt 'Melia and Papa was no cook.

We heard giggling in the sitting room, and Mama and I both hurried in.

Papa had got the kids to sit in a row on the sitting-room lounge, with shoestrings hanging out of their mouths to show Mama that they were starving and had had to eat their shoes. Waldemar Schwinn was with them, helping Harold to hold up Rose, and he had a shoelace too.

"You ninny!" Mama laughed, giving Papa a little hug. "You're a ninny, and you're doing your best to raise a tribe of ninnies. Harold, take that dirty shoelace out of the baby's mouth before he chokes on it." Then she quickly changed into a blue bungalow apron and went into the kitchen.

Harold and Waldemar started to make an elevator with the Meccano set. Papa got Jud and sat down in the big rocker, and as Mama worked she told him all about the sale and about Mrs. Marko and about little Land of the Leal who was paralyzed from the waist down.

"She asked me to come and see him," Mama said, "but how can I do that, Fred? I can't go to a Negro's house. I just can't. But she kept on asking, and it seemed to me . . .

121

I'd like to help her if I could, but how can I go to a Negro's house? She's being unreasonable, Fred."

Papa didn't agree or disagree, Papa with his gentle spirit, and it was a way he often had. Instead, he slid Jud down to his foot and let him ride the horsie. When Jud had had enough, he slipped softly to the floor. Then Papa got up and crossed the room to the washstand, and before the crinkly mirror he washed his face and wet-combed his hair. When that was all done, Papa said, "He's just a little black white boy, Mama Louise. It's just his skin and hair that are different."

"Touché!" Mama said. "All right. We'll go to see them someday. I'll plan on it."

Papa wiped his hands carefully on the brown huckaback towel, and then he said, "If you go after church tomorrow, Ivy will still have her Sunday dress on. The little boy will like it if you're dressed nice when you come." Papa, gentle Papa, he could wind you about like a string.

Mama dished the omelet onto a green and white platter and dressed it with snips of parsley from the plant on the window sill. Then she sighed, "I married a man by the name of Legree. First name Simon."

I didn't know what that meant, but I did know that tomorrow Mama and I would be going to Markoes' house to see little Land of the Leal, who couldn't move one single muscle from his waist down to his toes.

It was a strange feeling to know that Mama and I were going to go to a Negro's house, and I wiggled all through

122

Sunday school and forgot my Golden Text and lost the tithe money.

The tithe money was one cent put into a blue envelope Mrs. Powers had given us and written on the outside, "A tenth of my earnings for my Lord and Master." My earnings that week had been a nickel, but Mama said that you couldn't tithe a nickel so it had to be a penny. Mama said that Mrs. Powers had a wonderful way of teaching children, but I lost the tithe money just the same.

After Sunday school, Harold and Papa walked home, and Mama and I went the other way toward Lawrence Street where several Negro families lived. First came Lawrence Street and then Flower Street and then Hyde Court which was just a little alley. Markoes lived on Hyde Court in a sprawling double house with unpainted window frames and peeling gray stucco.

A crowd of little kids followed us to the door. Vina opened it, and before she let us in she yelled, "Go home, you all! Don't pesticate these folks."

Then she went in, and Mama and I followed. Inside the door was Osmand, grinning in a friendly way, and Booker W. hidden behind a funny paper with "The Timekillers" at the top. Vina ran to tell her mother that we were there.

Osmand went into another room and came back carrying a year-old baby in pink striped rompers. He dropped him into a shiny leather rocker and went into the other room again. When he came out he had another little rompered boy in his arms. He dropped him into the rocker too. They looked like a dish full of candy.

"There's this one and this one," Osmand said, "but the one I guess you wants to see is in there. Mama is in there."

Mrs. Marko stepped into the doorway then, and after she had greeted Mama and me both, she asked us to come into the bedroom where Landy was lying.

It was a happy little room with starched lace curtains. On a table under the window a beefsteak begonia stood, with a white knit doily beneath it. I saw the walls of the room with their garlands of yellow flowers, and I saw "Blessed are the Poor in Spirit" already hanging on a wall above a green-painted bed with twisty iron ends. And then I saw Landy.

I was used to Rose and had been used to her all my life, so I never felt sad when I looked at her, but with Landy it was different. He looked so small and black against his snowy pillows, and I ached seeing him, knowing that he could never in this world be better. Landy wasn't sad, though. He was like a tiny Osmand, with a big white grin splitting his shining black doll face. Mrs. Marko pulled the covers back to show Mama his legs. They looked like crooked little branches, with the feet falling flat and useless to the sides. The tears started to my eyes, and I brushed them away fast, for I knew it was bad manners to cry in front of strangers. I felt so hot and miserable, and I didn't know where to look; I didn't know where to hide.

Then suddenly I remembered the box—a tin Prince Albert box that I had brought for Landy. Pulling it out of my angora muff, I opened it for him, and he took out the things that Harold and I had put inside—a lead soldier, a whistle, a piece of Doublemint gum, and three green immies.

Landy looked at everything, then he put it all back in the

box and snapped it shut. He handed it to me and said, "Ope."

I opened it and handed it to him and he said, "Totchoo." Then he snapped it shut and gave it back to me again.

"Ope," Landy said. And when I had opened it and given it back to him, he said "Totchoo" once more. Over and over again we did it; it was just like playing with Jud. Ernie and Harmon, the other two little boys, ran into the room. Vina picked one of them up and I took the other. Mrs. Marko asked if we'd like to hear the big children sing, and Mama said, "Why that would be just lovely." So Vina and Booker W. and Osmand stood in a straight row, and without a piano or anything they sang, "Lead on, O King Eternal" and "There is a Green Hill Far Away," and it was as good as anything in church.

Mama thanked them all and said, "That was simply beautiful." Then Landy reached over and stroked Mama's finger in its fawn-colored glove. "Pretty," Landy said. Mama took his little black fingers in hers and held his hand awhile. Then she took out her handkerchief and made a Mathilda Spence doll and recited the piece that goes with it:

"Mathilda Spence, she loves to dance.
She'll do this much for fifteen cents,
But if another dime you pay
She'll dance the Tara-boom-de-ay!"

And at "boom-de-ay" the dollie would come all unwound. Landy liked it and all the others laughed, so Mama had to do it a few times more.

"Landy, he's real smart," Mrs. Marko said. "We figure we going to send that boy to college. The others going to be able to take care of themselves, singing or even hard work, but Little Landy here, he's going to have to use his head. We figure we got to save and get him to college."

"College!" Mama gasped, tilting her head to one side the way she always did when she was trying hard to understand. "College!" She looked at Mrs. Marko, and a slow smile crossed her face and her eyes got soft. Something had happened in that room. It was as though you had been kicking leaves along a curbstone and had found a tiara. It was as though it had rained all day and the rain had turned into flute-notes. It was as though you had gone into the fall garden to pull a turnip and found that you held an Easter lily.

For everyone there is a magic word, a word that is a dream, a flame, a mountaintop, a trumpet call, a star. For Mama there was such a word and Mrs. Marko had used it. "College" was just that word.

Mama herself had had a one-year teachers' course. She wanted college for Harold, and Jud too, and maybe Normal for me, but it was a distant and daring thing that she hardly let herself consider. But here was little Mrs. Marko actually planning and saving and counting on it! College!

Suddenly Mama jumped from her chair and I saw that she had pulled off her gloves.

"I'm going to Mrs. Latta's," Mama said. "That wheelchair wasn't sold yesterday, and I'll tell her that I want to buy it for Rose. With pillows it will do for now, and she'll soon grow into it. Then you can have Rose's gocart for the baby, for Landy. How would that be? That way, Vina can take him outside as soon as the weather gets nice, and he'll

126

learn faster, being with other children. I'm going to Mrs. Latta's to arrange it right away."

"Lord love you!" Mrs. Marko said, and Vina said, "Landy can be outside with us when we play hopscotch, and I'll take him to the store sometimes and downtown when they have the parades." Osmand and Booker W. just grinned.

Out on the sidewalk I tugged Mama's arm. "But what about Rose?" I asked. "Won't it make Rose a cripple to have a wheelchair? Won't it, Mama?"

Mama patted my shoulder. "Nonsense, Ivy," Mama said with her silver-bell laugh. "Of course not. Crippled or not, it's just in a person's mind."

The same little kids started to follow us down the street, but Vina opened the door again and screamed after them. "Look, you all! Don't you pesticate those folks," Vina yelled. "They're Landy's friends. Personally."

It had started to snow again. I caught a few tiny crystals on my mittens and studied them. They were all different; they were all alike; they were all wonderful.

The Hattish Hats

The kitchen lamp was swung on its hinged bracket into the open doorway, but the light wasn't nearly enough, so Mama lit the big lamp with the wide green shade. Its light glowed on the rosy damask tablecloth and made a small pool of warmth and brightness in the dusk of the sitting room.

I got out my spool knitting. Papa, Harold, and I all pulled our chairs nearer to the table. Mama sat down near us at the open sewing machine and began to stitch a patch on Harold's brown knickerbockers. As soon as the machine started, Jud said, "Minna-minna-minna."

Rose lay on the lounge playing with Charlie, her stocking doll with the pearl-button eyes, and Rose tried to say "Minna-minna-minna," too. Harold sat with his head under the table getting Mutzi-Putzi to growl by saying "Rats!" Grandma Hanneman rocked and sang,

> "Du, du liegst mir im Herzen,
> Du, du liegst mir im Sinn,"

and the frame of the platform rocker complained.

It wasn't what you'd call quiet in the sitting room, and so I thought I'd better wait with what I had in mind.

Suddenly the singing stopped. Grandma picked up Jud and bundled him off to bed. Harold quit teasing Mutzi-Putzi and went back to his blue-ruled paper that said:

Harold H.   B-6, Monroe School

March 23, 1914   Miss Poznanski

CARELESSNESS THE CAUSE OF FIRE

It is said that 83 per cent of all fires are caused by . . .

Beneath this Harold had drawn a picture of Mr. Lowry, our school principal, with his head on a chopping block and a label that said "Ole sorehead gets what's coming to him."

"Mama," I snitched, "Harold isn't doing his Language."

Harold made a face at me and chanted, "Tattletale, tattletale, hanging on a cow's tail!" Over Mr. Lowry's head he drew a dripping ax.

Mama snipped a tag of thread and started to baste a second patch in place, just as if she hadn't heard.

"I've decided to have a hat with pansies on it," Mama announced. "Mounds of them, all over the crown. Princess Alice had one on at a state reception. They showed it in the Sunday supplement. Shaded from lavender to purple. Lydia can get it done in plenty of time for Easter."

Papa reached for an apple from the majolica bowl and bent again over the old brown book he was going through for the eighth or ninth time, *The Habitant*. He could talk right along with his reading, our papa, but the conversation sometimes didn't amount to much.

"Mhmnhmn," Papa grunted.

"It will be gorgeous," Mama said, playing the thought as you might a mandolin string. "The veil should be purple too."

This was exactly the chance I was waiting for, but I carefully wound up my spool knitting so that I wouldn't have to look at Mama.

"I want a hattish hat too this year," I said. "I want a hattish hat the same as you get to have, Mama, only for a girl."

"Oh, but darling," Mama said, "I saw a little girl downtown in the Our Word Is Our Bond store, and she had on a green tartan kirtle and a jaunty tam. With a quill. You'd look dear in something like that."

Mama's eyes had a far-off creative look in them that seemed ominous when I already knew so well what I wanted. Tickie Wing's Easter hat—her mother had sent to Sears Roebuck for it—looked like a mold of strawberry Jell-O with a froth of cream-colored ruching around her face. It was trimmed with ostrich tips and apple blossoms. And Mama could speak of tams!

"It was very natty!" Mama said.

Papa looked up from his reading. "Trig!" Papa added.

"Trig, natty, and jaunty," Harold said, leering at me.

"You stay out of this, Mister Harold!" I warned. "I'm mad. I don't want anything trig or jaunty. This is Easter I'm talking about, and all I want is a hattish hat."

"I saw a magazine picture," Mama mused, "of three little New York girls. They had blue reefers and cunning round hats that looked like hot cross buns. Smart!"

This was the limit.

"I don't want to be a bun-head!" I screamed. "Every kid

130

in that Sunday school will be calling me 'Bun-head' and I'll die. I'll leave home. I'll go and be a nun rather. I only want a hattish hat."

Grandma came back into the room and heard me. "Ach, Louise," Grandma said. So I knew that at least someone was on my side. I kept wishing she'd argue, because Mama always gave in to her. But that was all Grandma had to say about it.

"It's silly and extravagant," Mama objected, biting off a fresh piece of thread and knotting it. "You know perfectly well that she only wears a hat that one time, and then it's swung back over her shoulders while some rough boy bats her over the head with his Bible history book. Little girls don't act like ladies any more."

"But *I* do, Mama," I protested. "I don't spit or say 'ain't' or let my pants show. I never yet snapped gum in Sunday school the way the Yaegers do. And you said yourself that I keep my gloves nice and clean. I don't want any jaunty bun-head. Easter is coming, and I want a hattish hat like you get to have, and Rose wants one too."

"Rose!" Mama stopped her work and looked straight at me.

Now it was out. That was the real reason I was so concerned. It had suddenly occurred to me that Rose, my own twin sister, had never had a real hat in her whole life. First baby bonnets and then little white starched Dutch caps, and last summer a turn-down linen hat almost like Harold's. My spring hats were usually plain straw, but Rose hadn't even had one of these. At first Mama had said that Rose couldn't wear a hat because she couldn't hold up her head, but now she lifted it all by herself and when her lower back was supported she held it quite well. Still, Mama didn't think she should have a hat.

"It'll make her look older," Mama objected.

"Not older than me," I said.

Mama didn't have an answer to that because, of course, I was right. Mama's real reason was that she wanted Rose to look younger than she was so that people wouldn't expect so much of her. That didn't seem to bother Rose, but I hated it. Besides, I had the idea that if Rose only had a real hat she could go to Sunday school. Ever since she had got the wheelchair I kept hoping for that. "She could sit right next to me in her own chair and not be a bit of trouble," I argued, but Mama wouldn't even discuss it. So I fussed about the hats instead. Rose didn't make a sound while I was talking, but she listened, and now she got excited.

"Rose wants a pink one and I want blue," I said. "We want them to have all sorts of stuff on them and stiff brims. If I have to wear a tam Easter I'll run away. And Rose too!" Rose laughed and crowed at this. It was a daring thought.

"Won't we, Rose?" I asked, and the sounds she made might have been meant for "Run! Run!"

I knew I had said too much, and it was a wonder that Mama hadn't sent me to bed long before, for it wasn't her way to let us be mouthy. Mama was in a gentle mood that evening though, and I couldn't ruffle her. "Your mother knows best what's suitable for little girls," was all she said, but by the tone of her voice I knew that I'd lost. No hats.

And then, just in time, Papa spoke up. "Why can't they, Mama Louise?" Papa said. "It's awful to want something

132

so bad. I remember when I was a little boy I wanted a bright red coat, but this tyrant," he smiled over at Grandma, "made me have a sensible brown one because it wouldn't show the dirt. I never forgave her," Papa said.

"Ach, Fred!" Grandma said. "It's lots you cared. Such a *Schmutzfink* as you were!"

"None the less," Papa answered, "sloppy I may have been, but I want my ladies to be beautiful." He spread his arms wide. "Let there be hats. Let there be hattish hats all around."

I ran to Mama and threw my arms around her neck. "Do we get them, Mama?" I asked. "Do we get to get them?"

Mama tapped her front teeth with her thimble. "Well, I seem to be outnumbered," Mama said. "I'll have to phone Lydia about it tomorrow and then we'll see."

Harold took a red Crayola from the box and drew a spreading pool of blood around Mr. Lowry's feet. Rose dropped Charlie, and Mutzi-Putzi picked him up in his mouth and dropped him on the lounge beside her.

Papa laid *The Habitant* on the table and reached for another apple. "You don' get drown' in Lac St. Pierre so long you stay on shore," Papa recited.

I went over to Grandma and inched myself up on her lap and leaned my head against her well-cushioned black waist.

"Rose's will be pink," I said happily, "and I want blue."

An all-day teachers' meeting with a holiday for Harold and me made it possible for us all to go to Aunt Lyd's house. It was easily arranged. Had we ever known her to say no? Mama said Mrs. Pahousek would come on Tuesday, so Monday would be fine. Aunt Lyd said to bring Grandma and Jud and everybody, and Mr. Evans would be over early to fetch us in the Overland.

That in itself was an exciting thing, because it wasn't too often that we had a chance to ride in anyone's auto. We drove out Alice Avenue, past the Bock beer signs, and every time Mr. Evans honked his horn, Harold would yell, "Sound your Klaxon!" and we'd holler, "Ah-oo-ah!" Even Rose tried to say it.

Mr. Evans didn't care how noisy we got. He was the shop teacher at Vocational High, and a bachelor, but Mama said you could see he was used to children. He was a fun person, and Harold and I kept wishing he'd hurry up and marry Aunt Lyd, but Mama explained that away by saying, "Well, he's of another persuasion." This persuasion was Christian Science, which was almost scandalous, but we liked Mr. Evans and his Overland.

After Alice Avenue we followed a different route from the streetcar but finally came to the corner that we called The End of the Line. There was a drugstore there with skinny wire tables and chairs outside for serving ice cream, and in the windows there were jars of beautiful blue- and red- and gold-colored water behind heaps of dusty-looking St.-John's-bread and strings of rock crystal candy. Mueller-leile's Drug Store with the mortar and pestle over the door, Muellerleile's Drug Store with the Beecham's Song Books, Muellerleile's Drug Store with the sleeping gray cat.

From there we'd follow a sandy, climbing road. If it were summer there'd be hot little bug sounds and wind flowers in the ditches. This time it was blustery March and there were neither, and besides, Mr. Evans whisked us along too fast to notice even if there had been.

Mama sat in the front seat holding Rose and making polite talk with Mr. Evans.

"Olga Nethersole . . ." Mama would say, and Mr. Evans would sigh and answer, "There'll never be another Olga Nethersole!" in a husky, tender voice.

Grandma had Jud in her lap, and she sat between Harold and me to keep us reasonably quiet, but there in the high, proud Overland, what use was there for Grandma to try? In the Green Fairy Book there were chargers, chargers and steeds; but this was an auto! "Ride! Ride!" Jud sang, and all our hearts sang, too. Everything was funny that March morning, and Harold and I both knew that we were the cleverest people alive.

"Press the button!" Harold would bellow, and I'd finish it for him, "Eastman does the rest!" The Overland was nifty. Mr. Evans was a daisy. It was keen. It was peachy. Oh gol! Oh gol!

When we got to the house we had to climb seventeen steps, it stood so high. Mr. Evans took Rose and Mama carried Jud. We crossed a tiny porch, and there was the sound of ferocious barking and of hurrying footsteps as Aunt 'Melia put the poodles away.

Krautkopf was penned up in the kitchen, and after he was used to our being there he could come into the room, but Schwester was banished upstairs. Schwester was afraid of steps and wouldn't come down by herself but stood there glaring at us with her angry raisin eyes.

135

"Doesn't she know we belong to Mutzi-Putzi?" I asked Aunt Lyd, but Aunt Lyd laughed and said, "Oh, that one is *ganz dumm!* She never learns anything!"

The smells at Aunt Lyd's house were always the same: oiled floor and Sunday meat and kerosene stove and Other People's House; a wonderful blend of smells like the sounds of an orchestra, with here and there way out in front of the rest something special, like the violins. At Aunt Lyd's house the violin smells were coffee and applesauce cake and ripe cucumber pickles. We never spent the summer at Stevens Point or had rabbits, or had cousins in Iowa, like some kids, but we did have this wonderful thing of going to Aunt Lyd's.

Mr. Evans left pretty soon to go to the teachers' meeting, and Aunt Lyd said he was to come back for supper and stop at Beckwith's to call for Papa. I thought how nice it would be to have him in our family, but Mama said we shouldn't ever ask Aunt Lyd anything about it because it was an unmentionable subject.

"Is a different persuasion always an unmentionable subject?" I wanted to know, but Mama said, "Oh dear, Ivy!" and so I knew I never would get a good answer to that.

Well, first the ladies had to have *Kaffee Klatsch*, and Aunt 'Melia fixed us some butter bread. Aunt 'Melia was a good cook, but because she read Dr. Graham, she always put a lot of bran in her bread. It was firm and severe, and Harold named it "Third Base." Jud licked the butter off of his Third Base and left it under the Hoosier White Beauty kitchen cabinet, but the rest of us ate ours. Mama asked Aunt 'Melia how her quinsy was, and Aunt 'Melia croaked,

"Oh, much better, thanks," and delicately touched her throat.

Aunt 'Melia was Grandma's sister, younger than she but wispy and not nearly so peppery. Her husband, the tanner, died long ago when Aunt Lyd was just a little baby, and Aunt 'Melia had to go out and sew to support them until Aunt Lyd was grown and could take her turn. Aunt Lyd lived with Grandma and Grandpa Hanneman during those years, and so she seemed more like Papa's sister than his cousin. Now Aunt Lyd did sewing for people at home, and the big bedroom off the sitting room had been turned into a workroom. It was a wonderful place of pins and patterns and silk and velvet scraps, and because of it our dolls were always the best-dressed dolls in town.

Aunt Lyd said, "I'll fix a place for Baby Rose on the Daveno-bed," and I got out some things for us to play with. At Aunt Lyd's house this was always easy because there was so much of everything. Usually, if the weather were nice, Harold and I would both go down the hill to find Osa and Wildie and a boy we called Dutch John. But this time Rose was there, and I wanted to be near the hats, so Harold went off alone.

In the workroom the hats began to be born, with Aunt Lyd's big scissors crunching against the table as she cut out purple taffeta for Mama's hat. I ran in once in a while to watch. Mama and Aunt 'Melia went to work on the frames for Rose's and mine, binding tape around the wires and sewing the underfacing into place. When the brim of Mama's hat was covered, Aunt Lyd set her to work spreading pansies over the crown and stitching them in place. Then Aunt Lyd

137

got out the pink *mousseline* for Rose's hat and cut a long strip to shirr around the crown. Rose went nearly wild with excitement, and I felt happy all over to remember that it was I who had helped bring this about. When Rose's hat was covered it was turned over to Aunt 'Melia to trim, and Aunt Lyd began on mine. The *mousseline* was tucked and gathered into delicate folds and flutings. Over it went ribbon, looped, turned, and tacked. Then, in and out of the ribbon, pink rosebuds and forget-me-nots. Aunt Lyd sat working and singing "Baby's Boat's the Silver Moon" around a mouthful of pins. Grandma and Aunt 'Melia talked about the Bon Ton three-dollar corset. I played "Everybody's Doing It" on the Grafonola.

I went into the workroom to have another look. "Ostrich tips too?" I asked, but both Mama and Aunt Lyd shook their heads.

"That's a little *too* much," Mama said.

"Tickie Wing . . ." I started.

"Precisely. Tickie Wing," Mama answered. "I don't see any very good reason why I should dress my daughters as copies of Tickie Wing, even if she is a little actress."

"Dancer," I corrected.

"Actress. Dancer. It doesn't matter," Mama said. "There will be no ostrich tips." And then to Aunt Lyd, "The mother p-a-i-n-t-s and there's been talk of a d-i-v-o-r-c-e." Mama and Aunt Lyd were apt to forget that all of us but Jud could understand spelling.

I didn't really care about the ostrich tips. A hat by Aunt Lyd was wonderful enough without them.

I got down the armadillo basket with the tail for a handle.

Aunt 'Melia had lined it with pink satin, and it was used to hold postal cards. We hunted for all of our favorites: a picture of a sad young man looking at a woman who had a big lemon for a head—"I picked a lemon in the Garden of Love," it said; a picture of a policeman carrying a girl out of a burning building over the verse:

> When flames consume and bravest flee
> From sights that rend the breast,
> In times like these you'll always see
> The Finest at their best.

There was "Sitting Bull" and "Florida Rattlesnake Ready to Strike" and the burnt-leather card that Papa had sent from San Francisco with "Why the DICKENS don't you write?" and a book by Dickens taking the place of the word. There was "Never trouble trouble until trouble troubles you," "Barry, the Dog Hero," and "The Tournament of Roses."

I laid them out in rows, and if they weren't straight Rose would show me she wanted them straight. We played until nearly suppertime with the armadillo and the cards. Harold came in yelling, "A soldier of the Legion lay dying in Algiers. There was lack of woman's nursing, there was dearth of woman's tears," and he showed us the finger that he had cut on a piece of glass when he and Dutch John were lagging for turns at Duck-on-a-Rock.

Aunt Lyd said, "Why, you poor little fellow!" and took him into the kitchen and washed his hand and put on some peroxide. I went out and watched to see if it would bubble when the poison boiled out, and it did. Aunt Lyd got a clean rag and tied it up.

139

Harold took out the Lotto set, and we played while Mama and Aunt 'Melia fixed supper and Aunt Lyd sewed linings into all three of the hats and packed them with pink tissue in a big box from the Our Word Is Our Bond store.

After that, Papa and Mr. Evans came, with Papa waving a two-pound box of Lowney's chocolates.

"For Lydia, a seller of purple!" Papa said.

"Papa, did you say 'smeller'?" Harold asked, and Aunt Lyd wagged her finger and said, "Now, now! No comments on my nose!"

"Well, I think it's classical!" Mr. Evans said in a gruff voice. Aunt Lyd giggled and went off in a hurry to fill a triangular cut-glass dish with pickled beets.

When supper was over Mama said we must get an early start because tomorrow was a school day, so Papa went out to watch Mr. Evans start the Overland. Harold followed them along and said, "Hey, Ev. You know what happened at school Friday? Ed Kubisch wore long pants, and Wally Schwinn and I asked him, 'What's the matter, Ed? Is your pa sick?' Old Ed got sore and he made some ice balls and laid for us in the alley behind the firehouse."

The back door slammed behind them, and I went into the kitchen to see if Aunt 'Melia knew about Adam and Eve and Pinch-me going down to the river to swim. "Adam and Eve got drowned and who was left?" I asked, and Aunt 'Melia said "Pinch-me" so I did. I was still laughing about that when Mr. Evans came back and said apologetically that the Overland wouldn't start. They had cranked and cranked it, he said, and it wouldn't budge.

Mama said, "Oh, that's all right, Ev. Fred's here now, and we'll manage on the trolley."

It was quite a little procession we made going down to The End of the Line to wait for the streetcar. Grandma walked ahead, Papa carried Rose, Mama carried Jud, Harold carried the diaper bag, and I carried the big gray box in which Aunt Lyd had carefully packed our hats. At first there were no other people on the car, and we had time to get arranged. Jud sat with Harold, and Rose and I with Mama. In a few blocks an old lady climbed on, with a little boy in leather gaiters and a blue reefer coat. Out of all the empty car they chose the seat right in front of Mama and Rose and me. The old lady went to sleep right away, but the little boy stood up in the seat and looked straight at us. He had the roundest, bluest eyes I had ever seen.

After a while he said to Mama, "Does your little broke-leg girl like to ride the streetcar?"

"Yes," Mama said. "Very much."

"Does your little broke-leg girl like to whiz around corners and look out at the houses and horses and wagons and the street lights and at one *big* beer wagon?" he wanted to know.

"Yes, very much," Mama said as if that were the easiest answer.

"Is she happy to be riding the streetcar and whizzing around and looking at all the things all the time?" the little boy asked.

Mama said, "Yes, unbearably happy," although Rose really didn't care for streetcars. The noise of them bothered her, and she rode them so seldom that she usually got sick.

141

The tracks curved and wound, and the car rattled and swayed. This had been a long, exciting day, and we had hurried from the supper table. Something was almost bound to happen. Then it did.

"Is your little broke-leg girl so happy that she has to throw up all over your pretty fur collar?" the little boy asked, but Mama was too busy cleaning up Rose to answer. We were lucky to have some clean diapers in the diaper bag. Papa helped Mama with the job.

There were more people on the car by this time, including two men in black shirts with plaster on their shoes. One of them still had some cold coffee from his lunch in a whiskey bottle. "Take it, ma'am," he said to Mama. "It'll help settle her stomach." I'm not sure if Mama liked the idea or not, but she wanted to be polite, so she gave a little of the coffee to Rose and thanked the man. It must have helped, because Rose began to look better after that.

By now the whole car was watching us, and several of the people were looking hard at Rose. I heard one lady say to her own little girl, "Well, thank God you aren't like that." I hoped Mama hadn't heard; then I knew she had. I felt bad and then suddenly I felt worse than bad. Much worse. The car started to lurch and sway, and through a great dark cloud that seemed to float down and surround me I heard the little boy's voice saying, "Is your *other* little girl happy to be riding the streetcar, too?"

Papa saw what was going to happen. He rang the bell and whisked me off the car, and the others must have followed. Papa took me into an empty lot until my trouble was over. Then he cleaned me up with his big handkerchief, and we went back to the street where the family was waiting. Mama was sitting on a low brick wall holding Rose, and her head was down on Rose's shoulder. She swayed a little as we came near her. Papa put out his hands to her and patted her shoulders. "What's the matter?" Papa said. "Is the pretty lady going to be unbearably happy too?"

Mama looked up at him, and I thought for a minute that she was going to cry. Then instead she laughed and laughed and laughed, until a lady in the house opened a window and yelled out, "Drunks! Move on! Don't you wake up by me the boysie!"

Mama was herself after that, and she handed Rose to Papa and reached to take Jud from Harold. Then for the first time we noticed someone running down the street. The streetcar had stopped on the corner a block away, and the conductor was hurrying back toward us with something in his hands—the box from the Our Word Is Our Bond store in which Aunt Lyd had packed the three very hattish hats. They had all been forgotten.

'Can We, Can We Rejoice?'

———————

April comes tripping on narrow feet, shaking her green-gold tresses in the rain, and we open our door to her. We open our doors and windows, and, smiling, we ask her to bide. Cool and lovely with blessing hands, Oh watch her then! Oh, watch her and be not caught napping, for she is no milkmaid month. Not langorous May with blossoms in her hair and a lulling voice. Not joyous June.

Watch her well, for here she comes, April the sorceress; and not to know her is to miss the secret of the whirling spheres. To meet her and not know her is like finding the philosopher's stone and using it to prop a gate post.

Touch the song-makers and hear them bray. They will tell you that she is a time of beginning. They will tell you of lovers, of young life, of leafing grass, but theirs is only half a story. In their braying and snorting and ground-pawing they will have missed the secret of April altogether, for she is not birth but rebirth, and how can you be reborn until death and decay have worked their miracle in you?

144

Silly as a sophomore you may gaze into the gold of a daffodil's cup, but in so doing you will be no more than a baby. It is gold. It is pretty. No more than that. But to bury the dry bulbs in the frost-tempered dust of fall, to watch for the pale, brave finger of returning life—that is to give birth to the daffodil itself. The death of our joy is sorrow, but the ultimate death of our sorrow is joy.

Lovely, lovely April with her tripping narrow feet!

Once, in April, Beikel the barber got hungry for liver salad. He told Papa and Harold when they were getting their every-other-Saturday trim, and Harold remembered and told Mama. So what was more natural than that Mama should make some the very next Monday, round it out with a wooden paddle, garnish it with halves of hard-boiled eggs, and send me over to Beikels' carrying it on a green and white platter with a Grecian key design?

Liver salad with onion and eggs. To tempt Mr. Beikel's palate. To soothe Mrs. Beikel's grief. Beikels' was on Henning Street, two houses down from Grandma's, and it was a house of grief, just as our house was. The same grief, the same pain; yet in their way of using it Mama and Mrs. Beikel were very different.

There are some people who crack and pick at grief as you would a black walnut, hoping they'll find something better inside. There are others who cradle and coddle and cuddle it, holding it close with soft little words.

Long ago on Henning Street, Mama picked and Mrs. Beikel crooned, and deeply each pitied the other.

145

Mrs. Beikel would say to me, "Oh, that poor, poor mama of yours! She is so brave! She is so brave!"

And, "Poor Mrs. Beikel!" Mama would sigh. "If only she would try more! She should *try!*"

Aching and wanting for each other like that, how could either of them teach what she did not know? Power for good can come only when we are able to see that good can come of ill; but this was something they had not learned. Then April came, and out of her own pain Mama reached, and covered a mounded platter with a fringed napkin for Harold or me to carry down the street. I begged to be the one, and for an odd reason. When I was at Beikels', Rose was dead. And when I came out she became alive again, and the joy I felt was like Papa's story about the nut. This big nut would sit and hit his head with a hammer, and when anyone would ask why, the nut would explain, "Because it feels so good when I stop."

Sometimes it seemed that I just had to go to Beikels'. Rose hadn't been sick in bed a day for months. She had gained a little weight, and her cheeks were round and pink. I would have been proud to take her out riding in her chair, but if I even hinted that I wanted to do it, Mama's answer was always no.

No! No flying around the block with me behind her on roller skates. No trips to all my secret places: to the empty house with foot-long grass and the mother dog with puppies under a sagging porch; or to the wall of the Catholic school, where by reaching just a tiny bit Rose could have touched my lucky stone that glittered with diamonds when the sun was right. But it was "No, dear, no! Not until she is

146

stronger." "No, dear, no," and her Easter hat still sitting in its box. Rose at seven wasn't really dead, but sometimes I had to go to Beikels' just to be sure that she was alive.

Beikels' was the brick house. I went to the side door between the budding honeysuckle bushes and wiped my feet on the cocoa-husk mat the way Mama always said we should.

Mrs. Beikel was cleaning a pair of her husband's white shoes. She lumbered to the door with the whiting brush still in her hand, and she was glad for the liver salad.

"Ach, dearie, dearie, the mama is so good!" Mrs. Beikel said. "She know how our papa love the liver salad. Come in once!" And she held the shiny brown door open for me. She smelled of soap as I passed her. She smelled of starch. She seemed, too, to smell of sorrow, but it was a sorrow that beckoned me, tempted me, urged me to come closer until suddenly I had had more than enough. Opal Tenn's scabbed knee, a mashed worm, and the acute angles of the brick house—when I was seven I had to go near them sometimes, if only to spring back again to the daylight world of Not Mine! Isn't So! and Never Touched It!

Well, the way it was at Beikels', I could go under the shell-and-bead lambrequin that trimmed the doorway, into the clean parlor; and by the light faintly sifting through stiff lace curtains I could read the *Daily News* and see the funnies that we didn't get at home. The way it was, I could sit high up on the slippery couch with a cross-stitched bee cushion, a gold-painted dragon cushion, and a red-printed Indian maiden cushion, and I could read "The Outbursts of Everett True" by Condo and "Freckles and His Friends"

147

by Blosser. And sometimes I'd even have time to read Dorothy Dix before Mrs. Beikel came in with the jelly bread. I was careful to keep the crumbs from falling on Mrs. Beikel's Crex carpet made of grass with a slippery feel. I was careful too not to touch the bee cushion or the dragon or the Indian maiden with my jelly fingers. Mrs. Beikel's house was always so very clean that you wondered what she found to do when housecleaning time came around. Here was a careful house, and a child could feel that without being told.

"Yellow tomato yelly," Mrs. Beikel was saying. "Poor Cissy she always like yellow tomato yelly. I make some yet for liddle girls."

Carefully I wiped my sticky fingers on my embroidered underpants and then leaned back on the bee cushion to listen. If Mrs. Beikel planned to talk about poor Cissy today, it was going to take a long time.

"Poor Cissy she was like that liddle Rose, *die Arme*," Mrs. Beikel said. "The poor thing. Such a poor back! Oh, it hurts yet to think of it!"

"How big was poor Cissy, Mrs. Beikel?" I asked, although I knew perfectly well the answer. Poor Cissy had died thirty years ago when she was not yet eight. My age. Rose's age.

"Liddle girl. Yust liddle girl. I show her picture," Mrs. Beikel volunteered as she had so many times before, and she crossed the parlor to the black walnut dresser and opened a creaking drawer.

It was old in that drawer, old and sad, and the old smell walked out to join the other sad smells at Mrs. Beikel's house—the varnish smell, the washed-paint smell, the

148

losed-room smell, and the strange grassy smell of the Crex arpet.

Out of the drawer came some of poor Cissy's things: her aptism dress and a little wool bonnet, both very old and ellow and the ribbons washed and soft. Mrs. Beikel solmnly laid them in my lap. She had a teardrop that stayed orever in a corner of one eye, and like the creaking drawer seemed to speak of sorrow too—of a sorrow that was ever boxed away with poor Cissy's seven-year-old body, but sorrow that lived on wanly in the parlor of the red brick ouse.

"See once Cissy, my liddle girl."

Mrs. Beikel's square-nailed fingers were handing me the ictures now, two tan ghost pictures of a wide-eyed, old ashioned child. On one she was shrinking among large vhite pillows, but on the other she was stiffly sitting in the ap of a dark, fierce man. The man had a wide moustache ike a floor brush, and pants with rounded stovepipe legs. 'ake away the moustache and put on him a white barber oat, and you had Mr. Beikel, although now the thick black air was streaked with gray. Behind them was a curtain raped back to show a window, and through the window a vinding path leading to a castle. I asked Mrs. Beikel if she nd Mr. Beikel and poor Cissy had lived in a castle once, nd she said no, it was just a screen the photographer had. was sorry that poor Cissy hadn't been able to spend her ew years in a castle because that at least would have been omething for Mrs. Beikel to remember.

I ached to think of anyone having to be dead. In Sunday chool Mrs. Powers, my teacher, used to talk quite a lot

149

about dying and the soul, but I always saw the soul as a large cold slice of something that looked like breast of chicken, and who would trade her seeing eyes or good fast legs for that? Never again to hang up a Christmas stocking? Never to gather maple-seed squirters in the spring? Never again to bring home a box from Dornzeif's and open it to find shiny black Mary Jane pumps? Never to get a new French dress with a pink waterized silk ribbon sash? Never, never again to eat hot popcorn or holler in an empty room? Dying must feel like cleaning the chicken house and choking with the smell of it. Dying must feel like drinking root beer and feeling sharp bubbles up your nose. Dying must feel like eating ice cream pig-fast and getting a stabbing under your ribs. Dying must feel like losing your mother's bar pin that you were never allowed to play with and being scared to go home. Dying must feel like forgetting to do your number work, like sitting on your feet and stepping down on needles and nothingness. Dying must feel like nothing—like senseless years of nothing. I hated it for Cissy and Rose. Rose and Cissy—we hate being dead, I thought. Cissy hates it. Poor, poor Cissy! Her little tan ghost face piled up a hard ball inside me that settled right on top of the jelly bread.

"Cissy was your only little girl, wasn't she, Mrs. Beikel?" I asked because my stomach hurt so much and I didn't know what else to say.

"Yust like the Rose," Mrs. Beikel said. "Ach, such a poor back! She cry, poor Cissy. She cry so much! And so we get her this. I show you."

And now I knew that Mrs. Beikel would be bringing out

150

the back brace as she had so many times before. It was made of muslin and canvas, with intricate straps and a row of heavy stays. It was harsh-looking and ugly, but in all the world this was the thing I wanted most. I wanted it so much that it seemed that my yearning must have stood out on me like stolen apples in a pocket. I dared not look at the brace, I dared not look at Mrs. Beikel. Instead I asked a foolish question.

"Could Cissy sit up in the brace, Mrs. Beikel?"

"Oh, then she could sit yust so good!" Mrs. Beikel said. "She could sit real good. See once."

"Rose should have a back brace," I said, forgetting for a moment. "Maybe then she could sit alone, too. Maybe Mama could get one for Rose and then she'd sit good, too. Only the Our Word Is Our Bond store doesn't have them, or Greenow's either. I bet Rose could sit up good in one though, and Mama would maybe let me wheel her places."

"Yah!" Mrs. Beikel clutched the back brace to her high black calico waist and held it tightly. "Yah. That be good for the Rose," she said, "but this one I keep. Poor Cissy she wear it until we bury her. Back in old country we have to leave her, but this I keep!"

Lovingly Mrs. Beikel folded the brace and laid it back in the drawer. "I show you the memorial too," she said. "My neighbor on View Street she make it for me when I come to this country. She make it for me when she hear about poor Cissy. See how pretty! Such stitches it got!"

I had seen the memorial many times before, but I couldn't remind Mrs. Beikel of that. The single tear shining in her eye looked extra sad, and I knew that she wanted

151

to talk and show the memorial, so I said I'd like to see it.

Paper came out of the drawer then, yellow newspaper first, then blue tissue paper and at last the memorial wrapped in a brown huck towel. It was all worked in shiny floss, in satin and seed stitch, on heavy, cream-colored linen, proud in a frame of velvet and gold. Too nice, surely, to hang on a parlor wall. Too nice to do anything at all with but lay in a drawer to show sometimes when sorrow came near to a bursting point.

I looked at the patient work of the memorial, at the dates, at the embroidered willow tree, and at the carefully lettered verses:

> She lived beloved, her charming ways
> Endeared her to her parents' heart,
> Who surely thought their latter days
> To cherish would be Cissy's part.
> So young, so tender, innocent and mild,
> Can we, can we rejoice to lose that child?

"It's beautiful. Just beautiful, Mrs. Beikel," I said, sliding off the slippery couch and crossing the Crex carpet to the door. Suddenly I wanted to be out of the little green parlor, away from the aspidistra and the umbrella palms, out of the red brick house. I wanted to be under the April sun, up the half-block of Henning Street and into the happy noise of home. Mrs. Beikel's tear hung sadly in the corner of her eye, and I felt as though I would drown in its sorrow. I was seven years old and tired of tears, tired of willow trees and old grief, and suddenly terribly, terribly tired of the little tan ghost of poor Cissy. Rose and I both were.

I ran up Henning Street with the fringed napkin fluttering from my hand, and I wondered if Harold would be around and if there would be time to play Kick the Can a little while before supper.

O Tuesday morning! O silky air! O plum-blossom breeze that dared even to come into Miss Bennet's second-grade room at James Monroe School! Harold and I walked home at noon and found that spring had suddenly settled everywhere. You could feel it. You could smell it. And then you could see it too where stubby little scillas had burst into blue-eyed bloom by board walks and porch corners; and oh, how you could see it where the clotheslines fluttered and every house had curtains out, or a man's beaver coat and a log cabin quilt!

Harold and I didn't say a word but we both started to run. We had to run! Housecleaning time was a special time, and if Henning Street had wakened that April morning and the ladies had all known that *this* was the day, do you think our Mama wouldn't have a towel tied over her hair like all of the rest?

Rose and I both loved the excitement and the pushed-about furniture, and I think Harold did too. Papa and Peezitch hated it of course, but Grandma Hanneman loved it perhaps the most of any of us. To Grandma it was a happy time, a time of opened trunks and pulled-out boxes and a chance once more to say, "I remember this well."

We turned the corner at Henning Street, and, sure enough, lace curtains were stretching in our own yard. Harold's reefer and my gray karakul-cloth coat were on the line, the Morris chair pillows were sunning on the side porch, and before we had climbed the fence and scrambled up the front slope and cut kitty-cross over the lawn, here came Aunt Lyd with the Alabastine bucket.

"Aunt Lyd! Oh Aunt Lyd!" I called. "Is my and Rose's room going to be blue the way Mama said we could?"

"It's a surprise. Just you wait and see now," Aunt Lyd said, and then Mama came out and said Harold and I should both wash up by the pump and wait outside until the kitchen floor was dry before we came in.

We washed in the cold iron-smelling water, and the Fairy soap got away from me once and squished off the platform into the rhubarb bed, and when I went to get it Harold dribbled water down my neck and I snapped the towel at him good and hard and caught him at least once. Then Grandma came down the walk from the chicken yard with Jud, and Mama pulled Rose in her wheelchair into the kitchen from the back stoop, so the floor was dry and we could go in and see not only the sky-blue walls of our little room, but the border of large pink roses that Aunt Lyd had cut from wallpaper and pasted halfway up around the wall and all around the windows!

"It's beautiful! beautiful! beautiful! Mama and Aunt Lyd," I said, "and Rose and I just love love love it!" Rose caroled and laughed and waved her arms and tried to talk, and Harold said, "It looks real nifty," and then Mama and Aunt Lyd took off their gloves and work-aprons and it was time to sit down to steaming hot potato soup.

You'd think that would be a wonderful enough thing for a Tuesday noon, but something more had to happen.

154

Grandma and Aunt Lyd and Mama were all talking fast and together about "No, Louise, that was the other one. It was Emma who married the shoe salesman and Kleinchen who had the bad eye. She went to teachers' college with the Haggard girl—the flip one with the Billie Burke hair."

Harold had finished and was sticking silver knives into the table edge and whanging out a tune on them, and Mama was in such a happy mood, visiting and laughing, that she didn't even notice.

I helped Rose hold her cookie, and we slipped a few crumbs to Mutzi-Putzi under the table and I giggled and Rose chortled over that, and then suddenly this knock came at the back door, and who followed it in of all people in the world but Mrs. Beikel? She never, never came to our house or anywhere hardly, and I don't really know now how I knew it—that what she was carrying, rolled in the *Daily News*, was poor Cissy's back brace—but that's what it was.

Mama rushed to meet her at the door, and I looked up and noticed that the one tear was in her eye again, even with her shawl on and in our kitchen. But here was poor Cissy's back brace, and that was the reason she had come. When Mrs. Beikel spoke she said it all of a rush:

"And I said to our papa this morning, I said, 'Such a brave woman with all those children and that poor little one and she makes always the liver salad that you like,' I said. 'I bring her the back brace,' I said. 'I bring her poor Cissy's back brace. I bring it *für die Arme!*'"

Then she pushed the long package into Mama's hands and pounded out of the door, out of our yard, and down

Henning Street before Mama could do one single thing more than call, "Thank you thank you thank you!" after her hurrying skirts. I wanted to run out and bring her back, but Mama said, "No, Ivy, don't. That poor soul is probably crying her eyes out this minute."

I still wanted to run after her. It didn't seem possible that Mrs. Beikel could ever cry more than just one tear at a time, and I started for the door, but Mama sent me a look that said "no," and another "NO!" so I stayed.

Rose? Oh, she was nearly tied into knots with excitement. She dropped the cookie, and Mutzi-Putzi gobbled it up, and Mama had to take her that very minute and lay her on the sitting-room lounge while we all crowded around, and they tried on poor Cissy's back brace. Of course it didn't fit right, but we had Aunt Lyd right there and Aunt Lyd could always figure out something. When Harold and I went back to school, there was Aunt Lyd down on her knees, pulling muslin out of Grandma's piece bag.

No more walls got Alabastined that day, but who cared? Who cared at all? When we came home from school at half past three, Rose was sitting on the couch by herself. Almost by herself, that is. It was really poor Cissy's back brace that was sitting up, with Rose, happy and proud, held inside of it. I hugged Rose and kissed her, and Mama brought her mending and sat down a minute, and we all giggled and laughed together. Aunt Lyd and Grandma stood in the doorway and brushed back a few happy tears, and then Harold came in and said, "By gum, that's pretty nifty!"

Well, what did he do next, Harold? He went straight to

Mama's drawer in the library table and got out a sheet of good paper and her thick black drawing pencils.

"What are you doing, Harold?" Mama wanted to know, winding off a little thread to mend the torn place in a curtain where Peezitch had caught his claw chasing a miller moth. And Harold said, "I'm going to draw a picture for Mrs. Beikel. I'm going to draw her a real nifty picture."

"You do that, Harold," Mama said. "You just do that."

'All We, Like Sheep...'

The *Courier* said it was May. Grandma's *Zeitung* said it was *Mai*. The coal company calendar, with the hunting dogs and the girl in the red coat, told us it was May, too. Grandma Hanneman said that now the Four Icemen would come, the cold days when the thornbush bloomed. Sure enough, the thornbush bloomed, the air turned cold, and Papa had to fire the Radiant Home heater again for four whole days. We waited for the squirters to drop from the maple trees, and there they were, the same as every year. Apple blossoms pinked and paled and fell, and Mama knew that this would be a good apple year. Harris' sparrows filled the yard; Papa said they'd be leaving for the North pretty soon, and the next day they were gone. Harold learned to recite,

> "Of all the idiocity of your curiosity!
> If I didn't have my white gloves on
> I'd spank your bombosity!"

I said, "Don't you let Mama hear you saying any such

thing, Mister Harold, if you don't want to be skinned alive!" And Harold did say it, and Mama gave it to him, good and plenty.

You see how it was? Long ago at our house, everything was for certain and you could depend on it. Grandma's old red hen sat on three different-looking eggs and we knew that ducklings would hatch and not chickens. We filled out slips of paper and sent them to our congressman, and sure as sure the garden seeds came back—Radish, Great Scarlet Globe; Onion, Prime Moon Globe; Candytuft, variegated; Salsify; Mourning Bride; Mangel-Wurzel—just whatever we had ordered. But with Rose it was so different.

With Rose no one knew, not Mama or anyone. She'd do a thing or maybe wouldn't, maybe couldn't. Something would work and then it would not work. Mama could never be sure. Mama could never plan.

Rose was growing stronger now, and with her strength she seemed to develop a new will, a will of her own. Sometimes she didn't want to do the exercises that Mama and Mrs. Pahousek planned so carefully for her. Sometimes she wouldn't work her Montessori frames. Mama would beg and plead with her, but Rose would only toss her head and laugh and wouldn't try at all. Once she dropped a whole boxful of reading cards on the floor just to get some more attention. She was often whiney and fussy too, and she cried when Mama said she must still wear her long-sleeved undershirt. Nothing like this had ever happened before, and Mama was at her wits' end about it.

There had been some discouraging times during the winter, but they were short, and after each one Rose had advanced a little further. You couldn't see it from day to day, but looking back to fall, we all knew how far she had really come.

Rose could hold her head well, and the back brace helped her sit for longer periods. Her back was getting stronger with exercise, her arms and legs were certainly stronger; but she was no nearer to walking than she had ever been. I still begged to take her to Sunday school, but Mama always put me off with "Not yet, dear. We must wait until she's a little better."

But now it was May, and Rose didn't seem to get better. She didn't get better and she didn't get worse; she just stood still. Mama worked harder with her than ever but had nothing to show for it. If you noticed only the outside of things, Mama was gayer than gay, but there was something about her that reminded me of Mrs. Schermerhorn's black string shopping bag the day she packed it too full and it burst in eight places all at once. It was one of the times when something had to be done. Something. Anything. Someone. Anyone. Even Milo Butters.

Milo was the most solemn person in our block, and for that reason Papa called him Laughing Allegro. He stayed at Mrs. Pulse's house with the gingerbread porches while he was finishing high school, but what he said he wanted to do after that was go away to college and seminary, and he already had a dignified black hat that he planned to wear there. To keep it clean, Milo kept his hat in a tin cakebox, and he sometimes took it out to brush and show off. Mrs. Pulse said that Milo had great spiritual qualities, but if he did neither Harold nor I had ever seen them.

160

I tried to warn Mama about him, but was it any use? Mama didn't see Milo as evil. To her he was just a solemn boy, and because of her own dreadful need she was quite willing to believe Mrs. Pulse's story that he had a healing gift. She told Papa about it at breakfast, dishing up pieplant sauce and serving Harold's and mine along with a look that said, "No comments, please, from either of you!"

Grandma's walnut house clock ticked loudly on the shelf, "Danger! Danger! Danger!" I ate my pieplant sauce without saying a word, but I had to put a lot of sugar on it.

Papa didn't say much either. He gave some grunts that could mean "yes," and after he got his Panama hat and put a little copy of *The Autocrat of the Breakfast Table* into his coat pocket to read at lunch, he kissed Mama goodbye and was on his way to work.

"Come on, men!" Papa called, and Mutzi-Putzi and Pee-zitch made ready to follow him as always to the corner. I decided to go too. Papa and I swung hands as we walked, and he didn't mind if I jumped hard on the good-luck blocks that had "Eureka Stone Company" on them and hopped over the bad-lucks with "Portland."

"Well?" Papa said.

"Harold's worried about confirmation," I told him. "He doesn't want Wally Schwinn to find out that his middle name is Sebastian."

"Confirmation is two years away," Papa said, "and when it comes, Harold Sebastian will learn that Wally's name is Waldemar Enos Melanchthon. Murder will out, and even the weariest river winds somewhere safe to sea. What really is on your mind this morning?"

161

"Papa," I said, "do you think Milo Butters can make a healing?"

"Ach!" Papa said. So I knew he couldn't.

"He says he can."

"If he can," Papa said, "I'll give him half my kingdom and the hand of my daughter Ivy in marriage."

"Then what does Rose have to have him for?" I asked, after holding my nose at the marriage part.

"She doesn't," Papa said. "Rose doesn't need him any more than I need to have that fool Ambler clean his nails with my hairspring tweezers, but it seems that Mama Louise does."

"Papa, Milo is bad. Harold saw him slip a piece of Jap Rose soap into Mrs. Pulse's drinking bucket. I don't see why Rose has to have him."

"Rose doesn't," Papa said. "It's Mama. It gives her peace of mind."

The street sprinkler was stopped in the middle of our block, and the driver was filling it at the tall hydrant with a dangling hose like an elephant's trunk. He waved at us as we passed. Papa and I waved back.

"But why, Papa?" I still insisted.

"Well," Papa said, "did you ever notice the way your Mama has to do something about everything? She's not like you and me, Chicken. When the Lord made us he put some watching-dust in our eyes. It helps us wait and see how the book turns out. Mama always looks at the last page, and if it doesn't turn out right she won't read further, because in a book you can't do anything about changing things. None of us knows how we'll come out with Rosie.

162

We have to wait and see. But Mama can't wait, and she has to do something. Laughing Allegro was handy, so today she wants to try him."

A big boy named Ralph passed us, walking out on the grassy boulevard. He had a tassel of lilac snapped into the visor of his cap. It would be a lilac day. Everyone would have them. We'd be painting them in school. "Lilacs are out, Papa," I said. And then I added, "Mama takes after Harold, doesn't she?"

"Yes," Papa said. "Mama takes after Harold, and if you don't get back home and get ready for school, our esteemed Miss Bennet is going to take after you. I don't think Laughing Allegro's prayers rise any higher than the shingles on Hafner's barn, but don't tell that to Mama Louise. Some good may come of it, after all."

"It would have to be a miracle," I said.

"Yes, it would have to be a miracle," Papa agreed.

He kissed me goodbye at the corner, and with Peezitch and Mutzi-Putzi tagging after I walked back to the house thinking about that.

Miracles were something we believed in. Rose and I both believed, and why on earth not? Hadn't we broken the sugar bowl to the doll's sugar-and-cream set that was exactly like Mama's? Hadn't we wept real tears over it? Hadn't I asked Aunt Lyd to fix it and then Tudyman, who between them could fix almost anything, only to be told that you couldn't glue glass? Hadn't I buried the pieces sadly under the syringa bush, singing "Heilig Heilig Heilig" over the grave?

This had all happened when we were all little-bitty kids, not more than five years old. The sugar bowl had a glass

163

cover with a little cross for a knob, and that cover had to lie all winter among the doll things, a reminder that if I hadn't been fighting with Veronica Klemmerer about who was going to play the mother, we might still have had the whole set.

But since there could be only one mother, we had argued about it and tugged and tussled at the pair of white-topped French-heeled shoes which were the mother's badge of office. And then it happened.

Veronica fell backward, knocking Rose out of the toy rocker onto the doll's table and from there to the floor. Grandma gasped, "Oh yay, oh yay!" Rose, who had never before fallen in her whole life, screamed in fear and outrage. No one was hurt, but when we cleaned up the mess we found the pieces of the broken sugar bowl.

Veronica knew we felt badly about it and said that she would try to do a miracle for us; and so, after the bits of glass were buried deep beneath the syringa, she took her little white rosary out of her apron pocket. Veronica knew a lot of fascinating things about miracles and the bones of saints; I loved to sit on the grass under the chokecherry trees listening to her other-worldly kind of talk.

"The saint in this chapel cried real tears," Veronica would say, "and when my Aunt Annie went there to pray she was cured of her Bright's disease," or, "Mrs. Ed Preston had consumption and all the doctors gave her up . . ." or, "My Great-grandmother Ott wanted a boy like anything . . ." I fought a great deal with the Klemmerers and Harold did too, but oh! I did love to listen to Veronica.

This day Veronica wanted to be kind because she was

164

orry about the sugar bowl. "You'll see!" she promised. "A miracle will happen!"

And then it did. Without question. Spring came, and Harold helped Papa spade up the garden so that on Maundy Thursday Grandma could plant the potatoes. With the first forkful of dirt, what did Harold turn up but a small cut-glass sugar bowl? Just the right size to go with the creamer and just the right size for the cover with the cross-shaped handle. No one would complain that the pattern was different. Of course we believed in miracles.

What we didn't believe in was Milo Butters, and no matter what Mrs. Pulse thought about him, we didn't think his prayers were worth as much as a Bull Moose button.

Harold and I couldn't stand him because he mouthed words as if he thought we couldn't possibly know what they meant, and the first time we saw him he was sewing on Mrs. Pulse's Household sewing machine, making the treadle go with his long, bare feet. Erma used to let him ride her bicycle, and that was another thing we didn't care for, the way he pedaled that girl's bike, slowly, like an old school janitor or somebody's uncle. We would have called him Laughing Allegro too, only Mama wouldn't stand for it.

Privately I had another reason for hating Milo Butters. I hated him for the way he used to sic the Pulses' dog on me.

"Sic her, Nig!" Milo would mutter, and I'd run home screaming all the way.

Fat old Nig, lamb-gentle and goose-simple! He was as harmless as a butcher's boat filled with leaf lard. Fat old Nig, shnoggling through his black nose—babies used to hug him and mash their gingersnaps into his curly fur. I knew

165

that he would never bite me, but there was something about Milo that was able to infect anything he touched with evil. He had, for me, an essence of evil that walked the day of Henning Street, goat-footed and musky.

Neither Harold nor I were unreasonable, though. We were willing enough to leave Milo Butters alone to sit on the front stoop, making goo-goo eyes at Erma in that spoony way while Mrs. Pulse sat in a hickory rocker painted pale blue, embroidering Campbell Kids on a pillow top. We were willing enough to let them all gather around Mrs. Pulse's Acme Cabinet grand piano, singing temperance songs like

> O Dermond, you look healthy now!
> Your clothes are neat and clean.
> I never see you drunk again.
> How came this happy change?

We were even willing to have Milo get mad when we caught him smoking a Cubeb behind our Mrs. Jones's House, and to have him swear, "Eo in eternum ignes!" This was a terrible thing to say to us because it meant "Go to H-E-Double Toothpick!" but if Milo wanted to use words that were worse than the doctor book and worse than Shakespeare even, we felt that was his business. Rose, my own twin sister, was not his business, and when I heard that Milo and Mrs. Pulse were coming, not only to our house but to see Rose, that was certainly too much.

For me, everything Milo did was evil. What, I wondered, if he put Rose into a witch's spell? What if, instead of healing her, he made her worse? An ice wagon stood in front of the house, and the water from it dripped into the

166

dust. "Danger! Danger!" the water said. I found a chip of broken ice to comfort me, and one for Harold. Then I went into the kitchen and got my Wheeler's reader and my jump rope. Harold was ready for school too, so we started out together. From our corner the church bells rang, "Danger! Danger!"

"We can't let him touch her," I said. "Maybe he's an ogre, really. He's liable to talk double pig-Latin to her and put her to sleep for a hundred thousand years. Poor Mama doesn't know what she's doing."

"He won't touch her," Harold promised, sucking ice. "Leave it to me."

So Harold would help. I made him carry my book, and I jumped rope all the way to school and did Red Hot Pepper forty-two times before I missed.

How can I describe an afternoon like that? We should have had the daylights whaled out of us for what happened, but we couldn't help ourselves. Milo and Mrs. Pulse got to our house about the same time we did. Mrs. Pulse wore her mother-of-pearl brooch from the Fair, the one with "Jessie" on it in gold wire. Milo wore his needle-toe shoes. They looked as wrong in our parlor as flies in a glass of plum jelly. They looked as wrong as a crooked picture or a table with "Dust Thou?" written on its dirty gray surface. "Harold will fix you!" I thought.

I've told you what Milo was; I can tell you better what Mrs. Pulse was not. Almost all I remember is that she had a nose that wiggled pinkly and an on-and-on-forever voice.

She wasn't a mother to put a fistful of dandelions into the best vase, to push back the dark of a nightmare's night, or to soften the dream wolves to nothingness. She was a finger-wagger, a window-knocker. She was a presence, always sitting in judgment.

Do you see how we couldn't help ourselves? *Mrs. Pulse and Milo, go away fast!* I thought. *Or Harold will fix you. Right now! Go!* But they didn't.

I stayed on the trellis outside the parlor window where I wouldn't miss a thing. Mrs. Pulse got out her tatting. Milo sat with his knees together on the two-sided wicker chair. He sniffed and ran his fingers inside his collar. Then he leafed through his little black book and said, "Since this is a judgment because of your sins, there's a certain passage in Isaiah that I think you'll find helpful, Mrs. Hanneman. It's . . ."

But he couldn't finish because just then Harold dashed through the room with a peach basket on his head, yelling "Crossington washing the Delaware!" Rose laughed and thrashed her feet, but before Mama could even say *"Harold!"* he was gone again.

Mama said, "The children are always in such high spirits after being cooped up in school all day!" Then she turned to Milo and said, "As you were saying, Milo?"

Mrs. Pulse tatted furiously.

Milo gulped a little as if it were hard to find his voice, and then he said, "I was saying there's a certain chapter here. I'll read it in case you are not familiar with it." He ruffled through the book once more, but now the door on the sitting-room side opened, and it was Harold again. This time he pushed his chest out and yelled, "I haf der schmall pox . . ." and then, after a short pause, he added, "of putter in der vagon."

Milo stared at him coldly, but Rose was overjoyed at the new turn of things. Mama said, "Please go out and play, dear. This isn't just the time for your jokes." So Harold left.

He came around to the front of the house and went up the other trellis where the purple clematis would climb. Harold poked his head in through one open window. I did the same through the other. Rose was happy to see us and burst into a delighted laugh. We held the curtains together under our chins.

"Good morning glory!" Harold said.

"Oh, how do you dewdrop!" I answered him. Then we jumped down from the trellises and rolled with laughter on the grass. From the parlor we could hear Rose's shrieks.

"Did you see old Milo's face?" Harold asked. "Good nightshirt! Oh, what a sight!"

We were good for a little while, but then Harold had a better idea. He went back into the house by the kitchen door and up the stairs. I got on the trellis again to watch through the curtains. From Grandma's bedroom Harold started dropping barley through the floor register. Not lots of barley. Just one grain at a time. Most of them landed near the part in Milo's hair. Right in the middle. He brushed at them, and he had a mad look on his face, not knowing what to think. Finally he looked up at the register, and Harold's voice hissed, "Cakebox hat!" I couldn't help myself. I remembered Nig. I put my head in at the window, and I said "Cakebox hat!" too.

169

Red-faced, Milo got up from the wicker chair and said that St. Paul himself couldn't make a healing in such a place. Mrs. Pulse got up too, and the two of them bristled all over. I began to be frightened. We had gone too far. Much too far. Mama said she was sorry, "but," she said, "you know how youngsters are. They don't realize things," Mama said. "They can't take things seriously, the way we older people do," Mama said. These were some pretty fine arguments, and I thought Harold and I should remember them, but when I looked hard at Mama I knew it was an outside thing. I knew it was a said-for-company thing.

We've done too much, I thought, and we'll catch it now for sure. Behind the house the rooster crowed, "Catch-it-now-for-sure! Catch-it-now-for-sure!" "Yes," I said.

But Mama smiled then and took Milo's hand, and she looked so pretty and appealing. Finally he sat down, and Mrs. Pulse's nose stopped wiggling and she sat down too. Mama went into the kitchen then for the plates of sandwiches and cake and the tea that Grandma had made, and in no time at all they were all sitting there and visiting.

Mrs. Pulse started to tell about Buster Hafner and what she told his mother. "It's not," she said, "that I begrudge a three-and-a-half-year-old child eating a pound of peanuts at my house, but as I told his mother, 'You've known me a long time,' I said, 'and you know that I don't begrudge anything a three-and-a-half-year-old child eats at my house. But you're his mother,' I said, 'and I think you ought to know what he done,' I said, 'when the griping starts in the night.'"

Mama said, "Well!" and passed the sandwich plate again.

Then Mama said if Mrs. Pulse would like some dusty

miller for her diamond flower bed she could have some, and she was sure too that Grandma could spare some fever-few and bergamot to put in the round bed. Why did she always have to be so nice to the terrible people?

She kept urging sandwiches and cake on Milo, and I saw that he had at least four sandwiches and I don't know how much cake. Rose had a piece of cake too, but Harold and I didn't dare come in to look for any.

Finally Mrs. Pulse picked up her tatting, Milo took his book, and the visitors went home. The rooster in back crowed and crowed. We went into the house. Mama took Rose out of the wheelchair and put her on the sitting-room lounge to rest awhile. We stood there and looked at Mama.

Catch-it-now-for-sure!

Here it comes, I thought, but nothing came. Just nothing at all. Mama didn't spank us. Mama didn't look at us. She walked into the big bedroom and closed her door.

Harold and I went out on the front steps to wait for Papa. "She didn't say a thing!" I said. I felt empty. Not only no-cake empty but empty-empty. Empty all over.

"I was sure we'd catch it," Harold said. He kicked at an ant-hill on the sidewalk and watched the ants scurry over his toes.

"She feels terrible," I said, "and I feel worse."

Late-afternoon sun washed our street with red-gold light. A catbird screamed from the crab-apple tree. Opal Tenn's Aunt Eeny walked by pushing Toddy in his gocart. He was holding Theodore, his bear, in one hand and a piece of bacon rind to chew in the other. There was bacon grease on Theodore and on Toddy too. Visiting relatives at Obsts'

171

on the corner got into a hack and, with hands and handkerchiefs waving, drove off to the Union Depot. Mrs. Obst went back into the house wiping her eyes, and in less than two minutes was upstairs shaking rugs and dresser scarves out of the guest-room window.

I picked a pansy from Grandma's flower bed beside the walk and took it apart to find the big fancy stepmother petal, the two fancy sisters, and the plain little yellow stepsisters. I was just taking the father out so that I could see the chest of money he was sitting on when I heard Papa's step.

He came up the walk with his coat swinging over his shoulder.

"Laughing Allegro has left his stamp of merriment upon you both," Papa said. "How did it go?"

"We were obnoxious," Harold said, kicking at ants.

"That does not surprise me. Did Mama Louise give you forty lashes with a cat-o'-nine-tails?"

Harold shook his head. "No. Mama didn't do a thing. She just went into her bedroom and closed the door."

"We didn't do it to be bad, Papa!" I insisted.

"Naturally not," Papa said.

"We were doing it to protect Rose," I explained. "Milo Butters is bad, and we didn't know what-all he'd do if he had a chance. He might have killed her. We were protecting Rose."

"I see," Papa said. "Does Mama Louise appreciate this thought?"

"Well, not exactly," Harold said. "She acts like we were mean to her."

Papa sat down on the step, pushed his hat back, and

172

oosened his collar and tie. "Maybe you were," Papa said. 'It's just possible you were."

The rooster crowed again.

"Are you going to send us to a good military school?" I asked.

"I've considered it," Papa said.

"Mama feels terrible." Harold kicked harder at the ants. I chewed the stem of the broken pansy. There was nothing I could say.

"What do you think would cheer her up?" Papa asked. "Do you suppose, for instance, that Mama would like to go to the theater to see Cyril Maude in *Second in Command* and have ice cream at the Boston candy store afterward? Do you think some such sort of program would help?"

Harold brightened. "Mama would like that fine," he said, "but you couldn't get the tickets so late, could you? Could you get tickets, Papa?"

"Just by chance," Papa said, "I happen to have two first-balcony tickets in my pocket. Now do you feel better?"

I said sure, and Harold said sure, but when we said it Papa looked at us sideways out of his narrow fox face. He held his chin in his hand, and his left eyebrow climbed high on his forehead. Papa was looking inside of us in a way that he could do. He could always see the things that even we didn't know were there.

Opal Tenn's Aunt Eeny came walking back. Toddy was asleep, his hands still clutching Theodore and the piece of bacon rind.

"And, in addition," Papa said, but his voice was gentle, cloud-soft and gentle, "I think I should crack your two little

173

kraut-heads together because you were obnoxious to Mama Louise. Crack them together," Papa said, "until your toenails rattle. I'll let you off, though, on one condition. Every single weed in that garden must be pulled by this time tomorrow night. There's a little time before supper, so I suggest that you start *now!*"

Harold was up like a shot and racing down the garden path. "You heard him," Harold said. "He means it!" I threw the pansy petals away and ran after him as fast as I could.

"Every single spicken-spacken weed has to go!" I said happily. The catbird flew down and began to hunt for bugs under the heart-shaped bean leaves. A baby wind whisked through fingers of the tender corn. Lilac fragrance was everywhere. May!

Up at the house I heard the screen door slam. I heard Papa calling Mama.

"Sweetheart!"

The Birthday

And now the wind came softly, and it was nearing the birth time, for it was June when we were born, the same as it is for many things—the time when the trees have their uncounted babies and the birds their ugly ones. For Mama, eight years before, there had been two, the one with an easy destiny and the other one with . . . what? No destiny at all, or a greater one than earth-bound Henning Street could see?

There was much in those days that we could not see: ants about their busy work, earthworms toiling, streams running clear in caverns far beneath us. And always there were the iris roots ripening underground, putting up edged leaves that no one in his wits would gather—leaves sharp, sword-like, and unlovely to the eye, leaves which were not bloom, yet were a promise of bloom. For, from the dark beginning, the flower was all there, fluttering petal and furry fall, delicate color and even more delicate scent, all waiting in the twisted lowly root.

And Henning Street understood the iris and expected the flower.

In some ways it was the best birthday we had ever had. Mama served lemonade and vanilla wafers out on the lawn. Aunt 'Melia and Aunt Lyd and Tudyman all came, and the Schwinns with their new baby. Papa lit joss sticks for all of us but the littlest to keep the mosquitoes away, and Grandma poured a canful of water into the joints of the lawn swing so it wouldn't squeak. Opal Tenn, with her hair clipped because of having had typhoid, was there, and the Klemmerers of course. But Mama said I couldn't ask my Sunday school class or any kids in my room because too much excitement wasn't the best for Rose.

We had snapper mottoes, though, just like at a real party, and we played Lead-man while the big people talked. Then Papa picked up Mutzi-Putzi and cranked his tail like a hand organ while he sang:

"Holdes Grün, wie lieb' ich dich!
Süsser Augen Trost für mich.
Alle Mädchen jung und schön
Sollen grün gekleidet gehen."

Rose wore her cross-stitched linen dress, and under the Japanese lanterns she sat in her wheelchair looking pretty and proud. Mama stood looking at her, and once when she thought no one heard she said to Rose, "We didn't make it this year, but . . ."

When we came to blow out the candles on our birthday

cake, Rose blew almost as hard as I did, and we all closed our eyes and wished. Well, sure as sure, I knew what Mama wished. It was a good wish, of course, but I wished for something different.

Mama I knew wished for Rose to walk because she felt so sure that a walking child would be a whole child, but I only wished for fun.

"Have fun, Rose!" I wished, squeezing my eyes tight and hard. "Have fun like everybody else." When I opened my lids again, the eight candles were out and sending little plumes of black smoke to the quiet June sky. My wish would come true. My wish would come true.

Everyone came up then and said, "Many happy returns of the day!" and do you know, it was years before I learned that a return didn't mean something you got? "Have many presents," I thought they were saying, and as politely as I could I'd always answer, "Thank you. I hope we do."

After the visitors went home, we had time to examine our returns, and they were wonderful. Hair bows of pompadour ribbon. Salt beads and Japanese teacups. A pencil box with a picture of a ball game called "Our Nine." Fans with kittens on them, beauty pins, voile for dresses, a box of butterscotch pillow candy, and a framed wall motto that said, "Thou Shalt Love the Lord Thy God, and Him Only Shalt Thou Serve." Last came the things from Harold, and those were the best, the very best of all.

Harold had worked hard on his presents, and I knew that there could be no others like them anywhere in all the world. The packages were wrapped in tissue paper left from Christmas and tied with pink ribbon bows, and on each was

177

a postcard with velvet flowers. Violets on mine and roses, of course, for Rose.

Inside, the presents were quite different. Rose's was a book Harold had made called *The Ten Worst Wonders of the Modern World*. Some of the wonders were "Mr. Snoddy Wearing his Wife's Sunday Waist to Work on the Section," "The Half-Cat, Half-Lion, and Half-Mud-Turtle," "Rassling for a Living on Top of the Flatiron Building in New York, N. Y.," and a better and more finished copy of "Ol' Sorehead Gets What's Comin' to Him." It was just what Rose wanted.

My *Komical Kuss Paint Book* was exactly what I wanted too. Harold had worked hard on it, but when Grandma saw it she tore out the pages with "Overcome by Sewer Gas" and "The Spanish Tortures" and threw them in the cookstove because she said that they were "rough talk." Even without these, though, it was a good present. When we went to bed that night I put it and *The Worst Wonders* into our doll trunk for safekeeping and drifted off to sleep knowing only one thing, a promise I'd seen in the candle smoke. My wish would come true. I knew it would.

When I awoke next morning I wondered what was new. Then I remembered. We were eight. But I couldn't make it real. We had been seven so long, and it was an age I liked. Rose was already awake, and, remembering *The Worst Wonders*, I got it out of the trunk, and Rose found all of the tiny things that Harold had drawn: a fleur-de-lis pin on a lady's dress, a goose flying high with a polka-dot necktie on, the tiniest frog peeking out of somebody's pocket. Nothing could be too small for Rose to find.

178

The weather man said rain, but it seemed he must be wrong; the day began with clear skies and a radiant sun. We played on the front lawn after breakfast, making clover wreaths and dandelion curls; and I made Rose a dolly with the pod from an Oriental poppy for a head.

Summer sang around us. Like sashes of deep blue, corn-flowers wandered between rows of blooming potato plants. Phoebes called their name from the elm tops, and, over a quilt of buttercups and pansies, lushly and lavishly the petals of the cabbage roses fell.

Jud was alone by the chicken yard when Mama caught him eating sand. She snatched him up and ran into the house with him. Harold and the Pokornys played One o' Cat in the lot behind Tudyman's tin shop.

Puffs of white cloud drifted. Bugs said their steely little phrases. June rounded to a perfect hour, and only I was out of step. I tried to feel eight years old. It couldn't fit. It wouldn't belong.

"Do you feel like eight, Rose?" I asked her. Rose grinned and nodded yes. *Yes, yes, oh yes!* She showed eight fingers.

So Rose could and I couldn't. It was an upside-down feeling. I pushed her wheelchair to a shady spot on the board walk near the house and sat down on a butter tub beside her. In the alley the produce man's bell rang. Both Mama and Grandma went out to price strawberries for canning. Mama's step was quick. She loved to can.

Tall against the little blue house stood the hollyhocks, double ruffled—Grandma's pride. Before them Kaiser Crown lilies made splashes of burning color. Gently a blos-som moved. It was the wind that did it. What happened after was the wind's fault, I say, because if it hadn't breathed on a hollyhock and made it bow low to a lily beside it, the idea of "ball" would never have come to me. I was unhappy with not yet feeling like eight, and I needed something different to do, so if the wind showed me a thing, wouldn't it be the wind's fault?

"Ladies and gentlemen at a ball," I said. "The hollyhocks are the gentlemen and the lilies are the pretty ladies. Now the fiddlers are playing, and they bow and they bow!"

Rose stretched her fingers toward the flowers, and I had an idea. There was a broken fishpole on the side porch that had once been used to prop up the matrimony vine. Mama pulled up the vine, though, because Aunt Lyd told her that the berries were poison, and she was afraid for everything-eating Jud. I got the pole and broke off two short pieces from the skinny end. Rose and I each took one.

"We're the dancing masters, Rose, and these are our teaching wands. Dance, you lovely ladies!" I said, and I poked at the lilies. Rose reached toward the hollyhocks and brandished her bit of pole.

"The gentlemen are dancing too!" I said. Rose laughed and beat harder. I swished and waved. Down bowed the hollyhocks. Down bowed the lilies. I could hear the fiddles scraping. I could see the rhythm of the bodies. I could feel the tapping of the feet. Dance! Dance!

Behind us there was a burst of angry German. "Shame! Shame you! My flowers! *Meine Blumen!*"

Instantly the ballroom vanished. The dancers disappeared, and what faced Rose and me from beside the little blue house were row upon row of broken stalks, shredded

180

leaves, hollyhocks and lilies that would never again lift up their lovely heads during that season's blooming.

Worse yet, Mama was there too, saying, "Girls! Girls! Girls!" and, in its silver-bell way, her voice was as angry as Grandma's. It was the kind of time when she would spank me first and ask questions later. Grandma paced and snorted, and her eyes were black with anger, for she hadn't heard the music, she hadn't seen the dancers. All Grandma had seen were two bad children and the ruin of her hollyhocks.

"The idea!" Mama said, and her hand was accurate. "Now," she commanded, "tell your Grandma that you're sorry, and then you can go right into the house and to bed. March!" Mama said.

I muttered something out of my shamed mouth and started to stub-toe my way to the door when Grandma's words stopped me.

"There are two of them, Louise," Grandma said. "The little one did it too."

Mama's eyes widened. "But Rose!" she stammered. "But surely Rose . . . She couldn't . . ." Mama said. "I mean, she didn't mean . . ."

"She did," Grandma insisted. "Will you let her grow up evil because she cannot walk? The little one was naughty too." And she looked up into Mama's face as though to say, "I am small and old but I know when I am right."

Mama gulped as if this were one of the times when she'd have to cry, but then suddenly she said, "You're right, of course. They both did it," and before she had a chance to change her mind, she had snatched Rose from the wheelchair.

As spankings go, this one wasn't much. Just a brushing of Mama's hand across Rose's little white pants, but Rose was my own baby, and it broke my heart. I howled worse than ever. I don't think Rose's heart was broken a bit, but the move was so unexpected that she shrieked with shock and fury. I cried right along with her, and Mama made us both go inside to bed.

We lay there a long time sobbing, and when one would forget to do it the other would remember and we'd start all over again. The rest of the house grew quiet. They had forgotten us completely. I slipped out of bed and, unnoticed by anyone, went sniveling to the barn. I wanted to go and die under the gunny sacks and not be found until Christmas and then they'd be sorry.

But when I went in, there was Harold. The Pokornys had gone home, and he was sitting on the chopping block making a boat. He smelled wonderfully of shellac.

"She spanked Rose!" I screamed. "Grandma had her do it! They're mean and I hate them both!"

Harold laid down his brush. "We'll need supplies for a three-days' march," he said, not taking time to consider. "We'll want some equipment. See what you can assemble."

I wiped my tears on my petticoat and began to feel light and airy. We were going to run away, Rose and Harold and I. After lunch would be the time. Harold knew just how to plan it.

We waited until Jud and Grandma took their naps and until Mama had gone down to the far end of the garden to attack the potato bugs with Paris green. Harold brought out our school bags. In the pantry was half of a pie. We slipped it into a school bag. Four potatoes and a handful of Newsboy cookies went in too. Rose would want a warm nightgown, I remembered. I packed our best little dolls, my sample of Sempre Giovine, and the stalagmite from the Cave of the Winds. Harold took his slingshot, matches, a collapsible drinking cup and some pieces from the Meccano set. We took the goat-cart picture for Rose. From the sitting-room lounge we took the red and green afghan, folded it into the wheelchair, and sat Rose on top of it.

Quickly we slipped from the yard. Mama was bending over in the garden. She didn't see us go. She didn't hear the wheelchair either. Its rubber-tired wheels made not a sound. I remembered our Sunday hats and made Harold wait while I ran back for them. Rose cheered with delight. She had never yet worn hers.

"Hush," Harold warned. "You'll wake the enemy!" I crammed the hats on our heads. Down to the corner of Dompatrick Street we raced. Harold pushed Rose, and I carried the school bags. They were lumpy with dolls and potatoes, and the Meccano set was heavy. Rose tugged at my skirt. It meant "Where are we going?"

"We're running away," I said. Rose laughed. We could go more slowly now. Harold took one of the bags. When we came to Porcher's drugstore he waited with Rose, and I went in to ask for a Free Puzzler. Mr. Porcher was there, and he stood in front of a stack of them and said they were all gone. He remembered that Harold and I had each got one when we came from midweek Bible school. I came out holding my nose.

"Mr. Liar!" Harold said. "I knew it. If it had of been

183

Woody Hecht, he would have given us three. Woody Hecht is a nifty guy."

"He bent a dime once," I said.

"He drives a Velie car," Harold said.

"He isn't a liar like Mr. Liar," I said.

"Mr. Liar is a liar!" We walked along Dompatrick Street singing it. Rose tugged my hand. It meant that she was singing too.

Out along Dompatrick Street we went, kicking the dust with our bare feet. Ed Kubisch came by, driving his father's yeast cart. "Ed Kubisch has all the luck!" Harold said.

Rose tugged at my hand again. It meant "Aren't we ever coming back?" "Rose wants to know . . ." I put the tug into words.

"No," Harold said. "Grandma had Mama spank you. Grandma is a Tyrol."

"What's a Tyrol?" I asked.

"A mean person," Harold said. "Like Gessler." It was hot in the sun. We walked along slowly, and Harold told us about Gessler's cap and William Tell.

"You know the *William Tell Overture* on Aunt Lyd's Grafonola?" Harold asked. "Prrr! Whang! Danga-danga-danga? Well, that's about Tell. Tell was a brave man and the best shot in Switzerland, and Gessler was a mean Tyrol. A Tyrol is when you make unjust laws and starve the peasants and don't give them any say in the government, so the people hated Gessler. Well, he had this cap with the green feather on it and he hung it on top of a tall pole and the people had to bow down to it and everybody did. Except Tell.

184

"Tell said, 'Look here, Gessler. I'll be darned if I bow down to any Tyrol.'

"Gessler got mad then, and he said, 'All right for you, Tell,' and he condemned him to shoot an apple off of his little boy's head because he hoped he'd miss and kill him. Only don't feel bad, Rose, because this story comes out good. You remember that Tell was the best shot in Switzerland. He picks up the old crossbow and takes aim, and here's the way the arrow goes through the apple—Zing! Splatt! Smasho!—and there's the apple busticated in a million pieces and the little boy wasn't even scratched. But then Gessler noticed Tell pulling a second arrow out from under his coat and he said, 'What's that for?'

"And Tell says to the Tyrol, 'That one was for you, Gessler, if I had harmed my son.'" Rose cheered. She loved stories.

When we got to Tetzkes' we were thirsty, so we stopped and had a drink at their pump. The Girl with Unripe Hair came out and yelled at us. She stamped her foot, and her white pigtails whirled.

"That's my papa's pump," she challenged us. "Who asked you to come and pump my papa's pump?"

We weren't real sassy to her, though. I made just one face at her with my eyes pulled down, and then we kept on going. Rose made a face too. She had never been in a fight before. It made her very happy.

"Crazy Boheeks!" the girl yelled after us. "Crazy Boheeks!" I looked back, and she stuck out her tongue. "If the clock strikes, it'll stay that way!" I warned her. "What a prune!" Harold said. "What a poor prune!"

When we came to Ben Bible's greenhouse, we asked him if we could come in and see the flowers. It was warm inside, and the air smelled of wet earth. Ben Bible smiled at Rose. "Going for a ride?" he asked. Rose reached her hands toward the flowers and smiled. Ben Bible smiled right back. He didn't ask a single foolish question but showed us all through his greenhouse. When we left, he took down a pink Busy Lizzie in its little pot and handed it to Rose.

"Because you're such a pretty girl," he said. He didn't notice her legs. He didn't notice the not talking. Rose went nearly wild with pleasure.

We went out into Dompatrick Street again and followed it to the country. Then we took the little side road that led to the German Lutheran cemetery. I climbed over the stile, but Harold pushed the wheelchair through the carriage gates and we followed the gravel path to Grandpa Hanneman's grave. Harold pulled up the Creeping Charlie that was choking out the flowers. We got water in a rusty sprinkle-can and watered the geraniums and lobelias.

Next to Grandpa's grave was Walter's with a flag on it, and then two little baby graves for Kenneth and Little Lily. It made me sad to think of two little babies lying down there.

Little Lily was Walter's twin, and they were Papa's own brother and sister. Little Lily was always out there, but Walter grew up and died of malaria in the Philippines, and he wasn't under his stone at all. Everyone told Grandma that it was better that way than if he had come back like Arch Rodumphrey with a hole in his head that his brains had leaked out of.

Arch Rodumphrey was in Mama's class at Engleman high school, and she said that he had had curly hair and belonged to the mandolin club. But after he got the hole in his head fighting in the Battle of Manila Bay, most of his hair was gone and he couldn't play the mandolin or work any more.

Arch walked all over town in his bare feet, summer or winter, with his hands folded, saying, "Adam, where art thou?" under his breath. Sometimes he stopped dead in his tracks and screeched out, "Sooey sooey sooey!" as if he were calling pigs. Harold and I were afraid of him, but Grandma only shook her head when he went by and said, "*Ach, der Arme!*" And, year after year, she grieved for Walter and always planted extra nice geraniums by his empty grave.

I felt sad thinking about Walter and Lily who were such different twins, and I felt sad thinking about Kenneth who was our brother and who had slept three nights in a basket at our house. I didn't want to think about them any more, so I began talking about Arch Rodumphrey.

"What did Arch Rodumphrey's brains look like, Harold?" I asked. Harold had never seen Arch Rodumphrey's brains or any brains, but he always pretended to know. "Like big bunches of angleworms squirming out of a can," Harold would say, and then he'd go on to tell me how the surgeon had put in a wad of cotton to fill the hole and sewed it up with a patch from a pig's stomach. "And that's why Arch is always calling pigs," Harold would say. But today out in the graveyard he didn't want to talk about it.

"Don't be a goop, Ivy," Harold said, "always wanting to talk about Arch's brains. Go and get some more water for Little Lily."

I got the water for Little Lily's flowers. Rose showed that she wanted to have a flower, but Harold said, "No. Those flowers belong to the dead people. We can't take them because lambs and flowers are all the stuff they've got."

We cleaned up all the graves and let Rose lean down to smell the flowers, the petunias and lobelias and the mignonette. Rose pointed to some little words on a stone.

"Oh, that's Geb and Ges," I said. "Geb and Ges are two eensy little men that stay out here all the time and pull the Creeping Charlie out of the ground." Rose laughed, but Harold gave me a shove.

"What do you want to tell her stuff like that for?" Harold said. "Geb and Ges is *geboren* and *gestorben*, and it means when you're born and then dead if you're German."

Rose nodded. She knew that all the time. I got out of Harold's reach. "Geb and Ges eat lobelia flowers," I said.

Rose looked at me and smiled. Her smile meant "I like this." She showed that she wanted to give Kenneth her Busy Lizzie, and so I put it by his lamb. It looked fine. Rose caroled with joy, and we left the cemetery by the back path through the little woods.

When we came to Clover Lake, Harold said, "We'll make the first camp here. You may address me as Captain de Garcia. We'll build a fire, and then Ivy and I can do sentry duty."

"Why?" I asked.

"In case of marauding catamounts or wolverines," Harold said. Rose tugged at my hand.

"What's a wolverine, Harold?" I asked for her.

"A she-wolf," Harold said, "only fiercer. First wolverine

188

comes to our camp, here's how she gets it zing-zing between the eyes!"

We found a round, grassy hill overlooking the lake, with a patch of level land below it, and decided to camp there. Harold took Rose out of the wheelchair and put her on the ground with her cushion under her. I took the afghan and spread one end of it over the chair's back. The other end we laid over some hazel brush. It kept slipping off, so I tied it at two corners with my hair ribbons. Harold and I weighed the bottom edge down with stones. It made a fine tent. Two people could almost get in. I took out the dolls and the Meccano set and put them inside. I picked a bouquet of Jenny-over-the-wall for Rose and helped her arrange it in the drinking cup. We put that in the middle of the tent floor, with the stalagmite and the goat-cart picture next to it. It began to look cozy. Harold took the cover off of the Meccano set and wrote "U.S.S. Kearsarge" inside of it with a red Crayola. He stood the sign by the tent door. Then he gathered wood and made a fire for roasting potatoes.

I took Harold's knife and tried to whittle a spoon for Rose. The knife slipped and I cut the heel of my hand. It didn't hurt much, and I wiped the blood away on some grass, but Harold said, "That ought to be cauterized, or at least have a tourniquet on it." He picked up Rose's flannel nightgown and tore it into strips. "It's warm weather and she won't be needing this," Harold said. Rose nodded in agreement.

"We'll use it to stanch the blood," Harold said. He tied it tight on my arm and used another piece for my hand. My arm felt sick-funny, but I left it on.

189

Then, while Harold said, "I've cut a lot of junk with this old knife," he cut the pie and we each had a piece. I broke Rose's up so she could handle it better. The potatoes got almost done and we each had one. They were black, and our faces got black too. After we were through eating, I took a piece of the nightgown, wet it in the lake, and washed Rose's face and hands. We let her sit by the water and dabble her feet while Harold and I waded. Rose and I both wore our hats. The water was warm; the hats were beautiful; I wanted it to last forever.

"I don't suppose I'll ever again ride in Woody Hecht's Velie," Harold said.

Rose laughed. She pointed to her hat. Nothing else mattered.

We knew it was late when we saw the cow man coming with the cows. Mr. Tegmeier used to get everybody's cow in the morning and bring them all back at night. When he came by our place he usually just had Hafners' Baldy and his own left, but now he was starting from the pasture, and he had nine or ten of them.

"Hello there," said Mr. Tegmeier. "Having fun?"

"We're camping here," I told him. "We're going to sleep in the tent!"

"So?" said Mr. Tegmeier. He laughed and walked on with his cows.

Rose tugged at my hand. Her cheeks were as pink as her Easter hat. Her smile said, "I love you, Ivy. I love Harold. I love being at Clover Lake the most of anything that's ever happened."

Harold twirled a maple branch and said, "I wonder who'll

feed my rooster?" I dried our feet on a piece of the night-gown. Ripples crossed the lake, first small and then bigger. The sky turned a lonesome color and a few tired little birds went screaming home. Something said "Swish!" in the cottonwood trees, and all the leaves were turning their vein sides up for dew.

Harold said, "Hey! I bet that old cow man tells where we are. I bet the old gink tells!"

I looked at the woods path again and began to think about the wolverines. "What will I do when I'm on sentry duty and a wolverine comes?" I asked. Harold didn't hear me. He twirled his branch faster.

"Gosh, I feel sorry for Jud being the only kid at home," he said. "I'll bet ol' Jud misses us. I'll bet my rooster misses me too. Maybe I ought to slip home tonight and see," Harold said.

"Look, Harold," I said. "Rose likes it here. Rose likes it the best of anything. Only . . . I wish I knew what to do about the wolverines."

Rose tossed her head and waved her hand at a puff of dust up on the wagon road. A horse and wagon were coming fast. When we looked closer, we could see that the horse was Blucher, with a spray of elderberry tucked into the hames. Tudyman was driving, and Mama was on the seat beside him. She had a yellow scarf tied over her hair, and she was still wearing her garden dress. Mama had come in a hurry.

Tudyman drove up close, and we could see that Mama was tight-lipped and cross. Tudyman roared when he saw our camp, but Mama couldn't laugh or even say a thing.

She stayed right where she was in the wagon. Tudyman swung down from the seat and came around the little hill—step-stump, step-stump, step-stump, the way he walked, his shoulders swinging widely. He peeked into the tent.

"Trudchen couldn't fix it nicer!" he said. "It's got everything but a downspout." Then he saw Rose and put out his arms to take her.

"I didn't think I'd live to see it," Tudyman said, "that you should be a *Zigeuner* too, with these other gypsies." He rubbed his stubby chin against her silky black bob and he said something strange. He said it just to Rose.

"Now that you've got 'er out of the dock," Tudyman said, "I want you to go right on paddling and keep 'er afloat. Don't wait around for thirty years like some big dumb *Esels* I could name."

I don't know what that meant, and I couldn't tell if Rose did either. I looked up into her face. She had her arms tight around Tudyman's neck, and her eyes were shining like winter stars. Rose was messier than Mama ever allowed, but she looked pretty and happy.

I remembered Christmas. "Rose reminds me of the Inchies," I said, "the way their little faces always shine when the candles are lit and Mama and Aunt Lyd are waiting with a wet dishrag."

Tudyman snorted. "It isn't a wet dishrag this time," he said. "It's a whole wet blanket."

I looked toward the wagon. Mama was sitting there perfectly still with her head in her hands. Poor Mama!

I untied my hair ribbons and began to take the tent apart. Harold put the wheelchair into the back of the wagon.

Tudyman carried Rose and put her into Mama's lap, still wearing her Easter hat. Harold put out the fire and I packed the school bags. We got into the wagon then and drove home. Tudyman hummed under his breath. The tune was "Tenting Tonight."

Blucher went into a stylish trot, but I didn't care. I couldn't care. I looked at Mama. I didn't hate her any more. I didn't even hate Grandma. I was sorry about the pie. I was sorry we were such mean kids but I couldn't say so. Harold didn't say anything. Mama didn't say anything. Tudyman didn't say anything either, but once he slapped his knee and shook with laughter. "Kearsarge!" Tudyman said.

Heavy clouds rolled in from the west. I thought lightning might strike us. I thought the end of the world would come. I almost wished it would.

At our gate Mama thanked Tudyman and carried Rose into the house. Harold and I followed with the things.

"Slaughter 'em kind of easy, Lou," Tudyman called out as he drove away. "Remember, you were young once too."

Young? Eight years old? I felt eight hundred. It was almost as dark as night. Harold and I walked slowly, trying to put it off. "Do you think we'll get Hail Columbia, Harold?" I asked.

"Good night nurse! What else!" Harold said. "Don't be a simp', Ivy!"

We opened the door from the side porch and walked into the kitchen, scraping our feet. Rose sat in the maple rocker, drinking milk through a straw as though she'd been rescued from starving. The swinging lamp was lit. Mama bent over the stove. She was saying, "Never been so worried in my life!" "Such children!" and "What next!" Grandma Hanneman was in the bedroom with Jud.

Mama spanked two of us that time without being told. Look. She had to, she was so glad to have us safe. Mama spanked us hard. First Harold, and then, when he was bawling good, me. She used the old felt Swatter. I screeched before she really got started. Peezitch ran and hid under the stove. Rose grew excited and spilled some milk. Papa came home just then.

"To what may we attribute this?" Papa asked, pushing back his hat and putting his hands on his hips.

"They ran off with Rose," Mama said. She stopped whacking me for a moment, but kept her hold; her fingers in my flesh felt like little steel clamps. "They had me worried out of my wits for half a day and the potatoes crying to be doused. Not a sign of one of them anywhere, and all the time that rough crew from the workhouse laying sewer pipes out behind. The man with the gun looked at me so oddly when I ran by. I could have sworn that they had something to do with it. They took a pie, and the heat was already so oppressive, and the nightgown is ruined. Harold and Ivy both." A sob stuck in Mama's throat, and she shook me hard.

My hand flung out against a chair-back with a snap, and I stopped feeling sorry for Mama and felt sorry only for myself.

"You're hurting my back! You're killing me!" I screamed, and I shrieked louder.

Papa watched us quietly. Rose grew more and more excited. She nearly fell out of the rocker. She pointed wildly at the washstand, but the gesture was meant for Mama. She dropped her milk glass.

"Tyrol!" Rose shouted. "Don' hu't kids!" It had a queer tinny sound as if it came, not from Rose, but from the tea box on the shelf; but it was Rose all right. It was Rose talking.

Mama stopped with the Swatter high. Papa's laugh split the air like a cannon cracker, and he snatched Rose from the rocker.

Her broken glass lay where it fell. Milk spread in a widening pool, and rounded fingers of it stretched along the floor boards and curled about the table legs. Mama didn't notice. Mama didn't say a word.

"She talked!" Papa shouted. "She talked! She talked!"

Mama dropped me and the Swatter, grabbed Papa and Rose and hugged them both. "Like everyone else!" Mama said. "She said it just like anyone!" Mama laughed and Papa laughed, and Grandma Hanneman came in from putting Jud to bed and she laughed too. "Iss goot!" Grandma said. "Rose learns from the *Kinder*."

Mama said, "Baby. Oh praises be. What's a Tyrol?"

Rose's face worked harder, her arms waved wildly. Mutzi-Putzi picked up the Swatter and tucked it under the pillow of his basket. Rose took a deep breath.

"Gess-ler!" Rose said.

Harold laughed and I laughed too. I looked up toward the lamp, and through my teary eyelashes I saw the rainbow. Not a big rainbow. I only saw a little one.

And After

———————

Now that's the way it was.

I can't tell you what all this means, or if it means anything at all. I only meant to show you how we lived long ago, when the wheeling of the seasons was sure and serene, when horses' hoofs clobbed in the soft dust of cities, and when street cries told how other men lived; a time of lines and brackets, good or bad, straight or crooked, noble or mean. Yet somehow, above it all, ran the whispers of a clear, clean thinking, and in the world of Henning Street as in the Henning Streets of all the world, little men began to know that they were big, and bigger men began to think about the little ones.

Then out of that time there came a time when people knew that there were others who were frail, who were weary, who were broken; that there were people who would never, never without help become real people. Here and there the tiny sparks of justice flamed. These were the sparks that spread and spread to lighten the rooms of shuttered lives, and the hands to spread the sparks were little hands when Rose and I were little.

It was coming. It was coming—the good that comes of seeing the good that comes of ill, the time when the arc we were part of would touch other arcs to form a circle, whole and complete. But long ago on Henning Street we were much too close to find the greater design of which we were a part.

Long ago at our house, that's the way we all were. That's the way Mama was.

Type used in this book
Body, 11 on 14 Electra
Display, Caslon

Paper: Gladfelters Publishers Antique

Anthropology and
the Public Interest
FIELDWORK AND THEORY

STUDIES IN ANTHROPOLOGY

Under the Consulting Editorship of E. A. Hammel,
UNIVERSITY OF CALIFORNIA, BERKELEY

Andrei Simić, THE PEASANT URBANITES: A Study of Rural-Urban Mobility in Serbia

John U. Ogbu, THE NEXT GENERATION: An Ethnography of Education in an Urban Neighborhood

Bennett Dyke and Jean Walters MacCluer (Eds.), COMPUTER SIMULATION IN HUMAN POPULATION STUDIES

Robbins Burling, THE PASSAGE OF POWER: Studies in Political Succession

Piotr Sztompka, SYSTEM AND FUNCTION: Toward a Theory of Society Western Bosnia

William G. Lockwood, EUROPEAN MOSLEMS: Economy and Ethnicity in

Günter Golde, CATHOLICS AND PROTESTANTS: Agricultural Modernization in Two German Villages

Peggy Reeves Sanday (Ed.), ANTHROPOLOGY AND THE PUBLIC INTEREST: Fieldwork and Theory

in preparation

Carol A. Smith, REGIONAL ANALYSIS, Volume I: Economic Systems, and Volume II: Social Systems

Frank Henderson Stewart, FUNDAMENTALS OF AGE-GROUP SYSTEMS

Raymond D. Fogelson and Richard N. Adams (Eds.), THE ANTHROPOLOGY OF POWER: Ethnographic Studies from Asia, Oceania, and the New World

Anthropology and the Public Interest

FIELDWORK AND THEORY

Edited by

Peggy Reeves Sanday

Department of Anthropology
University of Pennsylvania
Philadelphia, Pennsylvania

ACADEMIC PRESS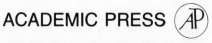

NEW YORK   SAN FRANCISCO   LONDON

A Subsidiary of Harcourt Brace Jovanovich, Publishers

ACADEMIC PRESS, INC.
111 Fifth Avenue, New York, New York 10003

United Kingdom Edition published by
ACADEMIC PRESS, INC. (LONDON) LTD.
24/28 Oval Road, London NW1

Library of Congress Cataloging in Publication Data

Sanday, Peggy Reeves.
  Anthropology and the public interest.

    (Studies in anthropology series)
    Includes bibliographies.
    1.   United States—Social conditions—1960-
—Addresses, essays, lectures.   2.   United States—
Social policy—Addresses, essays, lectures.
3.   Applied anthropology—Addresses, essays, lectures.
I.   Title.
HN65.S28   1976   309.1'73   75-26340
ISBN 0-12-617650-7

Contents

List of Contributors

Numbers in parentheses indicate the pages on which the authors' contributions begin.

Marcus Alexis (147), Department of Economics and Center for Urban Affairs, Northwestern University, Evanston, Illinois

Anthony E. Boardman (75), School of Public and Urban Policy, University of Pennsylvania, Philadelphia, Pennsylvania

Lilyan A. Brudner (293), Department of Anthropology, University of Pittsburgh, Pittsburgh, Pennsylvania

Otto A Davis (75, 309), School of Urban and Public Affairs, Carnegie-Mellon University, Pittsburgh, Pennsylvania

Patricia Lee Engle (247), Instituto de Nutricion de Centroamerica y Panama, Oficina Sanitaria Panamericana, Oficina Regional de la Organizacion Mundial de la Salud, Guatemala

Frederick Erickson (111), Harvard Graduate School of Education, Cambridge, Massachusetts

Margaret A. Frederking (309), School of Management, State University of New York, Buffalo, New York

Lucy Garretson (193), Market Research, Bell of Pennsylvania, Philadelphia, Pennsylvania

Ward H. Goodenough (15), Department of Anthropology, University of Pennsylvania, Philadelphia, Pennsylvania

John J. Gumperz (273), Department of Anthropology, University of California, Berkeley, California

E. A. Hammel (29), Department of Anthropology, University of California, Berkeley, California

Gary G. Hendrix (219), Stanford Research Institute, Menlo Park, California

Evelyn Jacob (95), Department of Anthropology, University of Pennsylvania, Philadelphia, Pennsylvania

Winthrop D. Jordan (37), Department of History, University of California, Berkeley, California

John R. Lombardi (205), City University of New York, New York, New York

Charles R. McGimsey III (25), Arkansas Archeological Survey, University of Arkansas Museum, Fayetteville, Arkansas

William D. Morris (167), Department of Political Science, University of Minnesota, Minneapolis, Minnesota

Robert Parke (333), Social Science Research Council, Center for Coordination of Research on Social Indicators, Washington, D.C.

Peggy Reeves Sanday (53, 75, 95), Department of Anthropology, University of Pennsylvania, Philadelphia, Pennsylvania

Henry A. Selby (219), Department of Anthropology, Temple University, Philadelphia, Pennsylvania

Carol B. Stack (205), Department of Anthropology and the Institute of Policy Sciences and Public Affairs, Duke University, Durham, North Carolina

Anthony F. C. Wallace (3), Department of Anthropology, University of Pennsylvania, and Eastern Pennsylvania Psychiatric Institute, Philadelphia, Pennsylvania

Anthony S. Walters (293), Graduate School of Business and Public Administration, Cornell University, Ithaca, New York

Douglas R. White (293), Department of Anthropology, University of Pittsburgh, Pittsburgh, Pennsylvania

Roxann A. Van Dusen (333), Social Science Research Council, Center for Coordination of Research on Social Indicators, Washington, D.C.

Acknowledgments

Recently there has been an increasing effort in the discipline of anthropology to rethink the underlying values that motivated students and professionals to concentrate their intellectual efforts mainly on the analysis of cultures outside the United States. This new awareness has been in part stimulated by the declining academic job market and in part by the social ferment of the 1960s which called for relevant research in the academic disciplines. In 1972, I drew up a proposal for a conference on the subject of the contribution of anthropology to U. S. public policy in an attempt to respond to some of the issues and problems being raised. The conference was held in Philadelphia in October of 1973. Ten of the nineteen chapters that appear in this book were first presented at the conference. The remaining chapters were solicited later. Without exception, all the chapters are published here for the first time.

From the start of this entire venture A. Kimball Romney and Roy D'Andrade were especially supportive, providing valuable comments on the original conference proposal. Through their efforts, the conference was funded under the auspices of the Mathematical Social Science Board. The Board is financed by a grant from the National Science Foundation through the Center for Advanced Study in the Behavioral Sciences, Stanford. I am grateful to these sources for support of the conference. In addition Anthony F. C. Wallace and Ward H. Goodenough afforded support through their willingness to take time from busy schedules to prepare papers and attend the conference. The Introduction went through many drafts benefiting along the way by comments from numerous sources. In particular, Winthrop D. Jordan, from the vantage point of an academic discipline where good writing can sometimes be found, tried to nudge me out of anthropologese into standard English. Eugene A. Hammel, in his capacity as editor of the Studies in Anthropology series, provided valuable aid in preparing the final manuscript for publication. Finally, and most importantly, I wish to thank all the contributors who inspired me along the way with their enthusiasm.

Introduction

This book is a part of the growing effort in anthropology and other social sciences to seek a greater understanding of how the culture in which we live affects our lives, and to use this understanding in formulating and implementing domestic social policy. This effort is more recent in anthropology than in other social sciences because of the need to study and describe other cultures in order to build a body of knowledge and theory that portrays and explains "both the similarities and the differences in the condition of mankind, to get at what is common through the differences that have arisen through the interaction of men with external nature and each other in different settings" (Hymes 1969:12). The study of other cultures has meant that anthropologists have not devoted much research or teaching attention to the study of their own national and social needs. Recent trends, however, indicate an increasing interest within the profession to include the United States as a legitimate subject for basic and applied research.

For example, the recent books edited by Hymes (1969), Nader and Maretski (1973), and Weaver (1973) all identify issue and provide examples of anthropologists engaged in action or research activities relating to U.S. social issues. In 1971, A.F.C. Wallace (see Chapter 1), in his capacity as president of the

American Anthropological Association, questioned the ethical and intellectual propriety of American anthropologists continuing to engage in research in other cultures while ignoring American national and social needs and the study of American communities. Margaret Mead, whose research and thought have frequently been responsive to social issues and problems, is presently stressing the importance of a change in the traditional role of science to include focusing on worldwide needs arising from environmental and population strains (*AAAS Bulletin* 1973).

There is a gap between the issues and problems being raised and a systematic framework within which students and professionals can pursue training and work toward solutions at either the research or action levels. The importance of filling this gap becomes more and more crucial for the training of students in view of the dismal projections for academic job opportunities. A recent assessment of the future of academic employment in anthropology indicates that, after 1982, over two-thirds of all anthropology PH.Ds will have to find employment outside of academia (D'Andrade, Hammel, Adkins, and McDaniel 1975). These authors predict further that the great majority of the nonacademic positions will be primarily administrative rather than research oriented. This raises the question of whether or not the present training programs are adequate for training students to find jobs and perform effectively in the nonacademic world.

The purpose of this book is to offer an intellectual perspective that might be useful to those students and professionals who wish to expand their knowledge so that they can operate effectively outside of academe. Working in a nonacademic setting does not mean that the academic commitment to the advancement of knowledge is rejected or neglected. On the contrary, intelligent and effective social action both requires and stimulates an ever expanding base of understanding and knowledge. Those presently operating in the arena where power is negotiated and public goods and services allocated—lawyers, legislators, and school officials—will find in this book rigorous empirical and theoretical studies of the range of cultural variation in the United States, its historical dimensions, and its effect on behavior, particularly behavior leading to inclusion or exclusion of various segments of our pluralistic society in the public domain of political and economic power.

One of the several commitments determining the perspective to be developed here is to an anthropology that serves the needs of both science and society. This requires formulating research problems that can be conducted sequentially or simultaneously at the basic and applied research levels. I would define basic research as contributing to knowledge, theory, and method—and hence to the advancement of social science. At this level, one is not necessarily concerned with the isolation of variables that can be manipulated by intervention strategies but with the understanding of all the factors contributing in some significant way to the phenomena under study. In addition, one also would be interested in developing theory and method that result in the most parsimonious descriptive statement of cause-and-effect relationships. The applied research level would be concerned with the isolation of variables that can be manipulated by public policy and with the identification of the point at which the cost of changing inputs outweighs the expected benefits. The *choice* of these variables—the intervention strategies—is based on underlying notions of how things are and how they should be. As many of the chapters in this book suggest, these notions are more often than not based on a narrow understanding of the American society and culture. Commitment to the democratic ideology demands knowledge of the full range of American sociocultural processes and how these processes—albeit, inadvertently as with a life of their own—may work for or against an egalitarian ideology.

The greatest potential payoff both for the advancement of social science and for enlightened social programming comes when basic research lays the foundation for applied research and the process of application uncovers new problems for basic research. For example, applied research can bring to light a class of previously neglected phenomena; Wallace (Chapter 1) shows that this was the case in applied anthropology with nativistic or revitalization movements. Thus, a by-product of involvement in policy issues can be the expansion of a discipline to describe and understand new processes.

Many of the chapters in this book will fall in the basic research category inasmuch as the authors are concerned primarily with developing theory or methods in a given problem area. The utility of these chapters lies in building a solid foundation for the development of a public policy that is based on expert judgments of the workings of contemporary sociocultural processes. While these judgments may be constrained in accuracy and scope by the level of existing knowledge and techniques, they at least provide a beginning.

Several other commitments have determined the selection of these papers. These are commitments to interdisciplinary research, to combing the quantitative with the qualitative approaches, and to listening to what others have to say. Part of listening to others involves working with and learning from policy-oriented researchers in other disciplines. The field of economics has had a long tradition of research and activity at the public policy level. The existence of a Council of Economic Advisors to the President and the projection of future economic trends, are examples of this activity. Initially, the entrance of other social scientists into the public policy domain would do well to include a careful examination of the analytic paradigms that have been developed and utilized with vary degrees of success by economists. Similarly, the success of political science in predicting trends in voting and citizen opinion also should be examined. The interaction between anthropologists and members of these and other disciplines may have the promising effect of generating new perspectives and more accurate predictions.

The success of this interaction will be greatly affected by the extent to which anthropologists can at least understand the quantitative methods utilized in other fields. This is necessary both for the critical evaluation of claims that are made and for combining some of these methods with the more qualitative approach of the anthropologist. Anthropologists must recognize and be prepared to deal with the fact that, although the traditional method of viewing behavior from the point of view of the participants is extremely valuable, it is not enough when the goal is to develop policy that affects a nation. The interdisciplinary approach is one means of joining the perspective gained from standard anthropological field work techniques with existing sophisticated methods for the empirical testing of hypotheses. Properly carried out, this approach has the promise of generating a body of theory and results that could revolutionize the participating disciplines.

To summarize, several commitments guide the perspective of this book. Social action is more effective when preceded by relevant research. Social programs should be based on knowledge of how and why things work, as well as on the ability to make things work. The most probable way of developing the appropriate knowledge base is through interdisciplinary research or at least through the understanding of the methods and results reached in other disciplines. For the anthropologist, this will mean an expansion of their facility with the language of statistics and other quantitative techniques. For other disciplines, this will mean giving attention to anthropological methodology and perspective.

Finally, there is the importance of listening to others—to all the parties who engage in the negotiation of social legislation, including "target populations." The pluralistic nature of today's negotiations, in which citizens' groups are frequently involved as well as government officials, social scientists, and legislators, requires extraordinary flexibility in understanding. Flexibility, at least in the social science component of the interaction, is more likely when exclusive adherence to traditional discipline lines is abandoned. Accordingly, I have included papers by nonanthropologists whose perspective enhances the common goal of expanding understanding in a way that can make social action more effective.

ANTHROPOLOGISTS' ROLE

Wallace (Chapter 1) discusses the development of anthropology in the United States from the 1920s to the mid-1960s and suggests that the traditional paradigm recently has come under severe challenge. The collage of assumptions underlying this paradigm saw anthropology as *(1)* essentially a graduate academic discipline; *(2)* primarily involved in basic research; *(3)* grounded mainly in non-Western cultures; *(4)* requiring no special ethical code; *(5)* entitled to call upon federal and foundation funds for unrestricted support. Since the mid-1960s, challenges have come from three major sources. First, there has been the increasing objection of foreign populations and governments to being studied under conditions of one-sided advantage to American anthropologists and their sponsors. Second, there is the challenge posed by the movement of socially concerned students and others to influence the academic disciplines to adopt practical issues, such as war, poverty, social injustice, and the misuse of the planet's natural resources. Third, there has been the pressure exerted by the centralization of federal science policy-making in a budgetary process that emphasizes practical payoff. Wallace believes that these developments are radically changing academic anthropology and that, among other things, there will be increasing questioning of the ethical and intellectual propriety of neglecting to study national and social needs.

Wallace makes two basic recommendations that could provide new directions both in training and research in anthropology and in national data-collecting activities. He suggests first that the census and other national survey activities be supplemented by the detailed ethnographic and historical study of a small number of ("index") communities selected carefully to represent major regional and social sectors of the United States. I think that anthropological studies of a representative sample of U.S. communities certainly would add a significant dimension to our knowledge of the national style and quality of life. What such a sample would be representative of or an index to, cannot be fully examined here. Wallace mentions regional and social sectors, which implies, although he does not specifically say so, the standard sociological sampling criteria—geographic location, race, ethnicity, and social class. These are primarily structural, not cultural, criteria; they are easy to quantify and, hence, to apply. Communities that are relatively homogeneous in race, ethnicity, and social class are easily pinpointed owing to housing segregation patterns. Stopping here in selecting "index" communities, however, might obscure our understanding of the full range of U.S. cultural variation. One might want to add cultural sectors to the sampling pool, perhaps using the typology suggested in Chapter 6. These are complex issues, clearly requiring much additional work.

Wallace's second suggestion concerns the study of past policy research and resultant changes in actual practice. Careful studies, paying attention both to the growth of knowledge and to the patterns of its public use, would help maximize both the quality and quantity of future research as well as its pragmatic relevance and value. This would amount to an ethnographic study of policy-related activities and could lead to uncovering the underlying assumptions and values motivating the cause of policy activity. It is only through an understanding of the paradigm covertly or overtly motivating policy research and action that we can find the means, if we wish, to change it. One can argue, for example, (see Chapter 6) that an Anglo-conformity model underlies major U.S. institutions, activities, and, hence, policy formulation. Qualitative change will require recognition of how particular assumptions and expectations have interacted to perpetuate this syndrome resulting, among other things, in the systematic exclusion of some segments of the U.S. population.

Goodenough (Chapter 2) proposes that we live in a culturally plural society, and he presents an insightful discussion of why cultural differences among us have gone so largely unrecognized. For example, the pattern of residential, school, and social segregation has served to promote intercultural ignorance among us and has reinforced cultural pluralism. The consequence has been that policy gets formulated in terms of the planners' ethnocentric view of the other sectors of our society. Goodenough believes that an important role for anthropologists will be to facilitate communication between policymakers and culturally different segments of the U.S. population. Anthropologists can do this because of their training in providing "emic" descriptions of a culture. The distinction between emic and etic, even though it is well-known in cultural anthropology, is virtually unknown in the other social and behavioral sciences. Understanding reality from the point of view of the participant is the goal of "emic" description in the delineation of the fundamental categorizations by which people perceive and order their world and in the statement of norms for behavior in terms of these categorizations. By contrast, an "etic" description states norms in terms of categories extrinsic to the culture being described. The point for public policy is that, if one is to anticipate how people are likely to respond to events, including the decisions of planners and policymakers, it is necessary to know the terms in which they perceive and interpret those events—to know their culture in an emic sense.

If planners want information on the aspects of a culture relevant to their planning, Goodenough suggests they consult anthropologists who already have acquired expertise in the culture in question or turn to bicultural nonanthropologists, to persons who can deal with the planners in their own terms and who, at the same time, are competent to deal with the other culture in question. The reasons he gives for the likelihood that the planner will turn to the anthropologist fit with my characterization of the United States as structurally pluralistic. Goodenough raises a few thorny issues, which are likely to inspire controversy. Whether or not one agrees with what he says in principle, he is probably accurate in his description of the planners' motivation in choosing an anthropologist as opposed to a bicultural nonanthropologist.

According to Goodenough, the most important role anthropologists will play when working as advisors will be to help the planner set priorities. Establishing priorities means that there will be an unequal distribution of the burden of sacrifice. This may put the anthropologist in the uneasy position of neglecting the needs of one group in order to advance the cause of another. Not to do so, on ethical grounds, however, means that priorities will be set by someone else who may be more inclined to be guided by the values of the dominant group. Anthropologists can also help to communicate the differences in cultural values in complex, plural societies and why such differences exist. Once these values are made explicit, as well as the consequences in setting priorities solely in terms of the dominant group, one moves closer to the position of being able to declare certain policies in conflict with rights guaranteed in the U.S. Constitution, thereby establishing the legal grounds for social change.

Most of the chapters in this book deal with cultural or language processes of contemporary U.S. populations. Unfortunately, for lack of space, it is not possible to include the work of physical anthropologists who have been actively involved with the U.S. Public Health Service in the study of physical and nutritional characteristics of the U.S. population. Archeologists also have contributed to motivating and shaping legislation involving the public interest—particularly preservation of the nation's past as it is reflected in the archeological record. A brief statement of some of these activities by McGimsey, an archeologist who has been active in this area, appears in Chapter 3.

In view of the emphasis in this book on what anthropology alone and in conjunction with other social science disciplines can offer in the way of increased understanding of the United States and its sociocultural processes, I believe it is important to include a contribution that addresses some crucial issues requiring self-reflection within the discipline, particuarly the issue of training. Hammel (Chapter 4) notes, as did Wallace in Chapter 1, that the environment that gave rise to the tremendous growth in academic anthropology is changing and that, if the discipline cannot respond to the new conditions, it will become vestigal. Although the traditional skills in which students have been trained are important for the effective study of the United States, new skills need to be developed. Hammel maintains that anthropologists can benefit from training in subsidiary subjects, such as business administration, law, and public health, in order to understand from the "native's" point of view the society in which they may eventually work. Another set of skills involves learning the languages other experts speak—particularly the language of mathematics and statistics. This is important because it places anthropologists in a better position to challenge the underlying assumptions of those employing these techniques when they are not validated by the ethnographic facts.

THE U.S. PUBLIC CULTURE

The substantive issue integrating the chapters in this section is variation in social performance. Social performance is defined in terms of those actions admitting an individual into the opportunity structure of the U.S. public domain, enabling individuals or groups to function effectively within the main-stream social system. Examples of such actions are educational achievement (Chapters 6–8), occupational mobility (Chapters 9,10), voting behavior (Chapter 11), adaptations to poverty (Chapters 13,14), and language (Chapters 15–17). The authors of these chapters are also in some way interested in the question of how groups are included in or excluded from the mainstream U.S. public culture.

This section begins with a contribution from a historian. Jordan's (Chapter 5) historical analysis of the heredity, race, and IQ issue suggests the possibility that, because the equation of inheritance, race, and mental ability is deeply rooted in the American past, associated discriminatory attitudes and behavior are not going to change very rapidly, very much, or very soon. It has been said that those who ignore history are doomed to repeat it. Certainly, Jordan's (1968) historical analysis of racial attitudes from 1550 to 1812 suggests that there has been little change—which raises the question of whether or not social scientists and those they train can change things at all. This is not a point likely to be warmly received by those among us who are committed to righting what we conceive as present wrongs, nor is it likely to inspire optimism in the student heading for a position in administration. Drying on the bureaucratic vine is the more likely possibility.

Jordan's contribution calls to mind the importance of greater self-awareness among the social science disciplines of their role in our ongoing social process. Until we become fully conscious of our role in this process, we can scarcely expect to be taken seriously when we expound on the roles of others. An illustration of the role of social science thinking in the history of racial attitudes is presented by Boardman, Davis, and myself (Chapter 7) in our analysis of how the American cultural template has affected the process of American education. Drawing from Jordan, we suggest that the nature–nurture model employed by Jensen and others for analyzing black–white differences in IQ is one more variant of a long-standing mode of thought deriving from social and cultural circumstances prevalent during the sixteenth-century Western European expansion into Africa and America. This kind of thinking continues to serve the same purpose—to exclude blacks. We present an alternative model for examining differences in measured ability, drawing from my analysis (Chapter 6) of cultural and structural pluralism in the United States.

In this chapter, I suggest that U.S. cultural variation is, for the sake of practitioners and policy formulation, best conceptualized in terms of who can or cannot adopt mainstream behavioral styles when the situation calls for it in public interaction. Accordingly, I present a typology of cultural variation in terms of those people or groups who can be classified as mainstreamers, bicultural, culturally different, and culturally marginal. Mainstreamers are those who display similar attitudes and modes of behavior in the private and public domains. Bicultural individuals are those who adopt mainstream styles in public interaction but who maintain a different cultural style in private interaction of the family, home, and community spheres. Culturally different and marginal individuals are those who either have not been exposed to mainstream styles or have rejected them as options for behavior in any setting. The difference between these two types and the importance of distinguishing them is discussed in Chapter 6.

The categories in this typology are conceived as being independent of race, ethnicity, or social class. While the latter classificatory criteria may be useful for understanding behavior in the family, home, and community spheres of interaction, they do not serve well as heuristics for understanding the outcomes of behavior in public interaction. Here, the important issue is the ability to communicate, to dip into a set of mutually agreed-upon standards for behavior. This latter point is picked up in different ways and approached from different angles in many of the chapters. Jacob and Sanday (Chapter 8) discuss the problem of interaction between teachers and Puerto Rican students and how the cultural typology presented in Chapter 6 helps in predicting which students will drop out of school. Erickson (Chapter 9) shows how the encounter between a counselor and student of different cultural backgrounds (particularly between white counselors and nonwhite students) can be seen as a screening device for social mobility. Morris (Chapter 11), in an elegant analysis of ethnic voting patterns, shows how coalition formation around certain issues, ethnic voting blocs, the 1965 Voting Rights Act, and the redrawing of congressional district lines, have increased the number of black incumbents. Garretson (Chapter 12) suggests that the tendency in our society to equate women with the realm of home and family (inside) and men with the world of work (outside) explains the resistance to passage of the Equal Rights Amendment. Engle (Chapter 15) reviews the arguments concerning the effects of learning the dominant language on children coming from a minority language group; and Gumperz (Chapter 16) discusses the effect of language on communication in public interaction.

Most of the chapters are problem-oriented in that they are concerned in one way or another with understanding the reasons for the disequilibrium in the distribution of power, resources, and rights in the United States. Alexis (Chapter 10) tackles this problem in his theoretical analysis of occupation discrimination against blacks. Stack and Lombardi (Chapter 13) vividly illustrate how the social and economic system maintains families in an urban black community in poverty. Selby and Hendrix (Chapter 14) apply an interesting methodology to the study of values of the poor and discuss how these values affect what might seem to the Anglo-oriented researcher and policymaker self-destructive behavior, but definitely is not.

THE ISSUE OF LANGUAGE

The relationship between language and social performance, particularly educational achievement, is intricate and is, in part, the subject matter of the field of sociolinguistics, a field now playing a central role in linguistic anthropology. Indeed one of the goals of education, according to Hymes (1974:119), is "to enable children to develop their capacity for creative use of language as part of successful adaptation of themselves and their communities in the continuously changing circumstances characteristic of contemporary life." A problem now well-recognized in the education of U.S. minority groups concerns language differences as well as cultural differences. Bilingual education is a sociolinguistic subject that has challenged linguists to develop conceptual and methodological tools able to analyze the place of speech in human life (Hymes 1974:119). Engle (Chapter 15) reviews the literature relating to the advantages of teaching initial reading and subject matter in a child's native language before the child is introduced to instruction and reading in the second language. It is clear from her conclusions that much additional work needs to be done before the question can be resolved. Gumperz (Chapter 16), following the lead of Erickson's analysis of nonverbal behavior in Chapter 9, asks how communication is facilitated or breaks down in public interaction. Brudner, White, and Walters (Chapter 17) deal with the issue of national language planning (in this case, Ireland) and present us with a model for national policy planning and some of the issues that must be resolved in this kind of policy formulation.

GOVERNMENT AND POLICY: TOWARD A NATIONAL SOCIAL AND CULTURAL REPORT

In 1966, the National Academy of Sciences and the Social Science Research Council jointly appointed the Behavioral and Social Sciences Survey Committee, which was charged with preparing a report on the present status and future needs of the component disciplines. The work of the BASSS Committee represented the first large-scale effort of the behavioral and social science disciplines to assemble an overall picture of the present state of these fields. The committee's report (BASSSC, 1969) was largely organized around the growing recognition of the need to apply the knowledge and wisdom of the full range of social sciences to the problems of our society. Throughout this report, the emphasis is on developing an increased depth of understanding of human behavior and the institutions of society and on finding better ways to use this understanding in formulating social policy and the management of our affairs. One way, not mentioned specifically in this report, of understanding an institution and how it manages its affairs is behavioral simulation. The major goal of behavioral simulation, as Davis and Frederking (Chapter 18) define it, is to determine the process by which individuals, groups, or organizations solve problems or make decisions. These authors review some of the uses of behavioral simulation in the study of governmental decision making and present a case study of the process by which the Federal Communications Commission issues broadcast licenses.

The BASSS Committee report presents six major recommendations that were considered to be ways in which the behavioral and social sciences could be strengthened both as sciences and as contributors to public policy. Three of these recommendations lie in areas to which anthropologists can contribute. The first concerns the development of improved social indicators measuring the quality of life, particularly in its noneconomic aspects. Van Deusen and Parke (Chapter 19) present an overview of social indicators research and discuss the potential role of anthropology in such work. This research calls for academic participation in policy making at a more basic level than that of the individual expert as consultant. As Sheldon and Parke state (see Chapter 19), it requires comprehension of the main features of society, how they interrelate, how these features and their relationship change, and the application of this knowledge to social policy development.

The second recommendation suggests preparing a privately developed annual social report for the purpose of interpreting social indicators data. The committee urged that such a report be developed privately until such time as it is felt that the problems involved in developing sound, workable social indicators have been solved. After a period of experimentation, if such an annual social report proves to be useful, it might then become a government responsibility like the annual economic and manpower reports prepared for the President. At this point, an important next step would be to establish a Council of Social Advisors to consider the policy implications of the report. Hopefully, anthropologists would be engaged in these activities. Anthropologists might stress the importance of including the concept of cultural indicators as well as the notion of the cultural state of the nation. Cultural indicators would refer to the underlying categorizations, the basic values influencing norms and behavior (including the norms and behavior of policymakers) that are so important for all the parties in a culturally plural society to understand. As Goodenough (Chapter 2) points out, and as is demonstrated in many of the chapters in this book, conflict in values and the lack of intercultural communication have a significant impact on many areas of social performance. The cultural dimension of a national report might provide an assessment of the current state of cultural conflict and communication.

The third recommendation is an essential complement to the first two. This concerns the development of a national data system specifically designed for the purpose of developing and monitoring change in social indicators as well as providing the basis for an annual report. The committee recommended that a special commission be established to investigate the problems involved in devising such a national data system, and that such a commission be charged with recommending solutions and proposing methods for managing a system that would make data maximally useful, while protecting the anonymity of individuals. Such a national data system should include the qualitative indicators that would come from in-depth anthropological studies of representative U.S. communities.

CONCLUSION: POLICY FOR ANTHROPOLOGY

I end this introduction by posing a question in the form of a challenge. Can anthropologists, or any body of social scientists, participate effectively in national policy making if they are ineffective in formulating and implementing policy to shape their own discipline? It is now common knowledge within anthropology that there is likely to be a shortage of job opportunities in the academic market place in the latter quarter of the twentieth century. At the same time, there is evidence of an increasing demand for anthropologists in the public sector at both the national and local levels. There is, however, little indication that this information is being communicated to students or that training programs are changing substantially to prepare students for the nonacademic market place. Rather, one is more likely to see an adherence to the traditional values, described by Wallace in Chapter 1, in both the training and direction of students in research activities. Perhaps the view presented in this book will provide some guidelines to those committed to change.

Another major issue related to policy for anthropology concerns the unyielding value in the discipline that emphasizes the pursuit of what one might call "scientific" truth as opposed to "folk" truth in studying their own society. This problem is evidenced, for example, in the tendency to disregard as "scientific" research that attempts to understand black–white patterns in IQ test performance on the grounds that these are not operational racial categories and that IQ is not a measure of "true" intelligence. Yet, while anthropologists reject such research, it is part of the everyday (folk) reality of many U.S. social interactions that a person's race and IQ often determine how he or she is treated. It is only when we can understand the nature of this reality and its use in the legal system that we can begin to shape it in the direction to which most anthropologists subscribe, namely to disregard these factors.

Finally, anthropology must find ways of helping to resolve the conflicting claims of social science research. Senator Walter Mondale (Sanday, 1972) has expressed both the policymakers' interest in the findings of such research and their confusion when confronted with results making opposing claims as to the effectiveness of a given intervention strategy. Perhaps this is one of the reasons the word "academic" is for many in policy-making positions a perjorative adjective. As Mondale has said (quoted in Sanday 1972:423):

No one seems to agree with anyone else's approach. But more distressing no one seems to know what works. As a result I must confess, I stand with my colleagues confused and often disheartened.

REFERENCES

American Association for the Advancement of Science Bulletin
1973   Interview with Margaret Mead. *AAAS Bulletin* **18**,(4):1.
Behavioral and Social Sciences Survey Committee
1969   *The behavioral and social sciences: Outlook and needs.* Englewood Cliffs, New Jersey: Prentice Hall.
D'Andrade, R.G., E.A. Hammel, D.L. Adkins, and C.K. McDaniel
1975   Academic opportunity in anthropology, 1974–1990. *American Anthropologist.* 77:753–773.
Hymes, Dell (Editor)
1969   *Reinventing anthropology.* New York: Pantheon Press.
1974   *Foundations in sociolinguistics: An ethnographic approach.* Philadelphia: Univ. of Pennsylvania Press.
Jordan, Winthrop D.
1968   *White over black: American attitudes toward the Negro, 1550–1812.* Chapel Hill: Univ. of North Carolina Press.
Nadar, Larua, and Thomas W. Maretzki (Editors)
1973   *Cultural illness and health.* Anthropological Studies, No. 9. Washington, D.C.: American Anthropological Association.
Sanday, Peggy R.
1972   On the causes of IQ differences between groups with implications for social policy. *Human Organization.* 31(Winter): 411–424.
Weaver, Thomas (General Editor)
1973   *To see ourselves: Anthropology and modern social issues.* Glenview, Illinois: Scott, Foresman.

I

Anthropologists' Role

1

Some Reflections on the Contributions of Anthropologists to Public Policy

Anthony F. C. Wallace

University of Pennsylvania and
Eastern Pennsylvania Psychiatric Institute

INTRODUCTION

A couple of years ago, I made some remarks on the increasing interest of anthropologists in research relevant to social policy, research that is responsive to the social needs not only of traditional areas of anthropological study, such as Oceania and the Indian reservations, but of the United States itself as a whole. I argued that recently there had been certain fundamental shifts in the conditions of anthropological practice in America. Let me repeat this argument here, by way of introduction to further comments.[1]

From the 1920s up to the mid-1960s, anthropology developed consistently along the lines of a clear-cut paradigm. As we all know, there were massive increases, especially after World War II, in numbers of anthropologists, in funding levels, in research and publication, but the pattern remained remarkably constant. It was a five-sided pattern which saw anthropology (1) as essentially a *graduate* academic discipline, (2) as a *basic science* with "application" following pure research, (3) as grounded in fieldwork and excavation in *non-Western* cultures, (4) as requiring *no special ethical code* beyond what

[1] The following discussion of shifts in conditions in anthropological practice is taken from the American Anthropological Association *Newsletter* 13(1) (January 1972): 10–11. Reproduced by permission of the American Anthropological Association.

simple patriotism and common decency would suggest and (5) as entitled to call upon federal and foundation funds for unrestricted *support of the discipline as such* (via fellowships and research grants).

Since the mid-1960s this paradigm has come under severe challenge and the challenge is becoming more and more intense. This challenge has come from three sources. Perhaps the earliest source of pressure was the increasing objection of foreign populations to ethnographic, physical anthropological and archeological scrutiny under conditions of one-sided advantage to American anthropologists and their sponsors. The story of much of this process has been told in Beals' book, *The Politics of Social Research*, and has resulted in the ethical code adopted by this Association. A second source of pressure, quickly following, came from the movement of socially concerned students and others to reform the university and to influence anthropology (as well as other fields) to take up such moral and practical problems as war, poverty, social injustice and the misuse of the planet's natural resources. The third, and still inadequately recognized, source of pressure is the accelerating centralization, under both Democratic and Republican administrations, of Federal decision-making on science policy, operating on principles of cost-benefit analysis. This centralization focuses especially in a cost-conscious Office of Management and Budget in the White House, which is administratively superior in budget matters even to the several Departments headed by the cabinet secretaries, and which synthesizes and edits in detail the budgets of the National Science Foundation, the National Institutes of Health, the National Institute of Mental Health, the Office of Education and other federal science-support agencies. It is interesting that this federal apparatus has taken up, in its own way, a parallel concern with many of the same social issues of interest to students and is *strongly* pressing the social sciences to be more "relevant."

The triple combination of the often mentioned problems of foreign area research, of the Movement's influence on the university scene and of the centralization of federal science policy-making in a budgetary process which emphasizes practical payoff is, I think, producing several massive effects which in sum radically challenge the old paradigm. I shall outline these effects under three headings:

(1) There is an increasing emphasis on many campuses on undergraduate education, sometimes to the relative neglect of graduate programs. This occurs in a context of generally tight college and university budgets and is coupled with a shrinkage of graduate predoctoral fellowship support (on the grounds of an anticipated overproduction of Ph.D.s), and of foreign area research support from Federal agencies and foundations.

(2) There is strong pressure on the federal agencies to which we traditionally turn for support—particularly the National Science Foundation and the National Institute of Mental Health—to give selective preference to research activities which clearly promise some practical benefit in such areas, to name a few, as child development, drug abuse and education. Possibly graduate students may find support as research assistants in applied research programs.

(3) Anthropology may have discovered its need to formulate more sophisticated ethical principles by contemplating its involvement in conflict-torn foreign areas. But issues of ethical relevance to the profession are not confined to social conflict in other parts of the world. The question will no doubt be increasingly raised, both within and without the profession, of the ethical and intellectual propriety of our *not* involving ourselves professionally in teaching, research and practical activities applied to our own national or social needs, and in not directing as much research attention to local

American communities as has been directed to Oceania, Africa and Latin America. The phrase "basic research" is no longer, to many, the invocation of an ultimate value.

In responding to this changing environment, the profession—anthropologists as individuals, and anthropology departments as groups—is, I suspect, evolving a new paradigm which accepts a definition of the discipline which, in some respects, is different from the present one and which nonetheless will preserve as central the basic elementary ethical principle of science itself—the obligation to develop and communicate systematic knowledge. I trust the Association will be helpful in assisting the profession in achieving a consensus in the course of this evolution.

These observations still appear to me to be generally valid, although I may have underestimated the precipitous nature of federal withdrawal from generalized support of predoctoral study in the social sciences. I would like to amplify them here, first by considering the policy-relevant activities of our forebears in anthropology, and then by suggesting, very tentatively, a typology of research related to public policy.

POLICY-RELATED RESEARCH IN OUR PAST

Although anthropology has been very much a basic science field, even to the degree of appearing to be esoteric to some, it was nurtured in its infancy in a context of immediate public policy concerns. (By "policy," I mean an articulate and relatively stable theory of how to cope with a certain problem, based on certain beliefs about the nature of the world.) In this country, for instance, one can hark back to James Mooney's classic study, *The ghost dance religion and the Sioux outbreak of 1890*. Mooney did his initial fieldwork in 1891, under the auspices of J. W. Powell's Bureau of Ethnology, and while a military investigation of the massacre at Wounded Knee was under way. Mooney dealt extensively with the causes of the "outbreak," and his report did little credit to the conduct of either the military or the Indian service. His report was published in 1896. During this period, public interest in the Indian policy of the United States was intense. and Mooney's monograph, although not published in a popular format, was intended to satisfy the need for facts not only about the Indians but also about the whites involved in the affair.

A similar example of early involvement in a comparable situation in another part of the world was F. E. Williams's classic study, *The Vailala madness and the destruction of native ceremonies in the Gulf Division*. Williams was employed in the Territory of Papua as "assistant government anthropologist"; the report was published by the Government Printer in Port Moresby in 1923. It had two aims that the author acknowledged: "First, to describe the Vailala Madness, as a matter of great interest in itself; second, to plead for the preservation of native culture—particularly of native ceremonies in the Gulf Division" (p. v). It is interesting that government responded immediately to Williams's plea by means of a memorandum, prefaced to the monograph, signed by J. H. P. Murray, Lieutenant Governor. Among other things, the Lieutenant Governor announced that he proposed "advising Government officers to adopt a sympathetic attitude toward the maintenance of existing customs and the revival of any that have gone—provided that such customs are not bad in themselves" (p. vi).

These two cases are illustrative of several points: Least important is the antiquity of anthropology's sense of policy concern; more important is the fact that the concern was largely felt, not about the problems of the dominant society, which generated the trouble, but for the immediate welfare of the natives whom anthropologists alone were able, in some measure, to understand and vouch for. Equally important is the circumstance that it was essentially this concern that attracted attention to a class of phenomena—what are variously called "nativistic" or "revitalization" movements—that had hitherto not attracted much theoretical interest. A valuable by-product of involvement in policy issues, in other words, is sometimes a heightened awareness of the need for basic knowledge of previously neglected processes.

It was, however, in the years following World War II—the only period of which I have any personal knowledge—that our quadranted profession produced a fifth wheel called "applied anthropology." In the years after the war, dozens, if not hundreds, of anthropologists served as advisors to the military governments of conquered territories and as consultants to our diplomatic representatives in more or less friendly allied countries. We have journeyed repeatedly, in droves, to Washington, New York, Chicago, and San Francisco, to sit at the green felt-covered committee tables of the National Research Council, the National Science Foundation, the National Institute of Mental Health, the Office of Education, the Social Science Research Council, the Ford Foundation, and so on. We have worked in psychiatric hospitals evaluating whether the care fits the needs and have gone to state capitols to advise the states on their mental health systems. We have served as witnesses before American Indian land claims commissions. We have read hundreds of dreary grant and fellowship applications (and some interesting ones too) and helped to set the evaluation criteria and the program needs for funding agencies. We have sat on ad hoc committees and signed explicit policy recommendations, addressed to senior government officials, even to presidents, in such areas as drug abuse, sexual behavior, and the effects of violence depicted on television. We have participated in symposia and press conferences and issued data and opinions on topics such as war, the future of the American family, and the generation gap.

Many of these post-World War II experiences have had a bittersweet quality for their anthropological participants. I pass over the more recent controversies over policy-relevant research in Thailand and over the ill-fated Project Camelot, which have been amply discussed and which have served to emphasize the fact that the days of colonialist anthropology have probably passed. Mildly patronizing efforts to aid a fumbling administration in its governance of misunderstood natives by providing ethnological insights are too easily perceived as hostile intelligence conducted on behalf of a foreign power and, ultimately, activities directed against the welfare of the anthropologist's own native hosts.

Since 1945, we have increasingly engaged in study of ourselves and of our own society for purposes of social welfare and social change. Often these activities are not undertaken by anthropologists alone but are joint enterprises of several disciplines. One early postwar instance was the activity of the National Research Council's Committee on Disaster Studies. In an era of anxiety about the Cold War turning into a nuclear Armageddon, it was deemed desirable by persons in such agencies as the Federal Civil Defense and the National Security Council to obtain scientific knowledge of how human beings responded to threats of disaster and to disaster itself. At the time, an anthropologist, William N. Fenton, was secretary of the old Psychology and Anthropology Division of the NAS–NRC. An interdisciplinary committee was formed, which first undertook to organize a bibliography and survey of the existing literature, and then proceeded to make contracts with a number of behavioral scientists, including some anthropologists, for original research. The major subjects of study included, in particular, panic in anticipation of disaster, the syndrome of emotional shock following disaster, leadership variables in postdisaster situations, and certain special problems, such as jamming of communication and transport facilities. The work was done in relatively leisurely fashion despite the doomsday atmosphere, a number of interesting monographs were published by the National Research Council, and there were several books and symposia produced by other organizations. The files eventually went to Ohio State where a program of studies of unprogrammed events, such as disasters, still continues. It is difficult for us to say what policy influence the project had. Toward the end, the National Security Council demanded, and got, a summary of the findings. The Disaster Studies project certainly reinforced the general lay impression that plans to evacuate major target areas while warheads were on their way were worse than futile. According to rumor, however, a simple political consideration deterred the federal establishment from instituting the alternate defense: a major deep-shelter program. The consideration was not unlike the logic of Fail-Safe: If the Russians saw us diving for cover, they might take it as a sign that we were preparing a pre-emptive strike and might, therefore, launch their own strike against a pre-emptive strike.

It all faded away in a kind of purple haze when Philip Wylie published a popular novel on the theme of *post*disaster panic. There was a nasty review by disaster-committee researchers in the *Bulletin of the Atomic Scientists,* pointing out to Mr. Wylie and anyone else who would listen that panic was a predisaster danger. After the event has occurred, people do not, by and large, panic; they are numb with shock. Then, Mr. Kahn reduced the whole issue to absurdity with celebrated calculations of mega-deaths resulting from various levels of nuclear warfare, and the issue somehow lost its urgency as a matter for policy-related research.

I have the feeling that some lives must have been saved somewhere as a result of the disaster committee's work, but it would take an extensive research program to discover the actual effects. A clearer case is the work of the late lamented Surgeon General's Scientific Advisory Committee on Television and Social Behavior. This enterprise proceeded in a glare of publicity; the avenues of possible influence on public policy were clear; and the practical results were clearly minimal. The policy issue was whether or not the public interest required that the major television networks reduce the amount of violence in their programs. Many people had been expressing concern about the heavy reliance of prime time dramatic programs on physical violence of all kinds, in Westerns, murder mysteries, detective stories, war films, and so on. Parents' groups were objecting to the even more violent content of children's weekend morning cartoons. A congressional committee, headed by Senator Pastore, requested the Surgeon General to conduct a scientific investigation of the question in order to guide Congress in its consideration of possible legislation. The Surgeon General, moving in the turbulent wake of the report of a relationship between smoking and cancer, turned to the National Institute of Mental Health (NIMH) to carry out the study.

NIMH staff developed a list of possible members of a committee that would supervise the study, evaluate the results, and eventually make the report. Perhaps anticipating a report that the television industry might construe as critical, the government turned the list over to representatives of the networks and invited their comment. Two of the three networks responded and several names (including scientists already distinguished in the field of television research) were consequently eliminated from the list. A furor developed when this information became public since, in addition to the fact that some members who were eventually appointed to the Committee were employees of the networks, it now appeared to the critics of television that the study would be biased in favor of the status quo: That is, it would find little evidence of a damaging effect of violent programming.

The Committee was interdisciplinarian, including several psychologists, a couple of psychiatrists, a couple of sociologists, and even one lone anthropologist. The NIMH staff (including the administrative personnel) were experienced and well-trained social scientists. Working together, the Committee and staff decided that, in view of the fact that a large but inconclusive body of literature was already available, new research should for the most part, focus on efforts to answer moot points. About one million dollars was available for contract research. With the Committee acting as a review board, several dozen contracts were let, many of them to researchers already established in the field (including some of the people who had been rejected from the Committee list earlier).

Studies dealt with such relatively uncontroversial matters as the total quantity of violent programming, the number of hours children spend watching television, and so on, but the focus of interest was the process of instigation. Instigation must be distinguished from imitation. A number of previous studies had shown that children will imitate the violent acts of adults (whether present in reality or seen on television or in movies), if given an opportunity immediately after exposure. This effect, however, was relatively short lived. The more serious question was whether exposure to violence (in real life and on television or in movies) would instigate the viewer to commit acts of violence later, in different settings, and far removed from the original spectator situation. Would it, in other words, not merely provide models for violence but actually motivate people to violence?

The critical data for answering this question came from an already completed longitudinal study of the mental health of a cohort of public school children who had been studied when they were in grades 1, 6, and post-12. Their television habits and reputations for aggressiveness had already been recorded. The question, then, was whether those children who had a history of higher violence-watching on television at grade 1 would have higher aggressiveness ratings 5 and 12 years later. As it turned out, such an association appeared in the data; but there were technical problems in the study itself, and the interpretation of the finding was ambiguous. Was watching violent television the causal factor? Or were both the violence-watching and the rating on aggressiveness the result of a third factor?

The Committee agonized over the interpretation of this study and of a few others that also dealt with the crucial issue and finally issued a report that declared that a slight, but significant, association had been found between violence-watching and aggressiveness, which probably applied to some especially vulnerable types of children. Contrary evidence was not emphasized, and larger issues (such as the effect on moral standards of communicating various attitudes about violence, war, law and order, civil rights, and so on) were noted but not seriously studied.

The report satisfied no one and probably convinced no partisan of either cause of anything except that it was wrong to give a committee of social scientists one million dollars to spend on research if all they could do with the results was equivocate. No federal legislation was passed as a result; the Federal Communications Commission imposed no new regulations on programming; and, as well as one can judge, the level of violence on television has not changed significantly.

Actually, of course, the Committee was not equivocating. There was abundant evidence to show, in a negative sense, that there was no *massive* instigating effect. There was evidence to show that some children, of not well-understood characteristics, probably were instigated by, among other things, violence on television. It was also apparent that many people, including children, liked to watch violent programs on television.

The only "good" consequence of the whole affair was, perhaps, the stimulation of more research into the matter. In the nature of the case, however, neither the social critics nor the defenders of television as it is could look upon the social sciences as having contributed anything of much value to the debate. Both sides had already settled, in their own minds, on a view of reality, and only the most startling, incontrovertible, black and white kind of discovery could be expected to change their minds.

TYPES OF POLICY-RELATED PROFESSIONAL ACTIVITY

In reviewing my own experience, and what I know of my colleagues' experiences, it seems that one can usefully generate a rough-and-ready typology of policy-related professional activity. (I prefer the word "activity" here to "research" because many of the more interesting contributions have had to do with evaluating other peoples' research rather than presenting work of one's own.) The typology is oriented to the identity of the policymaker and to the circumstances of policy decisions because it seems to me that these various factors call for different kinds of responses by anthropologists. Four categories seem to be clearly necessary:

1. "Public opinion" decides gradually, over a long time period via a multitude of individual legislative, judicial, administrative, and economic acts. Here I think of the research, essays, and theoretical, or even methodological, works that contribute to the formation, support, or destruction of a pervasive ideology. Although such work is apt to be diffuse and is rarely done at the explicit behest of government or foundation, it may have the profoundest impact of all on public policy. Studies dealing with human nature are of prime importance here, for they rationalize major policy orientations with respect to education, public welfare programs, war, civil rights, foreign relations, taxation—the whole range of a society's major policy postures. Of immediate relevance now are such issues as racial equality or inequality; sexual equality or inequality; whether or not man is inherently aggressive, acquisitive, and competitive; what is the most natural, or most appropriate, form of the family for a given society; and so forth. Considerations relevant to such issues may come from widely disparate fields—primatology, comparative human biology, paleontology, archaeology, psychology, and history, as well as ethnology and cultural anthropology. Such broad considerations also are directly relevant to immediate policy determinations (i.e., budget formation, troop commitment, etc.). Views of race and intelligence may influence a local school board's decisions on funding levels for various aspects of its programs. Beliefs about whether or not foreign peasants will fight and die for political beliefs against their own immediate economic interest may influence decisions about military commitments in underdeveloped areas. Anthropologists are not likely to be in a position to determine public

ideology all by themselves in such matters, but they can contribute powerfully to it in their role as "intellectuals."

2. Administrative structures (particularly government) are aware of a problem or issue, are dissatisfied with present modes of addressing it, but do not know what, if any, new options may be available to them, or how to choose between such options. Here, I think particularly of such large, but less diffuse than those mentioned earlier, problems as mental health, disasters (including nuclear attack), public housing, and the like: matters about which major governmental units must make decisions and which are more or less controversial. In Philadelphia, in the 1950s, for instance, there was much public debate over the relative merits of high-rise and low-rise housing. One of the parties, the Philadelphia Housing Association, employed me to prepare a report on the subject, which was later published by the Housing Authority itself. The state hospital systems are another governmental problem on an even vaster scale. As a result of a miscellany of new information and viewpoints, including the introduction of psychotropic drugs, the realization that milieu changes often improved the condition of psychotic patients, and a general research emphasis on chemical and situational factors in disturbed behavior, some state systems are now following the policy of emptying the state hospitals of most of their patients and of maintaining them in out-patient status in contact with community clinics and specially prepared housing situations. As a third example, one can cite the National Research Council's Committee on Disaster Studies and its research program shortly after the commencement of the Cold War; its research and publications no doubt contributed to a policy decision *not* to embark the nation on a program of deep-shelter building or Civil Defense evacuation plans.

3. Administrative structures are aware of the problem, have clearly defined options presented by law or custom, but need information before deciding which one to pick. One thinks here of more specific issues, such as whether the Corps of Engineers shall be ordered to construct a dam that will wash out an Indian reservation; whether the Congress should pass legislation legalizing marijuana; whether the Civil Service Commission should announce a policy that homosexuality is not a bar to employment; whether the Surgeon General should declare that violence on television is dangerous to the mental health of children; whether a given Indian tribe should be awarded financial compensation for past injury. All of these decisions are affected by the prior categories of policy, but more specific advice or data is required.

4. An administrative structure knows, as a policy matter, what it is going to do but will not move until more information is available to guide it in deciding how much to do it, when, where, how quickly, and so on. Here the input is not so much effective in determining policy as in rendering that policy effective. In one sense, these are the narrowest problems; but, precisely because they *are* narrow, the scientific problem that is exposed may be a basic one. Thus, a

housing authority may have decided to construct its buildings in such a way as to maximize neighborhood solidarity. There are, however, differences of opinion about what design factors under the authority's control will maximize neighborliness. The social psychologist or anthropologist who is consulted may be forced to admit that he does not know and that "basic" research is needed to find out.

PROBLEMS AND FRUSTRATIONS

The simple typology given here may need to be expanded, and I am sure that it is inadequate, at least in the sense that many individual enterprises will be classifiable in more than one category. If only as a device to force the consideration of a wide range of activities, however, it serves to show that the proper public policy activities of anthropologists are not confined to dealing with the special problems of minority groups; they deal with the very structure of the society itself.

As we have become painfully aware in the last few years, with the Camelot episodes and Thailand affairs, ethical problems bestrew the path of the social scientist whenever his work touches matters of public concern—and most of his work does. Sometimes the ethical problem is the possibility of the diversion of a discipline from the paradigmatic path (in the Kuhnian sense) by allowing its field of observation, its personnel, its jargon, and even its theoretical interests to be determined by action agencies, whether they be the military or the National Institute of Mental Health. At other times, the ethical problem is an intervention in other people's affairs, to the disadvantage of some of them, in the interest of special groups, whether by the discipline itself or by those who pay for its work.

Often, conscious involvement in policy matters—as in serving on an ad hoc committee or as an administrative advisor—is extremely frustrating, if not at times disillusioning. It is not merely that one's own contribution may be passed over, ignored, or even rejected; in addition, sometimes nothing at all happens. The contributions of science disappear down a rabbit hole, as it were, into an alien and incomprehensible governmental wonderland. One sometimes wishes that the world were governed by people who were willing to make classic Operations—Research-type contracts with social scientists just as the military did with mathematicians and physicists during World War II, but it is not realistic to expect this. The Operations Research model can only work in a clear and reasonably rational hierarchical system, and civil government—like university administration—is *not* (I almost venture to say "never and nowhere") a clear and simple hierarchy, but rather a complex network of consensual politics, intrigue, overlapping and competing administrative units, and bureaucracies so intricate that no single line of authority can direct them.

In a world like this, the frustration of the policy-oriented scholar and scientist is inevitable. But in a world like this, also, it is always possible to get someone to listen; in fact, the real problem is to generate information *without* some policymaker, on some level, hearing of it and using it, or attempting to destroy it, for some not-so-mysterious purpose of his own.

OPPORTUNITIES FOR CLARIFICATION

This book offers an opportunity for the consideration, not merely of new areas of potential contribution to policy, but also of the general problem of how these contributions can be made most effectively. As I have indicated, the interface between research and policy formation is not always a smooth one. Different types of situations—perhaps of the various aforementioned categories—may call forth different ethical principles and different patterns of association between administrator and scientist.

One of the promising new explorations, in this regard, is the newly developing field of *social indicators,* to which Chapter 19 is devoted. What is particularly interesting here is the possible opportunity for social science data and principles of interpretation, to be treated by various agencies of government as part of their standard informational input. Economic and demographic measures, of course, have traditionally been used by government to guide planning and as feedback with which to evaluate recent policy. Social and cultural considerations of other kinds, however, have increasingly been the subject of attitude surveys, or "polls," which supplement that other great coercive but ambiguous attitude survey, the electoral process. To the extent that the social indicators movement can amplify and regularize the flow of these kinds of information, the formation of policy can only be made more efficient and responsive.

My only criticism of social indicators is a typically anthropological one. The kinds of data used as indicators look, to me, very "thin." Quantifiable data in the social sciences are often thin because the criterion of countability and the demands of sample designs, where a large and diverse population is the subject, conspire to limit questionnaires to all but the most simple and apparently unambiguous response categories. Little can come through, on a national sample, about the organizational structure of any one community, or about the *meaning* of categories such as "college graduate," "Protestant," and "think a four-day work week is a good idea." I would suggest, therefore, that the census and survey type of data upon which social indicators rely be supplemented by the detailed ethnographic and historical study of a small number of communities, selected carefully to represent major regional and social sectors of the United States. About any one such community, studied continuously over years both by survey research methods and by the methods of the ethnographer and the historian, a body of data of great value for the analysis of process over time would accumulate, involving various dimensions. The study of these *index communities* would supplement, in an important way, the cross-sectional studies of national samples now being undertaken by survey research methods.

Let me conclude on the typical social scientist's note: "More research is needed." In this case, the research really lies in the domain of the history and sociology of that mixed "field" of science and its applications. Despite the fact that inquiry into the actual payoff of social scientific research is regarded by some of my colleagues as being in bad taste, if not slightly obscene, I believe that the question must be faced. Policy-relevant research needs to be the subject of research in order to know its influence (if any) on policy and to know the actual effects of that policy where implemented. It is not enough to accept the money, to do the study, and then to walk away. Too often—as Margaret Mead and her colleagues remarked in their report on the Thailand affair—the social scientist has regarded the bureaucrat who awards money in the hope of some tangible payoff as a candidate for wily exploitation via clever grantsmanship. Serious consideration of how to maximize both the quality and quantity of research, and also its pragmatic relevance and value to policymakers, must involve the careful study of actual cases, with attention paid both to the growth of knowledge and also to the patterns of its use by administrators and policy-makers. Careful empirical studies of the various ways in which policymakers have in fact influenced, and been influenced by, the social sciences are perhaps the proper domain of the sociology of science rather than anthropology per se. Whoever does the work, it needs to be done with an awareness that the relationship between science and public policy and administration is an enduring and complex one, involving systematic interactions among at least three parties or roles: scientists and scientific institutions, administrators and public institutions, and a general public and its culture. These interactions involve not only efforts to cooperate but also conflicts of interest and of values, to which the "factual" input of science bears an ambiguous relationship. Long-term processes of cultural change, which determine the issues about which policy is formed, are also involved. Such studies would, I believe, be of value to all parties in the collaboration.

2

Intercultural Expertise and Public Policy

Ward H. Goodenough
University of Pennsylvania

During World War II, my duties as an Army enlisted man with the Research Branch of the War Department's Information and Education Division included the pretesting of questionnaires used in surveys of attitudes and opinions among Army personnel. Designed for a variety of purposes, the questionnaires were drawn up by civilian sociologists on the staff of the Research Branch. Not having lived and worked as enlisted men among enlisted men, they had difficulty putting their questions in terms that were meaningful to the respondents. It was my job, in the course of pretesting, to figure out how to translate the original questions into appropriate langauge and how to refocus the questions, keeping them consistent with their original intent, so that they conformed with the clichés and stereotypes of the G.I. subculture. In morale studies, for example, indices of morale had to do with the things that preoccupied soldiers and with the various ways they expressed themselves about them. Soldiers' morale could not be measured by indices that would be appropriate to measuring the morale of social psychologists in the Pentagon.[1]

---

[1] For the kinds of studies undertaken, the findings from them, and the methodological problems involved, see the series of volumes by Stouffer and his associates (Stouffer 1949–1950).

Now we are used to thinking about the problem of bridging cultural gaps in connection with A.I.D. or Peace Corps programs outside of the United States. As the experience of the Army's Research Branch shows, however, the same problem of cross-cultural communication exists within complex, culturally plural societies such as our own. This problem is especially pronounced in communication between public planners or policymakers, drawn from professionally educated elites, and the other segments of our society for which they plan or make policy. Politicians are necessarily sensitive to this problem, as when they seek to find out what their constituents' main concerns are and to talk about them publicly in a "folksy" way. In recent years, moreover, research has made us increasingly aware of the depth of this problem in public education as it applies to our nation's economically most underprivileged groups as well as to such culturally and linguistically distinct peoples as Puerto Ricans, Chicanos, American Indians, and native Hawaiians (Sanday 1972, this volume).

We live in a culturally plural society. Cultural differences among us may be somewhat less marked than those we notice when we travel to other societies, but they are not less significant. Social structure tends to make our experience of cultural differences within our society, and out attitude toward them, different from our experience of these differences in other societies to which we travel. This difference in experience inclines us to overlook or to deprecate cultural differences in our own society. People from different classes or other sectors of our society deal with one another in narrowly circumscribed contexts: as employer and employee or as professional practitioner and client. We may spend a great deal of time in these contexts, but their narrowness of focus limits the kinds of dealings we have with one another in them and, hence, limits our chances of ever discovering the range of cultural differences among us outside of these contexts. If we become conscious of such differences, the highly structured nature of work and clinic situations prevents our having to do anything about these differences and allows us to remain ignorant of their true nature and extent.

To learn other people's ways of doing things and how to conduct oneself appropriately in terms of another set of customary procedures and values is hard work. No one who has mastered something likes to have to revert to being a neophyte again, unless he has some compelling reason to do so. People avoid, if they can, operating in situations where they are unfamiliar with what is expected and where they are likely, in consequence, to feel silly and incompetent. It is not surprising, therefore, that those who have the power to structure social situations regularly structure them so that they themselves will operate on familiar home grounds where others will have to do most of the adjusting. Doctors prefer to have their patients come to the office for their own emotional comfort as well as for reasons of economic and medical efficiency. Hospitals are arranged for the convenience of their staffs even, sometimes, at the expense of the patients, work situations for the convenience of employers at the expense of employees, public agencies for the convenience of the administrators at the expense of the public they serve. A superior regularly has his subordinates come to his office or other home grounds, where he is comfortable and they are in alien territory. He forces his subordinates to make the adjustments and minimizes his need to learn anything in order to function to his own satisfaction. If things go wrong for others because of his ignorance, his power advantage protects him from adverse consequences to himself. He can rationalize away his failures as someone else's fault and go on as before. I mention this all too familiar behavioral pattern because it works to minimize awareness by those in positions of power, and to minimize their desire to be aware, of the extent and importance of cultural differences between themselves and those for whom they plan and with regard to whose lives and welfare they formulate public policy.[2]

The pattern of self-segregation by those able to accomplish it is most clearly evident in colonial situations and among groups of expatriates, where the resident colonial officials or oil company employees tend to live in special compounds or distinct localities and to restrict very sharply their dealings with local people. It is no exaggeration to say that, in the United States, the pattern of residential segregation and of social and recreational club membership is essentially the same. Such social segregation serves both to reinforce cultural pluralism in American society and to promote intercultural ignorance among its members. The consequence for planning and policy making is that plans and policies are made in terms of the planner's ethnocentric view of the other sectors of our society.

Every culture's customs and beliefs rest on largely inexplicit categorizations of phenomena by which people perceive and order their world and the natural, social, and imaginary events within it. People's more explicit customs and beliefs are formulated in terms of these categorizations. In anthropological jargon, an "emic" description of a culture is one that seeks to delineate these fundamental categorizations and to state the culture's norms for behavior in terms of them. By contrast, an "etic" description is one that states its norms in terms of categories extrinsic to the culture being described. Etic description is, of course, necessary for delineating the basic categories intrinsic to a culture, what amount to that culture's primitive terms, but a fully emic description confines its use of "etic" categories and concepts to this task.[3] From there, it proceeds to describe the culture in its own terms.

---

[2] An added problem is that to point this out serves to confront planners and policymakers with their deficiencies and to put them immediately on the defensive, forcing them to deny that cultural differences are relevant to what they do.

[3] The terms "emics" and "etics" were coined by Pike (1954) on the analogy of phonemics and phonetics in structural linguistics. For recent discussion of these concepts in relation to anthropological method and theory, see Goodenough (1970, 1971).

Obviously, if one is to anticipate how people are likely to respond to events, including the decisions of planners and policymakers, it is necessary to know the terms in which they perceive and interpret those events, to know their culture in an emic sense. That much is clear. What is not so clear, perhaps, is where anthropologists come into the picture.

Anthropologists are increasingly being trained to learn and describe the emic categories of cultures. The methods by which they do this are still being developed. Furthermore, just as it takes time and effort to become competent in another language, it takes as much or more time and effort to acquire a command of another culture. To gain this competence, moreover, an anthropologist must rely on the already acquired competence of the people whose culture he seeks to learn. They are the experts. All an anthropologist does is to try to learn what they already know and describe it to others, but, in the end, he knows no more than they do. The difference is that he objectifies far more what he knows, both to himself and to others, and can, therefore, communicate that knowledge more accurately and directly. The point remains, however, that there is no way an anthropologist, starting cold, can go out and do a quick survey to learn the emic categories of another culture. If planners want information on the aspects of a culture that are relevant to their planning, either they must consult anthropologists who have already acquired expertise in the culture in question or they must turn to bicultural nonanthropologists, to persons who can deal with the planners in the planners' terms and who, at the same time, are competent in the other culture. Most of these persons grow up with that other culture and, through later, formal education and job experience, acquire competence in the planners' culture. They are more numerous than anthropologists and provide an obvious resource for developing culturally articulated plans and policies.

In practice, however, planners are hesitant to use this resource for serious, as distinct from token, consultation, especially at the policy-making level. They are more likely to use them to help implement policies and plans already decided upon; this is my impression, and it is also my impression that, when such consultations are sought, the relations between consulter and consultant are often difficult. There is, I think, good social psychological reason for this.

In a complex, multicultural society such as ours, planners and policymakers are members of and represent a cultural group that is politically dominant and socially prestigious. Their group's cultural values are the ones that define national interests. To give representatives of politically weak and socially un-prestigious groups a serious role in policy making is to surrender the power and prestige of the group the policymaker represents. It implicitly recognizes that other commonly derogated cultural values may have social legitimacy. Policy, moreover, is made with the interests of the dominant social group in mind. Even when policymakers decide to serve the interests of other, subordinate groups, the interests to be served are those that policymakers decide are "legitimate," by which they mean interests that can be served in ways that do not seriously jeopardize the interests of the dominant group. In making policy, to take as partners people who represent subordinate groups is to imply that the competing interests of the dominant and subordinate groups are subject to negotiation and compromise, a concession that members of a dominant group are very unlikely to make, except as the real power of formerly subordinate groups changes for other reasons. There is good reason, then, that planners and policymakers should hesitate to turn for serious consultation to bicultural "native" members of subordinate groups.

Thus, we come back to knowledgeable anthropologists, especially to those who are perceived as native or fully assimilated members of the dominant group. In this case, too, however, there are social psychological impediments to effective consultation.

In considering these impediments, we must first remind ourselves of a commonplace but largely overlooked aspect of social organization: People are continually called upon to sacrifice their personal interests to the interests of the groups to which they belong and to the interests of more powerful members of those groups, often advanced in the name of group interest (e.g., "national security"). Such sacrifice characterizes all societies, although in varying degrees. The more complicatedly interdependent that people are for the promotion of their respective interests, the more the necessity for making sacrifice. Every society has priorities as to what categories of persons make what kinds of sacrifice under what circumstances—including giving up their rights as members of society and even their lives. Some of these priorities are explicit and agreed to, at least in principle, by nearly everyone. "Women and children first" is an example in our society. Other priorities are less explicit but are no less systematically applied and are agreed to in practice, if not in principle. We see them at work in our society in connection with programs that get their budgets cut or eliminated or that are perennially underfunded in respect to their publicly announced objectives. Remedial reading in the schools and treatment of the mentally ill and physically handicapped are obvious examples. Clearly, low priority goes to the special needs of people who, without assistance, are unable to operate within our institutional arrangements. Moreover, people who occupy relatively powerless positions and who are perceived by those in power as "not their own kind" (by whatever criterion) are asked to make the greater sacrifices on behalf of the larger society. Land owned by members of so-called minority groups is more likely to be condemned for new schools or other public purposes. Those in power, moreover, resent persons who champion the interests of the powerless when the latter are called on to make the major sacrifices. The indignation of top officials in the Trust Territory of the Pacific at the successful defense of Micronesian interests by Peace Corps and OEO lawyers is a matter of record (Trumbull 1973). The Legal Services Program in our cities is under attack by public officials for similar reasons. Successful court suits on behalf of the poor led one member of Congress to complain, "What happens to the man in the middle class, the tax-paying and tax-providing millions who are not poor?" (Mathews 1973). His priorities are clear.

Anthropology developed in an age of Western political dominance of much of the world. Its concern with all of the world's ethnic groups inevitably has led most anthropologists to study politically dominated peoples, such as American Indians and the "tribes" of colonial areas; and their focus on small communities has meant that, even in Western countries, anthropologists have concentrated on peasants or on their urban equivalents, almost invariably people who are in weak power positions vis-à-vis political policymakers and national planners. The objects of anthropological study have been those peoples whose interests are the first to be sacrificed.

In order to learn their culture, an anthropologist must live in close association with the people he studies. He has to try to identify himself with them in order to learn to see and understand things as they do. As a result, he almost inevitably comes to feel a close kinship with them and to make their interests his own. To ignore their interests is to betray a trust that he assumed by virtue of the kind of association he had with them. It is not surprising, therefore, that anthropologists tend naturally to become resentful of the things policymakers and planners do in the interests of the dominant groups they represent. When asked to cooperate with policymakers, they are inclined to suspect that they are being asked to aid and abet policies that are not in the best interests of the people in whose culture they have acquired expertise. The "my people" syndrome is a natural consequence of the things anthropologists do. It necessarily restructures an anthropologist's priorities regarding who should make what sacrifices.

Here, then, is the crux of the ethical problem in applied anthropology. Here, too, is a source of great frustration for those who go into applied anthropology, who all too often see their recommendations, which favor the interests of those they study, ignored by policymakers who give low priority to those interests. In this regard, anthropologists and bicultural native members of minority groups stand in much the same kind of relationship to policymakers. Policymakers, however, perceiving anthropologists as members of their own social group, have difficulty understanding why they should be less than entirely cooperative.

The matter of priorities regarding sacrifice goes even deeper. To illustrate where it can lead, I want to recall what Raymond Firth (1959) found upon his return to Tikopia in 1950. Tikopia had just been hit by a devastating typhoon, and much of its food resources had been destroyed. Tikopian social organization ranks every family vis-à-vis every other family by criteria of genealogical seniority. The highest ranking household heads are the high chiefs, the next highest ranking household heads are the lesser chiefs, and so on. Stewardship of Tikopia's food resources is a traditional duty and prerogative of the chiefs, a stewardship they are expected to exercise in the interest of the survival of their society. When Firth arrived, he found the chiefs taking inventory of the island's resources in order to determine how many people could be sustained over the time it would take for the affected gardens and fruit trees to become productive again. The low ranking families were in dread of what the chiefs would then decide, for it was their traditional authority, having determined how many people could be sustained, to order all the remainder into permanent exile at sea, beginning with the lowest ranking families. In this instance, the ship that brought Firth to Tikopia took word of the disaster back to the Solomon Islands, and emergency supplies were sent in, making it unnecessary for anyone to leave the island. But the people understood that, in the absence of outside relief, there was really no alternative.

Tikopia provides an example of a rational procedure for deciding who is to be sacrificed, a procedure based on the Polynesian social system of genealogical rank and fully in keeping with Tikopian social values. Suppose, now, that the Tikopians had no established procedure for dealing with an emergency of this kind, and suppose that the high chiefs had taken advantage of Firth's arrival to ask him to advise them on how to deal with the problem of population reduction in a rational manner that would minimize sacrifice and be in keeping with the established values and ethics of their culture. He could not have come up with a better procedure. But what a spot for an anthropologist to be in!

That was the lonely little island of Tikopia, to be sure, and it may well appear that anthropologists are very unlikely to be asked to advise on matters of this kind. Only last August, however, a group of anthropologists was appealed to for advice in just such a matter by a member of the National Planning Commission of Bangladesh at a workshop on population problems preliminary to the International Congress of Anthropological and Ethnological Sciences. The problem confronting the Planning Commission, dramatically outlined to the workshop, was to devise an acceptable set of priorities as to who should survive and who be sacrificed in the face of an acute, insoluble food shortage. Some anthropologists present felt that they could not ethically take part in such an endeavor—a position that I think most anthropologists would endorse, as a "gut" reaction at least.

To decline on moral grounds, however, to develop orderly and culturally acceptable procedures in such situations is to leave the way open for greater misery and unnecessary sacrifice, the human cost of these same morals. Tikopians, it seems, knew they were better off for having an orderly procedure, however terrible it was to have to invoke it. When an anthropologist refuses on ethical grounds to advise on how to set up such procedures, he is opting for the greater human misery and social dislocation that result from their absence. Which position is morally more defensible is something each of us must decide for himself.

My point, of course, is that to advise on public policy is to advise on priorities and on how to make them socially acceptable and administratively capable of implementation. Priorities always imply an unequal distribution of the burden of sacrifice, but a society's collective interests cannot be optimally promoted without priorities. Such, then, is the arena of public policy. There are, to be sure, opportunities to help reduce human misery and to effectively promote human welfare. They represent the happy side of policy making and of applied anthropology in relation to it. Even such endeavors have their human costs, somewhere, as with the Legal Services Program. Public policy and its implementation necessarily involves some kind of sacrifice. If anthropologists are to take a more active role in regard to public policy, they must come to terms with this fact of life.

To come to terms with it well, it seems to me, requires a degree of compassion for all human beings (not just some of them) that is not easy to cultivate. It is not the setting of priorities that is morally wrong, but a lack of compassion in setting and administering them. To feel compassion for those who are called upon to bear the burden of sacrifice, people must have clearly in mind and be firmly committed to the values that determine the priorities. We need not harden our hearts against men when we invoke the principle of "women and children first," nor against our sons when we send them off to fight what we regard as a just war. Our values make the priorities clear, and we accept as unfortunate necessities the sacrifices to be made. When we all accept one another as fellow members of the same community of people and when we all subscribe to the same values, decisions as to sacrifice are compassionate, but, when people do not all accept one another and do not all subscribe to the same values, feeling for one's fellows can become a difficult moral exercise.

So we come back to the problem of differences in cultural values in complex, plural societies and to the need for policymakers to know what these differences are and to understand why they exist. Without such knowledge, cross-culturally acceptable priorities cannot be established. For without it, policymakers will be unwilling to grant that the different values of others deserve recognition; they will be unwilling to give up some of their own interest group's prerogatives and power to achieve cross-culturally acceptable priorities; and they will be unwilling to look upon policy making as a process of negotiation among representatives of their society's several groups. Rather, they will be more inclined to see policy as a determination of what is best for society solely from the viewpoint of their own interest group. Such policy is uninformed by compassion, and what it defines as necessary sacrifice is inevitably viewed by others as unjustly discriminatory and oppressive.

Because anthropology views all humans in all conditions as worthy of study, it is a discipline that enjoins us to accept the humanity of all, and it enjoins us to try to understand our common humanity within the context of our cultural differences. Thus, anthropology aims at cultivating the kind of knowledge and understanding on which compassion rests. I would like to think, therefore, that our moral obligation as anthropologists is not to avoid helping set priorities, but to go on cultivating our capability for compassion, so that we can bring fellow feeling for both policymakers and those affected by their policies to our work as applied anthropologists and to the end that we can help make policy making itself a more compassionate process.

REFERENCES

Firth, Raymond
   1959. *Social change in Tikopia.* London: Allen & Unwin.
Goodenough, Ward H.
   1970   *Description and comparison in cultural anthropology.* Chicago: Aldine.
   1971   *Culture, language and society.* Addison-Wesley Modular Publications, No. 7. Reading, Massachusetts: Addison-Wesley.
Mathews, Linda
   1973   Legal services threatened by White House. *Philadelphia Inquirer,* Sept. 27: 3-A.
Pike, Kenneth L.
   1954   *Language in relation to a unified theory of the structure of human behavior.* Glendale, Illinois, Summer Institute of Linguistics. (2nd rev. ed., 1967, The Hague: Mouton.)
Sanday, Peggy R.
   1972   The relevance of anthropology to U. S. social policy. *Council on Anthropology and Education Newsletter* 3(3): 1–8.
Stouffer, Samuel A. (Coordinator)
   1949– Studies in social psychology in World War II. 4 vols. Princeton, New Jersey:
   1950   Princeton Univ. Press.
Trumbull, Robert
   1973   U. S. lawyers in Micronesia stir up officials. *New York Times,* Sunday, Sept. 16: 16.

3

The Past, the Present, the Future: Public Policy as a Dynamic Interface

Charles R. McGimsey III

Arkansas Archeological Survey

Both the archeological profession and the general public are in the process of revising and reviewing their attitudes and approaches toward those objects and locations that provide the present and the future with all the knowledge we will ever have about the prehistoric past and that have, as well, the capability of vastly increasing our understanding of the historic period. There has also begun a marked increase in the interchange between these two generalized groups, the profession and the public. This interchange takes many forms, but all of these forms ultimately are reflected in public policy. That policy, in turn, becomes a dynamic force affecting the interchange.

In a very real sense, public policy represents the most effective statement or crystalization of today's thinking about our cultural resources from the past, their development and interpretation in the present, and their preservation for the future.

Archeology has long had an almost romantic appeal to much of the public, a not unmixed blessing. This public interest has led to occasional financial support of projects—which often were thought of, and presented, in a romantic light— and a rather high level of very generalized awareness. It also has occasioned a view of archeology as being slightly anachronistic (the doddering, bearded,

25

pith-helmeted professor) or at least on the far-out intellectual fringes. In short, a latent concern for and support of archeology has long been present, but the other side of the coin has frequently lead to uninformed (but largely unfought) attacks on archeological research by Congress or others ("You mean public monies are being spent to investigate the social attitudes of the Imbaguas in 2000 B.C.!") and too ready public acceptance of highly romanticized or highly problematic accounts most recently typified by what has been called the archeological astronaut approach.

Archeologists, while convinced themselves of the scientific validity and ulti-mate importance of their activities, have done little, with a few notable excep-tions, to communicate to the public this importance. Nor have they presented in a readable manner the achievements from which the public might discern this importance. Rather they have almost smugly gone about their own affairs content to comment almost exclusively to their colleagues and to the next generation of archeological students who would then perpetuate the process.

Both this generalized public concern and professional aloofness from public activity can be illustrated by the first two major pieces of legislation that established public policy: the Antiquity Act of 1906 and the Historic Sites Act of 1935. Both came into being because of the active concern of a few individ-uals, a concern which drew upon generalized public support for passage of the policy into law.

Despite this public declaration of policy, however, the strong professional and public apathy toward implementation caused both laws to be largely ineffective with respect to archeological resources. They served as the legal foundation for official policy and occasional platitudinous statements as to what that policy was, but there was almost no attempt to carry out that policy once it was declared. Persons have been taken to court for destruction of archeological or historical resources on federal property under the criminal statutes of the 1906 Act, but this has been extremely rare, and most of these have been within the past few years. The first court case appealed and, therefore, a case of published record, occurred in mid-1974, 68 years after passage of the law, and the appeal overturned the lower court conviction.

The 1935 Act charged the Secretary of the Interior with nationwide responsi-bility for the nation's historic and archeological resources. In some areas (e.g., the Historic American Buildings Survey) this responsibility was implemented, but there was no active program with respect to the nation's archeological resources. This dismal dereliction of a policy is a charge for which the profession and the public must be held more accountable than the Secretary. The Secretary must establish priorities, particularly when it comes to allocating funds, and he had little publicly expressed cause to consider a concern for the past as a very high priority.

Shortly after World War II, the public policy of reservoir construction implemented by the U.S. Army Corps of Engineers endangered large segments of this country's archeological resources. Perhaps because the threat was so direct and so massive, a number of archeologists, again drawing upon the generalized public concern for the past, were able to convince Congress to pass the Reservoir Salvage Act of 1960—an act that legalized a program actually already begun. This extraordinarily important if unfortunately all too restricted program saw, over a period of 20 years, the recovery of vast amounts of information which would otherwise have been lost.

Archeologists are probably the least publicly oriented of the anthropological disciplines. Frankly, I find it a very curious fact that, both at this time and later, archeologists, or rather a small but effective number of them, have been the most perceptive and the most active in terms of recognizing and utilizing public policy as the necessary interface between public concern and effective action. Prior to the mid-1960s, with the exception of the Reservoir Salvage program, public policy, while a potential force, showed little sign of actually serving as a dynamic interface between the past, the present, and the future, reflecting, no doubt, the absence of any widespread deep feeling of need on the part of either the public or the profession.

Facing up at last to a massive frontal assault on all aspects of the environment, the public began to be aroused and, in the 1960s, initiated what almost appeared to be a rearguard action. It was, however, action on a broad front and, because of this, rather than any specific input by the professions involved, the historical and cultural resources were included.

To their credit, archeologists, far more than historians, cultural anthropologists, or sociologists, accepted the challenge expressed by the general public policy which began to emerge in the late 1960s. For example, I seriously doubt that whoever drafted the National Environmental Policy Act of 1969 would have known an archeologist from an archaeopteryx and, in fact, archeology is not specifically mentioned in the law. Yet, because of an activist position adopted by a number of archeologists, occasionally leading to court decisions, NEPA has had a more far-reaching effect on archeology than any other, indeed all other, declarations of public policy. Because of NEPA, it has become possible for the archeologist to work with federal, state, and private agencies to begin to insure that cultural resources (though to date emphasis has been on archeological resources) are adequately incorporated into the planning processes of those agencies. The goal now is to first preserve those resources intact and only as a last resort to excavate unless there is an urgent and immediate scientific need to develop the knowledge which those resources represent.

The whole concept of cultural resource management has developed as a result and, in the case of archeology, is bringing about a rather rapid and drastic restructuring of the profession. Full-time professional managers of cultural resources and persons doing full-time research on those resources are taking their place alongside the traditional college and university professors who accompany their teaching, when possible, with some research on the side.

Even more recently, because of increased awareness on the part of both the profession and the public of the accelerating effect of public and private action on the nation's rapidly diminishing base of cultural resources, the archeological profession once again organized to crystalize this concern into public policy. NEPA brought archeology into the planning process, but many public agencies felt that their basic legislative charge did not permit them to take an active role in funding any program designed to implement the resulting plans, at least insofar as direct action with respect to any archeological resources was involved. The recently passed (May 1974) Archeological and Historical Conservation Act (PL 93-291) has eliminated that problem, in that every agency utilizing federal funds is authorized to utilize certain of those funds to mitigate the impact of the project on archeological or historical resources. The profession is now actively engaged in working with such agencies to develop means whereby this public policy can be implemented to the best advantage of the cultural resource base and in the context of the total public good.

Appropriately directed professional concern, which mobilizes an often generalized public concern, can result in the establishment of public policy. This is an essential step, but it is only the first of two essential steps. The second is effective implementation of that policy. This can only be accomplished by a profession that demonstrates to those agencies responsible for carrying out the policy that it can be implemented and that it is in the agency's best interest to do so because this is in the best interest of the public. This, in turn, can only be accomplished if there is indeed effective public support for the policy, and insuring this is also the responsibility of the profession.

In sum, the archeological profession has a responsibility for this nation's and, in a broader context, the world's cultural heritage from the past. This responsibility can be met adequately only through encouragement and the development of public policy. Once expressed, this public declaration of policy must be followed by an active program leading to its implementation and support. Public policy provides the key, but it alone will not unlock the door. That requires support by the public which, in the final analysis, must be generated by the profession.

4

Training Anthropologists for Effective Roles in Public Policy

E. A. Hammel

University of California, Berkeley

That anthropology has been involved in the formation, criticism, and execution of public policy for a very long time should be of no surprise. Like most academic disciplines, it has been nourished by the society surrounding it because it served some purpose of the body politic or was at least permitted to exist if it did not create too much nuisance. The criticisms of its involvement have been many—association with colonial or occupying regimes, a role as caretaker of subject peoples, advancement of personal careers based on the culture and experiences of informants. It has also been praised for the persistence of its humane point of view and the spirited defense by many anthropologists of the interests of the people they have studied. Exactly the same kinds of criticisms and praise can and have been, heaped on scholars and scientists of many disciplines concerned with the life and fate of human beings—historians, economists, physicians, members of the clergy.

For a substantial period of the history of anthropology, the social interest that permitted the field to exist and grow was that of commercial exploration and colonial control. The skills that anthropologists brought with them were knowledge of strange places, of exotic language and custom, and often the courage to face physical hardship. What they achieved will be judged best by our descendants, at a more objective remove—at its finest, the discipline was very much responsible for the overthrow of bitter and inhumane theories about human behavior. The ability to take a holistic view, to interpret exotic and apparently irrational custom as logical and understandable, and to do this in swamp, desert, and tundra was a great achievement. It is this achievement and the body of substantive fact and interpretive theory growing out of it that constitute anthropology as a field of pure scholarship, a pure-science core of the discipline that continues as the strongest interest for most of us.

In the last quarter-century, the social interest that permitted anthropology to exist and that, in fact, may have resulted in some obesity was higher education. In this sense, the subject peoples of the last two or three decades have been college students. Oddly, the anthropologists did not study the students; they continued to devour the exotica of the world, transformed it into various theoretical structures, and passed it on to student consumers. The connection with and effect on public policy in the area of education was mostly inadvertent. Those anthropologists directly involved in policy formation and execution were frequently brokers for their discipline, arranging for the transfer of largesse along networks of scholars. The skills they brought to this task were knowledge of the history of the subject, of its issues, and of the networks. Great departments were built, many students trained (a lot of them very well too), and much knowledge amassed and digested. It was, as others have observed, a polite, socially acceptable, and very substantial piece of extortion for the benefit of scholarship. Anthropology was joined in this caper by every other scholarly discipline you can name. The episode appears to have few competitors this side of the growth of the Church in the Middle Ages.

Now, it seems to me, the monasteries have been, or are about to be, secularized. Anthropologists have a choice between continued intonation of a liturgy in praise of a god important only to themselves, and finding a new source of nourishment. If this seems an excessively cynical point of view, let me stress that scholarship does not exist without a master who will be served. If anthropology is to continue to exist, if it is to succeed in maintaining its essentially humane view, in deepening its understanding of mankind, it must stay in the arena. The ethical dilemmas will be no easier than they have been.

If anthropology is to succeed, however, anthropologists must be effective. Anthropologists have always worked in an environment of competing ideas about human behavior, pitting their understanding and skills against those of other interpreters. For a time, the struggle was against theologians, then against the excesses of evolutionism, particularly against biological determinism, later against Western rationalism that denied the existence of other kinds of logic or cultural premises. More recently, the competition has been between different social sciences, in an almost Hegelian process of development of explanatory theory. The competition between the several social sciences in the period of academic expansion, a relatively easy one because of the abundance of resources, has set the stage for the next, a competition that will be more severe and in which arguments will be more severely tested. This time, if anthropologists do not win, they will lose, and, in losing, the discipline will become vestigial.

What do anthropologists have to know to win? What do they have to know to make their points accurately and convincingly, to keep their vision of human behavior an effective force? First, they must be careful not to forget what they already know. It will do no good simply to turn anthropologists into something else, for the victory over vestigiality would result only in extinction. All the skills that have been learned (and some, sadly, forgotten) ought to be maintained—the habit of working with small groups, of allowing one's self to be resocialized, of learning strange-seeming systems of values, the willingness to undergo the psychic isolation of fieldwork.

But that is not enough. Two other sets of skills are needed, both of which we now ignore almost completely. The first of these is knowledge of the society in which we will work. It is no good treating the U.S. government or a major corporation as though it were a valley in highland New Guinea, previously unvisited by civilized man (although the latter might be true). No anthropologist worth his salt would go to an exotic area without trying to find out everything he could about it first—unless obsessed with the notion that one had to go without any prior impressions at all. Nevertheless, the ideal of intellectual nudity seems to be not uncommon among some who would work in the jungles of bureaucracy. There is a great deal to learn about the fieldwork situation in advance—more if one is working in a complex society than in a simpler one—and, in many ways, it is easier to learn because a lot of it has been codified. This is not to say that the codified knowledge about the workings of a complex society is accurate but only that the natives have busied themselves with studying that knowledge before going to work in their bureaucratic vineyards. This means to me that the anthropologist working in public policy should make some effort to learn what some of the natives have themselves studied. In pedagogical terms, that implies, often, joint degrees or at least work experience.

Thus, one of the things we can do to make anthropologists more effective is to train them in subsidiary subjects, such as business administration, law, public health, engineering, or we can take individuals already trained in those subjects and make them into anthropologists. The advantages are twofold. Not only will the anthropologist have an excellent idea of what is in the natives' heads, having it also in his own, but the anthropologist will be recognized by some natives as a legitimate co-practitioner. Perhaps the most striking example of this situation would be that of the anthropologist working in public health or medicine with an M.D. degree. In a profession as status-ridden as medicine, possession of the basic degree would constitute a great advantage for the anthropologist. Of course, few students already embarked on the doctoral study of anthropology could afford to earn two major degrees. Most would have to be content with a master's degree in the minor subject or only with course work. It should be clear, however, that knowledge of the native system and legitimacy in the natives' eyes would increase, the greater was the double involvement. Similarly, we ought not to overlook the opportunity to give anthropological training to those in other disciplines, although it may take a period of proving our own effectiveness before we can attract many serious outside students.

The second set of skills has to do more with competing interpreters who are not working natives in the same sense—that is, with the other academicians competing for public recognition of their efficacy. These skills are the languages the other experts speak. The most important language they speak is one or another dialect of mathematics, in which our training is woefully deficient. I do not address myself here to the issue of the utility of quantitative techniques in anthropology for anthropology's sake, which I think is substantial, but to the ability to converse with economists, sociologists, statisticians, and others who may also be engaged in studying some group of "swidden" bureaucrats. The advantage of knowing their language is that you can argue with them in it. Most anthropologists studying the mechanisms of government and commerce seem to take the attitude of the proverbial English tourist—if you speak your own language loudly enough, the natives should understand. That won't wash. These natives have too much clout. At the very least, anthropologists should know enough about the mathematical models of linear programming, of game theory, of multiple regression, of path analysis to be able to point out, in no uncertain terms, when the assumptions of those mathematical models are violated by the ethnographic facts.

I will close this exhortation with a few observations from my personal experience—limited though it may be to the subordinate reaches of a university bureaucracy. Part of this experience comes from trying to be both a dean and an anthropologist for about 10 years. Part of it comes from watching some other social scientists place their students in positions of influence in government. As a dean, I have slowly (and sometimes painfully) learned how complex the process of bureaucratic decision making is—learned by watching practiced natives, sometimes seeing them scoop up the ball that I have fumbled. Sometimes, I have been able to force a little anthropological understanding by talking like a dean, sometimes to do a little deaning by talking like an anthropologist. In particular, I have learned how necessary it is to understand the system of values, the triggers to response, and the competing demands on officials who must decide every day from whom they should take away something in order to give it to someone else. This was all learned through what we usually call participant observation—a great many anthropologists of my generation and older have had similar experiences, usually as department chairmen, although, in that capacity, they perhaps do not come as close to the bank of the Styx as deans do.

Even more illuminating has been my observation of what my colleague, Aaron Wildavsky, has been able to accomplish by training students to operate in bureacratic roles. As dean of the School of Public Policy, he has placed bright young people in positions in which they evaluate social programs—for example, in the Department of Finance of the State of California—with remarkable effect. Six or eight years ago, when I endured the periodic audits of employees of that department—audits of the administration of fee regulations, of the disbursal of fellowship funds, and the like—I discovered that the visitor from on high had no understanding of the native system. As a native, subject to this colonial intrusion, I felt misunderstood, resentful of the auditor's authority, and sometimes downright angry. In the last three years, visited by Wildavsky's students, I have been amazed by their good understanding of how the native system worked. They were sympathetic to the premises of my culture and could criticize my operations in *my* terms. A useful symbiosis had developed between the native (me) and the anthropologist (them). I suppose it could be said that I have been gulled into participating in my own exploitation, but I would rather put up with their ministrations than the forced rape of their predecessors. These anthropologists in public policy disguise have often been our advocates in the Colonial Office in Sacramento. Of course, they make mistakes, and, from time to time, our knowledge of their methods, mathematical and other, enables us to take a few scalps ourselves. But they are a prototypical model of what an anthropologist could do in such a role. What enables them, and me, to operate at a level of reasonable mutual satisfaction is shared knowledge. It is that sharing of knowledge that we should strive for in training—teaching the anthropologist what the native is really like. As a native, I can vouch for it.

II

The U.S. Public Culture: Attitudes, Themes, and Behavior

5

A Sense of Success: Heredity, Intelligence, and Race in American History and Culture

Winthrop D. Jordan

University of California, Berkeley

The current debate concerning race and IQ is profoundly disturbing to many people, partly because it concerns public and particularly educational policy and partly because it touches deep nerves of moral concern in our culture. Frequently, the debate itself takes on a moral dimension; it seems to pit two very different armies of opinion against one another: on the one side, the vast majority of fuzzy minded academic liberals, ranged against a small number of academic spokesmen who articulate the presumptions of regiments of Archie Bunkers. Both armies know, of course, that they are in the right, as such armies always do.

The purpose of this essay is not to show that either side is right or wrong. Rather it is to suggest the possibility that the actual debate, and indeed the issue itself, is a product of the culture in which it has developed. My central contention is that the very essences of the concepts involved are culturally bound, that the conceptualization and application of the central terms, in particular ways at certain times, are part of the culture in which we participate—the whole debate governed, as cultures are, by cumulative experience.

HEREDITARIAN THOUGHT AND EUROPEAN EXPANSION

Some parallelisms and congruities in the perceptual realm appear so commonly in daily life that they are scarcely ever accorded explicit analysis. One such perception of life—one which draws all human beings together—is that likes produce alikes in the generative process. Sheep produce sheep, or, more precisely, sheep beget lambs, and lambs become sheep. All this is so obvious as to be irritating and one's response is: "Of course they do, and so what?" The only answer to that question is twofold: It is not immediately obvious that this should happen except that, in the realm of everyday experience, it does, and, when we do not know that it happens (as with some of the great whales), we simply assume that it does.

In very recent years, we have developed "scientific" reasons for this most fundamental assumption, and, therefore, the assumption has been proven "correct." We have endorsed, with the science of genetics, a powerful sense, very deeply embedded in our culture (most easily found by reading the Old Testament[1]) that many of the attributes we see in living creatures are somehow there because they are part of the procreative process.

At the same time, we have never assumed that the likeness of offspring to parents is exact. Alongside the assumption that the products of the generative process will exactly resemble the producers has stood the assumption that the products will be somewhat different, that is, alike but not altogether alike. There is a certain deliciousness of ambiguity in these twin assumptions, as indeed there is in our reactions to "identical" twins.

We are so immersed in our attempts to account for unlikeness that we find it hard to recognize the fact that it could be accounted for in different ways than those we are accustomed to. Indeed, some of our cultural ancestors were inclined to split the difficulty three ways: likeness by generation, sports (by which they meant random and playful variations), and conditions of growth—an ancient and largely Grecian formulation. Yet there have been profound continuities of cultural style from the ancient Greeks to our own world. Now we handle the same ambiguous dichotomy with an essentially similar triad: genes, mutations, and environment. We still use the same triadic model when confronting the "problem" of differences in mental-ability scores.

What seems to have happened over several thousand years of Western culture is that this triad, which was, in its original form, much less clear-cut than modern tastes would bear, became markedly more murky until relatively recently. To schematize the matter, our ancestors in the Middle Ages were unable to find much worthwhile disjunction between those attributes in people that resulted from their generation and those qualities that derived from their condition.

---

[1] For the topic of this paper, the most pertinent passage is Jeremiah 13:23: "Can the Ethiopian change his skin, or the leopard his spots?"

(They did find room, in their own way, for the miracles of God's providence and for inflictions by the devil.) In large part, their thinking on the matter was governed by their assumptions about society: Serfs were serfs, without question; so, also, knights were knights, with equal inherency; and so on with clerics, kings, and paupers. Who would think otherwise? Persons inherited the social status of their parents and inherited, as well, the attributes of that condition. Why question the obvious way the world was?

Then, in the sixteenth century, came the explosive transformation into our modern temper. Historians are far from agreeing on the timing, and, by and large, they tend, being historians, to stress antecedents and postcedents, but most would agree that, for the Atlantic nations of western Europe, the ones who invaded and settled the Americas, the sixteenth century was a crucial turning point not only in activity but also in mood.

One scarcely needs to point out that such major movements as the religious turmoil that we call the Reformation; the novel thrust of inquiry about the physical world that we associate with such names as Leonardo, Copernicus, Galileo, and Bacon; the formation of powerful nation-states in Spain, France, England, and the Netherlands; the breakthrough of commercial capitalism; and the thrust of European adventurers overseas all were parts of a single cultural shift. These developments have been very ably chronicled in detail; at the same time, they have been too frequently compartmentalized along national, periodic, or intellectual lines. In sum, what happened was that the peoples of western Europe began quite rapidly to alter their thinking and their activities into a mode that we now find recognizable as much our own. They began to master, dominate, restrain, count, and generally control themselves, their expanding environments, and other peoples. It is scarcely any wonder that they began to look at fundamental human matters in fundamentally different ways than they had before.

In order to make clear the relationship between this cultural revolution of the sixteenth century and our current perceptions, it perhaps is necessary to indicate more specifically what kind of social adjustments were then taking place among the people who began most successfully to conquer the entire globe with their novel mood of mastery and their growing technological grip upon their expanding environment. With Englishmen particularly in that period, social and economic arrangements were changing very rapidly; many of those developments were caused by and interwoven with the upheavals of the English Reformation and its resultant social, economic, and psychic dislocations: The changes in liturgical forms that had sustained the common people for centuries; the wholesale redistribution of landed property that followed Henry VIII's dissolution of the monasteries; the chronic unemployment that made the land seem to teem with wandering beggars; the decay of the wool trade with the continent and the successful shift to oceanic commerce. At the same time, this was an era of unmatched national exhilaration, governed by the political genius of the Virgin Queen, capped by the destruction of the Armada, and most evident of all in Shakespeare, the King James Bible, and the insistencies of the Puritan preachers that we most usually read in the works of Milton and John Bunyan.

Intimately linked with these developments and this new mood was the thrust overseas, for trade at first and then for settlement as well. Of course, this dynamic process resulted in contact with overseas peoples, especially the American Indians and the West Africans. Both these peoples seemed to Englishmen very strange: Not only were they radically defective in religion, in their lack of civil manners, and their beastly modes of living, but their physical appearance was so startlingly different as to seem defective as well. In their new mood especially, Englishmen felt that all these differences had somehow to be accounted for.

The history of the attempts at explanation has been a long one: We merely continue it when we debate the reason for the fact that blacks in the United States score lower on most IQ tests than whites. In order to realize the significance of the fact that the current debate is a continuation of a long-standing one, a very brief sketch of those attempts at explanation seems in order.

ENGLISH ASSESSMENTS OF AFRICANS

It is especially important for us to realize that, at the time of their initial expansion, Englishmen (and other Europeans) possessed notions about innate qualities that seem hopelessly fuzzy by modern standards. Until the latter part of the eighteenth century, they were simply incapable of making the discrete distinction between innate and acquired characteristics that comes so naturally to us. The very term *innate* was not frequently used, and, when it was, it possessed what now appears to be an almost nonsensical vagueness, as in the following description of a West African group, written in 1670: "Another (as it were) innate quality they have [is] to Steal any thing they lay hands of, especially from Foreigners . . . this vicious humor [runs] through the whole race of *Blacks*" (Ogilby 1670: 452).

Such thinking about cultural attributes was prevalent during the early years of European contact with the overseas peoples. One can sense, however, the seeds of change embedded in the previous quotation, where its author felt compelled to preface the term *innate* with an awkwardly nervous "as it were." What is more striking about this statement, though, is that it was one of the most precise ever recorded about the ingrained nature of African cultural characteristics prior to the mid-eighteenth century.

If early European commentators were a trifle vague, by modern standards, about the inherency of cultural qualities in other peoples, their comments on the intelligence of these bestial heathens were even more muddled. They were utterly unable to think about intelligence as being bipartitely a product of the reproductive process and of environment because, on the one hand, they made no such disjunction and, on the other hand, because their concept of "intelligence" was so very different from our own. At least until the eighteenth century, the very concept of what we call "intelligence" did not embody any full sense of inherent ability, rather it encapsulated prevailing notions about wisdom and about the human ability to achieve proper religious experience. As late as the end of the eighteenth century, the term *intelligence* was closely associated with the term *advices,* both of which by then suggested public information, what we would call "news."

Because the early expansionist years of European thinking about other peoples operated along these lines, it is scarcely surprising that there was then considerable confusion about physical qualities in mankind—a matter which one would think would have been much easier to handle. The question of physical differences among human beings was, of course, raised in startling form by the European "discoveries" of sub-Saharan Africa and of the New World. Here an interesting divergence took place. The peoples in those two regions looked different from Europeans—and different as well from each other. At first, in the fourteenth and fifteenth centuries, the confusion was monumental, owing largely to the prevailing assumption (a Greek—Arabic one) that peoples living on the same latitudinal line ought to be the same in appearance and temperament because they had to be living in similar climates. With increasing contact in the seventeenth century, it became clear that the natives of the tropical New World and those in tropical Africa possessed very different physical features. This discovery meant that the ancient Greek notion that barbarism was a function of climates either too hot or too cold had to be set aside; it meant also that long-standing explanations about the barbarity of the inhabitants of the British Isles could be chucked overboard.

As it came gradually to be accepted that the Indians were "tawny" and the Africans were "black," the question of physical characteristics became primarily a matter of deciphering the extraordinary appearance of the Africans. The Indians in America, it was decided, were not inherently tawny; their complexion was achieved by "natural" means. By the eighteenth century it had become an article of faith among Anglo-American commentators that the Indians were born white and that they darkened themselves with bear grease and other natural cosmetics of the forest. One senses in this very firm decision more than a whiff of a new apposition between environment and inherent condition, an apposition which derived much of its energy from the very different social, political, economic, and military conditions that prevailed during the first centuries of European contact with the peoples of the Americas and of Africa.

So it was, that the ultimate and most proper test of why the peoples of the globe existed in different colors became the case of the Africans. I am using here a kind of shorthand, not skirting issues: The much later European assessments of the peoples of the Orient fastened on issues of table manners rather than appearance; the "slant-eyed Chinee" and the "yellow peril" were much later and distinctly Victorian assessments, and they were partly extrapolations from earlier decisions about the Africans. The ultimate stanza in that interesting process is best read in the original editions of "Little Black Sambo," where the tale takes place in India, with a properly striped tiger (an animal not known in Africa) and a little black boy who is not Indian at all but a clearly African pickaninny.

That expansive Englishmen felt they had to explain blackness, rather than whiteness, is scarcely surprising. Their choice of explanations was fully logical in their world. For roughly a century and a half, from 1550 to 1700, two explanations competed with one another: One was what we would call environmental; the people in Africa had been partially fried by the sun because they lived too close to the Line. There was, in fact, good authority for this view; the pre-Biblical story of Phaeton's wild chariot ride through the heavens had been for centuries a standard gloss upon the problem.

But the Bible itself contained a passage that eventually came to be utilized as a competing explanation. The original story was very explicit: When Noah awoke in his tent from a prolonged bout with the product of his vineyard, he cursed the son of his son, Ham, who had "looked upon" his "nakedness" and had derided it. With those words, Noah condemned Ham's descendants to be forever the "servant of servants" (i.e., slaves) to the children of his brothers Shem and Japheth.

Why "blackness" ever became involved in a curse of slavery has never been satisfactorily explained except by very general reference to the predilections of Western culture. Until the sixteenth century, the story of the curse on Ham was used by Christian writers such as St. Augustine merely to explain the origins of slavery in the world in general. Apparently, early Medieval Jewish writers were the first to seize upon Ham's specific sexual transgression as an explanation for the Negro's appearance. Rather offhandedly, Talmudic and Midrashic commentators suggested that "Ham was smitten in his skin" and that Noah had told Ham that "your seed will be ugly and dark-skinned."[2] The first Christian glosses on this theme seem to have appeared in the sixteenth century—the first great century of overseas expansion. By the seventeenth century, the curse on Ham had become fully established as a compelling explanation for the puzzling blackness of Africans, as well as their notorious sexuality.

It was thus in this strange and not fully deciphered manner that the opening book of the Bible suggested (and contains to this day for a dwindling number of

---

[2] The original story is in Genesis 9:20–27. See Jordan (1968: 11–20). Quotations are from Epstein (1935–1960: 745) and Freedman and Simon (1939: 293).

adherents) a curse that "explained" both the slavery and the blackness of Africans. For several centuries, the curse on Ham, which has borne in Western culture the powerful sense that both the physical and social conditions of Africans were somehow inherent, competed with the climatic explanation of the Africans' perverse appearance.

It is revalatory of the change which took place in the minds of the expanding Europeans that the Biblical exegesis gradually gave way to the climatic one. By mid-eighteenth century, belief in the old story about the curse on Ham was well on its way to being relegated to the cellar of folk myth. The environmental analysis is still very much with us, accoutered in learned discussion about ultraviolet rays, skin cancer, and relative balances of Vitamin D. It would be a mistake, however, to say that environment has triumphed; we offer with equal confidence the proposition that the presence of melanin is governed by genetic transmission.

While we need to recognize these continuities, it is necessary also to appreciate the distance of our conceptual world from that prevailing in the early centuries of cultural contact. For present purposes, one more measure of that distance needs to be taken into account, a particularly tragic happenstance that has tinged racial thinking in the Western world from the very onset of contact and ever since.

In retrospect, it was an extraordinary train of events. As things actually happened, sixteenth-century European explorers encountered peoples on the West African coast who seemed very different in physiognomy. At exactly the same time and in exactly the same place, they encountered chimpanzees. These animals seemed to Europeans to be very different yet somehow very like both themselves and the aboriginals of the region. Travelers on the West African coast necessarily viewed these creatures through a haze of long-standing traditions about that continent that derived from Greek and Roman authorities. Centuries of learned opinions about Africa (including Aristotle's) suggested that, in that strange continent, various animals were forced to come together at the scarce waterholes and that there they "united." Indeed, there was considerable reason to believe, in the words of one of the foremost intellectuals of the sixteenth century, that "promiscuous coition of men and animals took place, wherefore the regions of Africa produce for us so many monsters" (Bodin 1945: 105; Aristotle 1910: 606b). A still more compelling notion about that distant land was the possibility that the menlike apes were some sort of men. It was in this way that the simultaneous discovery of the West Africans and the most human-seeming of the great apes were introduced into Western culture. The reverberations of that "discovery" are still with us, and not merely on gymnasium walls.

At the time, the resultant confusion was monumental. Did those "men of the woods" really kidnap human females? From those "spurious unions" could there be offspring and would they be fertile through another generation? The debate on these matters lasted for more than two centuries. At times, it wore the aspect of scientific discussion, as it focused on pressing questions as to whether or not mulattoes and mules were capable of fertile "generation," and whether or not the "spurious productions" of the African forests held membership in humankind. The psychic energy underlying this discussion was in large measure sexual; indeed, the linking of apes and Negroes was a special branch of the prevailing tendency of Europeans to attribute to blacks a special hypersensuality. Africans were said to be especially given to venery, the men sporting "large Propagators" and the women essentially "of a temper hot and lascivious" (Ogilby 1670: 451; Barbot 1704–1732: 34). Yet the fact that it took Europeans some two centuries to decide that apes were not human beings and that chimpanzees and Negroes could not produce offspring testifies not only to the power of the sexual imagery involved but to the vagueness of the notions with which Europeans initially approached any problem concerning heredity in peoples who seemed very different from themselves.

These assessments pertained to the Africans, emphatically not to the aboriginals of the New World. Our culture today still adheres (in very different terms, granted) to its original tendency to distinguish Indians from Negroes. Indeed, one of the most striking aspects of European contacts with the two peoples was their strenuous attempts to differentiate them. While it was being established as a firm fact that the Africans were especially lascivious, it was also becoming an article of faith that the Indians were not. The natives of America were, if anything, lacking in "ardor for their females."[3] They were continuously charged with savagery and with a luridly detailed catalog of physical brutalities but scarcely, if ever, with rape. The multitude of accounts about Indian raids upon white settlements do indeed include the carrying off of white women—to the awful fate of adoption into an Indian tribe. In contrast (and with much less good basis in historical fact) the accounts of black slave rebellions are replete with awful hints about slaughtering all the white men and sparing the women, whom they "intended to reserve for themselves" (*New York Gazette,* March 25, 1734).

From the very outset, America was sexually a more neutral arena than Africa. For English settlers in America, the animals that aroused the most interest obviously did not include the chimpanzee; there were, in fact, two such animals: the beaver, so much appreciated for the profit in his pelt and for his Protestant-ethic work habits, and the opossum, whose curious treatment of its young prompted one royal governor of North Carolina to submit to the Royal Society

[3] The words are the Comte de Buffon's as quoted twice in Jefferson's (1955: 58, 200) angry refutation.

of London a learned paper that contended that impregnation occurred of a forked penis fertilizing two parallel rows of teats. Along with these animals, surely, there would be no men of the forest, no strange monsters, and no spurious productions, certainly not in America. In addition, it had already been determined that the actual climate in America was different from that in Africa, no matter what the geographical parallels suggested. A multitude of factors, including mountains, forests, deserts, and so forth, meant that climatic conditions in the New World were altogether different. The ultimate conclusion as to the two different peoples was clear: Indians were different by reason of condition, Africans by inherent nature.

This intense and extraordinarily persistent distinction that English and other Europeans made between Africans and Indians was of course, in large part, a function of the very different circumstances of confrontation. The English invaded their beachhead on the Atlantic coast of North America and successfully conquered their way inland. They were intent on making that new land their home. By contrast, in Africa, the English and other Europeans had to remain content with a trading relationship with the coastal peoples, without settling there appreciably, until the latter half of the nineteenth century. Actual occupation of Africa by Europeans eventually took place in only a few areas of that continent, ones that were never heavily involved in the great migration of West Africans to the New World.

Given these contrasting social circumstances, it is scarcely surprising that "the Negro" became the testing ground for Anglo-American thinking about the question of human variation. In the New World, on the other hand, the circumstances of migration and cultural contact worked to chip away at the original conflation of inherent and acquired qualities in the peoples involved.

ANGLO-AMERICAN ASSESSMENTS OF AFRO-AMERICANS

For some 80 years following the first permanent English settlement in America, there were not many Africans present. Then, during the first two decades of the eighteenth century, there came a flood of Africans, so many forced migrants that, in sheer demographic terms, the population was altered with greater suddenness than with the immigration of the Irish and Germans in the decades before the Civil War and with the "new immigration" of southern and eastern Europeans in the very early twentieth century.

That early influx of Africans laid a carpet of social conditions that rapidly established a new basis for thinking about the Africans. For one thing, they produced offspring who were clearly not thoroughly African. The children (and theirs) were Afro-Americans, culturally increasingly more similar to English settlers who themselves were becoming more "American." This steady tendency was suddenly speeded in the 1740s by an outbreak of religious revivalism that spread throughout all the colonies during that time. The resurgence of evangelistic fervor known as the Great Awakening had important ramifications for the Afro-American population and for prevailing ideas about them. Increasingly, blacks, even in the lowly condition of slavery, possessed the opportunity of becoming Christian, by their own definition and by their masters'. Over the long term—it took more than a century—this development pressed upon white Americans the fact that blacks were spiritual brothers and sisters, fully capable of participating in the delights of the only world that was important. They might be forced into or choose separate churches, but there could be no question about their essential equal candidacy before the throne of judgment. The Great Awakening had begun cracking one of the most important walls of distinction.

It was only a generation after these initial shocks that the long-simmering ideas which animated the American Revolution broke to the surface. Given the context in which the words were written, "all men are created equal" could hardly be read as including blacks, not because they were not men (or human beings) but because the entire statement was intended as a gloss upon *political* rights, in which blacks obviously did not share. Indeed, given their experiences in the New World, it would have been surprising if white Americans had supposed for a moment that blacks were participants in their fraternal quarrel with England.

As things turned out, however, the implications of that explicitly stated equalitarian doctrine proved explosive. That the idea of equality was fixed in the foundation of our nation's ideology is familiar, but the full force of its naturalistic formulation is not. In his original version, Thomas Jefferson had written that "from that equal creation" men derived their inherent rights (Jordan 1968: 431). At the time, no one certainly—and least of all Jefferson—meant to include black slaves or women, but included they have been. The end result, so far as blacks were concerned, was formal inclusion in the political process. It is of the utmost importance that we recognize that formal Emancipation and the constitutional amendments of the Civil War and Reconstruction era conferred political rights, not social or economic equalities. Though these rights have been strenuously denied in practice, they have, in fact, been more comfortably acceded by the white population than other admissions of sameness.

In effect, during the middle years of the eighteenth century Afro-Americans came to be included at least potentially and of necessity in two of the most

important domains of our culture, religion and politics.[4] Yet there re....
the white population a profound disposition to keep blacks apart. It is no
accident that the origins of a novel exclusionary tendency dates from the era of
the American Revolution. It was exactly then that the question of African
intelligence began to become a matter of public discussion. At that time, a
handful of reformers began arguing that the prevalent "prejudice" against
Negroes was a product, in the minds of white persons, of the degraded social
position in which Afro-Americans were placed.[5] Some members of the same
band of enthusiasts suddenly found themselves making notable discoveries of
talent among the African race. The special variety of acclaim that fell upon
Phillis Wheatley and Benjamin Banneker is still with us. The point made then (as
it still is) by these purveyors of Negro talent was that slavery necessarily
degraded the sensibilities and still more the moral perceptions of its victims.
Accordingly, any evidence of intellectual ability became evidence of the survival
power of raw talent amidst the weeds of a degraded condition.

That there was more open debate among white Americans concerning the
"Negro's nature" in the years just before the Civil War is scarcely surprising.
From the late 1830s, it was becoming clear that the issue of slavery and its
extension into the "empty" lands in the west might possibly take the nation
apart, as it seemed to be doing in the 1850s and did in 1861. Much of that
recrimination, which did not merely affect the North and South but which
reverberated throughout the Western world, raged about the Negro's fitness (or
not) for freedom.

A key measure of the change that had taken place since the Revolution was
that, by the time of the American Civil War, the debate was being framed so
largely in terms of the Negro's head. In fact, measurement of intelligence by
reference to the dimensions and configurations of the skull were not completely
new at the time of the American Revolution, but it is also the case that we may
ascribe to the final quarter of the eighteenth century that predilection, once so
dominant and now so seemingly outmoded, for determining the possibilities of
any race or person by the simple process of describing their anatomy from the
neck up. In the antebellum era, thoroughly reputable American scientists were
standing in line to disclose their findings on this important subject.

The mood was general and did not revolve entirely about the question of race.
The science of phrenology, for example, by which the abilities and tempera-

---

[4] The matter of language is obviously pertinent here, but the process of Africans learning
English in the New World is so complex and poorly researched that I must omit any
discussion of the matter.
[5] The term "prejudice," as we apply it relative to ethnic groups, first came into usage
about 1760.

ments of individuals and races could be ascertained by feeling bumps on heads, was especially appealing in a fluid society in which the traditional indicators of status had so clearly broken down. The still-prevailing fusion of inborn and socially ingested qualities was evident in the claim made by the eminent Dr. Charles Caldwell before a large lecture audience in Lexington, Kentucky: "There are only three great heads in the United States: one is that of Daniel Webster; another that of Henry Clay; and the last . . . modesty prevents me from mentioning" (Quoted in Stanton 1960: 20).

Caldwell's suggestion was not then a laughing matter. Undoubtedly his audience craned their necks to see whether the lecturer's head really did measure up to the high standards suggested. What was then known as the "American school" of anthropology was dominated by polygenesists who thought of themselves as warriors embattled against the dark forces of insidious Biblicists who maintained in their obscurantism the doctrine that all mankind was one. That the battle should have been fought out along those antique lines was inevitable. What is most arresting about the pre-Darwinian debate is that it was framed in terms that were so persistently craniological.

The underlying problem was apparent. Why were blacks more stupid than whites and by such an impressive margin? And, therefore, how could blacks have possibly descended from that auspicious, though admittedly slightly tainted, start in the Garden? The dynamics underlying the choice of Africans as candidates for exclusion seem sufficiently clear; it is less apparent, though, why the discussion should have been waged with skull shapes, facial angles, and cranial capacities, carefully decked with drawings of the profiles of Grecian man, the elegant Caucasian, the hapless African, the ape, and a very long-snouted dog.

CHANGE AND PERMANENCE IN AMERICAN CULTURE

At this point, the reader may expect a review of historical developments during the century after Darwin, including the impact of scientific genetics, the development of the IQ test, and "the scientific revolt against racism" which began in the 1920s.[6] There have indeed been interesting changes during the last one hundred years, but there have also been profound continuities in thinking about race and intelligence despite Darwin, Mendel, Boas, and a changing climate in academia. Historians, who ought to know better, have not been fully alive to these continuities. For example, in 1963, historian T. F. Gossett (1963: 374) looked back with an air of finality and announced that "as late as" 1940 the psychologist E. L. Thorndike had been "willing" to discuss human intelligence in terms of percentages: 80% genes, 17% environment, 3% accident. One hears in

[6] The quotation is the title of Chapter 16 in Gossett (1963). On this matter, see Stocking (1968).

such an announcement two not very dissimilar voices: in the psychologist's, the reverberations of an old disjunction set into an elegantly precise mathematical triad and, in the historian's, the presumptive tone of retrospective conclusion that all this nonsense is behind us. That was in 1963. We know now that, "as late as" the 1970s, there is still similar willingness to embrace that same seductive reliance on numbers. One can almost hear the future historian's claim: "as late as the 1990s. . . ."

Rather than review these continuities of the past hundred years, however, it would perhaps be more useful to revert back to the one hundred years which preceded Darwin and the American Civil War. To state the matter baldly, it was in those years that thinking about race and heredity became "modern," that is, like our own. What characterized that thinking above all was its itch for precision of measurement and its stark bifurcation between qualities innate and acquired. To state the same proposition in a different way, there is a deep similarity between establishment of cephalic indices and determination of intelligence quotients; both were controlled by means of quantitative terminology, and both assumed an utter disjunction between innate and acquired mental abilities.

In order to give this proposition the force that it deserves, it is necessary to summarize rather arbitrarily a variety of complex historical developments. First of all, the last quarter of the eighteenth century saw the rise of comparative anatomy as an exciting field of scientific investigation whose spirit was reified in its technology—dissecting knives and calipers. Secondly, the initial intellectual challenge to slavery, in the 1760s, was accompanied, as we have seen, by strenuous assertions that the Negro was not naturally stupid but rendered so by his "condition." We have already touched upon a third category of historical development: the way in which the Great Awakening and the American Revolution, by including the Negro spiritually and politically with the white man, narrowed the terms by which he could be kept separate. Since he was no longer fully excluded in those realms, at least potentially, the question of his inclusion came into focus in a narrower and more intractable arena of debate, his inherent intellectual capability.

Finally, and most important of all, was the fact that the century preceding the Civil War was marked by certain social and economic developments that drew out to their extreme conclusions some of the most powerful cultural tendencies that had driven the original enterprise of English expansion overseas. The mood of mastery and control, of great adventure, of exhilarating and successful conquest came to reign virtually without challenge in Jacksonian America. The American Revolution seemed to contemporaries not the culmination but the auspicious commencement of a worldwide tendency. Ironically, the equivocal mixture of military disasters and triumphs that we call the War of 1812 did much to enhance this mood: Americans began to think that the new republic would succeed as a nation. It is difficult for us to recapture the power and pervasiveness of this feeling. The very term "Union" struck the mystic chords of memory with such force as to become the animating ideological reason for the greatest military conflict of the nineteenth century. Perhaps even more important was the enormous exhilaration of conquering a continent and peopling the vast "wastes" of the new empire of liberty. The continent was to be theirs.

At the same time, the very nature of man's relationship with his natural world was being changed by his own hand. Eli Whitney's cotton gin joined with the novel textile machines of Old and New England to transform both those societies and the American South as well. The steamboat, almost as much as the canals and railroads, revolutionized transportation. The telegraph and the daily newspaper changed "the latest intelligences" into "news." In sum, all this meant a mounting sense of the inevitability and rightness of change and of being on top of things.

It is exactly in that period that we can now see the death of the age-old assumption that each new generation would lead much the same life as the one preceding. It is no accident that one lapses here into an unavoidable pun. The very idea of "generations" of people assumes change through time, and "generation" is also, as one dictionary states, "the act or process of producing offspring." Embedded in the very idea of the procreative act was a new emphasis on change rather than continuity.

In and of itself, a sheer and pressing sense that things are changing does not lead necessarily to a sense of apposition between heredity and environment. What guided Western culture in the direction of presuming such apposition was its sense of mastery and control over the process. More than is usual in human affairs, nineteenth-century Anglo-Americans thought they were in control of change and that change itself was leading inexorably to a better world. The age has rightly been characterized as one that believed implicitly in "progress."

What this feeling led to was a need for placing signposts and benchmarks along the entire development. And what better way of laying out the path than deciding that certain qualities in human beings could not be changed and that, conversely, other qualities could be? Such a proposition suggests, of course, that the very making of such a disjunction was, in itself, a reflection of certain cultural predilections. To take the matter a bit further, one can argue that the patient and tightly planned fiddling with pea plants by an Austrian monk reflected personal preferences which were, in themselves, reflections of a cultural style that was already becoming evident in the careful (mis)calculations made by Christopher Columbus about the dimensions of the earthly sphere.

We are now beginning to have a fundamental change of heart, not because we sense any lessening in the pace of change but because we sense ourselves to be no longer in control of the process. With the study of human beings, the matter goes far beyond the fact that anthropologists are being unceremoniously tossed out of their ethnographical laboratories in the "third world" that they helped colonize. Our recent, budding discomfort with the radical disjunction between innate and acquired qualities is new in light of a century's experience, but old if one goes back to the pre-expansionist mode of thinking. Much of that discomfort derives from the fact that we are today less fully secure about the future direction of mankind than at any time in the last 500 years. While this novel situation may in part by attributed to current socioeconomic and technological conditions, it is important to remember that those conditions are themselves rooted in the expansion of Europeans overseas.

Those expansively migrating, maritime peoples (especially the English and the Dutch) were confident, exploitive, and narrow-minded, as conquerers usually are; they were also, more than many conquerers, riven with self-doubt. If they had not been so fundamentally ambiguous, they would not have been so successful. It is not simply technology that explains why western Europe took over the globe. It was partly their very inner ambiguousness, that sense of *torness* between steady *faith* (which they had inherited in the crystalizations of Church and Scripture) and boundless *possibility* (which they found in their venturous voyaging). It was that feeling of being torn that made them disjunctive concerning the essential nature of humankind—either the curse upon Ham *or* the sun; either they cannot read because they are born that way *or* our schools are all wrong.

This view suggests that because things have been going on in a particular way for a long time, they are not going to change very rapidly, not very much, nor very soon. Yet it also suggests that we are now on the cusp of an appreciable change because we are losing that sense of success that animated the overseas venturings and conquests. What this amounts to is a plea for greater self-awareness concerning our own part in an ongoing social process. The origins of our thinking about race, intelligence, and heredity are deeply rooted in the optative mood of the expansion of Western culture which was best summarized by Sir Francis Bacon, whose basic conviction and plea was that the accumulation of knowledge should be useful to mankind.

As we accumulate knowledge, it might be well to include in the growing mountain of data an appreciation of why we act in such a manner. Before we apply our controlling social sciences to any issue, we ought to be aware that the issues themselves may, in fact, be offspring of the itch-to-application that began to characterize our culture some five hundred years ago. Which is to say that the way in which we chop up the universal senses of insideness—outsideness, of permanency and change, or of we and they is itself a matter worth our consideration, particularly if we want to change it.

REFERENCES

Aristotle
1910   Historia animalium, translated by D'Arcy W. Thompson. In *The Works of Aristotle,* edited by J. A. Smith and W. D. Ross. Vol. 4. Oxford: Clarendon Press.

Barbot, John
 1704– A description of the coasts of North and South-Guinea. . . . In *A collection of*
 1832   *voyages and travels*. . . . , edited by John Awsham Churchill. 6 vols. London:
        J. Walthoe.
Bodin, John (Jean)
 1945   *Method for the easy comprehension of history*, translated by Beatrice Reynolds.
        New York: Columbia University Press.
Epstein, I. (Editor)
 1935– *Sanhedrin.* Vol. 2 of *The Babylonian Talmud.* 35 vols. London: Soncino Press.
 1960
Freedman, H., and M. Simon (Translators)
 1939   *Midrash Rabbah*, in 10 vols. Vol. 1. London: Soncino Press.
Gossett, Thomas F.
 1963   *Race: The history of an idea in America.* Dallas: Southern Methodist University
        Press.
Jefferson, Thomas
 1955   *Notes on the State of Virginia*, edited by William Peden. Chapel Hill: University
        of North Carolina Press.
Jordan, Winthrop D.
 1968   *White over black: American attitudes toward the Negro, 1550–1812.* Chapel Hill:
        University of North Carolina Press.
Ogilby, John
 1670   *Africa: Being an accurate description of . . . the land of Negroes.* . . . London: T.
        Johnson.
Stanton, William
 1960   *The leopard's spots: Scientific attitudes toward race in America, 1815–59.* Chi-
        cago: University of Chicago Press.
Stocking, George W., Jr.
 1968   *Race, culture, and evolution: Essays in the history of anthropology.* New York:
        Free Press.

6

Cultural and Structural Pluralism in the United States

Peggy Reeves Sanday

University of Pennsylvania

In 1970, nonwhite and minority students numbered 9.3 million or 21% of the total enrollment in public schools. Black students comprised 71.4% of this group, Spanish-surnamed students (i.e., students of Mexican, Puerto Rican, or other Spanish-speaking origin) 24.2%, Oriental 2.2%, and Indian 2.1% (HEW News Release, June 18, 1971). These children exhibit the lowest scholastic achievement scores, the lowest self-concept and sense of personal efficacy (Coleman *et al.* 1966). They also exhibit the highest drop-out rates. Of American Indian children, 50–60% drop out before they reach high school (Banks 1972: 293). The drop-out rate for Puerto Rican students by the twelfth year of schooling was 80% in 1960, compared to 46% for black students and 28.9% for Anglos (Bonilla 1972: 294). In some southwestern schools, one of the regions of the country where Spanish-surnamed students are the most highly concentrated, the drop-out rate for Chicanos was 20% (Guerra 1972: 313). Rural and mountain white children also exhibit the same patterns. When they are added to the numbers of nonwhite and minority pupils, the conclusion is inescapable that the American education system has failed in reaching a substantial portion of its children.

53

The aforementioned statistics suggest that systematic change in the delivery of education to American nonwhite, minority, rural, and mountain children is a must if a reversal of scholastic achievement, self-concept, and sense of personal efficacy is to occur for these groups. Such a reversal is imperative because of the evidence (Gurin, Gurin, Lao, and Beattie 1969) of the high correlation of these variables with successful participation in the occupational and political spheres of American public life. One major barrier to full participation in these spheres has been discrimination and prejudice on the basis of color and sex. While American educators cannot remove these barriers as they now exist in the adult population, they can structure educational environments that do not reflect the prejudices of the larger society and impart an understanding and respect for all of the cultural strands comprising the American culture. Educators can also maximize learning opportunities for all children through the development of curricular programs that employ the cognitive, emotional, sociocultural, and linguistic contexts that are familiar to children coming from culturally different homes.

Removing prejudice and discrimination in the schools is related to fighting against structural pluralism which, as will be shown later, exists in both the American society and in its schools. Structural pluralism will be defined as differential distribution of right, privileges, and scarce resources in the public domain. Promoting cultural pluralism and using it as a tool to maximize learning opportunities is related to fighting against the tendency to impose the values and norms of one cultural segment in the schools. The destructive results of the Anglo-conformity approach will be discussed later. Closely aligned with this discussion will be an emphasis on clarifying the concepts of structural and cultural pluralism and on demonstrating how the refusal to recognize the reality of the latter and the presence of the former has been among the most serious disadvantages minority children have had to face in the schools. Before embarking on this discussion, however, there will be a brief digression into the question of whether or not the schools can make a difference and whether or not social science knowledge has any impact on educators and on Congress in developing and funding responsive school programs.

CAN THE SCHOOLS MAKE A DIFFERENCE?

There are those who would dispute the contention that the schools must share the burden for the lowered performance of minority group students. The more widely publicized research of recent years has tended to stress the importance of factors in the home (Coleman *et al.* 1966; Jencks 1972) or of hypothesized genetic differences in cognitive functioning (Jensen 1969; Shockley 1972). Coleman *et al.* (1966) found that differences between schools account for only a small fraction of differences in pupil achievement. Jensen discusses the failure of preschool education programs to produce lasting changes in black children's IQ performance and implies that the "culturally deprived" child can never catch up with his more fortunate peers.

Recent research, not as widely publicized, contains powerful evidence that preschool programs can be effective and that schools do make a difference. For example Heber, Garber, Harrington, Hoffman, and Falender (1972) report the results of a maternal and infant 6-year intervention program in which the treatment effects on the cognitive development of the experimental group were observed over a 5½-year period and compared with the cognitive development of a control sample. At 36 months, there was a 30-point difference in mean IQ performance in the two groups, and, at 60 months, there was a 26-point difference between the groups. Stenner and Mueller (1973) describe a less costly and far more extensive program in terms of the number of children served. This is a major 6-year pre- and early elementary school program funded through Title I and administered by the Chicago Board of Education in low-income areas. Approximately 2100 children are enrolled in the program which offers up to 6 years of education. The preliminary results indicate that the traditional gap between advantaged and disadvantaged students can be systematically and substantially eliminated.

Several studies present dramatic evidence of the effect of the school. Guthrie, Kleindorfer, Levin, and Stout (1971) review the results of 17 studies dealing with the relationship between school services and student achievement and present their own findings from a study of Michigan schools. They conclude that a relationship exists between the quality of school services and academic achievement that is independent of the child's social environment. In a study of the pattern of IQ change over a 9 year period in an urban school system, I find (see Sanday 1973, and Kadane, McGuire, Sanday, and Staelin 1973) that change in racial and social class composition in the school were the two most important factors correlated with change in IQ scores. Finally, in a recent analysis of the twelfth grade tapes of the Coleman *et al.* (1966) study, Boardman, Davis, and Sanday (1973), using a quite different statistical procedure from those previously employed, find substantial evidence of the importance of teachers and schools. They report that teachers' verbal ability, class size, teachers' experience, school facilities, and problems in the school all have significant and important effects on the achievement measures.

The weight of this and other evidence (see Mondale 1972) suggests that the recent tendency to place all of the responsibility on the home environment for a child's school performance is simply a rejection of the overwhelming responsibility inherent in administering an enlightened public education system. The responsibility of the schools in serving minority children is particularly critical because of the evidence discussed by Coleman *et al.* (1966: 22) that the average minority pupil's achievement may suffer more in a school of low quality than might the average white pupil's. According to these authors:

> Whites, and to a lesser extent Oriental Americans, are less affected one way or the other by the quality of their schools than are minority pupils. This indicates that it is for the most disadvantaged children that improvements in school quality will make the most difference in achievement.

The school characteristics found to be most closely related to achievement for minority students were: existence of science laboratories, the quality of teachers, teachers' scores on the verbal skills test, educational level of teachers, and educational backgrounds and aspirations of other students in the school. It was also found that minority children in racially integrated environments were more likely than those in segregated environments to have a sense of control over their own destiny—an important attitude related to achievement.

IMPACT OF SOCIAL SCIENCE KNOWLEDGE ON SCHOOL LEGISLATION

Despite the well-publicized results indicating that home variables are, by and large, more important than school variables, Congress and educators have been firmly committed to school programs that were believed to narrow the gap between the educational outcomes of majority and minority children. For example, much of the busing effort is attributed to the results reported by Coleman *et al.* (1966) that integrated school environments were beneficial for minority children. In addition to the busing legislation, there have been, in the last decade, a number of programs that were specifically targeted for minority children. Most of the early programs were to enable the "disadvantaged" to "catch up." The failure of many of these programs to narrow the gap (see Jensen 1969) confirmed the opinion of many that the school can have no effect and that the cause of the gap must be sought in the genes or in irreversible trends that begin in the home.

Other scholars, particularly anthropologists and sociolinguists, pointed out the destructive, self-defeating tendency of these programs to ignore or to deprecate the child's cultural and linguistic background. The richness of the linguistic and cultural background of the so-called disadvantaged child has been amply documented (see articles in Williams 1970; Johnson and Sanday 1971; Sanday 1972; Valentine 1972; and Cazden, John, and Hymes 1972). An appreciation of the linguistic and cultural differences is now evident in bilingual legislation and in the educational research and development activities on culturally targeted curricular programs.

It is clear, then, that Congress and educators are responsive to an appeal to develop and appropriate funds for programs that promise to move us closer to a public school system where educational opportunities are linked to equal educational outcomes. It is also clear that the efforts of the past have not been wholly successful. Perhaps this is partially due to the absence of a pragmatic understanding of cultural pluralism and to the absence of a forceful commitment to eliminating structural pluralism.

MEANING AND USE OF THE CONCEPTS CULTURAL AND STRUCTURAL PLURALISM IN THE SOCIAL SCIENCES

Cultural and structural pluralism are subsidiary concepts that were derived from the general concept—the plural society. There have been two conceptual models in discussions of plural societies. The first, and oldest, has been called the equilibrium model of pluralism (Kuper 1969: 8). This view has been largely employed by political scientists and sociologists. The equilibrium model associates democracy with pluralism and defines pluralism in terms of the existence of different political positions, political parties, and in the separation of legislative, judicial, and executive branches. In such a society, there is also a number of competing interest groups all struggling more or less on an equal basis for the available power. The equilibrium model stresses integration as the major mechanism by which these different units are held together, as opposed to regulation by force. Integration is realized through a commitment to common values, one of which is that no interest group be eliminated by any other. Examples of these common values are respect for law and order, moderation in political involvement, commitment to gradual changes, and recognition of the dignity of other values in a society.

Such a model of the U.S. society appeals to those who have an idealistic view of the American reality, and it would provide an empirically accurate description of this reality if it were to be applied only to white America, since, during the course of U.S. history, only white immigrant groups have been incorporated to any significant degree into the political and economic domain. The equilibrium model is not an accurate description of the American historical reality when nonwhite groups are included. When these groups are included, a more accurate description of the United States is provided by the second model of the plural society, which is known as the conflict model (Kuper 1969: 10).

The conflict model originates in the work of Furnivall (1948) who developed it to describe colonial domination in tropical societies. In such societies, a Western system of values and attitudes and a Western superstructure of business and administration is imposed on the native world. Social pluralism in such societies is seen in the forced union of a "medley of peoples living side by side, but separated, within the same political unit. . . . Each group holds by its own religion, its own culture and language, its own ideas and ways" (Kuper 1969: 10). According to Smith (Kuper 1969: 12), it is cultural pluralism that imposes the necessity for domination by one cultural group over another.

Smith, the major proponent of the conflict model, defines cultural pluralism in terms of the degree to which groups within a given territorial and political unit share common institutions. An institution is defined by Smith (1960: 767) as "set forms of activity, groupings, rules, ideas, and values." According to Smith, a population sharing a single set of institutions is culturally homogeneous. A population sharing a common system of basic or "compulsory" institutions, but which has differing "alternative" institutions, is defined as culturally heterogeneous. The term cultural pluralism is reserved for the case in which there is a formal diversity in the basic system of compulsory institutions. The basic institutional system, according to Smith (1960: 769), "embraces kinship, education, religion, property and economy, recreation, and certain sodalities." Examples of alternatives are different occupations, class conventions, linguistic habits, and life styles.

Cultural pluralism is to be distinguished from cultural heterogeneity. Groups in a class system are culturally heterogeneous because they are held together by integration as opposed to regulation by force, and such groups share basic institutions although they may differ in occupation, conventions of dress, linguistic habits, and daily life style. The difference between the white-collar and the blue-collar family in white America is an example of cultural heterogeneity. Both would exhibit a similar family structure, go to predictable Protestant or Catholic churches, participate in a monetary economy, and share the same general set of values about recreation and education. The differences in a culturally heterogeneous system would occur in what Smith calls the alternative institutions. In a culturally heterogenous system, social mobility can occur with relative ease because it involves only the adoption of new alternatives and does not presuppose a change in basic institutions. Mobility is far more difficult under conditions of cultural pluralism because it involves the adoption of a totally new institutional system. This is particularly true where one cultural sector holds and maintains the balance of rights, privileges, and scarce resources.

U.S. white ethnic groups also are examples of cultural heterogeneity and not cultural pluralism (Smith 1960: 770–771). Smith believes that, in certain parts of the U.S., the black population has a distinct institutional system in his sense of the term. The evidence that certain black communities in the South differ markedly in their social, religious, and economic organization from those of the adjoining white communities leads Smith to call such populations plural communities. At the time of his writing, he did not choose, however, to refer to the United States as a plural society.

Later, Smith (1969: 440) does refer to the United States as a plural society and distinguishes between three levels or modes of pluralism: structural, social, and cultural. By itself, cultural pluralism consists of institutional differences that are independent of definable group collectivities. Social pluralism is the condition in which such institutional differentiations coincide with sharply demarcated and virtually closed groups or segments. Structural pluralism consists further in the differential incorporation and access of specified collectivities within a given society to the common public domain. Structural pluralism is manifested in the segregation of certain groups and the exclusion of the members of such groups from the valued occupational and political roles in a given society.

In discussing the existence of cultural, social, and structural pluralism in the United States, Smith points out that, although structural pluralism is unlawful according to the U.S. Constitution, in reality it does exist. The U.S. government is, according to its Constitution, explicitly organized as a consociation of territorially discreet collectivities. A consociation structure represents the formal opposite of differential incorporation of individuals or structural pluralism. A consociation of units excludes differential distribution of privilege, right, or opportunity in the public domain between its constituent collectivities, whether or not they share common institutions. In such systems, while citizenship may include identification with one or the other of a number of primary collectivities, formally there are supposed to be no differences in civil status in the common public domain and each collectivity is supposed to bear coordinate status. When it is effective, a consociation structure ensures that institutional differences (i.e., cultural differences) are treated as optional equivalents in the private domain, and social mobility across units always remains a possibility.

Actually, the United States is characterized by structural pluralism because of the long-standing exclusion of nonwhites and women. Both are differentially incorporated into the valued political and occupational roles. Through the mechanism of cultural, racial, and sex prejudice, Americans are allocated along a continuum that stretches from the preferred to the unpreferred.[1] The signals used to allocate people along this continuum are, in order of their strength, color, sex, and subcultural affiliation. The signal that has been employed with the most viciousness has been the race criterion. An example of the scurrility of the color bar appears in the following statement which appeared recently in a major education journal: "Nature has color-coded groups of individuals so that statistically reliable predictions of their adaptability to intellectually rewarding and effective lives can easily be made and profitably be used by the pragmatic man in the street" (Shockley 1972: 307). Ironically, the maintenance of struc-

---

[1] The notion of the preferred–unpreferred continuuum comes from discussion with Lloyd Hunter, with Antonio Pantoja, and from a statement entitled "The Concept of Cultural–Social–Economic Pluralism," prepared by the Committee on Cultural Pluralism of the U.S. Office of Education.

tural pluralism is ensured within the Constitution in the guarantees of States' rights.

CULTURAL PLURALISM IN THE UNITED STATES

The notion that the United States is culturally pluralistic has recently gained new acceptance. The classic statement of the cultural pluralist position as an accurate description of reality in America was made in 1915 by Horace Kallen in two articles under the title "Democracy versus the Melting-Pot" which appeared in *The Nation* (Gordon 1961: 277). At the time that he was writing, the prevalent view (still held by many) was that America was composed of a medley of groups who were merging together. It was believed that out of the melting pot would emerge a single American culture which would be strongly Anglo-American in the predominant norms and values. Kallen vigorously rejected the notion of the usefulness of the melting pot and Anglo-conformity models as accurate descriptions of what was actually transpiring in American life or as ideals for the future (Gordon 1961: 277). Kallen recognized that English would be the common language, but that "each nationality would have for its emotional and involuntary life its own peculiar dialect or speech, its own individual and inevitable esthetic and intellectual forms" (Kallen 1924: 116). In the introductory note to a volume of his collected essays, Kallen used, for the first time, the term "cultural pluralism" to refer to his position.

The position of cultural pluralism is now being reasserted in the theoretical analysis of American culture and, to some extent, in actual practice in the development of social programs (Sanday 1972). There is, however, some controversy and confusion over the applicability of cultural pluralism in the educational context. Wax (1972), for example, equates an emphasis on cultural pluralism with courses, programs, or schools in Black Studies, Indian Studies, and the like. Wax feels that it is misleading to portray Indianness as a homogeneous cultural entity. He argues, quite correctly, that American Indian groups exhibit a great deal of internal cultural heterogeneity. While some continue to use their native language or display other traits that have direct linkages to the aboriginal culture, others may have blended into one or another version of mainstream North America. Because of this, he believes that Indianness should be conceived as a socio-political rather than cultural identity. Wax raises important points; he errs, however, in assuming that an emphasis on cultural pluralism and culturally targeted programs means only the preservation and teaching of an aboriginal way of life.

While the surviving aboriginal traits must be recognized, cultural pluralism is more practically conceptualized in terms of variation in contemporary cultural themes, information components, and behavior styles within and across ethnically defined groups. If qualitative differences in these dimensions are found to exist across some groups as they do in the United States (see Chapter 7), then educational and public policy formulation must take these differences into consideration. But policymakers need to be informed of the meaning and impact of these differences in given problem areas through social science research. When a national sample is drawn for specific research purposes, such as analyzing the determinants of scholastic achievement, it may become necessary to disaggregate the sample along cultural dimensions because different explanatory models may apply in different groups. An approach somewhat like this was alluded to by the authors of the Coleman Report who state (quoted in Smith 1968: 387):

> White achievement appears to be highly sensitive to family background characteristics and apparently relatively insensitive to either of the two school factors. Negro achievement is sensitive to all three sets of variables but less so to family background than is the achievement of the whites. Discussion of the relative importance of these sets of variables without first defining the relevant groups is thus often misleading.

In a culturally homogeneous society, we would expect one explanatory model to hold for all members of the society (Sanday 1972). Cultural homogeneity implies that there is one scale along which the life styles exhibited by members of a given society can be judged and understood. There is the normative style, and anything departing from this norm is either an elitist or a defective style. Such an assumption has led, in the United States, to uniform welfare programs which treat all people needing welfare as if they were alike, that is, culturally homogeneous.

Another pitfall of the cultural homogeneity model is that it can easily lead to looking to the genes or to irreversible trends that occur in the home for the explanation of the failure of some children to achieve. In other words, it is a theoretical construct that leads responsible adults to shift the burden of the failure from social institutions about which they can do something, to sources beyond their control. Jensen's (1969) argument that the mean difference in IQ between blacks and whites must have a genetic basis because, among other reasons, middle-class blacks score lower than middle-class whites, is based on an assumption of cultural homogeneity. In order to reach this conclusion, Jensen must assume that middle-class blacks live in the same environment and internalize the same set of norms, values, and, above all, beliefs about themselves, as middle-class whites. All the current work demonstrates the opposite (see Johnson and Sanday 1971; Grier and Cobbs 1968; Hannerz 1969; Valentine 1972).

Emphasizing cultural pluralism is tricky and potentially destructive because of the tendency to associate cultural differences with such variables as race, national origin, or social class. To avoid this problem, I have suggested a typology of cultural units defined in terms of constellations of themes, behavior styles, and information components exhibited by members of a group that differ from those shared by members of other groups. In delineating such units in the United States, we must recognize the existence of a mainstream cultural unit that is the locus of power and control. When the concept of the mainstream or majority culture exists in a pluralistic society, people in such a society can be seen as falling into one of the following categories:

1. *Mainstreamer:* Member of the mainstream culture only (those people who have been exposed to and have assimilated the cultural components leading to mainstream life style and social performance).
2. *Bicultural:* Member of the mainstream culture and some other cultural unit (those people who have been exposed to and have assimilated the cultural components that allow them to perform acceptably in the mainstream culture and some other cultural unit).
3. *Culturally different:* Peripheral member of the mainstream culture, primary social performance is in some other cultural unit (those people who have been exposed to and have assimilated the cultural components related to social performance in a nonmainstream cultural unit).
4. *Culturally marginal:* Peripheral member of any cultural unit due to limited access and exposure to concepts and experiences (a characteristic often of institutionalized, sensorially limited individuals, and peer groups whose members have permanently disassociated themselves from their parents' culture).

These four types form a continuum in the degree to which mainstream norms are internalized and expressed. Taking the mainstream as the point of reference, competition, hardwork, striving for success, and future orientation characteristically underly prototypic transactions. Bicultural individuals have learned to behave predictably in mainstream transactions but maintain, in addition, another and distinct set of behavioral styles enabling them to behave predictably in nonmainstream transactions. Culturally different individuals are conversant only with behaviors characteristic of nonmainstream settings, while culturally marginal individuals are conversant only in very limited contexts. These contexts are radically different from those of the bicultural or culturally different individuals in that the associated behaviors are not part of a transgenerational patterned system but are developed in the present to meet certain transitory exigencies.

It is necessary to delineate empirically the cultural units making up the four types and to define operationally, in ways that can be employed in curriculum building, the cultural themes, information components, and behavioral styles characteristic of the units thus defined. A beginning in this direction can be found in several of the chapters in this volume (see Chapters 7 and 8). More than one cultural unit can be found in each type, and, as mentioned, it cannot be assumed that any type is defined by race, national origin, or social class.

For example, Black-Americans, Oriental-Americans, or American-Indians can fall into any of the categories named. In his discussion of Puerto Rican migrants, Fitzpatrick (1971: 98) describes three styles of adaptation to the mainland which can be classified as bi-cultural, culturally different, and culturally marginal. Bicultural adaptation is the effort to build a cultural bridge between the culture of the migrants and that of the mainland. Culturally different adaptation is the withdrawal into the old culture and a resistance to the new way of life. Cultural marginality can be a result of striving to become a mainstreamer. Fitzpatrick states that some migrants change their name, their reference groups, and seek to be accepted by the larger society. Unfortunately, by so doing, they are in great danger of becoming marginal because "having abandoned the way of life of their own people, in which they had a sense of 'who they were', there is no assurance that they will be accepted by the larger community" (Fitzpatrick 1971: 98). Bonilla (1971) makes a similar point when he says that those Puerto Ricans who assimilate must face the negative self-image and racial stigmatizing, which is a characteristic attitude toward nonwhites held by mainstreamers with a resulting loss of self-esteem. Jacob and Sanday (Chapter 8 of this volume) suggest that these styles may be present in the adaptation Puerto Rican school students make to cultural differences in the school.

Significant cultural differences in the United States are emphasized in the work of sociolinguists (Labov 1970; Cazden 1970; Cazden and John 1971; articles in Cazden *et al.* 1972). Gumperz and Hernandez–Chavez (1972: 85) state, for example, that the linguistic diversity characteristic of minority-group children also reflects far-reaching and systematic cultural differences. These authors state, further:

> Like the plural societies of Asia and Africa, American urban society is characterized by the coexistence of a variety of distinct cultures. Each major ethnic group has its own heritage, its own body of traditions, values, and views about what is right and proper. These traditions are passed on from generation to generation as part of the informal family or peer-group socialization process and are encoded in folk art and literature, oral or written. [Gumperz and Hernandez–Chavez 1972: 85.]

The distinct cultures referred to by Gumperz and Hernandez–Chavez in this quote are analogous to the cultural units referred to in the typology presented earlier. The value of this typology is that it includes, in addition, a way of looking at the options open to an individual in a culturally pluralistic society like the United States. Members of a nonmainstream cultural unit are, in differing degrees, articulated to the mainstream culture and, hence, can share elements of that culture. Depending on the barriers to interaction between members of the mainstream and other cultural units, these units over time may become assumed into the mainstream culture or remain separate. This potential pliability of cultural units suggests that social and cultural indices should be developed to monitor and describe changes.

Perhaps the most persuasive argument in favor of accepting a model of cultural pluralism comes from the evidence of the linkage between culture and learning. One of the prevalent views among those interested in cognitive processes in children is that children in some subcultures or cultures have certain processes while children in other subcultures or cultures do not. For example, Jensen (1969) talks about two kinds of cognitive skills—associative learning and conceptual learning. According to Jensen, groups do not differ with respect to their use of associative learning. However, groups do differ with respect to their use of conceptual learning. Jensen believes that whites possess this ability to a greater extent than blacks and, therefore, show superior performance on certain tasks.

The work of Cole (Cole 1972; Cole, Gay, Glick, and Sharp 1971), of Cazden and John (1971), and of Cohen (1971) leads one to question seriously such statements. These authors present evidence that indicates that there is a direct relationship between activities emphasized in some subcultures and not emphasized in others and cognitive styles and cognitive skills. Cole and his colleagues (1971), in work carried out in Liberia among children who have had some schooling and those who have not, show that cognitive skills are closely related to the activities that engage those skills. Their major conclusion (Cole *et al.* 1971: 233) is that "cultural differences in cognition reside more in the situations to which particular cognitive processes are applied than in the existence of a process in one cultural group and its absence in another." An important part of the method in this research is to identify the naturally occurring activities and associated cognitive skills for given cultural or subcultural groups. No research of this kind has yet been conducted in the United States. The work of Cohen (1971) and Cazden and John (1971) comes closest to this. Cohen, reporting on work with black and white children of varying socioeconomic classes, demonstrates a relationship between primary group structure and the way in which roles are enacted in this group and certain cognitive styles. Cazden and John (1971) review a number of studies that show how the life styles of American Indian children affect the way in which they learn in Anglo-American schools. Both Cohen and Cazden and John allude repeatedly to naturally occurring activities in the life styles of the different populations of children examined that are associated with unique learning styles.

If the relationship between culture and learning continues to be supported by more intensive work in the United States among minority children, and *if* it is found that the cognitive styles and skills associated with the activities that occur naturally for these children are significantly different from the skills emphasized in the schools, *then* to continue to ignore cultural pluralism and to refuse to understand it in a form in which it can be translated into the development of curricula and teacher-training programs must be interpreted as denying these children the opportunity to succeed in school. All the available information indicates that this is the case for most of the nonwhite minority children. It is now incumbent on the educational establishment to begin to identify the skills these children develop out of school and to think of ways in which these skills can be transferred to the school setting. At the same time, it will be important to discover how the cognitive processes learned by the Anglo-American child in the middle-class home, while engaging in the naturally occurring activities in this environment, can be freed from specific content and transferred to the content encountered by other children. For example, in Anglo-American homes, individualism and competition occur naturally, as well as an emphasis on abstracting from content. In the homes of many American Indian children and Puerto Rican children, it is known that the emphasis is on the family and the group and cooperation is encouraged along with an emphasis on the concrete. A question to be seriously addressed is how the bag of cognitive skills supposedly being communicated in the school can be communicated through the medium of the child's cultural background.

STRUCTURAL PLURALISM IN THE UNITED STATES

Prejudice, discrimination, and the subsequent exclusion of substantial numbers of Americans from choice occupational and political roles cannot be disputed. The question is whether or not the schools are a microcosm of the larger society. The empirical evidence indicates that this is overwhelmingly the case. It has been shown that an important function of the school is the transmission of culture as it exists in the larger society. Ethnographic studies of particular school situations show the very large role in the task of cultural transmission that is played by an unconscious enactment of role relationships in the larger society.

Parsons (1965), for example, describes activities in the schools in an Anglo-Chicano community that reinforce, in the minds of the children, the helper– helped relationship between Anglo-Americans and Chicanos in the wider community. Parsons used simple ethnographic tools, such as observing the number of times teachers asked Anglo-Americans to be helpers and Chicanos to take on the role of being helped. Byers and Byers (1972) made a film record of communication between two black and two white children and a white teacher in a nursery school setting. The film was then examined for contrasts in behavior between *(1)* white children and teacher and *(2)* black children and teacher. The authors assumed that there would be cultural differences between the communication behavior of the white and black children and that the teacher's cultural background would be closer to the white children's than to the black children's. The information on the film record supported this assumption. For example, one of the black children looks or glances at the teacher 35 times and "catches her eye" and exchanges facial expressions with the teacher 4 of those times. One of the white children, on the other hand, looks or glances at the teacher 14 times and "catches her eye" and exchanges expressions 8 of those times. It would appear, from this information, that the teacher does not pay as much attention to the black child as she does to the white child. Actually this is not the case. A careful analysis of the film indicates that the white child times her glances at the teacher to catch pauses or general "searching the scene" behavior of the teacher, whereas the black child's attempts are not so timed. This and other similar instances, such as the difference between the way in which the teacher touches the white children and the black children, indicates that there is a communication gap that occurs at the unconscious level. It was found that the black children and the white teacher cannot communicate in a mutually rewarding manner because they do not know the appropriate language. This inability to communicate at an emotional, nonverbal level can, the authors suggest, inhibit the black child's ability to learn from the teacher. This could eventually lead the teacher to treat the black children in the only way she knows how—that is, the way she has learned blacks are treated in the larger society.

Perhaps the most convincing study of cultural transmission in the schools is Leacock's (1969) study of teaching and learning in four city schools. The study investigated how and what children are learning in school, in order to arrive at a fuller understanding of what aspects of classroom life are most significant for their intellectual growth and understanding. Its purpose was to yield greater insight into the process of teaching and learning, in the context of observing ways in which children are being socialized into various roles in American society (Leacock 1969: 9).

The second and fifth grades were studied in a low-income black school, a low-income white school, a middle-income black school, and a middle-income white school. Data were collected through observations of classroom proceedings and interviews with the teachers and children. All classes were observed from February through May. Two observers recorded classroom interaction: One concentrated on the teacher and the children with whom she was immediately interacting, and the other focused on the children. Both observers recorded the time at the beginning and end of transitions, interruptions, disciplinary episodes, and any other slightly unusual incidents. The teacher-observer recorded as much of the teacher's verbatim evaluative, disciplinary, and motivating statements as possible, the general content and specific techniques of her teaching, and the names of all the children she called on, referred to, or signaled. They also recorded the correctness or incorrectness of a child's reply to the teacher and generally noted classroom reactions to specific teacher actions that the child-observer might not catch. The child-observer tried to record as much of the quality and atmosphere of the class as possible in terms of child—child interactions, degree of attentiveness, content of elaborated or initiated statements by the children, the behavior of a child after a significant interaction with the teacher was finished, and the reactions of other children (Leacock 1969: 11–12).

The results showed that the school experience of the low-income black children contrasted sharply with that of the white middle-income children. It was found, for example, that the teacher working with white middle-income fifth-grade children took the children's lack of attention as a cue to her, indicating the need for her to arouse their interest. On the other hand, the teacher of the low-income black children attributed boredom on their part to their presumably limited attention span. In general, the expectations for the low-income black children were low, and there was little respect shown for their ability to learn. It was found that the contributions of the low-income black children would be cut off and undermined and that the interest shown by the children would be stifled with irrelevant personal remarks. It was also found that, in the classroom, there was no attempt to "impose middle-class goals" on the children, but rather a tacit assumption that these goals were not open to at least the vast majority of them. The middle-class values being imposed on them defined them as inadequate and defined their proper role as one of deference. Lowered expectations on the part of teachers were expressed by a low emphasis on goal-setting statements altogether. In a 3-hour period, clear-cut overt goal-setting statements numbered 12 and 13 for the low-income black school, 15 and 18 for the low-income white school, and 43 and 46 for the middle-income white school.

These and other results indicate how the reality of the school experience contributes to the progressive falling off of interest and decrement in cognitive performance of the black child. The value of studies like Leacock's is that it provides vivid detail of the experience of the black child in school. In discussing the relative role of the home, community, and the school in perpetuating the inequities in our society, Leacock states (1969: 204):

> Social organization comprises an interlocking network of institutions, each reinforcing the other, and the school can no more be entirely responsible for perpetuating inequalities in our society than can any other single institution. However, the importance of the school is equally undeniable, and our data indicate its complicity despite its formal commitment to ameliorating, rather than aggravating, the difficulties of poverty.

STRATEGIES FOR CHANGE

A multi-pronged strategy will be necessary for bringing about enlightened change in the delivery of education to nonwhite and minority children. Thus far, it should be amply clear that promoting cultural pluralism without fighting structural pluralism will not be enough. Children, in order to find the necessary self-confidence, must feel both that their cultural heritage is admired and that they will be accepted as equals. In addition, in order to develop the appropriate cognitive skills, children need to start from the linguistic and sociocultural context they are most used to. The types of strategies that will aid in accomplishing these ends are listed and discussed briefly

1. *Development of alternative school social structures.* Considerable thought is currently being given to alternative schools. It is important to consider how family constraints may limit some children's ability to attend school. For example, migrant children or those who must find jobs to help support their family should have an opportunity to get a schooling at their own convenience. Furthermore, attempts should be made to think carefully about the number of hours school is in session, the time at which it begins, and the social structure of the school. The open classroom is a new idea, but there are other ways of structuring the school experience which may be more effective. Furthermore, it is possible that attending school in a central location and being herded together with students all of the same age is ineffective. Thought needs to be given to utilizing other physical facilities for schooling.

2. *Change in the role relationships enacted in the school.* Teachers are socialized in a structurally pluralistic system and, whether they like it or not, will consciously or unconsciously communicate prejudice. Teachers must be trained to understand consciously how this can happen and learn to change their behavior. This can be done in a way that is not threatening to the teacher and that becomes an integral part of the requirements for certification. Parsons (1970) has developed a technique to aid teachers to adopt new and more productive roles in the classroom. He assumes that it is first necessary to get teachers to change their role behavior and that this can be accomplished by the technique of engaging the teacher in a process of self-confrontation through self-observation.

This technique has four main features. A brief segment of classroom behavior is recorded on video tape. The teacher views the tape a number of times, each time performing a single coding task that involves focusing sharply on some very select aspect of the total behavior on tape. After each viewing, the teacher performs a programmed analysis of the results. The preliminary evidence, derived from the pilot use of the Guided Self-Analysis technique by over 2,000 teachers, indicates that the behavior changes induced by the technique are impressive.

This technique is offered only as an example of what might be done. It is important to think of many different ways in which teachers can learn to monitor the quality of their interaction with children. Teachers may also need to be judged in terms of the quality of this interaction together with their teaching ability.

3. *Development of teacher-training programs that prepare teachers to understand and deal emotionally with culturally different students.* While teachers can generally be taught something about the cultural differences that exist at one point in time, the literature does not allow one to keep abreast of the diversity in culture and the rapid changes. All teachers must, therefore, learn to be ethnographers. That is, they must learn to observe and to understand the cultural differences that children may bring to their classrooms each year. In order to do this, perhaps teachers can learn from the work of Maria Montessori (1913, 1964, 1965a, b). Montessori insisted that teachers practice ethnography incessantly and that they look at children as a naturalist looks at bees. She felt that the main task of teachers was to watch what the children did. When it became evident that a particular device was not working for a child, the task was then to devise some modification or some alternative device on the spot. These devices would then become part of the bag of offerings to children who could pick and choose what most suited them. According to Gearing (1973), the educational practices Montessori said would work did, in fact, work dramatically in the slums of Rome.

4. *Basic research activities on the relations between naturally occurring activities in different cultural contexts and associated cognitive skills.* To date, the work in cognition in children has usually used white middle-class children as subjects. When culturally different children are used as subjects, the analysis usually revolves around how they do not have the skills exhibited by Anglo-American children which long ago became the model of how children should perform cognitively. It is extremely important to begin working on the cognitive skills culturally different children have developed and to learn the cultural context in which these skills develop. Research also needs to be conducted on the mechanisms by which cognitive skills can be freed from specific cultural context and transferred to new content. The work of Cole and his colleagues (1971) can be used as a guide.

5. *Development of new curriculum materials.* Gearing (1973) discusses the curriculum efforts at the primary, secondary, and college levels with which anthropologists are currently working to bring about change in the schools. The importance of these efforts, according to Gearing, is that through them the student discovers that he can vicariously enter the experience of other people, which means that he can discover how he is alike or how he is different. The anthropological message that is communicated in these materials involves the concept of cultural relativity, or the notion that all cultures of all peoples are to be equally respected and understood. This message may be in conflict with the teacher's or a school's emphasis on conformity to Anglo-American norms. Hence the anthropological message may compete with the processes of cultural transmission in the society at large and in the school in particular. It could be that, as

Gearing (1973) suggests, such curricular materials are "out in front of the culture, anticipating and perhaps generating culture change" (p. 1243).

CONCLUSION

Cultural and structural pluralism in the United States have been defined and described in the school context. It was suggested that both cultural differences and structural exclusion from the opportunity structure affect minority children's performance in school. However, for the sake of developing optimal educational strategies given funding limitations, it is important, in future research, to sort out the degree to which minority group scholastic achievement is a function of adaptation to minority status and/or cultural differences between home and school. The chapters by Sanday, Boardman, and Davis (Chapter 7) and by Erickson (Chapter 9) make beginnings in this direction.

The typology of cultural pluralism presented earlier implies that intervention strategies should be flexible. Clearly, those who are culturally different or marginal will require a somewhat different intervention strategy than those who are bicultural or mainstreamers. Those who are marginal will probably require the most attention. In the schools, these may be the individuals in most need of special ethnic history and culture programs. On the other hand, those who are culturally different may want mainstream oriented programs especially if they are seeking to adopt a bicultural mode. The marginal individuals may also display the most personal frustration, anxiety, and disruptive behavior. Because they have been isolated (or have isolated themselves) from positive interaction with the adults who are the purveyors of culture, they may not have internalized standards to guide their behavior in a way that would be acceptable to the members of any cultural unit. The process by which such standards can be internalized by older children or young adults may require an intervention strategy that goes beyond the school and into the home and community.

REFERENCES

Banks, J. A. (Editor)
  1972   The imperatives of ethnic education. *Phi Delta Kappan* **LIII** (5) (January): 266–269.
Boardman, A. E., O. A. Davis, and P. R. Sanday
  1973   A simultaneous equations model of the educational process: The Coleman data revisited. *Proceedings of the Social Statistics Section,* American Statistical Association, Washington, D.C. Pp. 62–71.
Bonilla, E.
  1971   Ethnic studies and cultural pluralism. *The Rican* (Fall): 56–65.
  1972   Cultural pluralism and the education of Puerto Rican youths. *Phi Delta Kappan* LIII (5) (January): 294–296.

Byers, P., and H. Byers
  1972   Nonverbal communication and the education of children. In *Functions of language in the classroom,* edited by Courtney B. Cazden, Vera P. John, and Dell Hymes. New York: Teachers College Press. Pp. 3–31.
Cazden, C. B.
  1970   The neglected situation in child language research and education. In *Language and poverty,* edited by Frederick Williams. Institute for Research on Poverty Monograph Series. Chicago: Markham.
Cazden, C. B., and V. P. John
  1971   Learning in American Indian children. In *Anthropological perspectives on education,* edited by M. L. Wax, S. Diamond, and F. O. Gearing. New York: Basic Books. Pp. 252–272.
Cazden, C. B., V. P. John, and D. Hymes (Editors)
  1972   *Functions of language in the classroom.* New York: Teachers College Press.
Cohen, R.
  1971   The influence of conceptual rule sets on measures of learning ability. In *Race and intelligence,* edited by C. L. Brace, G. R. Gamble, and J. T. Bond. Anthropological studies, No. 8. Washington, D.C.: American Anthropological Association.
Cole, M.
  1972   Toward an experimental anthropology of thinking. Paper presented at the joint meeting of the American Ethnological Society and Council on Anthropology and Education, Montreal, April.
Cole, M., J. Gay, J. A. Glick, and D. W. Sharp
  1971   *The cultural context of learning and thinking.* New York: Basic Books.
Coleman, J. S., E. Q. Campbell, C. J. Hobson, J. McPartland, A. M. Mood, F. D. Weinfeld, and R. L. York
  1966   *Equality of educational opportunity.* Washington, D.C.: U.S. Government Printing Office.
Fitzpatrick, J. P.
  1971   *Puerto Rican Americans.* Englewood Cliffs, New Jersey: Prentice-Hall.
Furnivall, J. S.
  1948   *Colonial policy and practice: A comparative study of Burma and Netherlands India.* London: Cambridge Univ. Press.
Gearing, F. O.
  1973   Anthropology and education. In *Handbook of social and cultural anthropology,* edited by J. Honigman. Chicago: Rand McNally.
Gordon, M. M.
  1961   Assimilation in America: Theory and reality. *Daedelus* 90:263–285.
Grier, W. H., and P. B. Cobbs
  1968   *Black rage.* New York: Basic Books.
Guerra, M.
  1972   Educating Chicano children and youth. *Phi Delta Kappan* LIII (5) (January): 313–314.
Gumperz, J. J., and E. Hernandez-Chavez
  1972   Bilingualism, bidialectalism, and classroom interaction. In *Functions of language in the classroom,* edited by C. B. Cazden, V. P. John, and D. Hymes. New York: Teachers College Press.
Gurin, P., G. Gurin, R. Lao, and M. Beattie
  1969   Internal–external control in the motivational dynamics of Negro youth. *Journal of Social Issues* 25: 29–53.

Guthrie, J., G. Kleindorfer, H. Levin, and Stout
   1971   *Schools and inequality.* Cambridge: Massachusetts Institute of Technology Press.
Hannerz, U.
   1969   *Soulside: Inquiries into ghetto culture and community.* New York: Columbia
           Univ. Press.
Heber, R., H. Garber, S. Harrington, C. Hoffman, and C. Falender
   1972   Rehabilitation of families at risk for mental retardation: Progress report. Rehabili-
           tation Research and Training Center in Mental Retardation, Univ. of Wisconsin,
           Madison.
Jencks, C.
   1972   *Inequality: A reassessment of the effect of family and schooling in America.* New
           York: Basic Books.
Jensen, A. R.
   1969   How much can we boost IQ and scholastic achievement? *Harvard Educational
           Review* 39: 1–123.
Johnson, N., and P. R. Sanday
   1971   Subcultural variations in an urban poor population. *American Anthropologist* 73:
           128–143. Reprinted in Volume III of *Educating the disadvantaged* New York:
           AMS Press.
Kadane, J. B., T. W. McGuire, P. R. Sanday, and R. Staelin
   1973   An econometric model for estimating IQ scores and environmental influences on
           the pattern of IQ scores over time. In *Proceedings of the Social Statistics Section,*
           American Statistical Association, Washington, D.C. Pp. 72–81.
Kallen, H.
   1924   *Culture and democracy in the United States.* New York: Boni and Liveright.
Kuper, L.
   1969   Plural societies: Perspectives and problems. In *Pluralism in Africa,* edited by L.
           Kuper and M. G. Smith. Berkeley: Univ. of California Press.
Labov, W.
   1970   The logic of nonstandard English. In *Language and Poverty,* edited by F. Williams.
           Institute for Research on Poverty Monograph Series. Chicago: Markham.
Leacock, E.
   1969   *Teaching and learning in city schools: A comparative study.* New York: Basic
           Books.
Mondale, Walter P. (Chairman)
   1972   *Toward equal educational opportunity: The report of the Select Committee on
           Equal Educational Opportunity, United States Senate.* Washington, D.C.: U.S.
           Gov. Printing Offic.
Montessori, Maria
   1913   *Pedagogical anthropology.* New York: Stokes.
   1964   *The Montessori method.* New York: Schocken.
   1965a   *Spontaneous activity in education.* New York: Schocken.
   1965b   *Dr. Montessori's own handbook.* New York: Schocken.
Parsons, T. W.
   1965   Ethnic cleavage in a California school. Unpublished doctoral dissertation, Stan-
           ford Univ.
   1970   Guided self-analysis system for professional development—education series. Lim-
           ited distribution by the author: 2140 Shattuck Avenue, Berkeley, California
           94704.

Sanday, Peggy R.
1972   The relevance of anthropology to U. S. social policy. *Newsletter of Council on Anthropology and Education.* **III** (3): 1–8.
1973   *A diffusion model for the study of the cultural determinants of differential intelligence.* Final Report submitted to the U.S. Department of Health, Education, and Welfare, National Institute of Education. To be revised for publication.
Shockley, W.
1972   Dysgenics, geneticity, raceology. *Phi Delta Kappan* **LIII** (5) (January): 297–308.
Smith, M. G.
1960   Social and cultural pluralism. In *Social and cultural pluralism in the caribbean. Annals of the New York Academy of Sciences* **83**: 763–785.
Smith, M. G.
1969   Some developments in the analytic framework of pluralism. In *Pluralism in Africa,* edited by L. Kuper and M. G. Smith. Berkeley: Univ. of California Press. Pp. 415–458.
Smith, M. S.
1968   Communications. *Journal of Human Resources,* **3**: 387.
Stenner, A., and S. Mueller
1973   A successful compensatory education model. *Phi Delta Kappan* **LV** (4) (December): 246–248).
Valentine, C. A.
1972   *Black studies and anthropology: Scholarly and political interests in Afro-American cultures.* Addison-Wesley Modular Publications No. 15. Reading, Massachusetts: Addison-Wesley.
Wax, M. L.
1972   Cultural pluralism, political power, and ethnic studies. Paper presented at the annual meetings of the American Ethnological Society, Montreal, April.
Williams, F. (Editor)
1970   *Language and poverty.* Institute for Research on Poverty Monograph Series. Chicago: Markham.

7

The Cultural Context
of American Education*

Peggy Reeves Sanday   Anthony E. Boardman   Otto A. Davis
University of Pennsylvania   University of Pennsylvania   Carnegie–Mellon University

For the cultural context of American education it is instructive to reach back in time and note certain developments that occurred in sixteenth century England. This is the period marking the birth of the European expansion overseas, the enslavement of Africans, and the development of a technology pressed forward by an urge to order, control, and classify—to count time, money, and people. These developments were part of a multi-faceted cultural revolution when they began and have reached new pinnacles of absurdity and inhumanity in the twentieth century. In the administration of the American education system, the urge to order and classify—to master and control—has resulted in the nailing of children on the impersonal cross of verbal, mathematical, or some other kind of achievement—

*The authors gratefully recognize the support of the National Institute of Education (NIE-G-74-0070) in the funding of the research on which this chapter is based.

This chapter is a product of the interaction, over a number of years, between an anthropologist (Sanday), a public policy analyst (Boardman), and a political economist (Davis). The analysis of the cultural context of American education, in the first section of this chapter stems from Sanday's anthropological focus, while the simultaneous equations formulation of the educational process was jointly conceived by Boardman and Davis.

always summarized in a number. This is now so pervasive, so much a part of the American culture that we may be both incapable of seeing other possibilities and powerless to change our present ways, locked as we are in a way of doing things that has roots in a centuries old cultural pattern.

All Americans have paid the price. While the twentieth century technological and scientific expression of these sixteenth century cultural values has taken us to the moon and has enabled us to advance to thermonuclear warfare readiness, it has locked us out of the internal life. White American children have paid one price, minority children another. In being pressed into becoming cognitive whiz kids, a sense of playfulness, imagination, and love is muted for white children. Nonwhite children simply never reach the door of opportunity because the education process burdens them permanently with the cross of their lower achievement and IQ scores, impeding their ability ever to succeed. Scores have become the means for assigning certain groups of people to an inferior status. Questions about differences in group scores invariably become naive discussions of nature versus nurture in this supposedly most sophisticated age of analysis.

With respect to sex differences in behavior, it is now possible to find agreement for the view that there is a complicated and inseparable relationship between culture, biology, and prenatal–postnatal environment (Money and Ehrhardt 1972). It is still impossible, however, to find such agreement in the area of black–white differences. In a simplistic linear model, Jensen (1969) leads the field of those assigning most of the variance to nurture leaving a small part to be attributed to nature. This kind of thinking can be traced to nineteenth century attitudes toward the Negro. The nature–nurture issue rose concurrently with abolitionism and the Civil War. Thomas Jefferson talked about freeing Negroes on the same pages that he proposed the idea of Negro mental inferiority based in nature. One is tempted to the conclusion that the nature–nurture issue took the place of slavery as a device for keeping Negroes in their place. Indeed, Jordan (Chapter 5 of this volume) has so suggested.

Since the days of Thomas Jefferson, in spite of having reached the moon and having made numerous other exotic discoveries requiring great complexity of thinking, we have not moved far in our thinking about mental ability and learning. While his language may be dressed up with terms like heritability and his conceptualization presented in twentieth century analysis of variance terms, Jensen's conclusions still dissolve into the same simplistically orchestrated nineteenth century dichotomy opposing nature and nurture only now with numbers attached giving the relative weights—80% for nature, 20% for nurture. The nonsense of Jensen's approach is just as neatly shown by Sanday (1972), Lewontin (1970), and Layzer (1974).

In what follows, we propose a radically different theory, quantitative methodology, and a set of conclusions with which to evaluate mental ability (in this case achievement) and other outputs of the American educational process. Being products of the aforementioned Euro-American cultural urge to quantify, we stress the importance of using simultaneous equations estimation procedures in empirical analyses of the education process. We think that the simultaneous regression model is the most faithful to the complexity of the process we are studying. We promise, however, not to let numbers get in the way more than is minimally necessary. In the light of our theory and analysis, we suggest certain educational policy research strategies in pursuit of that still allusive goal of our democracy, equality of educational opportunity. Our data come from a sample of 16,000 representing six ethnic groups selected randomly from the Coleman *et al.* (1966) twelfth-grade tapes.

THE CULTURAL CONTEXT OF AMERICAN EDUCATION

Because the educational process takes place in a home, school, and community context consisting of individuals interacting, teaching, scoring, and making grades, we tend to concentrate our study of it at these levels. We treat the educational process as a *thing* that exists in a vacuum, that is observable, and that can be understood by applying linear cause–effect models to snapshots of behavior taken at one point in time. We argue endlessly as to how much of the variance can be assigned to home, school, or community and proceed to change one of these contexts depending on how the numbers turn out.

The process of education takes place in the much larger, historically determined, amorphous cultural template of the American society. The cultural template is the set of ideal forms that informs and guides all transactions in all social networks independently of our conscious awareness. The axis on which the constellation of mainstream American ideal forms rotates is the urge to order and classify—to count time, money, and people—to control. Rooted in the social ferment of the sixteenth century (see Jordan, Chapter 5 of this volume), its contemporary cultural expression is found in the Protestant work ethic, future orientation, sexual repression, and an overemphasis on intelligence and cognitive learning. Psychological and spiritual health, joy, love of society, optimism and humor, trust in people, and tolerance for others and their opinions are either considered much less important or are not emphasized at all.

Inseparable from the sixteenth century developments was the evolution and acceptance of bond slavery. The mood for control and expansion interacting with labor necessities in the colonies, the equation of black, evil, heathenism, baseness, and unbridled sexuality, all provided the necessary cultural support for the enslavement of Negroes in an atmosphere where freedom and personal liberty became the watchwords of American independence (Jordan 1968). So, right from the beginning of the development of the cultural axis still so pervasive was the inseparable interweaving of the notion that Negroes were different and, therefore, rightfully to be excluded and debased. The inherent contradiction of freedom, liberty, and opportunity for whites, as opposed to debasement, slavery, and exclusion for blacks, survives into the present. It has created a condition of cultural and structural pluralism in the American social system.

Cultural pluralism (defined by Sanday, Chapter 6 of this volume) refers to opposed sets of beliefs, values, attitudes, communication, and behavior styles characteristic of certain groups. Such differences may have been originally based in unique historical and cultural traditions. They survive in the present to the degree that they are consciously maintained, or to the degree that members of different culture-bearing groups are excluded and segregated from mainstream America. Exclusion and segregation are the prerequisites of structural pluralism, defined as differential incorporation of groups of people into the opportunity structure (Sanday, Chapter 6 of this volume). Blacks and American Indians were excluded from the beginning of the colonialization period. Late in the nineteenth century, this practice was extended to Orientals and Mexican-Americans, and, in the twentieth century, to Puerto Ricans. As we will argue later, the Orientals, because of certain cultural congruities with the American mainstream, have been more successful in breaking the structural barriers. The non-Anglosaxon white immigrants, while they may have been temporarily excluded, were able to pass into the mainstream once divested of their cultural identification.

Cultural and structural pluralism mean that many of the nation's children are socialized outside of the American mainstream. The standard intelligence and achievement tests are, however, measures of specific knowledge and problem solving skills predictive of social performance in the mainstream. Excluded as they are in their home and community contexts, these children do not have the same exposure to the knowledge and skills these tests call upon. Since educability depends upon a fund of prior knowledge, skills, and acquired cognitive habits, these children are behind mainstream children even before they begin school. Based on this Sanday (1972, 1973) has hypothesized that the nature and degree of contact with the mainstream culture will explain group differences in mental test scores. Since this notion is something of a break with a long scholarly tradition opposing genetic versus environmental factors in the explanation of group differences, we will illustrate how the degree of contact with mainstream America is related to the average test scores of nonmainstream groups. Two sets of data are employed, one collected in the first quarter of the twentieth century, the other in the third quarter.

1. Army mental test scores published in the early 1920s. In 1923, Carl Brigham published a study of the relationship between intelligence, nation of origin, and length of residence in the United States. The analysis was based on the published army mental test scores of "about 81,000 native born Americans,

12,000 foreign born individuals and 23,000 negroes" (Brigham 1923: xx). In making these group distinctions, it is quite clear that Brigham, reflecting attitudes of the time, does not consider the last two groups to be part of mainstream America. He says in his introduction, "Army mental tests give us an opportunity for a national inventory of our own mental capacity, and the mental capacity of those we have invited to live with us" (1923: xx).

The native- and foreign-born samples were separated by officer and draft status. The scores of the foreign-born who could not speak English were based on a nonlanguage test. The remaining scores were based on a test given in English. The analysis of the mean scores of native- and foreign-born draft yield very interesting results and conclusions on Brigham's part. Even though the tests were to measure "native or inborn" intelligence, the native-born draft scored higher, on the average, than the foreign-born draft. The foreign-born draft scores were directly related to years of residence in the United States. With increase in time of residence, the difference between the native- and foreign-born became less significant. The foreign-born group in this country over 20 years had an average score identical with the average score of the native-born. This very remarkable fact of increase in the intelligence scores with years of residence led Brigham to the following statement:

> It is sometimes stated that the examining methods stressed too much the hurry-up attitude frequently called typically American. The adjustment to test conditions is a part of the intelligence test. We have, of course, no other measure of adjustment aside from the total score on the examinations given. If the tests used included some mysterious type of situation that was "typically American," we are indeed fortunate, for this is America, and the purpose of our inquiry is that of obtaining a measure of the character of our immigration. Inability to respond to a "typically American" situation is obviously an undesirable trait [1923: 96].

Of course, if the tests did include some mysterious "typically American" situation, it would be difficult to argue that they measure "native or inborn intelligence." Brigham handles this problem by concluding that growth in intelligence cannot be explained by an increased length of residence, but by "gradual deterioration in the class of immigrants examined in the army, who came to this country in each succeeding five year period since 1902" (1923: 111).

We would argue that the army tests were culturally biased and that Brigham's data showing a relationship between years of residence and increase in average score reflects this bias. Further testimony to the cultural bias of the tests appears when the scores of the foreign-born draft are compared by country of birth. The differences among the foreign-born draft are listed below in terms of the percentage from each country who exceed the average (white) native-born American. These figures are taken from Brigham (1923: 119).

England	67.3%	Sweden	41.7%	Turkey	25.3%
Scotland	58.8%	Norway	37.3%	Greece	21.3%
Holland	58.1%	Belgium	35.3%	Russia	18.9%
Germany	48.7%	Austria	28.2%	Italy	14.4%
Denmark	47.8%	Ireland	26.2%	Poland	12.2%
Canada	47.3%				

Those coming from the Protestant industrializing economies do better than those coming from the Catholic or Eastern Orthodox and Jewish rural economies. This means that those coming from the countries most culturally similar to the American mainstream do better. These are, of course, the countries supplying the original settlers of the American colonies who brought with them the ingredients of the mainstream American cultural template. Not surprisingly, the foreign-born draft who score the highest are those born in England. This suggests to us that the greater the cultural similarity between the draftee's country of birth and his new country the more likely he is to do well on the army test. Years of residence are confounded with these results since those countries at the top of the list happen also to be those with the longest history of immigration to the United States and, therefore, those having the greatest familiarity with the American culture.

Brigham's conclusions, however, are quite different. His major conclusion provides a vivid picture, in the language of the 1920s, of the ethnocentrism and urge to control inherent in the still enduring mainstream American way of thinking. Brigham says (1923: 182), quoting the famous Nordicist, Madison Grant (1922):

> In a very definite way, the results which we obtain by interpreting the army data by means of the race hypothesis support Mr. Madison Grant's thesis of the superiority of the Nordic type: "The Nordics are, all over the world, a race of soldiers, sailors, adventurers, and explorers, but above all, of rulers, organizers, and aristocrats in sharp contrast to the essentially peasant and democratic character of the Alpines. The Nordic race is domineering, individualistic, self-reliant, and jealous of their personal freedom both in political and religious systems, and as a result they are usually Protestants. Chivalry and knighthood and their still surviving but greatly impaired counterparts are peculiarly Nordic traits, and feudalism, class distinctions, and race pride among Europeans are traceable for the most part to the north" (p. 228). "The pure Nordic peoples are characterized by a greater stability and steadiness than are mixed peoples such as the Irish, the ancient Gauls, and the Athenians, among all of whom the lack of these qualities was balanced by a correspondingly greater versatility." [pp. 228–229]

2. Scholastic achievement scores published in 1966. The Equality of Educational Opportunity Survey, conducted in 1964–1965 and published in 1966 by Coleman *et al.,* produced the most comprehensive body of data ever collected on public schools and their students in the United States. Mosteller and Moynihan (1972) refer to it as the most important source of data on the sociology of

American education yet to appear. Achievement tests were administered to approximately 900,000 students in the first, third, sixth, ninth, and twelfth grades in a nationwide sample of schools. Over a hundred items were collected on each student's personal background, aspirations, and attitudes. In addition, the school principals provided information on school characteristics, and teachers filled out a questionnaire on their background and attitudes and took a verbal achievement test.

In Table 7.1 we present a set of variables that we suggest are measures of the degree and nature of contact with mainstream America. These are by no means the only measures of this sort; however, they are the only ones available in the

Table 7.1
Rank Order of Nonmainstream Groups Reflecting Degree and Nature of Contact with Mainstream America

Variables	Whites	Oriental Americans	American Indians	Mexican Americans	Blacks	Puerto Ricans
Home						
Student social class	1	2	4	5	3	6
Two parents in home	1	2	4	3	6	5
Number of older siblings	1	2	5	6	3	4
Average rank	1	2	4.3	4.7	4	5
School composition						
Average student social class	1	2	6	3	4	5
Proportion of white students in class last year	1	5	3	2	6	4
Mainly black school (<30% white)	1	5	4	2	6	3
Proportion of white teachers in class last year	1	5	2	3	6	4
Average rank	1	4.3	3.8	2.5	5.5	4
Teacher Ability						
Teacher's average verbal score	2	1	4	5	6	3
School characteristics						
Teachers have problems with administration	2	6	1	3	4	5
School facilities	1	2	3	4	5	6
Problems in school	1	2	3	4	6	5
Mental tests given in school	3	1	4	2	5	6
Average rank	1.8	2.8	2.8	3.3	5	5.5
Total average (average of average rank)	1.5	2.5	3.7	3.9	5.1	4.4

Coleman *et al.* data. We used a sample of 16,000 selected randomly from the twelfth-grade sample, which we grouped into six subsamples. We assume that the White subsample (N = 4530) constitutes the mainstream and that Oriental Americans (N = 1332), American Indians (N = 1332), Mexican-Americans (N = 2420), blacks (N = 4364), and Puerto Ricans (N = 1352) constitute the nonmainstream groups.

Group means on each of the variables presented in Table 7.1 were computed (see Appendix 1 for a brief description of each variable and method of scoring). Each of the groups were then ranked on each variable in order of closeness to what we hypothesize to be the value most reflective of the mainstream. In most cases, this simply means that the highest mean value is the closest and the lowest the most distant. A rank of 1 is assigned to the highest and 6 to the lowest (unless there are ties). Thus, student socioeconomic class is scored so that the highest value reflects higher social class and the lowest value lower social class. In a few cases, such as number of older siblings, the lowest mean value is assigned a 1 and the highest a 6. In this case, it is assumed that having fewer sibling results in a greater degree of contact.

The rank order decisions were made independently of the mean values for the white student sample. If we are correct in assuming that this group constitutes the mainstream culture, we would expect that, in most cases, this group would have a rank of 1 on each variable. Examination of Table 7.1 illustrates that this is, in fact, the case. The group closest to the white group is the Oriental-Americans with American Indians, Mexican-Americans, Puerto Ricans and blacks following respectively.

Table 7.2 presents the rank order of each group on the five scholastic achievement tests administered to the twelfth-grade sample. If Sanday is correct in her hypothesis that degree and nature of contact with the mainstream culture explains group differences in mental-ability scores, the group ranks on these tests

Table 7.2
Rank Order of Ethnic Groups on Achievement Tests (EEOS Twelfth-Grade Data)

	White	Oriental Americans	American Indians	Mexican-Americans	Blacks	Puerto Ricans
Achievement Test						
Verbal	1	2	3	4	6	5
Nonverbal	2	1	3	4	6	5
Reading	1	2	3	4	5	6
Mathematical	2	1	3	4	6	5
General informational	1	2	3	4	5	6
Average rank	1.4	1.6	3	4	5.6	5.4

should be the same as the ranks on the cultural variables. This is exactly the case. The rank order correlation of the overall average group ranks in both tables is nearly perfect.

By these measures, Orientals are closest to the mainstream, and blacks are the most distant. American Indians fall in between, a fact which needs to be underlined since, in arguing for black genetic differences in intelligence, Jensen (1971: 13) says: "American Indians, though considerably more impoverished than Negroes in the United States, score higher than Negroes on tests of intelligence and scholastic achievement." Jensen based these remarks on the reported Coleman data. His interpretation is definitely not borne out by our more systematic analysis.

In spite of severe and systematic racial discrimination and past exclusion from the mainstream opportunity structure, Orientals appear similar to whites in mental-ability scores and on the cultural variables. Insidious comparisons between Orientals and blacks would lead some to suggest genetic superiority as an explanation for Oriental success. It would be argued that they "have made it" in spite of racial discrimination. This argument takes structural pluralism into consideration but not cultural pluralism. The framework of cultural pluralism suggests a quite different explanation. Part of the cultural baggage brought by Orientals to this country included certain beliefs, values, and attitudes that were similar to the American cultural template. In addition, Orientals brought certain core economic and community political institutions that enabled them to survive and overcome racial discrimination in this country.

Rigid self-control, motivation to succeed, and emphasis on education and learning are deeply embedded in the Chinese and Japanese cultural traditions. A study of Japanese immigrants showed that most of them came from localities in which, in 1900, 51% or more of the men had at least 8 years of schooling. The authors of this study believe that educational attainment prior to immigration is a prime factor explaining Japanese occupational success in the United States (Levine and Montero 1973: 40). In the United States, Japanese and Chinese communities were segregated from the mainstream but tightly knit and organized in what proved to be powerful economic and political associations. A sense of ethnic, tribal, clan, territorial, and family honor was maintained through the provision of a group-sanctioned, community-based cultural mechanism for controlling individual behavior. Such mechanisms did not exist in American black communities (Light 1972: 187).

The Oriental immigrants also brought with them culturally derived consumer preferences and a culturally preferred style of economic organization which Light (1972) argues enabled them to achieve economic mobility in the face of severe economic discrimination. This preference was a penchant for partnership rather than solo entrepreneurship. A similar preference also existed in the economic organization of West Indian blacks that was derived from West Africa, but did not survive among American blacks. It was a preference that made it possible for these groups to go into retail proprietorship.

Retail proprietorship has been a classic avenue for movement into the American mainstream. Orientals used this avenue successfully, American blacks did not, although their West Indian counterparts did. By 1919, 47% of the hotels and 25% of the grocery stores in Seattle were Japanese owned. In 1940, 40% of Japanese men in Los Angeles were self-employed (Light 1972: 10). In 1929, there were enormous differences between the business development of Chinese and Japanese as compared to American blacks. On the other hand, West Indians in Harlem distinguished themselves from native born Negroes by their remarkable propensity to operate small business enterprises. In the 1920s, the black-run retail businesses were largely in the control of West Indian blacks. While American blacks tended to be involved in noncompetitive service enterprises, the West Indians operated businesses in direct competition with whites. Thrifty, stingy, and grasping were adjectives used to describe them (Light 1972: 33).

Light (1972: 22) attributes these differences in business activities to the existence of culturally derived, but structurally similar, customs labeled by Geertz as "rotating credit associations." These are credit institutions that existed in south China, Japan, and West Africa and were employed by Orientals and West Indians in the United States as the principal device for capitalizing small business. American blacks did not employ a similar institution. "Why" makes for interesting speculation.

Rotating credit associations have been well described in West Africa and probably existed in the societies supplying the major portion of the slave trade. It was not lost in the West Indian slave culture, but it was in the United States. Light hypothesizes that this is a function of the demography of slavery in the two areas. Throughout the slavery period, the black population dramatically exceeded the white in the Caribbean. As Jordan put it, "West Indian planters were lost not so much in the Caribbean as in a sea of blacks" (quoted from Light 1972: 37). By 1860, approximately 50% of all slaves in the United States lived on farms of up to 20 slaves who worked in close association with whites. In addition to the contrast in size, the mostly black West Indian sugar plantations were often owned by absentee planters, and there was, in many cases, a dependence on the food raised by slave farmers. By the mid-nineteenth century, for example, the entire population of Jamaica was completely dependent on the black economy for its subsistence (Light 1972: 38–41). In such an atmosphere, traditional economic institutions were able to flourish.

Light establishes the viability of the rotating credit association among Chinese, Japanese, and West Indian migrants to the United States and argues that American-born Negroes did not employ such an institution because it had apparently vanished from their cultural repertoire. In addition to being scattered mostly on small farm units during the slavery period, there was, during the period from 1790 to 1860, a vast interregional redistribution of slaves in the United States. Some 835,000 slaves were moved from the exporting to the importing slave states. Even if Fogel and Engerman (1974) are correct in their assertion that 84% of this number moved with their owners in farm units, the fact of this movement would suggest a severe fragmentation of any regional black unity of the kind found in the Caribbean. The absence of the rotating credit tradition inhibited the development of American-Negro owned business. Thus, racial discrimination in lending affected American Negroes more deleteriously than it did the other minority groups (Light 1972: 36).

The other nonmainstream groups in our sample have also experienced exclusion and discrimination. Unlike the Orientals, their cultural heritage contrasts more with the Anglo-American tradition, further handicapping them as they seek to realize the opportunities afforded by the "American dream." Mexican-Americans, now the second largest minority in the United States, number over 5.5 million of which 90% live in the Southwest, representing at least 12% of the population there. Although the Southwest Chicano community can trace its origins to 1598, the largest influx of Mexican immigrants occurred in the years 1920–1929 and 1953–1964. They came as unskilled field laborers but soon became urban dwellers. In 1960, the median age was 17, and the median education for men and women 25 years old and over was 7.1 completed years of schooling as compared with the 12.1 for the Anglo-American population (Trueba 1974: 9).

From the beginning, discrimination against Chicanos was of the same form as that against blacks. They were denied entrance to public parks, public swimming pools, movie theaters, stores, and restaurants and went to segregated schools. In the 1940s, restrooms, churches, and cemeteries carried signs: "For Colored and Mexicans." Trueba (1974: 9), speaking of Chicano children, says that they have

> suffered the psychological oppression of being humiliated, laughed at, neglected, or even despised and abused, not only by private individuals and groups of this society but by the very authorities and institutions, schools included, that claim to represent the quintessence of American democracy.

The story for Puerto Ricans is not much different. They are newer migrants, the largest influx beginning in the 1940s and concentrated in New York City. The migration pattern traditionally has been one in which, proportionate to the Island population, there were more women, nonwhites, literate persons, urban dwellers, and skilled and semi-skilled workers (Glazer and Moynihan 1970; Kantrowitz 1973; Mills, Senior, and Goldsen 1950). Exclusion from the mainstream through residential segregation, job discrimination, and a low voting rate owing to the language barrier has been characteristic. In 1960, only one-third of the New York Puerto Rican population voted (Glazer and Moynihan 1970). Contrary to the economic and political community unity among Orientals, there was none in the U. S. Puerto Rican population. This is still somewhat the case, although the situation is changing. The major ties seem to be still with the Island, as witnessed by the flow of Puerto Ricans back to their homeland.

It is interesting to compare the migration to the United States to the migration of Puerto Ricans to St. Croix where they were very successful and now dominate the economic life of the island. There they aroused the same resentment with their energy and competence that Jews and Chinese aroused in the United States. The Puerto Ricans in St. Croix, as reported by Glazer and Moynihan (1970: 110), were thought to work harder and produce more than the natives. They were preferred in the sugar fields because it was thought that they were more intelligent and adaptable. At a time when they formed one-quarter of the population, they owned and ran more than one-half of the 122 businesses on the island. Reporting in 1947, Senior presents evidence that they used a form of rotating credit association in the development of these businesses. According to Senior:

> On every hand one hears the assertion that the Puerto Ricans are "clannish," that they hire only fellow Puerto Ricans, that they help each other in financial crises, that the larger and wealthier storekeepers will help newcomers start businesses in competition with the local people. [quoted from Glazer and Moynihan 1970: 111]

Glazer and Moynihan state that the St. Croix Puerto Ricans were not much different from the New York Puerto Ricans. Both had the same impulse to better themselves and the same business-minded instincts. In spite of heavy competition and lending discrimination, there were 4000 Puerto Rican-run businesses in New York City in the late 1950s, considerably more, at that time, than Negro-run businesses. This can be explained by the Puerto Rican cultural food preferences, the language ties, and the rotating credit institution—all of which helped to nourish consumer-oriented businesses. Puerto Ricans have not yet been able to move, as did the Orientals, into businesses servicing the mainstream community. However, according to Glazer and Moynihan, this may be simply a matter of time.

The American Indians in the twelfth-grade Coleman sample are more than likely very unrepresentative of the full range of American Indian culture. Of American Indian children, 50–60% drop out before they reach high school (Sanday, Chapter 6 of this volume; Johnson 1968) which suggests that our twelfth-grade sample is skewed.[1] It is clear from the rank order presented in Table 7.1 that the American Indians in our sample may come from more

---

[1] Referring to the drop-out figures presented by Sanday (Chapter 6 of this volume), it should be noted that Puerto Ricans also exhibit a very high drop-out rate by the twelfth grade, suggesting that our Puerto Rican sample is also skewed. However, the rank order presented in Table 7.1 does not indicate that the skewing is toward mainstream styles, as is indicated for the American Indian sample.

assimilated families. It is difficult, therefore, to speak about the degree of their cultural difference. Considered as a whole, however, it is clear that American Indian cultures are vastly different from the mainstream culture of Anglo-Americans. Emphasized in the literature are the very different value patterns (cf. Zintz 1967; Krueger 1973). Where Anglo-Americans emphasize mastery over nature, American Indians emphasize harmony with nature. Anonymity and submissiveness are valued rather than individuality and agressiveness. The purpose of work is to satisfy present needs and to share with others rather than to "get ahead" and save for the future. Aspirations are to follow in the way of the old people, to maintain a fluid continuity between past and present rather than to move from the present into a materialistically oriented future. Orientation is to persons rather than to things. There is an interest in decisions arrived at by concensus rather than by the majority vote. Fluid and nonhierarchial leadership is stressed instead of assigned leadership patterns arranged hierarchically. All of these values, as many authors have pointed out, are in direct conflict with classroom expectations. It is not surprising, therefore, that many American Indians drop out of school. In addition to the personal hardship they and their families must endure, they obviously cannot find much solace in the schools.

DISCUSSION: A SIMULTANEOUS EQUATIONS APPROACH TO THE ANALYSIS OF THE EDUCATIONAL PROCESS

We have sketched the cultural backdrop of American education and have shown that the average achievement scores of the nonwhite groups were related to their degree and nature of contact with the mainstream unit. By ranking each of these groups on a mainstream culutral continuum and comparing the rank order with group ranks on achievement scores, we can be accused of evaluating groups relative to a mainstream-conformity model. However, it has been our purpose to show how closely related mainstream conformity is to performance on mainstream achievement tests. This finding has, we believe, important implications for the legal issues surrounding the equality of educational opportunity question. In our future work, we will begin by assuming a cultural difference model and proceed to examine empirically the question of what broad educational policy strategies are suggested by cultural differences. The issue to be framed is whether home, school, and pupil attitudinal variables interact differently in the various ethnic groups in accounting for variation in educational achievement in each group.

In addressing this question, we will use the data collected by the Coleman report research team. These are valuable data because of the large nationally drawn sample, the inclusion of ethnic group identification, and the large number of home, school, and pupil attitudinal variables. In our previous work with these data tapes, we specified a conceptual model of the educational process and an associated analytic technique which will be briefly summarized (see Boardman, Davis, and Sanday 1973 and n.d.).

The education process produces students with a certain amount of knowledge, motivation, set of expectations about the future, and sense of individual efficacy. In addition, this process forms, in the pupil's mind, a perception of teachers' and parents' expectations. We refer to these six outputs of the education process as the endogenous variables. The endogenous variables both determine each other and are determined by home and school variables which are called the exogenous variables. The notion that the education process has multiple outputs which are jointly determined (i.e., there is a feedback relationship between the outputs) is not new. Mosteller and Moynihan (1972) point out, for example, that the sense of individual efficacy can both affect and be affected by scoring well on an achievement test. An individual's expectations for the future can affect and be affected by all of the factors just listed. Because we conceptualize the education process as one with multiple outputs with feedback between the outputs, we employed simultaneous equations estimation procedures for modeling the process where the multiple outputs constitute the set of endogenous variables. Home and school factors are considered to be exogenous to the feedback system but, at the same time, to have an important effect on each of the variables included in the endogenous system. Home and school variables are, thus, included in the analysis in what is called the exogenous variable system.

We can use this procedure to analyze the educational process in each of the six groups. We assume that the cultural differences between these groups mean that the endogenous factors will be related differently in each group, and different exogenous factors will be important when the endogenous factors are considered separately. For example, sense of individual efficacy might be prominent in affecting all of the endogenous factors in the analysis of one ethnic group but might play a less important role in another group. For one ethnic group, home variables may be the most important in explaining achievement, and, in another group, school variables may override home variables. Furthermore, certain school variables, such as racial integration, may turn out to have no effect on achievement in one group and an important effect in another.

In order to further illustrate our approach and its relevance to educational policy formulation, we review briefly the work of others who have employed the Coleman data. Many of these researchers have perceived multiple, jointly determined outputs in the educational process. Unfortunately, most of them did not use the proper statistical procedures for handling such a system, favoring instead the use of single equation production function models. An educational production function consists of a single output, usually an achievement test score, which is explained by a set of individual teacher and school characteristics. Emphasis centers on identifying various inputs that appear to affect pupil achievement. Each coefficient of a variable measures the marginal increase in achievement per unit increase in that particular variable. A parameter estimate gives the expected increase in the dependent variable per unit increase in an explanatory variable.

Coleman *et al.* (1966) used a variant of the single equation model or the educational production function. In order to determine the importance of an explanatory variable, these authors used step-wise regression in which the criterion for the entry of additional variables into the regression may depend upon which variables add more to the amount of the variance explained in the dependent variable (measured by R^2, the coefficient of determination which equals the square of the multiple correlation coefficient). The authors report that, after including home background characteristics in the model, adding variables measuring school characteristics did not greatly increase the R^2. In other words, they say that differences between schools account for only a small fraction of the difference in pupil achievement whereas differences between families tend to account for most of the differences in achievement. Of all the school variables, the characteristics of a pupil's peer group added most to the R^2. After adding these variables to the regression, it was found that teacher characteristics added more to the R^2 than any other school attributes. The authors concluded that *other resources, on which school systems spend much money, appear unimportant.* These results, combined with the finding that school facilities differ little from school to school, suggested that the school can do little to overcome the differences between pupils associated with race and home background.

Numerous authors have criticized the methodology of what came to be called the Coleman Report. The most fundamental of these criticisms concerned the use of addition to R^2 as a measure of the importance of a variable. Cain and Watts (1970) state that the regression coefficient is a most useful statistic for measuring the importance of a variable for the purpose of policy action. Coleman *et al.* did not report the regression coefficients. Not surprisingly, numerous authors have reanalyzed the data using ordinary least squares which estimate regression coefficients. Marshall Smith (1972) performed one of the most careful regression analyses. He concluded, however, that the results of his re-examination affirm and strengthen the overall conclusions of the Coleman report. Virtually all of the reanalyses reported similar findings.

While all the results of the Coleman Report come from a single education production function, the authors clearly note that achievement is not the only output of the educational process. They state, for example, that the orientation of the children to feelings about themselves, their motivation in school, and their aspirations toward further education and toward desirable occupations are, in part, an outcome of education and, in part, a factor that propels the child toward further education and achievement. They also note that a pupil's self-concept is affected by his success in school and, as a factor in its own right, is an important outcome of education. In sum, these statements imply that the educational process has many outputs and that there might be feedback relations among the outputs.

The book edited by Mosteller and Moynihan (1972) contains the most recent series of reanalyses of the Coleman data tapes. None of these analyses employ a nationwide sample at a given grade. Most of them concentrate on a given region or regions. None of the reanlyses come to conclusions that depart significantly from those drawn by the authors of the Coleman Report.

Levin (1970) should receive considerable credit for first publishing the notion of modeling the educational process by a system of simultaneous equations. We have extended Levin's work and have estimated a simultaneous equations model of the educational process with 6 endogenous variables and over 30 exogenous variables. Our endogenous variables were: pupil achievement, motivation, expectations, efficacy, and perceived parents' and teachers' expectations. The exogenous variables included home characteristics, such as number of brothers and sisters, social class of parents, presence of two parents; individual characteristics, such as reading before school, number of hours watching television, length of time in present area of residence; and school characteristics, such as racial and peer social class composition in the school, teachers' verbal ability, number of teachers per pupil (Boardman, Davis, and Sanday 1973).

Our results indicate that both home and school variables significantly influence scholastic achievement. The exogenous variables having the most influence on achievement were ethnic group affiliation, region of the country, certain of the individual demographic characteristics, and many of the school and teacher characteristics. The surprising discovery of our analysis was the indication that good teachers and good schools are important for educational achievement—a finding contrary to previous analyses of the same data. In particular, teachers' average score on a verbal ability test, class size, teachers' experience, and problems in the school and peer group social class were significant. These results question the controversial conclusion obtained previously that the school can do little to overcome the differences between pupils associated with race and home background.

The difference between our conclusions and those of others raises the question of the degree to which the empirical results that form the basis of our thinking about educational or social policy might be an artifact of the statistical model and the procedures used. Admittedly, the authors of the Coleman Report did an excellent job given the fact that they worked under many externally imposed constraints (especially time constraints) which led them to use an inadequate methodology. This methodology, however, led to what now appears to us to be an erroneous conclusion. With respect to the IQ issue, it has been shown that Jensen's conclusions were also based on an inadequate methodology leading to erroneous conclusions (Sanday 1972; Lewontin 1970; Layzer 1974). We refer to these two examples in order to underscore the danger of accepting as unassailable truth the results of statistical analysis in formulating public policy.

In our previous research, we did not disaggregate the total sample by ethnic group. While we included these as dummy variables, this did not allow us to investigate the questions raised earlier. The only statement we can make with reference to the ethnic groups concerns the degree to which the achievement score gap between these groups and the white sample is closed when the exogenous factors included in the model are controlled. Before these factors are controlled American Indians, Mexican-Americans, blacks, and Puerto Ricans obtain, on the average, 12 to 14 fewer correct answers than whites on the verbal achievement test. Oriental-Americans obtain, on the average, 2 fewer correct answers than whites on this test. When the exogenous variables are controlled by including them in the regression, the score gap between each of the first four groups and whites drops by two-thirds, on the average. The gap between Orientals and whites disappears all together. This suggests that there are some exogenous variables that have a similar effect on verbal achievement in all of the ethnic groups. However, the fact that the gap is not completely reduced in some of the groups suggests that each should be analyzed separately utilizing the cultural difference framework. Once this has been accomplished, culturally targeted educational policy strategies can be suggested.

CONCLUSION

We have tried to demonstrate the degree to which educational measurement is culturally biased. This is not a new discovery—it has been known for a long time. The question is, why, knowing this fact, are we unable to change the educational process. We suggest that the reason is quite simple. We are dealing with the most basic and cherished roots of the American culture, and our inaction is simply due to a fear of change— a fear of what will happen if minorities are given an equal place. It is the same fear that faced Thomas Jefferson and many abolitionists when they realized that slavery was wrong but could not bring themselves to admit Negroes into the Anglo-American mainstream. The educational process is inseparable from America's cultural roots. How can children be taught to respect and admire these roots at the same time that they learn how devastating they were to nonwhites, particularly to blacks? How can children be taught that change is more crucial than unquestioning admiration of their cultural heritage? Even if they learn the good and the bad of the American past, we are still left with the urge to master and control, to compete and succeed at the expense of others. In short, as many anthropologists have noted, schooling is a reflection in microcosm of the American culture. It is not simply a matter of changing tests—it is a matter of changing the American culture. It is unlikely that a centuries old tradition will change very rapidly, if at all.

APPENDIX: BRIEF DESCRIPTION OF VARIABLES USED IN TABLE 7.1

Variable name	*Description*
Student social class	An index constructed from father's occupational level, father's and mother's educational level, presence of encyclopedia in the home, whether student attended nursery school and kindergarten, number of hours student works for pay, number of people per room in student's home. High value indicates higher SES.
Two parents in home	Two parents alive and living at home = 1, otherwise = 0.
Number of older siblings	Number of older brothers and sisters. None = 1, . . . , 8 or more = 9.
Average student social class	Average socioeconomic background of students in school.
Proportion of white students in class last year	Proportion of white students in class last year. No whites = 1, . . . , All white = 5.
Mainly black school (<30% white)	Less than 30% white = 1, otherwise = 0.
Proportion of white teachers in class last year	No white teachers = 1, . . . , All white teachers = 5.
Teacher's average verbal score	Teacher's average verbal right on a verbal test (the average refers to all teachers in the school who took the test).
Teachers have problems with administration	Teachers complain of lack of effective leadership = 1, no problem = 0.
School facilities	A combination of principal's responses about library, auditorium, gymnasium, laboratories, etc.
Problems in school	A combination of principal's responses about problems of damage, discourtesy, and violence to teachers.
Mental tests given in school	School gives intelligence tests *and* standard achievement tests = 2, school gives intelligence *or* standard achievement tests = 1, otherwise = 0.

REFERENCES

Boardman, Anthony E., Otto A. Davis, and Peggy R. Sanday
  1973   A simultaneous equations model of the educational process: The Coleman data revisited with an emphasis on achievement. *Proceedings of the Social Statistics Section,* American Statistical Association, Washington, D.C. Pp. 62–71.
  n.d.   A simultaneous equations model of the educational process. Unpublished manuscript.
Brigham, C.
  1923   A study of American intelligence. Princeton, New Jersey: Princeton Univ. Press.
Cain, G. G., and H. W. Watts
  1970   Problems in making inferences from the Coleman report. *American Sociological Review* 35: 228–242.
Coleman, J. S., E. Q. Campbell, C. J. Hobson, J. McPartland, A. M. Mood, F. D. Weinfeld, and R. L. York
  1966   *Equality of educational opportunity.* U.S. Department of Health, Education, and Welfare. Washington, D.C.: U.S. Government Printing Office.
Fogel, Robert W., and Stanley L. Engerman
  1974   *Time on the cross. The economics of American Negro slavery.* Vol. I. *Time on the cross: Evidence and methods.* Vol. II. Boston: Little, Brown.
Glazer, N., and D. P. Moynihan
  1970   *Beyond the melting pot.* Cambridge, Massachusetts: M.I.T. Press.
Grant, Madison
  1922   *The passing of the great race: Or, the racial basis of European history.* New York: Scribner.
Jensen, A. R.
  1969   How much can we boost IQ and scholastic achievement? *Harvard Education Review* 39.
  1971   Can we and should we study race differences? In *Race and intelligence,* edited by C. L. Brace, G. R. Gamble, and J. T. Bond. Anthropological Studies, No. 8. American Anthropological Association, Washington, D.C. Pp. 10–31.
Johnson, Lyndon B.
  1968   The American Indian, a message relating to the problems of the American Indians. In *Appendix of Hearings before the Subcommittee on Indian Education,* Part 2. U.S. Senate. Washington, D.C.: U.S. Government Printing Office, 1969.
Jordan, Winthrop D.
  1968   *White over Black: American attitudes toward the Negro 1550–1812.* Chapel Hill: Univ. of North Carolina Press.
Kantrowitz, N.
  1973   *Ethnic and racial segregation in the New York metropolis.* New York: Praeger.
Krueger, D. W.
  1973   The effect of urban-industrial values on the Indian lifestyle. In *Chincano and native Americans,* edited by R. O. de la Garza, A. Kruszewski, and T. A. Arciniegu. Englewood Cliffs, New Jersey: Prentice-Hall. Pp. 78–89.
Layzer, D.
  1974   Heritability analyses of IQ scores: Science or numerology? *Science* 183 (4131): 1259–1266.
Levin, H. M.
  1970   A new model of school effectiveness. In *Do teachers make a difference?* edited by A. M. Mood. Washington, D.C.: U.S. Government Printing Office.

Levine, G. N., and D. M. Montero
  1973   Socioeconomic mobility among three generations of Japanese Americans. *Journal of Social Issues* **29**: 33–47.
Lewontin, Richard C.
  1970   Race and intelligence. *Bulletin of the Atomic Scientists* **26** (March): 2–8.
Light, Ivan H.
  1972   *Ethnic enterprise in America.* Berkeley: Univ. of California Press.
Mills, C. W., C. Senior, and R. K. Goldsen
  1950   *The Puerto Rican journey.* New York: Russell and Russell.
Money, J., and A. E. Ehrhardt
  1972   *Man & woman boy & girl.* Baltimore: Johns Hopkins Univ. Press.
Mosteller, F., and D. P. Moynihan (editors)
  1972   *On equality of educational opportunity.* New York: Random House.
Sanday, Peggy R.
  1972   On the causes of IQ differences between groups with implications for social policy. *Human Organization* **31** (Winter): 411–424.
  1973   A diffusion model for the study of the cultural determinants of differential intelligence. Final Report submitted to the U.S. Department of Health, Education, and Welfare, National Institute of Education.
Smith, M.S.
  1972   Equality of educational opportunity: The basic findings reconsidered. In *On equality of educational opportunity,* edited by F. Mosteller and D. P. Moynihan. New York: Random House. Pp. 230–342.
Trueba, H.
  1974   Bilingual–bicultural education for Chicanos in the Southwest. *Council on Anthropology and Education Quarterly* **V**(3) (August): 9–15.
Zintz, Miles V.
  1967   Problems of classroom adjustment of Indian children in public elementary schools in the Southwest. In *Education of the disadvantaged,* edited by A. Harry Passow, Miriam Goldberg, and Abraham J. Tannenbaum. New York: Holt. Pp. 88–100.

8

Dropping Out: A Strategy for Coping with Cultural Pluralism

Evelyn Jacob and Peggy Reeves Sanday

University of Pennsylvania

In this chapter, a framework for the analysis of certain behavioral conse-quences of cultural pluralism will be developed and related to specific aspects of the behavior of culturally different children in U.S. schools. A number of recent studies have demonstrated differences in communication style (Erickson, Chap-ter 9 of this volume; Byers and Byers 1972) and differences in dominant values (see articles in Cazden, John, and Hymes 1972) between members of minority and majority groups. These studies also document vividly the effect of such differences on the outcome of these encounters. More frequently than not, the outcome is one in which differences are exacerbated rather than reduced, with the result that the minority group member is often excluded from further meaningful interaction. For an overall framework from which such outcomes can be deduced as well as ways in which they can be averted, we offer the following discussion of the effect of cultural pluralism on behavior.

SOME BEHAVIORAL CONSEQUENCES OF CULTURAL PLURALISM

Using the traditional definition of culture, Sanday (Chapter 6 of this volume) suggests a typology of cultural units in the United States. Cultural units are defined in terms of the constellation of themes, behavior styles, and information components exhibited by members of a group that differ from those shared by members of other groups. Applying this approach to the United States, cultural units are classified in terms of the degree of assimilation and exposure to the life styles of the mainstream cultural unit. The resulting typology (i.e., main-streamer, bicultural, culturally different, and culturally marginal) needs further empirical delineation and operationalization of specific behavior patterns constituting the various types before it can be useful in social policy formulation. For example, we need to understand more specifically the behavioral consequences of interaction between members of the various cultural units when developing social programs or intervention strategies.

Goodenough (1971) presents an ideational definition of culture that is useful for the analysis of possible outcomes of interaction between the culturally different. He defines culture as a "system of standards for perceiving, believing, evaluating, and acting" (1971:41). At the individual level, culture can be identified as a person's *propriospect*, consisting of the various sets of standards for perceiving, evaluating, believing, and doing that the individual attributes to groups of other persons as a result of experiencing their actions and admonitions as well as those standards, beliefs, and values the individual has developed from experience and attributes to no one else (Goodenough 1971:36–37). In this approach, the set of standards that a person attributes to a particular set of others is, for him, the culture of that set. Many such cultures can be included in an individual's propriospect. The particular set of standards that he choses to guide his behavior on a particular occasion is his *operating culture* for that occasion. An individual could be competent in several operating cultures.

According to Goodenough (1971:39), it is to the advantage of people who deal with one another regularly to be competent in what they perceive as the same or at least equivalent set of standards. The standards that such people agree on as appropriate in their mutual dealings are defined as the *public culture* for those activities. There may be individual versions of this public culture, but the range of variation is limited. By developing an understanding of the public culture of his group, an individual is able to *predict* the behavior of others in the group and behave *predictably* to them. Predictability does not mean that an individual can anticipate specific behavior, only that he is cognizant of the range in which it will fall and is able to interpret the behaviors falling within that range.

The importance of predictability is also discussed by Wallace (1970) who states that, as any set of persons establishes a system of equivalent behavioral expectancies, an organized relationship comes into existence. Equivalent behavioral expectancies provide the mechanism whereby relationships are organized and maintained and implies the recognition—as the result of learning—"that the behavior of other people under various circumstances is predictable, irrespective of knowledge of their motivation, and, thus is capable of being predictably related to one's own actions" (Wallace 1970:35). Wallace defines culture as a set of standardized models of equivalent mutual expectancies.

The question of concern in this chapter is what happens when persons with nonequivalent public cultures engage in mutual interaction. If both parties continued to operate according to their respective public cultures, behavior would not be mutually predictable. It would seem advantageous, then, for these groups to develop a public culture to govern the areas of mutual activity. If this public culture consists of a "composite" of the contributing cultures, the resulting standards might be ones that most of the individuals involved in the interaction would be comfortable with. If, on the other hand, one of the groups is more powerful than the other, the individuals in the dominant group might try to impose their own standards on the others. In such a case, the minority group members would be faced with learning new standards by which to govern their behavior, that is, to become competent in a different public culture.

Competency in a particular public culture can be defined in terms of the degree to which an individual can employ standards for behavior that enable him to behave predictably to those others with whom he is engaged in mutual activity. We suggest that the degree of competency a person exhibits is a function of exposure to the standards in question and incorporation of these standards into one's operating culture. Exposure occurs through social interaction, and incorporation is influenced by motivational factors.

Goodenough (1971:38) states that competence in the standards of sets of others can be developed only through intensive interaction with at least some of those others. When there is no interaction between members of different sets (such as urban blacks, suburban whites, migrant farm workers, to take just a few examples in the United States), one would not expect knowledge of the others' standards for behavior to develop. However, interaction is necessary but not sufficient. Motivation to incorporate and utilize standards in guiding behavior is also important. The amount of reinforcement an individual receives for behaving in certain ways may have an important effect on the process of incorporation and learning of new standards. Using exposure and incorporation as the defining dimensions, competency can be scaled as follows:

1. No competence: no exposure to the standards of the public culture in question.
2. Some competence: some exposure but little motivation to incorporate the standards.
3. Adequate competence: exposure with sufficient motivation to incorporate the standards.
4. Native competence: fluency in the use of the standards through frequent interaction and employment of these standards in guiding one's behavior.

This discussion can now be related to the typology of cultural pluralism presented earlier by Sanday. An individual whose propriospect consists of more than one nonequivalent public culture can be classified as bicultural or multicultural. An individual whose propriospect does not include the mainstream public culture, but which does include at least one other definable public culture, can be classified as culturally different. An individual whose propriospect contains only the mainstream public culture can be classified as a mainstreamer. Finally, an individual whose propriospect does not include a definable public culture can be classified as culturally marginal.

There are important policy implications of competency and predictability which can be illustrated in the context of the public schools, where we often find groups of individuals who are competent in different native cultures, that is, the system of standards an individual incorporates into his propriospect during the socialization process. There are many students in the U.S. schools who have had little or no exposure to, or little or no motivation to incorporate, the standards of the mainstream public culture. Since the public culture of the school is often synonymous with the mainstream public culture, nonmainstreamers are at a disadvantage because they may be unable to predict the behavior of their peers or of teachers, and they may experience certain consequences of behavior unpredictably.

Byers and Byers (1972) and Erickson (Chapter 9 of this volume) illustrate how nonpredictability on the part of students can result in teachers and counselors rejecting and ignoring them. Marlowe's discussion of the social psychological aspects of nonpredictability is suggestive of other behavioral consequences. He states:

> We perceive the social environment by matching our responses against the standards provided by other people. Stability will be found only if our social perceptions are similar to those of others to whose standards we subscribe (or would like to subscribe). If they are dissimilar, stress results. Stress motivates the individual to reduce it with the least effort or the fewest changes in his interpretation of the social environment. [Marlowe 1971:54]

In the public school situation, both students and teachers may be motivated to reduce stress resulting from nonpredictability in one of the following ways:

1. Contact with individuals of the other culture is avoided.
2. Contact is kept to a minimum or regulated to areas where differences are minimal.
3. Contact occurs regularly, but misunderstanding and misinterpretation leads to open conflict and hostility.
4. Contact occurs regularly, but the individual changes his operating culture to incorporate the standards of the culture of the individuals who hold the balance of power in the contact situation.
5. Contact occurs regularly, and all involved in the interaction work toward the development of a composite public culture.

The first four strategies impose a harsh burden on the child or adolescent. One of the most promising aims of present educational policy and intervention strategies is the working out of mechanisms whereby all the parties involved are enabled to develop a congenial and mutually predictable public culture. Gearing's (1973) discussion of intervention research in the schools is suggestive of ways in which such an end could be accomplished.

To conclude, any policy-relevant discussion of cultural pluralism must include more than speculation about and delineation of cultural differences. Cultural pluralism in a contact situation may have powerful effects on the behavior of certain individuals, depending on where they fit into the paradigm which has been presented. It is important that these effects by empirically delineated. In the remainder of this chapter, we will apply this approach to an analysis of some aspects of the behavior of Puerto Rican children in U.S. schools.

THE EFFECTS OF CULTURAL PLURALISM ON THE SCHOOL BEHAVIOR OF PUERTO RICAN CHILDREN

Previous research indicates that many Puerto Rican children come to school without having incorporated into their operating cultures the standards for behavior characteristic of the public culture that is transmitted in the schools (see Fitzpatrick 1971; Koss 1965; Padilla 1958).

If such differences exist in the school setting, nonpredictability may occur in the behavior of Puerto Rican students and teachers. Furthermore, these students must face and deal with the behavior of their peers, which may also appear strange to them. Another complication arises when we consider the fact that Puerto Ricans may be the object of prejudice. As one Puerto Rican boy in our sample put it when asked if he felt badly about being a Puerto Rican: "I felt bad at first, because when I moved into this white neighborhood, the kids started teasing me and calling me a spic. . . . Three years ago, I had a natural tan and the kids around my way started calling me a spic." Prejudice may lead to lowered self-esteem which, in turn, makes it less possible for the youngster to deal effectively with the stress resulting from nonpredictability. As Marlowe puts it:

> Persons low in self-esteem react to stress with anxiety, and anxiety disrupts complex cognitive behavior. To some degree, stress increases group cohesion, but if the group persistently fails to cope with the stressor, they lower their level of aspiration and do not try so hard subsequently. [1971:620]

This suggests that many Puerto Rican children must cope with stress resulting from nonpredictability and prejudice.

The reported high drop-out rate of Puerto Ricans in U.S. schools suggests that they are coping with stress resulting from nonpredictability and prejudice by avoiding contact or keeping contact to a minimum (strategies one and two mentioned earlier). The school drop-out rate for Puerto Rican children by the twelfth year of schooling in 1960 was 80%, compared to 46% for black students and 29% for Anglo-Americans (Seda Bonilla 1972:294). In the empirical portion of this report, we examine the relationship between dropping out of school and the match between a sample of teachers' and Puerto Rican students' perceptions of the acceptability of selected behaviors in school. The hypotehsis to be tested is that the response pattern of Puerto Rican drop-outs on questions concerning acceptable behavior in school will be different from the response pattern of teachers and Puerto Rican stay-ins. If this hypothesis is supported, we can speculate that drop-outs cope with cultural difference by avoiding contact or by engaging in open conflict and hostility and that stay-ins cope by keeping contact to a minimum or by changing their operating culture to incorporate the standards of their teachers. Another possibility is that at least some stay-ins come to school with an operating culture that includes standards that are present in the school public culture.

PROCEDURE

In any behavioral setting, there are types of people to whom different behavioral expectations are attached (Goodenough 1969). These types are called "status identities," and, in the school setting, they refer to categories of people such as black student, white student, Puerto Rican student, gym teacher, shop teacher, and so on. There are also certain behaviors that can be seen to occur or not to occur between status identifies, such as between black student and white student or between gym teacher and Puerto Rican student. In this study, we compare the responses of Puerto Rican students (stay-ins and drop-outs) and their teachers to questions regarding what they consider acceptable behaviors between persons having particular status identities.

Since interaction requires at least two persons, status identities can be combined into dyads: the "doer" and the "receiver" of a particular behavior. The dyads can then be combined one-to-one with behaviors to form a set of stimuli (each stimulus consisting of one dyad and one behavior). Respondents can be asked whether or not it is acceptable for *status identiy A* (doer) to do *X* (the behavior) to *status identity B* (receiver). They can also be asked whether or not it is acceptable for *status identity A* (doer) to be punished for doing *X* (behavior) to *status identity B* (receiver).

Following this approach, which was adapted from the procedure presented by Goodenough (1969), we first determined status identities and behaviors that are important in the school setting. Groups of Puerto Rican students were asked to discuss their school experiences. Initial lists of behaviors and social identities were compiled from these discussions. These social identities and behaviors were used to construct pilot questions using the format described earlier.

It is important to note that this set of questions was administered as part of a larger questionnaire. In the pilot study, the first part of the larger questionnaire contained about 180 questions on demographic, sociocultural, and attitudinal variables and was administered only to students. The second part contained the questions on acceptable behaviors discussed earlier as well as a parallel set of questions asking if it is acceptable for the "doer" to be punished for the particular behavior. It was also asked (for each dyad–behavior combination) how often the informant thought the "doers" actually performed the behavior to the "receivers" and if the "doers" were punished for it. This second part contained over 200 questions and was administered to both teachers and students. As can be seen, the total pilot questionnaire was very long. In order to reduce respondent fatigue, it was necessary to reduce the size of the questionnaire and, therefore, to select a smaller number of status identities and behaviors. The final set of behaviors was chosen from the initial set because: (*1*) They have the potential to occur often in the school setting; (*2*) they are related to the concept of *respeto* (respect) which some informants stressed as being important in the interaction of children and adults in Puerto Rican culture; and (*3*) they showed a varied response pattern in the pilot studies.

For this analysis, we will deal with only those dyads that involve a teacher and a student. These dyads are listed in Table 8.1. The behaviors selected for this analysis are also presented in Table 8.1. Pairing each dyad with each behavior resulted in 18 possible combinations. Combinations 14, 16, and 18 in Table 8.1 were not included in the questionnaire because they seemed illogical in a school setting. Thus, our analysis deals with 15 behavior–dyad combinations. We will deal with those questions asking whether or not a behavior–dyad combination is acceptable and whether or not it is acceptable for the "doer" to be punished for the behavior. This gives a total of 30 questions. Sample questions are:

1. Is it acceptable for a Puerto Rican student to argue with a teacher?
2. Is it acceptable for him (her) to be punished for it?

Table 8.1
Possible Dyad–Behavior Combinations in the Questionnaire

	Behaviors		
Dyads	*Argue with*	*Accuse*	*Refuse to obey*
Puerto Rican student to teacher	1	7	13
Teacher to Puerto Rican student	2	8	14
Black student to teacher	3	9	15
Teacher to black student	4	10	16
White student to teacher	5	11	17
Teacher to white student	6	12	18

Sample

This instrument was administered to a sample of 15 teachers and 266 Puerto Rican students (43 drop-outs and 223 stay-ins). The data were collected in New York City, Philadelphia, and Vineland, New Jersey. The breakdown of the sample by city is as follows: Of the teachers, 8 were from Philadelphia, and 7 were from Vineland; 120 of the students were from New York (91 stay-ins and 29 drop-outs), 78 were from Philadelphia (69 stay-ins and 9 drop-outs), and 68 were from Vineland (63 stay-ins and 5 drop-outs).[1]

RESULTS

Of the 30 questions asked of teachers and Puerto Rican students, our hypo-thesis predicts that the response distribution on each question for teachers and stay-in students will be more often the same than that of teachers and drop-outs. To test this hypothesis, we divided the questions into those asking if the behavior is acceptable and those asking if the behavior is punishable. Fifteen questions were of the first type and 15 of the second. Using the X^2 statistic, we examined whether the response distribution for each question was significantly different between (*1*) teachers and stay-ins and (*2*) teachers and drop-outs.[2] The results in Table 8.2 do not support the hypothesis. The number of questions in which the response distribution is either the same or different between the two student groups and their teachers is about equal. One interesting fact that does emerge from Table 8.2 is that both student groups agree with the teachers more on the questions about punishable behavior than on those about acceptable behavior.

These results led us to subdivide the stay-in and drop-out groups in terms of the degree of daily contact each student had with school (measured in terms of frequency of "playing hooky"). In the discussion presented earlier, we suggested that students experiencing culture conflict, stress, and anxiety may cope by varying the degree of contact or by incorporating into their operating cultures the standards of teachers. In the cases in which culture conflict is a contributing factor to dropping out, we would expect this to be the final outcome of a process of increasing stress and anxiety. Playing hooky might be an early

[1] The data used here to explore the consequences of cultural pluralism for the Puerto Rican children in the sample come from a larger study on the causes of the Puerto Rican drop-out rate. This study is being conducted by the Puerto Rican Research and Resources Center (now Universidad Boricua). This larger study will be published by members of the Universidad Boricua and will include a comprehensive analysis of the Puerto Rican drop-out rate of which this study will be a small part.

[2] Yates' corrected chi-square was used; .10 was the cut-off point. The most obvious statiscal technique, a standard analysis of variance, was not performed since variance in subgroups was not homogeneous.

Table 8.2
Comparison of Response Distributions by Type of Question for Two Student Groups and Teachers

Comparisons	Acceptable behavior questions		Punishable behavior questions	
	No significant difference	Significant difference	No significant difference	Significant difference
1. Stay-ins and teachers	7	8	13	2
2. Drop-outs and teachers	7	8	12	3

indicator of the behavioral response to increasing stress. The stay-ins who play hooky often may be in the process of dropping out—if so, we would expect their response pattern to be similar to that of the high-hooky drop-outs and the pattern of both groups to be dissimilar to that of teachers.

The stay-ins who do not play hooky often may either feel comfortable in the school setting or may begin to incorporate into their operating cultures the standards of the school. The low-hooky drop-outs, on the other hand, may feel comfortable in school but choose to select other options open to them, such as getting married or getting a job.[3] Consequently, we would expect the response pattern of the low-hooky students to be more similar to that of teachers.

The sample sizes for the high- and low-hooky stay-ins and drop-outs are presented in Table 8.3. Table 8.4 presents the number of questions on which the four student groups and the teachers agree.[4] While the response distribution for the two low-hooky groups is similar, as is the distribution for the two high-hooky groups, their similarity with that of the teachers is the reverse of what we expected. The high-hooky stay-ins and drop-outs exhibit a response pattern similar to teachers on 11 of the 15 questions about acceptable behavior, as compared to 5 and 8 for the low-hooky groups. There is, however, a similar response distribution between all of the groups and the teachers on the questions about punishable behavior. To summarize, the results of Table 8.4 show that there is a low degree of agreement between low-hooky students and teachers on what is acceptable and a high degree of agreement between them on what is

[3] The larger study conducted by the Universidad Boricua found that 24% of the low-hooky drop-outs were married, while only 1% of the low-hooky stay-ins and 11.6% of the high-hooky drop-outs were married. When asked why they dropped out of school 24% of the low-hooky drop-outs gave pregnancy as the answer, 18% reported illness, 12% said that they were bored or depressed, and 6% said it was because of a job.

[4] Yates' corrected chi-square was used; .10 was the cut-off point.

Table 8.3

Sample Sizes of Stay-In and Drop-Out Groups
Subdivided by Hooky Question

Responses to hooky question	Stay-ins N	Drop-outs N
High hooky	48	27
1. Almost every day		
2. About once a week		
3. Once or twice a month		
Low hooky	175	16
4. Less than once a month		
5. Never		
Total	223	43

punishable. High-hooky students and teachers seem to have a relatively high degree of agreement on both what is acceptable and what is punishable.

Clearly these results do not support our hypothesis as originally stated. However, three additional analyses of the data yielded some unexpected and interesting results which, although not confirming the hypothesis, supply additional insights to our general discussion of the behavioral consequences of cultural differences.

In the first analysis, means were calculated separately for each type of question for the teachers and each of the four student groups. A "yes" response was set equal to 1, and a "no" was set equal to 0. Each respondent was given a

Table 8.4

Comparison of Response Distributions by Type of Question for Four Student Groups and Teachers

Comparisons	Acceptable behavior questions		Punishable behavior questions	
	No significant difference	Significant difference	No significant difference	Significant difference
1. Low-hooky stay-ins and teachers	5	10	13	2
2. Low-hooky drop-outs and teachers	8	7	15	0
3. High-hooky stay-ins and teachers	11	4	12	3
4. High-hooky drop-outs and teachers	11	4	12	3

score that equaled the sum of the "yes" responses (maximum = 15). The mean for each group is the sum of these individual scores divided by the total number of respondents in a group. A higher mean, then, implies that more "yes" responses were given by a group. This can be used as a measure of the number of questions (i.e., behavior–dyad combinations) that the group considered acceptable or punishable. The results are displayed in Figure 8.1.

Teachers see many of the behaviors as being acceptable; they have the highest mean on questions of acceptable behavior of any group. They also see many of the behaviors as being punishable. Low-hooky students (stay-ins and drop-outs alike) see few behaviors as being acceptable (they have the lowest means) and many as being punishable (low-hooky drop-outs have the highest mean). High-hooky students fall between teachers and low-hooky students. They see more behaviors as acceptable than do low-hooky drop-outs, but they see fewer as acceptable than do the teachers. They see fewer behaviors as being punishable than either teachers or low-hooky students.

What is striking about these results is the evidence of inconsistency on the part of the teachers. It appears that the teachers find the same behaviors punishable and also acceptable. An analysis of the degree of inconsistency in each group was

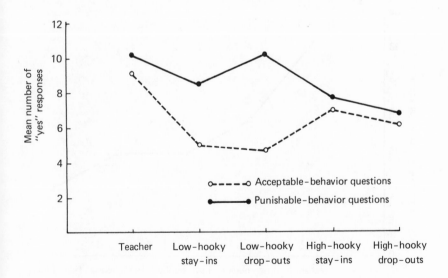

Figure 8.1 Mean number of "yes" responses over all questions by teachers and student groups.

carried out. Inconsistency was defined as the case in which a respondent answered: "Yes" a behavior is acceptable, and "yes" the same behavior is punishable. Each respondent was then scored for the number of inconsistent responses, and the percentage of such responses for each group was computed. As can be seen from Figure 8.2, teachers display a much higher percentage of inconsistent responses than do the student groups. Low-hooky stay-ins have the next highest percentage, and high-hooky drop-outs have the lowest percentage.

In the third analysis, we separated the questions dealing with acceptable and punishable behaviors into those in which the teacher is performing the action and those in which a Puerto Rican student is performing the action and computed the percentage of responses in which each group answered "yes":

1. It is acceptable for a teacher to perform action X to a Puerto Rican student.
2. It is acceptable for a Puerto Rican student to perform action X to a teacher.
3. It is acceptable for a teacher to be punished for performing action X to a Puerto Rican student.
4. It is acceptable for a Puerto Rican student to be punished for performing action X to a teacher.

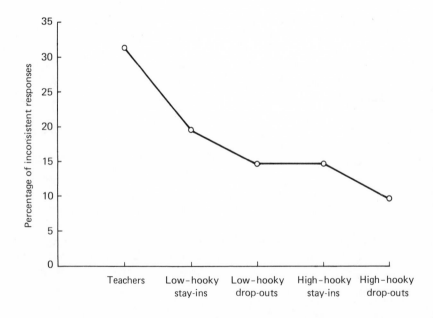

Figure 8.2   Percentage of inconsistent responses by teachers and student groups.

Table 8.5
Percentage of "Yes" Responses by Type of Question for Four Student Groups and Teachers

Response groups	Acceptable behavior questions		Punishable behavior questions	
	Teacher to Puerto Rican student (%)	Puerto Rican student to teacher (%)	Teacher to Puerto Rican student (%)	Puerto Rican student to teacher (%)
Teachers	70	54	63	68
Low-hook stay-ins	42	36	53	60
Low-hooky drop-outs	41	28	54	73
High-hooky stay-ins	51	43	49	55
High-hooky drop-outs	39	49	45	44

Table 8.5 indicates that, with the exception of the high-hooky drop-outs, all of the groups find *more* behaviors acceptable for teachers than for students and *fewer* behaviors punishable for teachers than for students. Furthermore, the low-hooky students find a *very low* percentage of behaviors acceptable for students and a *very high* percentage of behaviors punishable for students. The high-hooky drop-outs display a much different pattern. They find a higher percentage of behaviors acceptable for students than for teachers and about the same percentage of behaviors punishable for teachers as for students.

To summarize the data which have been presented, contrary to our expectations, the high-hooky students are more like the teachers in their response distribution on the 15 questions asking if a behavior is acceptable (Table 8.4). The low-hooky students are more like the teachers in their response distribution on the 15 questions asking if a behavior is punishable (Table 8.4).

Teachers' responses are inconsistent in that most behaviors are scored both punishable and acceptable. The low-hooky groups find few behaviors acceptable and most punishable (Figure 8.1). Those behaviors that the low-hooky groups find acceptable are more likely to be behaviors in which the teacher is performing the action, while those that they find punishable are more likely to be behaviors in which the student is performing the action (Table 8.5). The reverse is the case for the high-hooky drop-outs. They find a greater percentage of behaviors acceptable for students than for teachers and about the same percentage of behaviors punishable for teachers as for students.

DISCUSSION

We began this chapter with the suggestion that cultural differences between students and teachers lead to stress, anxiety, and eventual withdrawal or to the incorporation of new standards into one's operating culture. It was hypothesized that the response pattern of Puerto Rican drop-outs on questions concerning acceptable behaviors in school would be different from that of teachers and Puerto Rican stay-ins. The data did not support this hypothesis. In the first place, the students are more aptly categorized by the degree to which they maintained daily contact with the school (low-hooky versus high-hooky). Secondly, the response pattern of these recategorized groups is both similar to and different from that of teachers. The response pattern of the high-hooky students is different on the questions about punishable behavior and similar to that of teachers on the questions about acceptable behavior. The reverse holds true for the low-hooky group—their response pattern is similar on the questions about punishable behavior and different on the questions about acceptable behavior.

These results are possible only because of the inconsistency of the teachers who rate the same behaviors as both punishable and acceptable. Whether inconsistency is, in fact, a part of the teachers' behavior and not simply an artifact of the instrument being used is something that must be established in future research, which should include natural observations of teacher–student interaction. Inconsistency, of course, would make it very difficult for culturally different students to learn to distinguish the appropriate from the inappropriate behaviors. Students, in effect, would be placed in the double bind of having to cope with nonpredictability *and* with the absence of clear signals that they might use to guide their own behavior and to understand that of their teachers. It could be that the low-hooky students cope with this dilemma by restricting the range of what they perceive as acceptable and widening the range of what they perceive as punishable—perhaps, in order to "play it safe." The high-hooky students, on the other hand, may cope by making themselves "masters of the action," in which anything is acceptable and nothing is punishable.

An alternative explanation for our results might be that the instrument we have used has not uncovered coping strategies on the part of culturally different students (as suggested earlier) but has tapped typical behavioral styles of the Puerto Rican child in U.S. schools. The playing it safe behavior of the low-hooky students may be an extension of attitudes toward authority that the child learns at home. According to some (Fitzpatrick 1971), Puerto Rican children are more submissive to authority in comparison with American children who are more aggressive and competitive. Strong authority patterns are characteristic of the Puerto Rican family and are also evident in Puerto Rican schools where the teacher is viewed as an extension of the family (Fitzpatrick 1971:183). The low-hooky students who drop out of school may be choosing to remain *culturally different*. They may be opting for the adaptation described by Fitzpatrick (1971:98), which is a withdrawal into the old culture to resist the new way of life they are exposed to in the American school. The low-hooky students who remain in school may be struggling toward a *bicultural mode.* They may be the offspring of parents who are making an effort

> to build a cultural bridge between the culture of the migrants and that of the mainland. These are the people who have confidence and security in their own way of life, but who realize that it cannot continue. Therefore, they seek to establish themselves in the new society, but continue to identify themselves with the people from whom they come. [Fitzpatrick 1971: 98]

It is interesting to note here that these are the students (see Figure 8.2) who have the highest incidence of inconsistent responses of the student groups. Could it be that part of developing an operating culture that matches the public culture of the school includes incorporating inconsistent standards?

The tendency of the high-hooky students to view everything as acceptable and nothing as punishable for students is reminiscent of the observations that many Puerto Rican youth reject their parents and all adults as models and elevate the peer group as the prime reference group. It has been suggested (Fitzpatrick 1971:96) that this may be a reaction to the confinement imposed by the Puerto Rican family in an effort to protect their children. Such confinement may appear excessive to the child growing up in a society in which the dominant values are self-reliance, agression, competitiveness, and questioning. The problem is that, in abandoning their family culture and life patterns as well as that of the school (as evidenced in dropping out or in playing hooky), these students are in great danger of becoming *culturally marginal.* By abandoning the way of life of their parents as well as that of the American school, they cut themselves off from all adult socialization agents. As Fitzpatrick (1971:98) puts it, "They may find themselves in a no man's land of culture." Unfortunately, for those selecting this option, the dangers of mental illness, delinquency, drug addiction, and generalized personal frustration are acute.

We conclude by raising two issues. First, there is the question of the reliability and validity of the instrument used in this study. This can only be established in further research. We would suggest that the following modifications be incorporated in future applications: (*1*) describe specific situations and then ask if behavior X is acceptable or punishable, (*2*) increase the number of behaviors sampled, (*3*) offer a wider range of response options, and (*4*) use an incomplete block design to reduce the size of the questionnaire. One way to test for validity might be to compare questionnaire results with analyses of student–teacher interaction.

Second, there is the question of the processes by which culturally different individuals might develop a mutually predictable public culture. Our bias is toward the development of "composite" public cultures in which the standards of all the participating individuals are represented. The question, of course, is how do the individuals involved learn these standards. This is another area requiring additional research in which, we would expect, a great deal of attention would be directed toward what we know about the processes involved in second language learning.

ACKNOWLEDGMENTS

The authors gratefully acknowledge the encouragement and the opportunity provided by Antonia Pantoja, Victor Alicea, and Roberto Aponte to include the instrument described in the data collection process and to explore the implications of the cultural pluralism model.

REFERENCES

Byers, Paul, and Happie Byers
    1972   Nonverbal communication and the education of children. In *Functions of language in the classroom*, edited by Courtney B. Cazden, Vera P. John, and Dell Hymes. New York: Teachers College Press. Pp. 3–31.

Cazden, Courtney B., Vera P. John, and Dell Hymes (Editors)
    1972   *Functions of language in the classroom*. New York: Teachers College Press.

Fitzpatrick, Joseph
    1971   *Puerto Rican Americans*. Englewood Cliffs, New Jersey: Prentice Hall.

Gearing, Frederick O.
    1973   Anthropology and education. In *Handbook of social and cultural anthropology*, edited by John Honigman. Chicago: Rand McNally, Pp. 1223–1249.

Goodenough, Ward H.
    1969   Rethinking 'status' and 'role': Toward a general model of the cultural organization of social relationships. In *Cognitive anthropology*, edited by Stephen A. Tyler. New York: Holt. Pp. 311–330.
    1971   *Culture, language and society*. Addison-Wesley Module. Reading, Massachusetts: Addison-Wesley.

Koss, Joan
    1965   Puerto Ricans in Philadelphia: Migration and accommodation. Doctoral dissertation, Dept. of Anthropology, Univ. of Pennsylvania.

Marlowe, Leigh
    1971   *Social psychology: An interdisciplinary approach to human behavior*. Boston: Holbrook.

Padilla, Elena
    1958   *Up from Puerto Rico*. New York: Columbia Univ. Press.

Seda Bonilla, E.
    1972   Cultural pluralism and the education of Puerto Rican youths. *Phi Delta Kappan* LIII (5) (January): 294–296.

Wallace, Anthony F.
    1970   *Culture and personality*. (2nd ed.) New York: Random House.

9

Gatekeeping Encounters:
A Social Selection Process*

Frederick Erickson

Harvard University

INTRODUCTION

This account is written to illustrate how one can move from (1) relatively general ethnographic work in a field situation through (2) specifying a particular type of recurrent event and identifying key features within it to (3) sampling those events and (4) summarizing quantitatively the sociocultural regularities discovered in analysis of those events. At the end of the chapter, I will suggest ways by which the behavioral indices and analytic procedures I have described could be used on a larger sample, from which inferences might be drawn relevant to social policy decisions. Depending on how one defines the functions of social scientific evidence in policy decision making, the data reported here may have policy implications as they stand, despite a relatively small sample size.

It is worth noting here the significance I attach to the adjective "simple" in this chapter. I maintain that the nature of order in the sociocultural phenomena

*The research reported here was sponsored by the Center for Studies of Metropolitan Problems, NIMH (MH 18230 and MH 21460) and also supported by the Ford Foundation. The support of both is gratefully acknowledged.

I studied is such that regularities can be illustrated by quite elementary descriptive and inferential statistics. I think this is potentially true for much anthropological research, although I do not mean to suggest that more elaborate quantitative procedures are never appropriate. But given the ways in which anthropologists tend to approach the study of social life through fieldwork, some aspects of their descriptions of everyday social behavior and its underlying rules lend themselves to quantitative summary of a quite straightforward kind.

The research reported here can be characterized as "microethnographic." Gumperz and Hymes (1964, 1972) have called for "ethnographies of communication." This would include a survey of the range of different ways of speaking in the various speech situations found in a given sociocultural unit considered as a whole. My work has been more a "microethnography of communication," in that I have focused mainly on one class of speech situations—"gatekeeping encounters" between United States male school counselors and job interviewers, and the young men they interview. The work is "ethnographic" in the sense that it considers as a whole the organization of behavior in these interactional events—considers nonverbal and situational aspects of interaction[1] as well as verbal aspects—and identifies customary features of interactional form and function in the events. It is also "ethnographic" in that the selection of the gatekeeping encounter as a socioculturally salient class of interactional events was preceded by field experience in familial, educational, industrial, and social service settings in an urban neighborhood. In particular face to face encounters, the social meaning of form in language, nonverbal behavior, and interactional strategy is only apparent in the light of knowledge and experience of the larger sociocultural system within which the encounter takes place. This kind of "microethnographic" research can only be done by reference to a "macroethnographic" context.

The unit of analysis in the study reported here was the gatekeeping encounter. This is a type of interactional event; specific instances of it were junior college counseling interviews and job interviews. These are "gatekeeping" events because one person, the interviewer, has authority to make decisions about the social mobility of the interviewee. At the discretion of the interviewer, advice was given and/or permission for mobility was granted or withheld. In the junior college interview, permission could be granted to continue for further education in one of a number of possible "programs"; in the job interview, permission for hiring could be given or withheld. We collected films and videotapes of 52 such encounters.

---

[1] Definition of situation within particular encounters is considered in the analysis, following Goffman's notion of the encounter as generating its own rules as a situational variation on general sociocultural rules for interaction (cf. Goffman 1961:19–29).

THE FIELDWORK EXPERIENCE: DISCOVERING THE GATEKEEPING ENCOUNTER

It was through fieldwork that I gradually came to identify the gatekeeping encounter as theoretically salient and appropriate for detailed study. I did not begin by looking for gatekeeping encounters. From 1963 through 1966, I worked first as a volunteer, then as a staff member, at a youth agency in a predominantly black neighborhood on Chicago's West Side.[2]

At that time, little had been published, either by black or by white authors and researchers, about contemporary urban ghettos in the United States. Gatekeeping was not on my mind. I had been hired by the Y.M.C.A. because I brought with me a research and curriculum development grant. I came to study African survivals in musical idiom, social uses of music, and folklore in the neighborhood. Based on this research, I developed an after-school curriculum for young people. Through the youth agency, I became involved in other aspects of youth work, education, and community affairs that eventually led to the study of gatekeeping.

My activities in the neighborhood ranged from straight ethnomusicological work—learning the idiom of songs composed by teenage singing groups and writing down songs for the groups in standard notation for copyright—to helping welfare families move from one apartment to another, going to parties, sitting in meetings with aldermen's assistants, police lieutenants, school principals, and businessmen, having a beer after work with friends at a local tavern, and teaching in an on-the-job training program at a local steel company.

The "buzzing and blooming confusion" of everyday life reduced gradually into units and patterns. Some struck me "etically," as an outsider. Others were pointed out to me "emically" by informants and co-workers,[3] by the issues and analyses focused on by social movements and community organizations in the neighborhood, and by local opinion (which, as best I could judge it, sometimes differed from that of people "in the movement" or in "organizing" just as it differed from newspaper accounts or the reports of elected officials).

Many of the orderly features of neighborhood life may seem obvious to American readers, but I will list those relevant to the salience of gatekeeping because their utter famliarity makes them easy to overlook.

---

[2] An adjoining neighborhood is described in detail by Keiser (1969), who was doing an ethnography of a teenage street club during the years I was working at the youth agency.

[3] The distinction made by Pike (see Goodenough 1971) and many others between the "etic" and the "emic" is useful here. I am using the terms in their simplest sense, in direct analogy to linguistics: "etic" referring to the categories for describing everyday life brought by the scientifically trained researcher to the social behavior he perceives as a participant observer, "emic" referring to the "folk" categories used by members to describe the same phenomena. In the "folk" system, classificatory distinctions may be made on the basis of features unaccounted for in the researcher's "etic" system.

"Etic" indicators: The geographical distribution of social rank and organizational access

a. *Geographic location:* The neighborhood was located between the downtown shopping district and the outermost neighborhoods of the city that bordered on the first ring of suburbs.

b. *Formal Organizations:* There were three main classes of formal organizations in the neighborhood; *business organizations* (some large scale with a national market, some small scale with local clientele), *service organizations* (police and fire departments, public and private hospitals, public and parochial schools, public and private youth and adult-serving agencies, and "the Welfare"), and *churches* (most not affiliated with "mainstream" denominations, some large, occupying church and synagogue buildings left by previous white residents, others small, occupying storefronts).

c. *Geographical locus and organizational status:* With the exception of janitorial and "entry level" jobs in the formal organizations, and entrepreneurship in a few "special" local businesses—beauty parlors, rib shops, pool halls—and ministerial positions, virtually all jobs in formal organizations were held by persons who lived outside the neighborhood. Most jobholders were white. The neighborhood population was over 95% black in 1963, over 99% black by 1966. Black occupation of the neighborhood was recent. Population density rose from approximately 7000/square mile in the late 1950s to upwards of 35,000/square mile in the mid 1960s with no increase in housing units.

d. *Political—social influence:* There were three classes of networks through which influence might flow or collective action might be mobilized. First, there were *"local" networks*, which are fully indigenous (such as the churches—storefront churches were often made up of a few extended kin groups—and teenage street clubs, often including with a few exceptions, an entire 4—5 age cohort of males in four or five square blocks). Second, there was a level of *local "outreach" arms of various organizations whose central governance came from somewhere else* (numbers runners and drug pushers and their contacts, local precinct captains and their assistants, local ministers who received support either from central denominational sources or from a citywide political organization, public and private youth agency personnel, school teachers and lower echelon administrators, and welfare workers). This group often acted as mediators, brokers, or spokesmen for neighborhood residents. Third, there were *the top public and private officials of the area* (nonresident business executives, aldermen and committeemen, school superintendents, hospital administrators), who often served on the local governing boards of organizations in the second class of networks. Organizations in this third class were directly linked to the social structure of the city and nation as a whole. Persons at this level had the most influence to negotiate. Often they set policy for the operational personnel of the organizations at the second level, who carried out policy in relationship with persons at the first level, who were neighborhood residents.

For black young people and young adults of the neighborhood, as I knew them, the daily round usually involved face-to-face contacts with some white "outsider." Each day one went to school and met the teacher, to work and met the boss, or to a shop and met the storekeeper. Then one returned home. Often, although not daily, one dealt with a social worker or clerk in an office of "the Welfare" or some other public agency. The continual presence of cruising police cars meant that, when on the street or sitting on the front steps of the apartment building, one had the continual experience of being "watched" by outsiders.

From the time a child was 5 years old, the ebb and flow of everyday life involved "going to meet *the Man* and then returning home to one's own. The people on the outside had the influence: you did not. They could do you a favor, or "run you through those *changes*,"[4] or "whup the game" on you.[5]

All this was apparent from my vantage point as an "outsider" who was part of the buffer system of youth work professionals. I saw children after school, walking into the youth agency; many went through a "decompression" period of a half hour or longer with their friends before the normal outside-school energy level returned, and one had gotten one's "front" together again. Before and after job interviews, I talked with young people, sometimes giving them a ride to the interview or picking them up afterward and "debriefing" them on what happened over a coke. When I worked in the factory as a "teacher," I saw the young neighborhood trainees at their machines under the supervision of the "outsider" foreman. I also saw the trainees in the lounge we used as a classroom and watched them switch styles back and forth each day, turning on the "front" as they walked through the classroom door and turning it off as they walked out, managing alternative presentations of self as did the waiters in the resort hotel described by Goffman (1959: 116–117).

An "Emic" Distinction between Inside and Outside

As a participant observer, it was apparent to me that people in the neighborhood moved back and forth across "inside" and "outside" territories. The salience of this movement was apparent not only from "etic" descriptions of the spatial behavior of persons in their daily rounds, but from the "emic" characterizations of daily life that occurred in the everyday conversations of neighborhood

---

[4] Chord changes—an analogy between harmonic sequences and standard organizational procedure sequences, proliferated or repeated over and over again if a bureaucrat were using the rules to give you a hard time, attenuated if he or she were bending or breaking the rules to make it easy on you.

[5] Trick you.

residents and from cultural production in the form of song texts, jokes, and metaphors for social relations (e.g., "the Man" and "whupping the game").

For example, there is *Stormy Monday*, an "urban" blues introduced by T-Bone Walker. The version that follows was sung in the early 1960s by Bobby Bland (words were transcribed during a live performance, presumably at the Regal Theater in Chicago by Keil (1966: 138—139) and shortened slightly here). In the early 1960s, "urban rhythm and blues" artists like Bland were regarded as "country" (another kind of outsider) by teenagers in the neighborhood, who would not admit to knowing much about blues. Among some adults over 30, the age range most directly involved in working for "the Man" or dealing with his service organizations, urban blues was still popular.

Stormy Monday

They call it stormy Monday
But Tuesday's just as bad
   (repeated)

Wednesday's worse
Lord, and Thursday's oh, so sad

The eagle flies on Friday
And Saturday I go out to play

Sunday I go to church
And I kneel down 'n' pray.
. . . And this is what I say, baby (spoken)

Lord, have mercy,
Lord, have mercy on me . . . (repeated and varied)
. . . You know I'm trying, trying to find my baby
Won't somebody please send her home to me . . . Yeah (spoken)

Stormy Monday speaks to the inside—outside polarity. Seven days are segmented into weekend (inside) and weekdays (outside), which begin "stormy" and continue that way as you work for "the Man." The Eagle (dollar) comes from outside. It flies on Friday, the pivot between outside and inside. After getting paid (on a weekly rather than monthly basis), you get your clothes "out the cleaners" after work and get your "front" together.

Many jokes and sayings further illustrate the relationship between insiders and outsiders.

If you're White, you're right
If you're Brown, stick around
If you're Black, get back.

Q. Where can you find the most Negro Ph.D.s in the United States?
A. At the Chicago Post Office. [current in 1964]

Used to call "the Man" "Mr. Charlie" [before 1967] ; now he's "Chuck," [after 1967] but he's still "the Man." [comment on the Civil Rights Movement]

The outsider clearly has the power and resources. Relations with him may be friendly ("Charlie") but not that of equals. The difference in rank is continuously present and alluded to ("Mr.") or is continuously present and not alluded to ("Chuck").

Other emic indicators could be found in the issues that were salient in the Civil Rights Movement. When the Southern Christian Leadership Conference, under the direction of the Rev. Dr. Martin Luther King, began to organize in Chicago in 1965, it focused most of its activity on the western region of the city in which our neighborhood was located. "The Movement" identified the related issues of "education, employment, and housing" as highly salient. A song sung in demonstrations in the South came to be sung in Chicago, with local names inserted:

No more *Massa Daley–Massa Quigley* [mayor–ward committeeman]
No more Massa Daley
No more Massa Daley over me, over me
And before I'll be a slave
I'll be buried in my grave
And go home to my Lord and be free.

As racial conflict escalated and lay (or "folk") social structural analysis became more differentiated, newer voices in "the Movement" identified an issue that struck close to home for me—"welfare colonialism." The first time I heard the term used was an evening meeting early in 1966 at the downtown office of the Church Federation (an alliance of Protestant denominations that had been involved with Dr. King), at which the issue was identified in these words by a black woman from the Student Nonviolent Coordinating Committee. The "colonial" meaphor struck a number of my white youth work colleagues and me as descriptive of our "buffer" position in the neighborhood (we had been urging our agency director and board to "hire more black staff," but the ring of "welfare colonialism" stayed with us and produced more cognitive dissonance than did our own language). No matter how benevolent the intent, local "helping" by white "buffer" professionals functioned to prevent black professionals and neighborhood residents from organizing self-help and indigenous social change strategies. During that spring (with what we thought was mostly insight and only partly liberal guilt), we disengaged from our jobs. The following year (1967), a citywide group of black social service and education professionals organized an alliance to promote the hiring of black professionals in such interface positions of mediation–brokerage–advocacy between the black and mainstream social systems as youth worker, teacher, counselor, and job interviewer. In response to the alliance of black professionals, a number of predominantly white professional organizations in the city reacted very strongly. The issue was joined.

COLLECTING EVIDENCE ON GATEKEEPING ENCOUNTERS

Summary of Indicators of Salience

It was apparent from experience in the neighborhood that "talking to 'the Man' " was a speech situation that occurred fairly often for most residents. Since "the Man" had resources and influence that residents did not have, the outcome of the talk with him could occasionally be very important. At certain points in the life cycle of an "insider," his survival might be contingent upon the disposition of "the Man" either not to hinder him or to help him in his dealings with mass society. These were the conditions of "colonialism" that had been identified by "the Movement." As "the Movement" rapidly evolved into "the Black Power Movement," members asserted that "talking to 'the Man' " resulted in being victimized either because of "the Man's" malevolence or because of his well-intentioned but naive incompetence. From this logic, it follows that the brokers or advocates for black people should be black, ideologically as well as racially. Encounters with mass society should be conducted together with persons who were one's "own." This would change the character of the relationship between the helper and helped from one of patronage ("the white man's burden") to one of advocacy and, ultimately, revolutionary solidarity.

I wondered what "the Man" did as a gatekeeper, whether he dealt with interviewees of his own ethnic group differently from black and Latin interviewees. If so, how were these differences played out in interactional performance, and what social meaning did such difference have for interviewees and for the gatekeeper himself? Two points of gatekeeping contact with mass society could occur between late adolescence and the beginning of young adulthood: going to see a school counselor or a job interviewer. Issues of well-being and (occasionally) survival could be at stake in these encounters. Because most persons in educational and business organizations occupying the status of interviewer were white, going to see them meant "talking to 'the Man'."

I wanted to see what effect ethnic and racial similarities and differences between the two persons in the encounter had upon the character and outcomes of interaction face to face. Identifying the *character* of interaction involved considering not only speech forms and speech functions but the form and function of nonlinguistic behavior as well. Identifying the *outcomes* of interaction involved considering how a gatekeeper disposed of the case before him: whether he fostered or hindered social mobility and by what interactional means he performed these gatekeeping functions.

Two additional aspects of the situation made gatekeeping encounters appropriate for study. First, they usually took place between only two persons seated across a desk in a room or partitioned space. This made it relatively simple to make unobstrusive audiovisual records of the encounters in their natural settings. Second, because the gatekeeper's day consisted of one interview after another dealing with the main theme of the structure of his organization—each interview manifesting a "variation" in terms of the place of a particular interviewee in that organization—the interview became quite stylized. Standard "routines" and optional subroutines were employed by the interviewer. This meant that particular encounters were a fairly coherent semantic and interactional domain, and that one encounter was likely to be comparable to another.

The Sample: A Natural Experimental Design

The city of Chicago is organized geographically and socially such that as citizens in their daily rounds pass through social territories and social time there are regular patterns of alternation between intraethnic contact and interethnic contact. (cf. Suttles, 1968). This is true for gatekeeping encounters at schools and factories as well. In some parts of the city and in some organizations, contact between persons of particular ethnic statuses is more likely than in others. In a sense, the city itself presents a "natural experimental design" (Campbell and Stanley 1966) for the study of interethnic relations. We selected field sites for observation and recording at which contact between three main ethnic classes was most likely. These classes were *white ethnic* (predominantly Polish-American and Italian-American), *Latin* (predominantly Mexican-American), and *black*.

Later in the course of our research, it became clear that this three-way classification was inappropriate. Ethnic and racial identification was one indicator by which our informants categorized persons, and gatekeeping behavior varied according to ethnicity and race. Although our informants did not refer explicitly to any categories of ascription more general in inclusiveness than ethnicity, we found, as we analyzed our data, that such categories emerged. For example, Italian-Americans and Polish-Americans were ethnically distinct and subculturally different. Yet relations between an Italian-American interviewer and a Polish-American interviewee, while not as symmetric behaviorally as relations between two Italian-Americans, were much more symmetric than relations between an Italian-American interviewer and a black interviewee. The same held for black—Mexican encounters in comparison with black—black and black—Polish encounters. There seemed to be a category of ascription and identification more general than *ethnicity* within which Polish-, Italian-, and Irish-Americans clustered, on the one hand, and blacks, Chicanos, and Puerto Ricans clustered, on the other hand. We called this category "pan-ethnicity," by analogy with the "Pan-African" movement, in which Africans of diverse regions and cultures established solidarity with one another within a superordinate category of identification as "Africans." In our sample there were two pan-ethnic classes; we called them "white ethnic" and "Third World."[6] Interaction between members of ethnic groups within these two classes was more symmetric than interaction across the classes. The significance of this will be discussed later on.

Eighty-two cases of encounters (10- and 5-minute sound films and videotapes) were collected. Background ethnography was done at all field sites, varying in extent according to the number of films we intended to make at the site. Table 9.1 shows the distribution of cases across sites and the ethnic combinations of persons in encounters. We were not able to get a "clean" sample of ethnic combinations by recording natural encounters in the field. In the second of the 2 years during which we collected films, we made films of nonnaturalistic encounters between student pairs controlled for ethnicity. (University students who were strangers were told to talk about problems of registration at the university and were then filmed.) These student–student encounters appear also in Table 9.1 and in Table 9.2, which summarizes the cases by ethnic class. We were supplementing our "natural experimental design" with more traditional experimental material to meet the exigencies of the real world. Most of the evidence and conclusions reported here, however, come from the naturalistic cases collected at field sites.

CONVERTING RAW DATA INTO EVIDENCE

The 82 cases collected represented approximately 30,000 feet of film: 600 minutes of face-to-face interaction. Since cinema film is exposed at 1/24 second per frame, we collected 864,000 individual pictures of two persons talking, each picture containing much information. The problem was how to reduce this mass of information, together with background ethnographic information, into usable form.

The reduction and analysis of data took 2 years. First, a number of research assistants coded the films to retrieve various aspects of verbal and nonverbal behavior. Then a smaller group of assistants and this writer, all of whom had watched all the films a number of times at regular speed and had watched portions of many of the films in slow motion, combined their intuitive judgments with quantitative summaries of the coded evidence and began to write

---

[6] While most of the white ethnic students could be classified as lower middle class, and most Third World students could be classified as working class or "underclass," the differences between the two groups and similarities within groups did not seem to be primarily a matter of "social class," although social class may have been partly a factor.

summary "microethnographic" descriptions of various aspects of the character and outcomes of interaction found in the films. The research team also began to manipulate the quantitatively summarized evidence statistically.

Development and Application of Coding Strategies

Verbal, nonverbal, and "interactional process" behavior occurring in the encounters was coded for. Two principles were followed in developing the codes. First, we wanted independence, both between individual raters using a single code and between the various kinds of codes so that we could demonstrate the intersubjective reliability of our evidence. Second, we wanted interdependence among different codes, both for conceptual consistency, and also so that we could key all the codes to each other to get a synoptic view of the whole interactional process and structure. On the basis of this picture of the whole, relationships among parts could be inferred. All the codes are briefly described as follows:

1. Speech behavior
   a. two codes for paralinguistic phenomena, one for voice pitch, one for voice intensity and rhythm.
   b. three codes for dealing with linguistic phenomena, one for the "referential functions" of speech (explicit semantic content manifested in lexicon and syntax), one for "social functions" of speech (implicit semantic content), and one for (symmetric) verbal overlapping or (asymmetric) verbal interruptions of one another by the two speaker—listeners.
2. Nonverbal behavior
   a. one code for gaze direction and involvement, indicating when speakers looked at or away from each other
   b. one code for proxemic phenomena, indicating when speakers moved closer to or farther away from each other
   c. a notation system for describing kinesic rhythm—the timing (not the quality or specific content) of body motion and gesticulation—at microsecond intervals.[7]

---

[7] This is the microanalysis procedure used with the abstracted segments described in the earlier section. Kinesic rhythm is identified through manual coding at 24 frames per second, and speech rhythm is identified through a polygraph print-out of the film sound track segmented into 24 frames per second, the print-out of the time unit being synchronized with the cinema projector. This procedure locates voice intensity patterns in synchrony with body motion patterns. The kinesic code is a simplified version of the one developed by Prost (1967). The whole procedure follows the orientation of Byers (1972).

Table 9.1
The Sample, by Site, Ethnicity, and Interviewer

Site	Interviewer–Counselor	Applicant–Student	Number of cases
1: Large company	1 German-American	German-American	2
		Italian-American	1
		English-American	2
		Polish American	1
		Czech-American	1
		Jewish-American	1
	2 black	black	1
		German-American	3
Total			*12*
2: Public high school	Polish-American	black	3
Total			*3*
3a: Small company	Polish-American	Mexican-American	1
3b: Small company	black	black	1
Total			*2*
4: Public high school	Participant observation of school counseling interviews		
5: Large company	Participant observation of white–white and white–black job interview training sessions		
6: Small company	1 white	black	3
	2 black	black	1
Total			*4*
7: Private junior college	1 black	black	3
		Puerto Rican	2
		Irish-American	1

2 black	black	5
	white	3
	Puerto Rican	1
Total		*15*
8: Public university	black–black	2
	black–Mexican-American	1
	black–Polish-American	1
	Polish-American–Polish-American	1
	Mexican-American–Mexican-American	1
Total		*6*
9: Public junior college	1 Italian-American	Italian-American	5
		Polish-American	3
	2 Irish-American	Polish-American	2
		black	3
		Puerto Rican	1
	3 black	black	1
		Polish-American	5
		Puerto Rican	1
Total			*21*
10: Public university	Polish-American–Polish-American	2
	black–black	2
	Mexican-American–Puerto Rican	1
	black–Mexican-American	2
	black–Polish-American	3
	Polish-American–Cuban	1
	Polish-American–Mexican-American	1
Total		*12*
11: Public university	Polish-American–Polish-American	1
	Mexican-American–Mexican-American	1
	Mexican-American–black	1
	Polish-American–Mexican-American	4
Total		*7*

Table 9.2
The Sample, by Sites and Pan-Ethnic Class

	Job interviews	School counseling interviews	Student–Student encounters	Total
Black–Black	3	9	4	16
White–White	8	10	4	22
Latin–Latin	–	–	3	3
Black–White	6	15	4	25
Black–Latin	–	4	4	8
White–Latin	1	1	6	8
Total	18	39	25	82

3. Hierarchical ordering of natural units (segments) of speaking/listening behavior
   a. "etic" codes for segmentation (in which units are defined from the "outsider" perspective of the research staff—analogous to phonetic analysis in linguistics)
      1. a code for overall behavior asymmetry, identifying sections during which the smooth flow of interaction broke down between speakers—an "asymmetry sections code"
      2. a procedure for identifying segments within the sections of behavioral asymmetry—an "asymmetry segments" code
      3. a procedure for identifying microsegments within the asymmetry segments
   b. "emic" codes for segmentation (in which units, demarcated as whole "events," are identified impressionistically by the encounter participants themselves from a "insider" perspective or by naive judges from a "quasi-insider" perspective)
      1. The "emic" codes for the overall impressions of the encounter participants themselves, one code indicating the location of a viewing session comment in relation to the flow of interaction in the original encounter, another code indicating the content of viewing session comments
      2. A group of "quasi-emic" codes for overall impressions of interaction process administered as a questionnaire to naive judges who viewed videotapes of the original encounters and scored a questionnaire for each encounter.

By these means, we gathered independent evidence of the hierarchical integration of interactional phenomena. Independence was maintained by having different individuals code for different behavioral phenomena and by controlling for different combinations of sensory media through which the behavioral phenomena could be apprehended by an individual coder (see Table 9.3).

Summarizing Evidence from the Various Codes

We had transcripts of the original counseling interviews and transcripts of the comments made by participants in viewing sessions, as counselor and student watched a videotape of their interview and commented on changes of topic and emotional tone.[8] It was a simple clerical task to key the viewing session comments to points in the encounter transcript being referred to. Once this was done, and once shifts in referential content of talk and other nonverbal aspects of interaction that had been coded (shifts in proxemics, paralanguage, and eye contact) were cross-referenced to utterance numbers, it was possible to prepare summary tables that indicated the presence or absence of change along the various coded dimensions and indicated the location of changes relative to one another across dimensions (see Table 9.4).

From these summary tables and the original code charts, we could retrieve information about the relation of various verbal and nonverbal behavior classes to each other by marking situational shifts and smaller segments within the section bounded by situational shifts. For example, from the differences in "texture" of presence or absence of change illustrated in the summary table, it is apparent that a change in the organization of interaction occurs between utterances 33 and 34–35, then a less gross change occurs at utterances 37 and 38, and another major change occurs at utterances 42 and 43. The *content* of the change is not indicated by the summary table, but the *location* of the change is indicated. The table combines "etic" evidence (such as the code for proxemics and for referential speech content) with "emic" evidence from the code indicating presence or absence of viewing session comments. This procedure combines evidence differing in source and in kind in the demarcation of "units," "segments," or "microsituational shifts" in the filmed examples of interaction.

Clearly, different raters, experiencing the raw data through different sensory media (some looking at film with sound, others at film without sound and backward as well as forward, others working from typed transcripts), were retrieving features of interactional structure that associate together. In addition, some of the "sections" identified in this exhaustive manner are the same as those identified by raters watching the sound film at regular speed, identifying what seemed to them intuitively to be "uncomfortable moments" during the course of the filmed conversation.

Furthermore, the "uncomfortable moments" identified by raters were usually accompanied (in 16 out of the 18 cases of counseling interviews in which we have an uncomfortable moment and viewing session data) by a "viewing session comment" by one or both of the encounter participants, as they watched their conversation on videotape in viewing sessions. The counselor and student had

---

[8] The location of a viewing session comment was indicated on the audiotape by the point at which the audio track of the videotape being viewed by the informant went "off" and the voice of the informant commenting on that point went "on".

Table 9.3
Sources and Kinds of Coded Data

Code (behavioral phenomenon)	"Data Source"		"Data kind"
	Sensory modality	Information medium	
Proxemic	visual	cinema (silent)	etic
Eye contact	visual	cinema (silent)	etic
Kinesic–asymmetry—segments	visual	cinema (silent)	etic
Kinesic–asymmetry—microsegments	visual (first)	cinema (silent)	etic
	auditory (second)	cinema (sound)	
Paralinguistic (pitch)	auditory	audiotape	etic
Paralinguistic (intensity accents)	"auditory" (machine print-out)	cinema sound track	etic
Kinesic–asymmetry—sections	auditory–visual	cinema (sound)	emic (encounter participants and judges)
Overlap–interruption	auditory–visual	cinema (sound)	"quasi-emic" (judges)
Interaction process	auditory–visual	video	"quasi-emic" (judges)
Viewing session	auditory–visual	video	emic (encounter participants)
Topic (referential function of speech)	visual	transcript	etic
Time reference (referential function of speech)	visual	transcript	etic

Illustration of a Summary Table

Line	Topic	Overlap—Interruption	Proxemics		Paralanguage		Time reference shift	Viewing session comment	Eye contact
			Coder 1	Coder 2	Coder 1	Coder 2			
28	1								2
29									
30									
31	1								
32									
33	1				1				22
34		1	1		11				2
35	11111			1	1	1			3
36				1	1	1			
37	11			1	1	1	1		
38	1			1	1	1	1		32
39				1	1	1			
40					1	1			24
41									
42	1						1		
43	11111111	1		1	11	11	111	1 (1)	4342
44		11							2
45	111				1	1	1		
46									
47	1				1	1	1		23
48					1	1		1	32
49	1	1			1	1	1	1	2342
50					1	1			2
51	1				1	1			2
52									
53	1111	1			1	11	11		2434
54					1	11			
55	111	1							4
56					1				

been asked, in separate viewing sessions, to stop the videotape "each time something new happens—a change in topic or emotional tone." One of the places they stopped the tape to comment on what had been happening was almost invariably within an "uncomfortable moments section" identified by the naive raters.

In the summary table of the interview (Table 9.4), lines 34–43 were identified by raters as the most uncomfortable moment in the whole film. Table 9.5 presnts a transcript of the actual interview (lines 37–43) together with comments by the participants in later viewing sessions.

We decided to focus on these "uncomfortable moments," etically and emically identified by raters and by the participants themselves. We considered these segments of interaction as units that were comparable across films. A number of measures were used to describe the character of uncomfortable moments. Two of the measures used to describe degree and character of discomfort in the uncomfortable movements are the "asymmetry segments code" and the "rhythmic asymmetry code."

ASYMMETRY SEGMENTS CODE

The asymmetry segments code (ASC) identified subsections within the whole uncomfortable moment and ranked each subsection in terms of the degree of behavioral asymmetry—low, medium, and high. A single rater used this code. She watched the sound film of the whole uncomfortable moment, at regular speed forward without sound, at regular speed backward with sound, and forward and backward in slow motion. In this manner, she could watch the faces, postures, and motions of both speakers but could not distinguish their words.

Essentially what the rater was doing was making a judgment of the "ratio" between the amount of activity in the speaking behavior of the speaker and the listening behavior of the listener.[9] If the speaker were speaking with great animation—rapid speech, leaning forward, broad gestures, eye contact with listener—and the listener were listening with animation—rapid head nods, leaning forward, eye contact—this was characterized as "symmetric speaking–listening." If the listener nodded rarely, slouched in his seat, averted his eyes or looked out the window, this was considered inconsistent with the speaker's animated quality of speaking and characterized as "asymmetric speaking–listening."

For 26 cases, the subsections within the asymmetry section identified by the ASC rater *corresponded exactly with the subsections appearing on the summary tables.* Somehow, even watching the film backward, she was able to attend to whole gestalts of interactional cues that were apprehended part by part by the

---

[9] A more detailed description of this code and the rhythmic asymmetry code referred to later is available in Erickson (1973).

Table 9.5
Transcript of Part of an Interview and Later Viewing Sessions

Student viewing session	Transcript	Counselor viewing session
H	G	I
Researcher: The ah, information he gave you on the counselor, were you satisfied with that?	(White counselor) 2: As far as next semester . . . Why don't we give some thought to what you'd like to take there? . . . Do you plan on continuing along this P.E. major?	2: Right now, we both seem to be concentrating on giving information. He on the other hand is concentrating . . . on accepting the information and putting it together. (CVS P # 4)
5: Not especially, you know.	(Black student) 5: Yeah, I guess so. I might as well keep it up . . . my P.E., and I wanna go into counseling too, see . . . you know, to have two way . . . like equal balance.	J
R: Why?		2: . . . he's got aspirations for the future, P.E. and uh . . . uh, counseling . . . he's a little bit ahead of himself as far as the counseling. . . . (CVS P # 3)
5: Well . . . well I couldn't really say, but I wasn't satisfied with what he wanted to push . . . I guess he didn't think I was qualified you know. That's the way he sounded to me. (SVS P # 5)	2: I see, Ah . . . What do you know about counseling?	
	5: Nothing.	

Continued

129

Table 9.5 (continued)

Student viewing session	Transcript	Counselor viewing session
(H-1)		K
	2: Okay . . .	3: As the year progressed, I guess I got the question so often that it became one of my favorite topics an' I was ready to uh numerate . . . essentially what he did was he started me off on my information. (CVS p. 11)
R: Does he make you feel comfortable or uncomfortable?	5: I know you have to take psychology course, of some sorts, and counseling.	
5: Well, I was like uncomfortable. You know I wanted ta . . . you know, mouth off (L) but I didn't.	2: Well, it's, this is a . . . It'll vary from different places to different places. . . . But essentially what you need. . . . First of all you're gonna need state certification . . . state teacher certification . . . in other words, you're gonna have to be certified to teach in some area . . . English or history, or whatever happens to be your bag . . . P.E. Secondly you're gonna have to have a master's degree . . . in counseling . . . which as you know is an advanced degree (laugh). That's what you have to do to get a counseling . . . to be a counselor. (9-2-5 L, 37–43)	
R: But why didn't you?		
5: I didn't want to start something.		
R: I don't mean start something but, you know, then maybe things would have gotten into . . . to more of what you wanted. Do you think he was leading the conversation?		
5: Yeah, he was spicing it, like card stacking you know. He was doing a little propaganda, you know. (SVS p. 6)		

Student 5: This guy here seems like he was trying to knock me down, in a way, you know. Trying to say no . . . I don't think you can handle anything besides P.E.. You know, he just said it in general terms, he just didn't go up and POW like they would in the old days, you know. This way they just try to use a little more psychology . . . they sugar coat it this way.

Researcher: They sprinkle it . . .

5: They sprinkle it with sugar.
(SVS P # 10)

2: Well, it's, this is a . . . It'll vary from different places to different places. . . . But essentially, what you need . . . First of all you're gonna need state certification . . . state teacher certification . . . in other words you're gonna have to be certified to teach in some area . . . English or history, or whatever happens to be your bag . . . P.E. Secondly you're gonna have to have a master's degree . . . in counseling . . . which as you know is an advanced degree (laugh). That's what you have to do to get a counseling . . . to be a counselor.

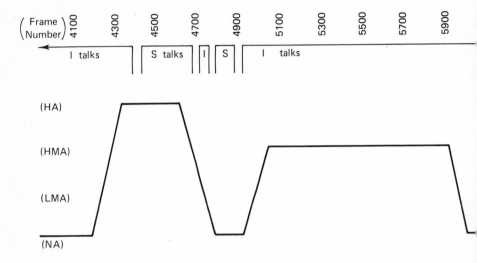

Scale: 1 inch = 200 frames (24 f.p.s.) = 8.3 seconds

Figure 9.1 An asymmetry segments code chart. NA = no asymmetry; LMA = low moderate asymmetry; HMA = high moderate asymmetry; HA = high asummetry.

coders of paralanguage, proxemic shifts, and the like, who operated on one or two sensory "channels" at a time. Here was a nonstandard demonstration of interrater reliability. Figure 9.1 shows a chart summarizing the asymmetry segments code for the asymmetry section illustrated in the previous tables. Notice that segments of high relative asymmetry alternate with segments of little or no asymmetry.

On the chart used by the coder, each 100 frames of film (approximately 4 seconds of interaction) are reduced to 10 squares. There are 10 squares per inch on the graph paper. This converted a measure of time to a measure of length. Using an ordinary ruler, I measured the lengths (duration) of charted segments of asymmetry at different levels of asymmetry and averaged these for all cases.[10]

Rhythmic Asymmetry Code

On the basis of the asymmetry segments code, segments were picked for even more fine-grained analysis. Adapting a notation system developed by Prost (1967), we developed a procedure for charting the *motions of body parts* (head, arms, torso, legs) and *intensity accents in speech* along a time line calibrated in

---

[10] The chart appearing here in the text is reduced by half from the original; 100 frames of film equals five squares on the graph paper.

twenty-fourths of a second. This gave us a record of the rhythmic organization of kinesic (body motion) and speech behavior immediately preceding and during the "uncomfortable moment." Using a different measuring system and approach from Chapple (Chapple and Lindemann 1941) our findings were consistent with his—at moments of discomfort, the even flow of interactional rhythm between speakers is distorted. I identified four kinds of rhythmic asymmetry from the charts, scaled the kinds according to degree of asymmetry, from low to high, and tabulated the results for the 26 cases of "uncomfortable moments."[11]

Measures of Affect and Special Help

Our two measures of asymmetry in face-to-face interaction were considered together with rater's judgments of the level of affect (emotional tone) of each encounter, and the amount of special help (bending or breaking of organizational rules, extra assistance involving counselor time after working hours) given by counselors to students.[12]

Ethnicity and Behavioral Asymmetry, Affect, and Special Help

There was a clear relationship between ethnicity and the "match" between speaker–listener behavior as measured by the asymmetry segments code. There was an even closer relationship between the speaking–listening ratio and the social category termed *pan-ethnicity*.[13] We identified two pan-ethnic classes of

[11] These measures are also discussed in detail in Erickson (1973).

[12] These measures are also discussed in detail in Erickson (1973). It should be noted that the inferential statistics presented in the following discussion only illustrate patterns in the descriptive statistical data and indicate approximate differences in the strength of relationships among various factors. The data do not meet all the conditions required for the parametric statistics employed.

[13] Each informant belonged both to a particular ethnic group (Polish-American, Chicano, etc.) and to one of two pan-ethnic groups ("white ethnic" or "Third World"). All encounters designated "intraethnic" were between members of the same ethnic group. Some encounters designated "interethnic" were between members of groups within the same pan-ethnic class (e.g., Polish-American and Italian—American); other encounters designated "interethnic" were between persons from different pan-ethnic classes (e.g., Polish-American and black). Since we found that encounters across pan-ethnic lines were qualitatively different from encounters within the same pan-ethnic class, we decided to separate these in our quantitative summaries and analyses. The distinctions "intra-pan-ethnic" and "inter-pan-ethnic" accomplish this. The category "intra-pan-ethnic encounters" includes encounters between members of the same ethnic groups within the same pan-ethnic class. By making comparisons according to these categories (and by adding a third distinction between "co-members" and "non-co-members"), we are able to show what portions of variation left unexplained by comparison according to more restrictive categories of identification (ethnicity) are explained by comparison according to increasingly general categories of identification (pan-ethnicity and co-membership).

ethnic groups—"Third World" (black, Mexican, Puerto Rican) and "white ethnic" (Polish, Italian, Irish). For all features of interaction except rhythmic asymmetry, pan-ethnicity explained more of the variance in our data than did ethnicity.

The mean amount (time expressed in inches) of asymmetric speaking–listening for same and different ethnic pairs follows: the higher the number, the longer the duration of asymmetry within a section.

Encounters	Mean length of asymmetry segments
Intraethnic	5.99
Interethnic	8.31
Intra-pan-ethnic	5.86
Inter-pan-ethnic	9.75

N = 26 cases

This is a difference, but it is not statistically significant. In addition, the pan-ethnic difference is slightly greater than that between same ethnic and different ethnic pairs.

One of our initial working hypotheses was that differences in cultural communication style would affect the amount of discomfort in gatekeeping interviews. We assumed that there would be greater similarity in communication style among persons of the same ethnic group than among ethnically different persons. (This assumption turned out to be only partially true, for reasons to be presented later.)

The ASC results suggest that factors other than intraethnic cultural similarity and interethnic difference in communication style are affecting the degree of discomfort. We found that, among these intervening factors, were situational conditions—especially the social *persona*, or "composite social identity" presented by the student in the gatekeeping encounter (see Goodenough, 1965). Some attributes of the social identity of students that are independent of communication style—bad grades, courses taken in the wrong sequence or dropped without permission—when revealed suddenly in the encounter caused a rapid change in the definition of situation, in the relationship of rights and obligations obtaining between student and counselor—a "situational shift," to use the terminology of Blom and Gumperz (1972). These situational shifts might result in an uncomfortable moment. Conversely, some features of the "micro-social structure" of the encounter seemed to reduce interactional asymmetry, as measured by the ASC. These were attributes of social identity that revealed a common bond between the two speakers apart from ethnicity or cultural similarity; for example, an Irish counselor and a Chicano student learning that they had attended the same parochial school, or an Italian counselor revealing

Table 9.6
Differences in Symmetry, Affect, and Special Help in Counseling Encounters by Ethnicity[a]

	Asymmetry segments	Affect	Help
Intraethnic	5.99 (NS)	2.89[b]	10.7[c]
Interethnic	8.31	1.30[b]	6.0[c]

[a] $N = 26$.
[b] $p < .05$.
[c] $p < .025$.

that he had been a high school wrestling coach and a Polish student revealing that he was on the junior college wrestling team. We used the term "co-membership" for this generalized sharing of particularistic attributes of status (including ethnicity but also in addition to it). The following three tables show the relationship between ethnic, pan-ethnic, and co-member social identity; speaker–listener asymmetry; the "outcome" measures of emotional tone; and special help given in the school gatekeeping encounters. The "intra–inter" gap widens for *asymmetry segments* and affect when cases are compared according to pan-ethnicity rather than ethnicity, even though the greater difference is not statistically significant. Co-membership explains more of the variation in the data than does ethnicity or pan-ethnicity. (In Tables 9.6 and 9.7 analysis of variance was computed separately for the *intra–inter ethnic* comparison, the *intra–inter pan-ethnic* comparison, and the *high, medium, and low co-membership* comparison. The widening difference in means across the three tables illustrates the increasing explanatory "power" of the three kinds of social classification.)

Table 9.7
Differences in Symmetry, Affect, and Special Help in Counseling Encounters by Pan-ethnicity[a]

	Asymmetry segments	Affect	Help
Intra-pan-ethnic	5.86 (NS)	2.65[b]	8.4 (NS)
Inter-pan-ethnic	9.75	.82	6.6

[a] $N = 26$.
[b] $p < .10$.

Table 9.8
Differences in Symmetry, Affect, and Special Help by Co-membership[a]

	Asymmetry segments[b]	Affect[c]	Help[d]
High co-membership	3.15	8.78	12.57
Medium co-membership	7.17	7.03	10.51
Low co-membership	11.58	4.81	6.61
Overall	*7.40*	*6.72*	*9.69*

[a]N = 26 (N for asymmetry segments = 43, including student–student encounter).
[b]Anova $p < .025$.
[c]Anova $p < .01$.
[d]Anova $p < .05$.

Rhythmic Asymmetry Code

Results from the rhythmic asymmetry code turned out to be more closely associated with ethnicity than with pan-ethnicity or co-membership. This suggests that the rhythmic asymmetry code is retrieving aspects of interactional form that are cultural rather than social structural in origin. At this writing, our measure of interactional rhythm is our best indicator of "match" or "mismatch" in cultural communication style between speakers. The close association between the amount of rhythmic asymmetry and the ethnicity of speakers is illustrated in Tables 9.9 and 9.10. In Table 9.9, while both pan-ethnicity and ethnicity are associated with rhythmic asymmetry at the .01 level of significance, the χ^2 value for ethnicity is higher. In Table 9.10, the relationship between rhythmic asymmetry and co-membership, while not nonexistent, is quite low, and the χ^2 value falls considerably below the .05 level.

In contrast to Tables 9.6, 9.7, and 9.8, which show that more general and inclusive categories of social identification explain more of the variation in the

Table 9.9
Rhythmic Asymmetry at "Uncomfortable Moments" by Ethnicity and Pan-ethnicity[a]

	Intraethnic	Interethnic	Intra-pan-ethnic	Inter-pan-ethnic
Low or none	15	11	21	5
Middle	0	4	2	2
High	0	9	2	7

[b]$\chi^2 = 12.88$ ($p < .01$).   [c]$\chi^2 = 10.369$ ($p < .01$).
[a]N = 39 (including student–student encounters).

Table 9.10
Rhythmic Asymmetry by Co-membership[a]

Co-membership	Rhythmic asymmetry		
	Low	Medium	High
High	11	1	1
Medium	13	1	2
Low	7	2	6

[a]χ^2 = 6.614 (NS). N = 44 (including student–student encounters).

Table 9.11
Rhythmic Asymmetry and Affect[a]

Affect	Rhythmic asymmetry		
	Low	Medium	High
High	7	0	1
Medium	6	0	2
Low	4	1	4

[a]χ^2 = 4.598 (NS). N = 44.

data than does ethnicity, the reverse is true for Tables 9.9 and 9.10. As the category of social identification becomes more general, the χ^2 decreases with the highest χ^2 for ethnicity, the next highest for pan-ethnicity, and the χ^2 for co-membership not only lowest but considerably lower than the χ^2 for pan-ethnicity.[14]

The amount of rhythmic asymmetry during the most "uncomfortable moment" is also clearly related to rater judgments of overall emotional tone and the amount of special help given during the counselor–student interviews. Because the numbers in some cells are so small, the relationships are not statistically significant, but inspection of Tables 9.11 and 9.12 does reveal a clustering of high affect and help in the region of low rhythmic asymmetry, and *vice versa*.

All this suggests that similarity in cultural communication style (as indicated by the rhythmic asymmetry data) and one's composite self-presentation as a social personage (as indicated by co-membership score) have a strong effect on the character and outcomes of the gatekeeping encounters in our sample, and also on the conduct of encounters between pairs of students who were strangers. The relative strength of communication style and co-membership in influencing the outcomes of interaction is difficult to estimate. Under some conditions of co-membership, differences in communication style seem to be overridden or overlooked, and some students may receive considerable special help despite much "difference."

What is important here is that *both communication style and particularistically defined social identity* (defined in terms of particularistic attributes of identification rather than universalistic attributes, such as grades, test scores, and courses completed) *stand outside the formal organization's rules for what is situationally relevant in a gatekeeping encounter* (cf. Goffman 1961: 25). Whether or not a

[14] Here again, as with the analyses of variance, χ^2 was completed separately for classification of cases by ethnicity, pan-ethnicity, and co-membership.

Table 9.12

Rhythmic Asymmetry and Special Help[a]

	Rhythmic asymmetry		
Special help	Low	Medium	High
High	8	0	1
Medium	5	1	3
Low	4	0	3

[a]χ^2 = 4.341 (NS).

student is a wrestler, or has black skin, or has a communication style that is incompatible with that of the counselor is not, according to the official charter of the junior college, supposed to affect the way in which the student is "treated" by the counselor—the way in which the counselor encourages or discourages him to continue his formal education, the amount of assistance offered by the counselor to help the student achieve a desired educational goal. The college catalogue, a "grammar book" of ideal rules for the formal social system of the organization, states that students are evaluated in terms of universalistic features of social identity. Yet our evidence from actual encounters shows that, invariably, particularistic attributes of the status of social persons, such as ethnicity, are "leaking" into the gatekeeping encounter, affecting definition of situation and the gatekeeper's treatment.

Table 9.13

Rhythmic Asymmetry and Special Help by Race of Counselor

	Rhythmic asymmetry		
Special help	Low	Middle	High
White counselors ($N = 2$)[a]			
Low	5	0	0
Middle	2	1	2
High	1	0	2
Black counselors ($N = 2$)[b]			
Low	3	0	1
Middle	3	0	1
High	3	0	1

[a]N = 12 cases.
[b]N = 12 cases.

One interesting finding concerning the effect of this particularistic "leakage" on the treatment received by the student is illustrated in Table 9.13. Even though our sample of counselors for this portion of the data is extremely small, differences exist in the relationship between special help and rhythmic asymmetry, according to the race of the counselor.

What this may suggest is that the black counselors, members of a "different" group themselves, are more tolerant of differences in cultural communication style than are the white counselors, or they may be more willing to give special help despite the race and culture of the student. It may be that some members of ethnic groups ranking at the bottom of American society in terms of influence, having themselves been "run through the changes" of the standard operating procedures of bureaucracies, are more willing to help all comers, whether "same" or "different," to find shortcuts through organizational mazes. This last is speculative, but it could become an empirical question.

IMPLICATIONS FOR POLICY AND FOR THE CUMULATION OF LARGER SAMPLES

Summary of Findings

As a researcher with anthropological training, I had focused on gatekeeping as a result of my field experience. I had wanted to demonstrate that cultural style in communication behavior was the most powerful single factor affecting the outcomes of gatekeeping encounters for students from a variety of ethnic backgrounds in a major American city. After 4 years of collecting and analyzing evidence, this formulation of the research problem seemed too simple; ethnicity and communication style seemed to have much influence on gatekeeping outcomes in many encounters but seemed to have much less influence in other encounters. This seemed to be true partly because ethnicity did not predict cultural style directly—there was considerable cultural variability within ethnic categories. (cf. Barth 1969). In addition, some "bi-" or "tricultural" ethnics "style switched" to adapt to the person they were talking to.[15]

The differential influence of cultural style over gatekeeping outcomes is also partially explained by considering social identity as a variable in its own right,

---

[15] "Style switching" to accommodate the other was much more likely in intra-pan-ethnic encounters than in inter-pan-ethnic encounters. This may be partly because fellow pan-ethnics (who are more likely to live in the same or contiguous neighborhoods and to attend the same schools) are more likely to have been exposed to the interactional style of their culturally different fellow pan-ethnics, and thus style switching is easier for them. Another reason may be that fellow pan-ethnics are more likely to be motivated to accommodate one another than are persons of different pan-ethnic backgrounds.

interacting with and occasionally overriding the influence of cultural style. Features of social identity other than ethnicity were situationally relevant to the counselors and students and influenced their behavior, as indicated by the figures in our tables for *pan-ethnicity* and *co-membership.*

If a student were Italian-American talking to an Italian-American counselor who had been a wrestling coach, it helped if the student were also a wrestler. If a student talking to such a counselor were Polish-American and a wrestler, he was likely to receive more special help and friendliness than a Polish-American student who was not a wrestler. Occasionally, co-membership in such situationally defined ascription categories as "fellow wrestler" or even "fellow history major" (ascription categories to which persons could belong despite ethnic, racial, or cultural difference) seemed to override the effects of differences in cultural style, ethnicity, or even race. Conversely, it was in those interethnic and interracial encounters in which very few features of particularistic co-membership were revealed that cultural difference seems to have been most troublesome, and rhythmic assymetry scores tended to be highest.

Overall, some form of "leakage" of particularistic features of social identity seemed to be occuring in every gatekeeping encounter, whether at school or at work. Some mix of communication style and co-membership affected how much emotional warmth and help toward social mobility each student or job applicant tended to receive from each gatekeeper.

It appeared that Third World students and job applicants fared less well at the hands of white ethnic gatekeepers than did white ethnic students and job applicants. This was what the alliance of black human service professionals had maintained in 1967 in the city of Chicago. It is what I and many other Americans, black and white, knew intuitively.

The next finding was unexpected. Apparently, white ethnic students and job applicants were likely to get more special help from Third World gatekeepers than their Third World counterparts were likely to get from white ethnic gatekeepers.

Finally, the main contribution of the study may be methodological—at least some aspects of *cultural communication style, co-membership, emotional tone, and special help* could be operationally defined and empirically measured in ways that articulated with an overall ethnographic context.

The Issue of Generalizability

Our conclusions are "true" for a sample of 82 encounters. They are most "true," in terms of both validity and reliability of empirical evidence, for 26 encounters between junior college counselors and students. The question that remains is: "Do these findings generalize to the whole city of Chicago or to the entire United States?" It could be that we collected a biased sample or that certain features of the sociocultural history of Chicago make it unique, and, therefore, we cannot generalize our findings to, say, Los Angeles. Intuitively I would say that cities like Pittsburgh, Boston, Philadelphia, New York, and St. Louis are similar enough to Chicago for findings from Chicago to apply to them.

The issue of generalizability could be taken one step further and it could be argued that, since in *no case collected* did particularistic attributes of social identity *not* affect the conduct and outcomes of face-to-face interaction, we can assume that this is true universally for face-to-face encounters until contrary evidence is supplied. I would be willing to assert this and to make policy recommendations for this society on the basis of it. But one counter example could destroy the argument, and without further evidence such statements are suspect.

Microethnographic procedures, that make use of an audiovisual record of behavior that can be viewed repeatedly involve continual cross-checking of evidence across different kinds of codes and across different raters. Behind the conclusions reported here stand the interlocking judgments of more than a dozen research assistants, as well as the intuitions of two ethnographers (Leonard-Dolan and myself). The analytic power of all these procedures applied to 26 cases (or 44, including the student–student encounters) may give considerably more weight to conclusions derived from those cases than to conclusions derived from traditional ethnography done by a lone ethnographer, armed only with lead pencil, toothbrush, and hunting knife.

Increasing the Size of the Sample

It might be wiser to cumulate a larger sample of cases. This could be done quite readily. We have developed three measures of interactional quality that associate closely with the outcomes of gatekeeping, with ethnicity, and with co-membership. These measures are derived from the asymmetry sections code (whole uncomfortable moments), the asymmetry segments code (parts of an uncomfortable moment ranked according to degree of asymmetry), and the rhythmic asymmetry code (subparts ranked according to degree of rhythmic distortion).

Rhythmic asymmetry coding is the most precise procedure we have developed, but it is extremely time consuming, hence impractical for use on a larger sample. The Asymmetry segments code is more time consuming than the Asymmetry sections code but gives a more precise measure of interactional quality. These two codes could be used together. We could identify the most uncomfortable moment in the encounter, using the asymmetry sections code and then use the asymmetry segments code to give us a measure of relative uncomfortableness and behavioral asymmetry across interviews.

An alternative would be to teach asymmetry sections coders to attend to some of the behavioral cues retrieved by the asymmetry segments code. Then, in one coding operation, they could identify the most uncomfortable moment and rank its uncomfortableness in a way that would be comparable across interviews. Coder training could be done using the videotapes we already have made. The validity of the coders' work on new videotapes could be checked by periodic "segments" analysis of the "sections" they were coding.

Two other coders could judge emotional tone and the amount of special help given to each student. A brief questionnaire to be filled out by the counselor and the student after the interview could be prepared and field tested during this phase of research. Our experience with viewing session comments by encounter participants suggests that a questionnaire of this kind could produce valid data. If we were to demonstrate a close relationship, in perhaps 100 cases, between the questionnaire and our coded data on interactional quality and special help, then the questionnaire could be used alone on a much larger sample.

Media technology now makes it relatively simple to collect videotapes of interviews. A video camera with a self-activating microphone can be pinned to the wall of an interviewer's office. It could be equipped with a device to randomize the times it turns itself on when speech begins. There could also be an override switch the interviewer could press if a student did not want his interview taped. All students would be asked for consent, but the camera would be on only for some of the interviews for which the consent was given. Neither the interviewer nor the student would know when the camera was on. They would know that it was off only when the override switch was engaged. By this means, many cases could be collected in various sites simultaneously.

In the original study, we ended up focusing primarily on two junior college sites, one public and one private, in a single city. There are other site variables. One might want to collect cases from public and paraochial high schools. Some videotapes might be collected in different cities. Questionnaires could be distributed in a variety of cities.

The question is: "Where does one stop?" Its answer lies only partly in methodological considerations, which are relatively simple. A sample of 100 videotapes, randomly collected in a variety of setings, together with one or two hundred brief questionnaires could demonstrate a clear relationship between the ethnicity and communication style of the "gatekept" and the gatekeeper's treatment.

Policy Implications

The stopping point is also determined by policy considerations. Do policymakers want certainty from policy research? If so, then no amount of empirical evidence is sufficient. On the other hand, do policymakers want to be told what they want to hear?

The controversy over the *Equality of Educational Opportunity Survey* (EEOS) conducted by James Coleman and associates (1966) is a case in point. Here, a study done hastily, with a nationwide sample of 600,000 students, is character-ized by different researchers as statistically ambiguous, methodologically wrong-headed, or valid and embarrassing in its conclusions. Some national and local policymakers have welcomed its conclusions and acted on them; others have ignored them; others have hired consultants to declare the results invalid. Here, a large-scale sample survey, with a complex multivariate statistical design, seems to function for researchers and policymakers alike as a TAT picture or Rorschach ink blot.

I think that the kind of research reported here, because of the richness of its data and because of the high redundancy in the systemic organization of the phenomena studied, produces results that are less problematic than survey research like EEOS and more amenable to illustration by simple statistical procedures. But others may disagree. It seems that the culture of academia requires professors to go to great lengths to refute one another. This is called scholarly criticism. One of my teachers, Raoul Naroll, spoke to this issue whimsically in identifying as a methodological problem in social science the "problem of the lurking variable." It could be formulated as Naroll's law, although he did not state it in quite this way: "The training and temperament of any social scientist is such that he will invariably overlook a variable that confounds his data. This lurking variable will always be identified by some other researcher."[16]

Because of the problem of the "lurking variable," it seems to me that social scientific research does not produce certain answers even in "basic" studies, much less in applied "policy" studies. Anthropologists who study complex polyethnic societies are only beginning to be called upon to do policy research. I think that the best of what they have to offer is informed intuitions about the workings of sociocultural units (however defined) considered as wholes. Hope-fully, these intuitions can be backed up by some of the kinds of procedures for summarization and verification used in other branches of social science. Among these procedures are various means of quantification.[17] What the intuitions of anthropologists in our own society can do is to provide policymakers with a new framework within which to consider a social "problem"; a framework that makes visible aspects of the problem that may have gone unnoticed because they were so obvious. Viewing the problem in a new or broader context can, perhaps, suggest a new or wider range of "solutions" or may suggest that a particular issue is not amenable to "solution" in Western melioristic terms.

[16] Gluckman discusses some of the reasons for this in *Closed systems and open minds: The limits of naivety in social anthropology* (1964).
[17] This is a simplified statement of what Pelto (1970) advocates in his treatise on method and what John Whiting has advocated throughout his career by calling on anthropologists to frame jeopardizable hypotheses.

In my own study of gatekeepers I have tried to provide such a new framework. I conclude that it is meaningless to think of gatekeeping encounters as "sealed off" from the "leakage" of particularistic attributes of persons, such as cultural communication style and co-membership. This runs counter to a major theme of American ideology—that meritocratic sorting procedures for assigning social rank are objective. The obvious policy implication is that the personnel and the organizational context and structure of the institution of gatekeeping should be fundamentally changed to take into account ethnic, racial, social class, and other kinds of particularistic attributes of the statuses of persons meeting face to face.

ACKNOWLEDGMENTS

The author is indebted to Carolyn Leonard—Dolan and Jeffrey Shultz, collaborators in the initial and final stages of research, respectively. Shultz designed the scales for affect and special help and conducted the statistical analysis of data reported here.

REFERENCES

Barth, Fredrik
　1969　*Ethnic groups and boundaries: The social organization of culture difference.* Boston: Little, Brown.
Blom, Janpetter, and John Gumperz
　1972　Social meaning in linguistic structures. In *Directions in sociolinguistics: The ethnography of communication*, edited by John Gumperz and Dell Hymes. New York: Holt.
Byers, Paul
　1972　*From biological rhythm to cultural pattern: A study of minimal units.* Doctoral dissertation, Columbia University. University Microfilms No. 73-9004, Ann Arbor, Michigan.
Campbell, Donald T., and Julian C. Stanley
　1966　*Experimental and quasi-experimental designs for research.* Chicago: Rand-McNally.
Chapple, Eliot D., and Erich Lindemann
　1941　Clinical implications of measurements of interaction rates in psychiatric patients. *Applied Anthropology* 1:1–10.
Coleman, James S., E. Q. Campbell, C. J. Hobson, J. McPartland, A. M. Mood, F. D. Weinfeld, and R. L. York
　1966　*Equality of educational opportunity.* Washington, D.C.: U.S. Government Printing Office.
Erickson, Frederick, with J. Shultz, C. Leonard-Dolan, D. Pariser, M. Erder, J. Marchese, and C. Jean
　1973　*Inter-ethnic relations in urban institutional settings.* Final Technical Report, Projects MH18230, MH21460, National Institute of Mental Health.
Gluckman, Max
　1964　*Closed systems and open minds: The limits of naivety in social anthropology.* Chicago: Aldine.

Goffman, Erving
  1959   *The presentation of self in everyday life.* Garden City, New Jersey: Anchor.
  1961   *Encounters: Two studies in the sociology of interaction.* Indianpolis: Bobbs-
         Merrill.
Goodenough, Ward
  1965   Rethinking "status" and "role": Toward a general model of the cultural organiza-
         tion of social relationships. In *The relevance of models in anthropology*, edited by
         Michael Banton. London: Tavistock.
  1971   *Culture, language and society.* Addison-Wesley Modular Publications, No. 7.
         Reading, Massachusetts: Addison-Wesley.
Gumperz, John, and Dell Hymes
  1964   The ethnography of communication. *American Anthropologist* **66**, (6): Pt. II.
  1972   *Directions in sociolinguistics: The ethnography of communication.* New York:
         Holt.
Keil, Charles
  1966   *Urban Blues.* Chicago: Univ. of Chicago Press.
Keiser, R. Lincoln
  1969   *Vice lords: Warriors of the streets.* New York: Holt.
Pelto, Pertti
  1970   *Anthropological research: The structure of inquiry.* New York: Harper and Row.
Prost, Jack
  1967   Bipedalism of man and gibbon compared using estimates of joint motion. *Ameri-
         can Journal of Physical Anthropology* **76** (2): 135–148.
Suttles, Gerald
  1968   *The social order of the slum: Ethnicity and territory in the inner city.* Chicago:
         Univ. of Chicago Press.

10

Two Theories of Discrimination*

Marcus Alexis
Northwestern University

INTRODUCTION

Economists are often criticized (and, unfortunately, too often rightly so) for their preoccupation with displays of technical virtuosity and for too little application of their not insignificant talents to the solution of high priority real-world problems. The corollary of this, namely, that economists have little, if anything, to contribute to an understanding and possible solution of this class of problems, is, fortunately, false. Attention to the problems of their day characterizes the writing of such stalwarts of the classical school as Smith, Ricardo, and Malthus (see Robbins 1953). The importance of Marx in economics and social thought is so well known as not to need further discussion.

What, then, is the basis for the criticism of economics? The answer is to be found in the methodology and problems emphasized in neoclassical economics. Maximizing behavior and the roles of measurable economic quantities—prices, wages, profits, and so on—are mainstays of the analysis, but noneconomic

*The work reported in this chapter was supported by the Center for Urban Affairs, Northwestern University and the Urban Institute. Neither the Center for Urban Affairs, Northwestern University, nor the Urban Institute is responsible for the views expressed here.

variables are not absent. Indeed, underlying the apparent scientific objectivity of much neoclassical writings are models of man and society which, though often unspecified, enter into the economic models nonetheless.[1]

Alfred Marshall, as representative as anyone of the neoclassical tradition, is a case in point. For half a century, students in the English speaking world were introduced to economics through his *Principles of Economics*, which went through eight editions. Marshall's *Principles* is the precursor of modern economic texts; it is important for both its methodological contributions and for its interpretation of economic behavior. The latter is often passed over in critiques of the *Principles*. But there can be no doubt about the influence of Marshall's own philosophical bent and perceptions of the environment on his interpretation of economic behavior.

> Experience seems to show that the more ignorant and phlegmatic of races and of individuals especially if they live in a southern clime will stay at their work a shorter time and will exert themselves less while if the rate of pay rises so as to give them their accustomed enjoyments in return for less work than before. But those whose mental horizon is wider and who have more firmness and elasticity of character will work harder and longer the higher the rate of pay which is open to them; unless indeed they prefer to divert their activities to higher aims than for material gain. [Marshall 1890: 528–529]

It is said that Marshall had India in mind when this passage was written (Parson 1931). His attitude is similar to current attitudes of Latins (Italians, Spaniards, and Latin Americans) and of black Americans. In any case, we have here an early example of a perception of human behavior (influenced by environment) that affects economic behavior.

Economic anthropologists are divided on the question of whether economic analysis, as currently practiced, can be meaningfully applied to the study of traditional societies. There appears to be agreement on the usefulness of such analysis in studies of peasant societies with production for exchange and market structures (Dalton 1969). The substantivists and formalists disagree on whether or not economic concepts appropriate to market societies can be applied to traditional (nonmarket) ones. It would be too ambitious a goal to seek to resolve this conflict. But even if it is true that such concepts as "efficiency" and "maximization" are inappropriate to studying traditional societies, it does not follow that economic concepts and techniques are inappropriate to studying all nonmarket aspects of behavior.

Without suggesting or implying that the approach can be transfered to traditional societies, this chapter demonstrates that nonmarketable quantities can be integrated into an economic theory of market behavior.

[1] For a related discussion of unspectified assumptions in the economic development literature, see Seers (1967).

Two approaches to the analysis of discriminatory behavior are presented. The first is in the neoclassical tradition. The second views market behavior as part of a larger scheme or purpose.[2] In both, nonmarket considerations are a central part of the theory.[3]

It should be stated at the outset that the subject of this chapter is labor market discrimination against blacks. In a sense, this is a narrow concern because there are other groups who are discriminated against, namely, women and youths. Discrimination is also present in the markets for residential housing and educational opportunities, to name but two. The models discussed in analyzing employment discrimination against blacks should, however, be useful tools for investigation of other forms of discrimination. This emphasis is not justified when one considers the fact that the numbers of women and youths are greater than the number of blacks and, furthermore, that black women might require an analysis different from what is presented here. In response, all that one can say is that, at this time, the theory is most developed for black workers without regard to sex (but black males probably fit the models best). Surely, this accident of historical development will not continue to obscure the unique aspects that apply in the cases of women in general, black women, and youths (black and white).

Although the theory is not well developed, some comments on the differential position of women and youths should be made at this time. Discrimination against blacks differs from some other forms of discrimination (against women, for example) in that blacks occupy a different social position and the potential power of blacks, in a numerical sense, is less than that of women. Attempts to treat discrimination against women as a mere variant of discrimination against blacks are ill-focused. To begin with, women are in a political position, should they choose to exercise their franchise, to end discrimination against them through the electoral process. Being a political as well as an economic minority, blacks do not have this option. Furthermore, even in economic terms, some women are potential beneficiaries of discrimination against other women. To the extent that entry restrictions based on sex are effective, some men's incomes are larger than they would otherwise be. In the case of married women, this gain in their husband's income might well be greater than the loss in their own income due to sex discrimination. If it is joint income that is important, these couples gain.[4] Discrimination against women differs from race discrimination in another important way. Discrimination against blacks extends to opportunities to reside

---

[2] Becker (1957) and Arrow (1972) are in the neoclassical tradition; the second view is Alexis (1973).

[3] Interestingly, in the Marxian formulation, economic considerations, that is, capitalist accumulation, dominates the analysis, and discrimination against certain segments of labor is seen as a means to an economic end. For a discussion in this tradition, see Harris (1971).

[4] For an innovative discussion, see Becker (1973).

in particular neighborhoods, to attend certain schools, and to enjoy freedom of movement and association. Women are not excluded from residential areas, and public schools certainly admit both male and female children without discrimination. Exclusions that affect women are to be found in "male only" activities, which center around private clubs, men's bars, and the like. These are almost certain to exclude blacks too.

Discrimination against youths is different from race discrimination in that (*1*) it is temporary and (*2*) the exclusions are limited; that is, some of the "surplus" received by discriminating adults is shared with the youngsters who are discriminated against.

DEFINITIONS

It is common in everyday usage to treat "discrimination" and "segregation" as if they were synonymous. In a general way, the two words can be differentiated by noting that "discrimination" refers to differential treatment of those in like situations. For example, discrimination between two workers of equal productivity exists if one is treated as if he were more productive than the other. This could result in the worker(s) being discriminated against receiving lower wages, having higher unemployment rates, or both. In the case of "segregation," on the other hand, one refers to the separation of individuals or groups. If workers who perform the same task are separated from one another on some basis, such as race, then the work force is segregated.

More formal definitions of discrimination and segregation are:

> If an individual has a 'taste for discrimination' he must act as if he were willing to pay something, either directly or in the form of a reduced income to be associated with some persons instead of others. When actual discrimination occurs, he must in fact, either pay or forfeit income for this privilege. This simple way of looking at the matter gets at the essence of prejudice and discrimination. [Becker 1957: 4]

Segregation is defined as follows:

> In general, if various members of different factors (such as laborers and foremen) are combined into one group by a criterion such as color or religion, one can say that market segregation of this group exists if its members are employed with each other to a significantly greater extent than would result from a random distribution of members of such a factor. [Becker 1957: 49]

Both definitions contain subtleties. First, the notion that the discriminator must pay something for discriminating comes down to meaning that, by discriminating, the discriminator forfeits an opportunity to make his income or profit larger than it would if he did not discriminate. If presented with two equally productive employee candidates, one of whom is black and the other white, an employer who discriminates against blacks will hire the white candidate. If the black candidate is willing to work for something less than the white candidate and the employer still hires the white, he will forfeit the additional income (profit) he could have earned by employing the less expensive worker. We shall see in the formal theory of employer discrimination that, under specified conditions, white employers will choose to hire the more expensive white employee. Clearly, such employers forfeit profits by so doing. Economic theory is not helpful in establishing a reason for such a decision. One of the purposes of this chapter is to extend the scope of considerations beyond the purely economic ones.

The definition of segregation refers to being "employed with each other to a significantly greater extent than would result from a random distribution. . . ." According to this, separation of groups need not be complete for segregation to exist. All that is required is that the "mixture" of groups of employees (factors of production, or, if you will, inputs into the production process) be other than would occur if random mixing were allowed to take place. This can be tested by statistical methods. Therefore, the definition is operational as it stands.

We can have discrimination without segregation and the reverse. If equally productive workers receive the same wages but are separated into groups based on color, we have segregation without discrimination. If, on the other hand, there is no separation of workers by color but one group receives less than the other (and is equally productive), there is discrimination without segregation. Furthermore, both discrimination and segregation can be achieved in not-so-obvious ways. One way to both discriminate and segregate is to regularly assign one group to a lower job classification even though it does the same work. A plumber's helper might be required to do all that a journeyman plumber does (and do it quite as well) but receive lower wages. If in addition, racial groups are separated into one or the other classification, with a distribution that cannot be explained by change, then we have both discrimination and segregation.

In cases such as this, it is possible for a discriminating employer to enhance his income (profits) rather than have them lowered. It is true that such an employer can earn even larger profits by hiring all blacks and having them perform all the plumbers' tasks. If this were done, it would not matter then whether they are called plumbers' helpers. In a free market, such choices are open to employers. In constrained markets. such as when there are union contracts or when white workers, by collective action, can prevent employers from taking such actions, both the incomes of black workers and of white employers are reduced.

EMPLOYER DISCRIMINATION: A TRADITIONAL VIEW

What might be called the "traditional" theory of discrimination in labor markets argues that there are two types of workers who are indistinguishable in all respects save one; this can be color, sex, religion or anything else. This difference does not affect their production of marketable output, but it does affect the production of nonmarketable output. That is, the two groups are perfect substitutes in the production of market goods, but they also produce subjectively valued utilities (disutilities).

If the value of the nonmarket goods is positive to the employer, members of such a group are said to be preferred; if it is negative, they are nonpreferred; and if it is zero, they might be called neutral. The value to an employer of a particular employee is equal to the sum of the marketable plus nonmarketable outputs. Accordingly, workers with negative nonmarketable outputs receive lower wages than workers with nonnegative nonmarketable outputs. The wage differential is a measure of the extent of discrimination between groups of otherwise identical workers.

Economists tend to shy away from questions about the formation of preferences; the discipline is more adept at deriving consequences of different preference structures. Accordingly, economic literature is mostly silent on the question of why the nonmarketable output of some workers is valued positively and of others negatively. Instead, economists say that agents act "as if" they preferred some outcomes (situations, goods, employees, etc.) to others.

To understand wage differentials based on discrimination, it is useful to think in terms of costs as distinguished from prices. The wage price paid to workers is only part of the cost of employment. There are also nonpecuniary costs. If an employer finds the presence of some workers distasteful, he has an aversion to such workers; or their presence is a disutility to him; then their nonmarketable output is negative and imposes a nonpecuniary cost on him. The net cost of employing such a nonpreferred worker is

$$W_{np} (1+d) = W_p \tag{1}$$

where W_{np} is the money wage of the nonpreferred worker, d is a nonpecuniary cost, and W_p is the money wage of the preferred worker. Accordingly,

$$d = \frac{W_p - W_{np}}{W_{np}}$$

which is the discrimination coefficient—relative wage differential.

This formulation has been criticized on the groups that it (*1*) merely formalizes the observed phenomenon, (*2*) ignores the structure (i.e., environment) that generates such preferences, and (*3*) more importantly, is silent on the question of the dynamic social consequences of such wage discrimination. What, for example, is the impact on incentives to invest in education and accumulate capital and on other social relationships in which economic resources are important? If, for example, it is true that housing discrimination is merely income discrimination in the sense that the only barrier to blacks living in certain neighborhoods is their ability to pay, then wage discrimination affects housing markets, and we know that housing arrangements are responsible for de facto school segregation. Thus, wage discrimination does affect other aspects of the lives of blacks and other "nonpreferred" persons.

INTERPERSONAL COMPARISONS OF UTILITY

Rules for making interpersonal comparisons of utilities cannot in general be derived from economic considerations alone, but economic reasoning is useful in understanding and interpreting some situations in which the well-being of two or more persons is involved. It has been argued that, if "preferences of participants" is defined as an "economic" concept, long-run outcomes, which are the product of processes of negotiation, propaganda self-sacrifice, arbitration, spiteful self-destruction, and war and which are generated by preferences of the participants, are economic outcomes. Furthermore, when long-run equilibrium is reached, weights for making interpersonal comparisons are implied by the underlying "economic" factors, namely, resources, technology, and the like (Valvanis 1958).

For direct interpersonal comparisons, following Valvanis, we require that: (1) each man's (woman's) utility function be at least an ordered metric; (2) one party manifests his utility to another and that manifestation increases with utility; (3) the other party correctly perceive the manifestation and that perception increase with manifestation. Let U_j be the satisfaction (utility) of an event to the jth person. Define a function M_{ij} (U_j) as the manifestation of the satisfaction to another person—the ith person. Also define P_{ij} (M_{ij}) as the perception by the ith person of the jth's satisfaction level. By requirements (2) and (3) just listed each person's utility is directly comparable to another person's utility. Furthermore, if one person's utility (satisfaction) depends on another's, we have, by the requirements stated earlier, a means of determining the other person's utility. All we need now is a way of connecting the two utilities. This is accomplished via V the vicariousness function, which relates U_j (U_i)—the utility of person $j(i)$ to $i(j)$. Symbolically, the direct utility comparisons are expressed thus:

$$U_i = V_i (U_j)$$
$$U_j = V_j (U_i). \tag{3}$$

In Figure 10.1, note that a high value for U_j is associated with a low value for U_i and vice versa. This illustrates the operation of envy—malice. To see how the entire process operates, consider Figures 10.2–10.4. In Figure 10.2, we show the relationship between an event, such as income during a period, and the utility of that income to person j. The way in which j manifests that utility is shown in Figure 10.3. Figure 10.4 shows the perception of that utility (satisfaction) manifestation.

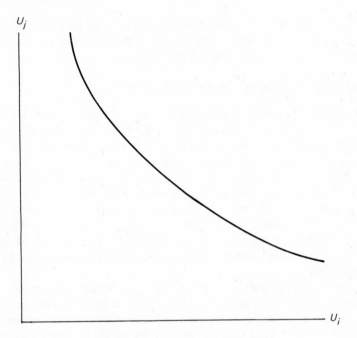

Figure 10.1 Correspondence of U_i and U_j.

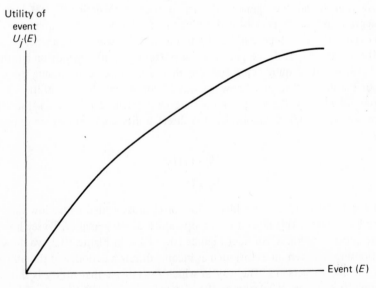

Figure 10.2 Relationship between an event (E) and the utility of the event $U(E)$ to the jth person.

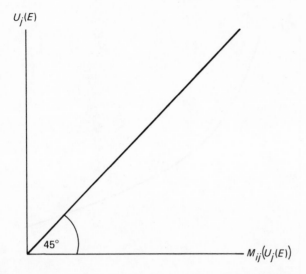

Figure 10.3 Relationship between utility (U_j) and manifestation $M_{ij}(U_j)$.

It should be noted that, in Figures 10.3 and 10.4, the relationship portrayed is a 45 degree line from the origin. This means that the coordinates of the vertical and horizontal axes are the same. In other words, the utility of the event is manifested from j to i exactly as j feels about it (Figure 10.3). From Figure 10.4, we see that i perceives the manifestation from j in the same units that j transmits

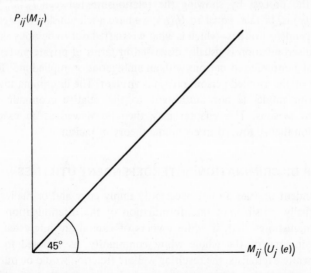

Figure 10.4 Relationship between manifestation (M_{ij}) and perception (P_{ij}).

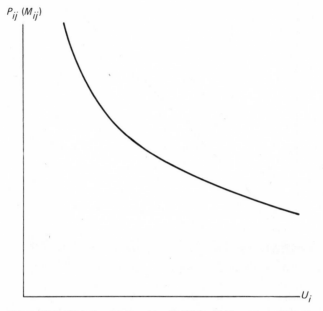

Figure 10.5 Relationship between $P_{ij}(M_{ij})$ and U_j: envy–malice case.

it. Putting Figures 10.3 and 10.4 together, it is clear that the ith person now knows exactly what utility the jth person receives from the event. Figure 10.5 completes the process by showing the relationship between $P_{ij}(M_{ij})$ and U_i. Since $P_{ij}(,M_{ij})$ is, in fact, equal to $U_j(E)$, we have a relationship between U_j and U_i—interdependent utilities—which is what we started out to demonstrate.

Whereas discrimination is usually discussed in terms of private preferences for avoidance of nonpreferred persons with an ambiguous or implied indifference to the welfare of the avoided person, racism is virulent. The discriminating decision maker in our model is not indifferent to the relative economic status of nonpreferred persons. This chapter may then be viewed as an extension of discrimination theory toward an economic theory of racism.

EMPLOYER DISCRIMINATION: INTERDEPENDENT UTILITIES

Interdependent utilities do not necessarily imply envy and/or malice; benevolence is equally possible. In one formulation of the discrimination problem, Krueger demonstrates that, if white owners of capital are interested in maximizing the income of the whole white community, as opposed to only the income of white capitalists, the resulting welfare function would be quite similar to Becker's, except that discrimination would be directed at maximizing white real income rather than avoiding the distastefulness of working with black workers (Krueger 1963). Krueger's inference that wage rates of black workers would be less than wages of perfect substitute whites is incorrect, but as we shall see, the magnitudes could differ from those in the Becker–Arrow model.

Even granted that white capital owners do have an aversion to blacks in terms of their being present, it does not follow that discriminatory wages are a consequence. Much capital is employed where the owner(s) are not present; take the case of large publicly owned corporations. In such instances, the aversion effect is zero, but the wage differential ($W_p - W_{np}$) is positive. Two ways in which this can happen are that managers have an aversion to black workers and/or white workers have such an aversion. In either case, the observed wage differential could exist. A third possibility is that white managers believe that white capital owners prefer not to hire black workers in their firms. Even here, however, the motivation is unclear; it is not aversion. But wage discrimination is consistent with envy–malice regarding black workers by white owners of capital. This subtle distinction is the economic essence of the difference between discrimination and racism.

We shall be arguing that white capitalists and white workers consider the effects of their actions on the relative well-being of black workers and will see that envy or malice, in the absence of aversion, is sufficient to produce depressed black wages.

DISCRIMINATION MODELS

Detailed discussion of the assumptions in the models and derivations of results are not discussed here.[5]

From economic theory, we know that profit-maximizing employers will pay a worker (in real terms) an amount equal to his (her) incremental (marginal) contribution to putput. The white wage rate (w_w) will equal the incremental output of labor (its marginal product–f'), whereas the wage rate of blacks (w_b) will be less than f' and, therefore, less than the white wage rate.

"Exploitation" of blacks takes place in the sense that the equilibrium wage rate is less than the value of product produced (at the margin). Stated another way, the *money* value of output (at the margin) is greater than the money cost of black labor input, whereas nondiscriminatory equilibrium would require equality of the two. Again, from the white employer's standpoint, black labor produces both a marketable output (its marginal physical product) and a nonmarketable output. The latter (the negative value of the presence of blacks in the work force) has to be subtracted from the value of the physical output. Thus, blacks always receive less than the value of their marketable physical out-

---

[5] The interested reader is referred to Becker (1957) and Alexis (1974).

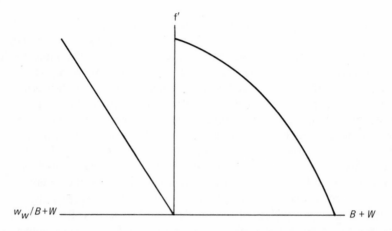

Figure 10.6 Relationship between incremental (marginal) product and white wage rate.

put because white employers subtract from it the value of their negative) non-marketable output.

The relationship between incremental product, as the number of black and white workers $(B+W)$ is increased, and the white rate is shown in Figure 10.6. The same relationship, but with black wage rate substituted for the white wage rate, is shown in Figure 10.7. The 45 degree line in the left quadrant of Figure 10.6 indicates that white workers receive their marginal product. From Figure 10.7, it is clear that black workers receive less than their marginal product. If the difference between black wages and their marginal product is constant, then the relationship between black and white wages is as is shown in Figure 10.8. If, however, the discrimination coefficient increases as either the number of black workers or the percentage of blacks in the labor force increases, then the relationship between black wages and marginal product is as is shown in Figure 10.9. These results are obtainable from either the traditional or the interdependent utilities approach. The wage differential with the envy–malice hypothesis will always be at least as great as with the traditional view.

The discrimination coefficient is then the trade-off between money profit and the presence of an additional black (or the profits the employer is willing to forego if he can reduce his black employment by one) which leaves the employer indifferent to the hiring (firing) of an additional black worker. The theory is silent on *why* white employers have this "taste for discrimination." It is concerned solely with the effects. In that respect, it is not a complete theory of discrimination but rather a theory of the market mechanisms through which it acts and the consequences of that action.[6]

---

[6] An attempt to provide such a rationale is found in Alexis (1973).

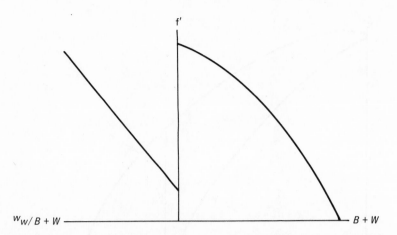

Figure 10.7 Relationship between incremental (marginal) product and black wage rate.

Who benefits (i.e., gains in pecuniary terms) from discrimination against black workers? How is the discount from black wages divided between white employers and employees? The answers to these questions depend on (*1*) the difference in profits of discriminating and nondiscriminating firms, (*2*) the distribution of any difference in profits. Differences in profits are divided between white employees and employers (also white). Profits of discriminating firms are

$$\pi = f(B{+}W) - f'(B{+}W)(B{+}W) + d_b B + d_w W, \qquad (4)$$

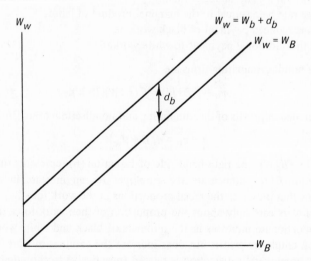

Figure 10.8 Black and white wage differential independent of black proportion in the work force.

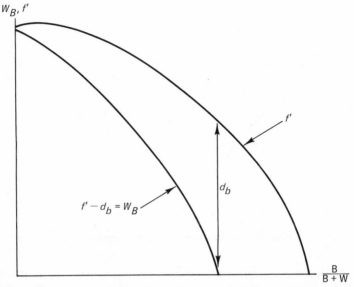

Figure 10.9 Black and white wage differentials related to black proportion in the work force.

where

π = profits of the firm
$f(B+W)$ = output
$f'(B+W)(B+W)$ = the nondiscriminatory payments to black and white workers, the wage rate being equal to the marginal product of labor,
$d_b B$ = the reduced payment of black workers
$d_w W$ = the additional payment to white workers.

Profits of nondiscriminating firms are

$$\pi_0 = f(B+W) - f'(B+W)(B+W). \tag{5}$$

The difference in profits of discriminating and nondiscriminating firms is

$$\pi - \pi_0 = d_b B + d_w W. \tag{6}$$

Divided by $(B+W)$, the right-hand side of Equation (6) represents the additional profit required to compensate the employer for an increase in the scale of operations that preserves the racial proportions in the work force.

If employers care only about the proportion of their work force that is black, then proportionate increases in the numbers of black and white workers has no impact on employer profits but does increase the earnings of white workers. If, however, employers' satisfaction is related (negatively) to the number of black employees and this is little offset by the increase in white workers, then white employers (and possibly white workers too) gain. It is an open question empirically whether employers' satisfactions are a function of the proportion of blacks in the work force or of the absolute number fo blacks.

Even if one assumes that it is the proportion of blacks in the work force that is governing here, it does not follow that such a utility function has no effect on black employment opportunities. Rather, it is clear that increasing proportions of black employees will require larger compensations to white employers. If blacks have higher unemployment rates than whites, it means that black workers will have to accept more depressed wage rates. This need not be a consequence if market intervention is permitted.

The question of gains from discrimination is sufficiently important to be looked at more closely. Our results are based on the assumption that all capital is owned by whites and that blacks own only one productive resource, labor. We shall relax that assumption and substitute the following: *There are two sectors, a black (B) and a white (W); the black sector has a smaller capital–labor ratio than the white sector. Furthermore, there is the possibility of trade of labor and capital between the two sectors.*

In this revised model, a "taste for discrimiantion" is interpreted as meaning: "Whites prefer to use their capital with white labor and can be induced to export capital only at a higher return than they can get at home." By "home," we mean the white sector. It can be shown that, under plausible conditions, white owners do earn a premium (in money terms) on the capital they export to the black sector.

In the absence of discrimination, white owners of capital (capitalists) would export capital (or import labor) to the point where the capital–labor ratios (and hence the marginal products of capital and labor) are equal. With discrimination, white capitalists prefer to use their capital with white labor and can be induced to export capital only by receiving a higher price (return) from the black sector (Krueger 1963).

EMPLOYEE DISCRIMINATION

If it is reasonable to assume that white employers have an "aversion" to black employees, is it not equally reasonable to assume that white worker, who work side by side with black workers have an aversion at least equally as large? Furthermore, if one assumes that black and white workers are not only economic competitors but also competitors in the political (power) and social (status) sense, attempts by white workers to lower the demand for black workers are all the more to be expected.[7] In both the traditional and envy–malice cases, discrimination by complementary white labor leads to black wages being less than white wages.

[7] These subjects are discussed in Becker (1957) and Alexis (1973, 1974).

So far, we have assumed that discriminatory wage differentials arise because of the aversion of either employers or complementary inputs. What can be said about discrimination by perfect substitutes? The traditional view is that it is difficult to demonstrate that employee discrimination can lead to market discrimination, although it might quite easily lead to segregation. For example, if white workers demand a higher wage when they work with black workers, then it will pay for (nondiscriminating) employers to hire all blacks or all whites. Under some conditions, discriminating employers might have an integrated work force; all that is required is that the (discriminating) employer have a preference for hiring whites to offset the presence of disliked blacks.

Suppose that white workers have the following indifference map between white wages (w_w) and the proportion of whites in the labor force (W/L) (Figure 10.10), then, for a given level of satisfaction (I,II,III, *etc.*), w_w is a decreasing function of the proportion of the labor force that is white.

The cost to any firm of hiring B (black) and W (white) workers is

$$C(B,W) = w_b B + w_w (W/L) \qquad (7)$$

where $L = B + W$. For an all white labor force, the cost is $C(O,W) = w_w (1) L$, and, for an all black labor force, the cost is $C(B,O) = w_b L$. Since $w_w (1) < w_w (W/L)$ for $W < L$, it follows that an all white labor force is less costly than an integrated one.

If blacks and whites are perfect substitutes, as we have been assuming, and if employers do not discriminate, then $w_b = w_w$, and all firms will be segregated, but there will not be wage discrimination. Therefore, employee segregation, but

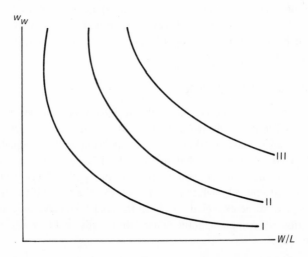

Figure 10.10 White wage rate as a function of the proportion of whites in the work force.

not discrimination, is the consequence of employee discrimination that is expressed in terms of a decreasing wage rate as a function of white employees. Currently accepted theory argues, therefore, that employee discrimination does not produce wage discrimination. However, if white employees use nonmarket devices, such as the ballot box, they can force employers to discriminate (in a wage sense) against black workers.

How can this be done? Suppose that white workers organize and successfully enact legislation that requires government licensing or certification in terms favorable to whites but unfavorable to blacks, such as culturally biased tests or completion of courses given only in segregated white schools. Then, blacks, who are, in reality, perfect substitutes, will find themselves "unqualified" for certain jobs. They might have to work in a lower job category and be paid less. Union organization can produce the same effect. In fact, a credible threat by white workers properly signaled and interpreted is sufficient to translate discriminatory tastes of white workers into wage discrimination. It is not always easy to discern discrimination in this form because workers in the same job category might receive the same wages or persons doing the same job might receive the same wages. A well-designed licensing or certification scheme would reserve the higher wage jobs for the political majority. The traditional view, by focusing on discrimination through ordinary market channels, misses the variety of opportunities for a white majority to induce market discrimination by means of nonmarket devices.[8]

CONCLUSIONS

An attempt to circumvent the conceptual problems associated with the traditional view of employer and complementary factor discrimination based on the argument that whites seek to avoid association with blacks raised questions about the reasonableness of the "aversion principle."

No satisfactory answer to the question of why absentee owners should care about the skin color of their workers that was consistent with the aversion principle was found. The possibility that another measurable economic quantity not so dependent on physical association and that envy—malice considerations normally beyond the scope of economic analysis might be a useful vehicle to study discrimination suggested that a model involving interpersonal comparisons of some sort should be investigated. In our formal model, we focus on the proportion of the wage bill going to blacks and whites.

The choice of relative wages going to white labor is not arbitrary. Ceteris paribus, white capitalists can reasonably be expected to prefer giving income to

---

[8] For a discussion of how the political mechanism can be put to the economic advantage of political majorities, see Demsetz (1965).

"their own kind" and might even be willing to sacrifice some profit to improve the relative income position of laboring whites. There are several reasons why white employers might find this sensible. First, economic resources are of importance not only in traditional economic activity, such as exchange, but also as surrogates for standing in the social order and in power relationships. What common benefit there is in being white is likely enhanced by some intraracial "benevolence."

While variables other than the relative income of white workers could have been investigated, our approach has the advantage of being a natural extension of the aversion model by dealing jointly with wages and the numbers employed in absolute and relative terms. These first results suggest that further research of this type is likely to be productive and out of it will hopefully grow sufficient knowledge about discrimination as a phenomenon to end or at least greatly reduce it.

Neoclassical, partial static, full employment equilibrium analysis models of racial discrimination in labor markets are based on two important limiting assumptions: (*1*) Capital markets are perfect, and (*2*) wage rates are perfectly flexible. Such analysis of behavior at the margins and the derivation of partial static equilibrium conditions in the context of a two sector, single commodity model are useful as a first step. Such a context is not, however, productive in providing answers to policy-related questions, the essence of which involves dealing with unemployment, wage rigidities, and imperfections in capital markets. To do justice to the study of such phenomena, we require a general equilibrium model with employee and employer search. A model of such richness presents a great many analytical difficulties but is certainly a direction that policy-oriented research will have to pursue.

REFERENCES

M. Alexis
  1973   A theory of labor market discrimination with interdependent utilities.*American Economic Review* 73 (May): 256–302.
  1974   The political economy of labor market discrimination: Synthesis and exploration. In *Patterns of racial discrimination*. edited by Ann R. Horowitz and George von Furstenberg. Vol. II. Lexington, Massachusetts: Lexington Books.
K. J. Arrow
  1971   Some models of racial discrimination in the labor force. Santa Monica, California: Rand. RM6253-RC.
  1972   Some mathematical models of race in the labor market. In *Racial discrimination in economic life*, edited by A. H. Pascal. Lexington, Massachusetts: Lexington Books.
G. S. Becker
  1957   *The economics of discrimination*. Chicago: Univ. of Chicago Press.
  1973   A theory of marriage, Part I. *Journal of Political Economy* 81 (July–August): 81–47.

D. Bell
  1971a Bonus schemes and racism. *Review of Black Political Economy* 1 (Summer): 111–120.
  1971b Bonuses quotas and the employment of black workers. *Journal of Human Resources* 6 (Summer): 309–320.
  1971c Occupational discrimination as the source of income differences: Lessons of the 1960's. *American Economic Review* 62 (May): 363–372.

George Dalton
  1969 Theoretical issues in economic anthropology. *Current Anthropology* 10 (February): 63–80.

H. Demsetz
  1965 Minorities in the market place. *North Carolina Law Review* 43 (February): 271–297.

D. J. Harris
  1971 The black ghetto as an internal colony: A theoretical critique and alternative formulation. Mimeo.

A. O. Krueger
  1963 The economics of discrimination. *Journal of Political Economy* 71 (October): 481–486.

A. Marahll
  1890 *Principles of economics.* London: Macmillan.

T. Parsons
  1931 Wants and activities in Alfred Marshall. *Quarterly Journal of Economics* 46 (November): 101–140.

A. H. Pascal
  1972 *Racial discrimination in economic life.* Lexington, Massachusetts: Lexington Books.

L. Robbins
  1953 *The theory of economic policy in English classical economics.* London: Macmillan.

D. Seers
  1967 The limitations of the special case. In *The teaching of economic development,* edited by K. Martin and J. Knapp. London: Gass.

S. Valvanis
  1958 The resolution of conflict when utilities interact. *Journal of Conflict Resolution* 2: 158–159.

F. Welch
  1967 An interpretation of income differences in the rural South. *Journal of Political Economy* 75 (June): 225–240.

11

The Plight of the Ethnic Candidate: A Spatial Analysis

William D. Morris

University of Minnesota

INTRODUCTION

"Atlanta is too young to die!" was the campaign slogan utilized by the white incumbent mayor of the city in his reelection bid in 1973 against a black councilman. Such polarizing slogans are becoming more the rule than the exception in many urban areas. Detroit, Cleveland, Los Angeles (twice) have all been the setting for political campaigns exacerbating racial and ethnic lines. The consequences of these tension-inducing campaigns and elections have caused many observers to wonder whether our urban centers will be able to survive as viable social and political units.[1] Admittedly, some have concluded that the prognosis does not look good.

Until the Civil Rights Movement of the 1960s, the political power monopoly of white Americans had remained unchallenged except for the Reconstruction governments imposed on the South one hundred years before. It was the aim of the radical Republicans of that era to form a biaracial partnership with southern blacks to dominate politics nationally. The northern radicals allied with southern blacks completely controlled the policy institutions of the federal and state

[1] The most penetrating and interesting analysis that we are familiar with is Jacob (1961).

governments. Through disenfranchising southern whites who had been loyal to the Confederacy and simultaneously granting the vote to newly freed slaves, the alliance was able to control every southern state at the end of the war. In some states, such as Tennessee, Virginia, Georgia, and North Carolina, the coalition lost power very quickly. Elsewhere, blacks and radical Republicans dominated the state legislatures of South Carolina and Mississippi and even elected a black United States senator. Mutually advantageous to both groups, this power sharing arrangement was to continue in some areas for nearly a decade.[2]

The presidential election of 1876 finally ended the southern black–northern Republican modus vivendi. Although the Republican candidate, Rutherford B. Hayes, lost in the popular vote count to his Democratic opponent, he became President because disputed electoral votes in three southern states were ceded to him. In order to obtain these votes and quell any general outcry of a "stolen election," Hayes won the support of conservative southern Democrats without whose aid bipartisanship would have been absent in the final decision of Congress on the election results. Without bipartisanship, Hayes's power as president would have been gravely jeopardized from the outset of his term. The southerners, however, were willing to break with the northern wing of their party and deal with the Republican. The offer they made Hayes was simple: Hayes would be traded the electoral votes for an end to Reconstruction. Specifically, all federal troops that enforced the Reconstruction governments' policies were to be removed, and the federal government was to terminate all interference in the politics of the South. In effect, Hayes could have the presidency if the white conservatives could have the South. The bargain was very quickly struck: Hayes became the first president to lose in the popular vote to his opponent but win in the all-important electoral college vote, and very quickly thereafter radical Republican state governments were replaced by conservative white Democratic administrations.[3]

In the South, a period of 80 years of undisputed white political supremacy followed the Hayes bargain. Gerrymandering, discriminatory registration requirements, and even vote fraud were utilized by the white power structure to insure its dominance. In states such as Mississippi, where blacks constituted an absolute majority of the population, the "race issue" overshadowed all other considerations and certainly set the tone of the state's politics throughout much of the

---

[2] Several historical analyses were particularly helpful in the writing of this synopsis: Broderick (1969), Franklin (1961), and Hyman (1967).

[3] The standard reference is Schlesinger (1971). The final vote of the Election Commission that investigated the disputed returns was along party lines; however, the southern Democrats did not protest the final decision very loudly. Had the Commission decided to "go behind" the official returns and investigate irregularities, many observers believed they would have found the Democratic nominee victorious in all three of the states; southern Democratic collusion prevented such an in-depth investigation.

twentieth century (Key 1949). Legislation, the official use of force, and outright terrorism were frequent tools of the white power elite in eliminating the threat of any black voting majority. Not until the passage of the first federal Civil Rights Act of 1957, and the more sweeping legislation of 1964 and 1965, were blacks finally given the opportunity to make their numerical strength felt at the ballot box.[4] But events in the South are really only half the story.

In the twentieth century, as blacks moved northward because of the availability of jobs in the major industrial centers of the North, the functioning of the white Democratic urban machines became impaired. At first, in return for the usual provision of social services and political aid, the machines could count on massive voter support in black areas; the long-standing successful formula for the assimilation of ethnic groups into the existing power structure worked well. Eventually, however, two factors weakened the machines: First, the federal government began to perform many of the social services heretofore provided by the machines, thus eliminating one of their greatest bargaining assets; and, second, the white movement to the suburbs coupled with the massive influx of southern blacks during the 1940s and 1950s fundamentally changed the ethnic composition of the machines' clientele. In short, blacks no longer had any great need for a white political machine in many areas of the country. If serious accommodation with black leaders were not forthcoming, the old-style urban political machine would lose a significant pool of voters. Several machines did adapt; others did not and have disappeared or been replaced.

The impact of these legislative and demographic changes on black political progress can best be appreciated through an examination of the growth in numbers of black elected officeholders. Table 11.1 shows figures for the period 1964–1974. Quite clearly, a large gain was made in both the North and South between 1964 and 1968 with a steady upward trend thereafter. The results are a testimonial to the 1965 Voting Rights Act which, in 10 years, has increased black registration in Dixie alone from less than 1.5 million to 3.5 million (U.S. Bureau of the Census 1974). With their newly protected right to vote, blacks have been able to exercise deserved power much more proportional to their numbers in both state and federal election districts.

Aggregate data alone, however, does not provide any insight into the effects of political pluralism on the American political system. Unfortunately, much of the current research on ethnic politics ceases to go beyond simple vote counting or ungeneralizable discussions about specific campaigns.[5] Political scientists have failed to construct a paradigm from which ethnic politics can be evaluated: the

[4] For the effect of black votes on Lyndon B. Johnson's victory in the border states, see White (1965).

[5] A typical series of extended case studies can be found in Kimball (1972). A fascinating overview of ethnic life, in all of its many aspects, can be found in Novak (1971). The most extensive data analysis is found in Levy and Kramer (1972).

Table 11.1
Black Elective Officeholders[a]

Subject	1964	1968	1970	1972	1974
Total black	103	1125	1860	2625	2991
U. S. Senate					
North	0	1	1	1	1
South	0	0	0	0	0
U. S. House of Representatives					
North	5	9	11	11	12
South	0	0	2	4	4
State legislatures					
North	78	119	128	148	149
South	16	53	70	90	90
Mayors					
North	(NA)	12	34	34	45
South	(NA)	17	47	49	63

[a]Source: U. S. Bureau of the Census (1974: 125). NA: not available.
South: District of Columbia, Delaware, Maryland, Virginia, West Virginia, North Carolina, South Carolina, Georgia, Florida, Kentucky, Tennessee, Alabama, Mississippi, Arkansas, Louisiana, Oklahoma, and Texas.

political and social conditions leading to divisive elections, the logical choices of positions on issues and emphasis by candidates running in polarized multicultural areas, and the exploration of mitigating forces in the environment.

This chapter is an attempt to add a theoretical perspective to the myriad data that many urban politics studies have produced. Through the construction of a rational choice model, which will be explained in detail later, we appraise the developing character of politics in a plural American society. At the same time that we deduce certain results from the framework of the model, we shall also isolate aspects of the political system that particularly lead to interethnic conflict or harmony. Wherever feasible, policy recommendations are made. In short, we hope that the model may serve as a productive, albeit greatly simplified, means to understanding and evaluating current tendencies in ethnic politics in this country.

THEORETICAL FOUNDATIONS

The classic work by Anthony Downs, which first appeared in 1957, laid down the framework utilized here (Downs 1957). Downs essentially has borrowed the economic concept of the "rational man" and applied it to campaigns and elections: hence the emergence of the "rational voter." Through the construction of axioms and postulates about individual political rationality, he systematically deduced several rather interesting results about the behavior of political parties questing for power. Later we relax several of the Downsian assumptions about the political universe and arrive at a very different set of conclusions; however, for now, a survey of the traditional assumptions of Downsian (or spatial) models follows.

The first assumption deals with the voter: Voters are granted the cognitive ability to evaluate candidates' and parties' positions and systematically to employ a decision rule in their determination of which candidate to vote for. For simplicity, it is postulated that there is only one issue dimension upon which calculations take place: for example, an ideological dimension ranging from reactionary to revolutionary or a political issue dimension ranging from laissez faire to planned economy. Although this may prove unrealistic in terms of many elections, it greatly reduces the mathematical intricacy of the model without impairing its explanatory power. Along this issue continuum, the voter is able to place any candidate according to the position he adopts in his campaign; furthermore, all voters place the candidate at this same perceived point on the continuum—in other words, no individual variation among voters is permitted. Consider Figure 11.1:

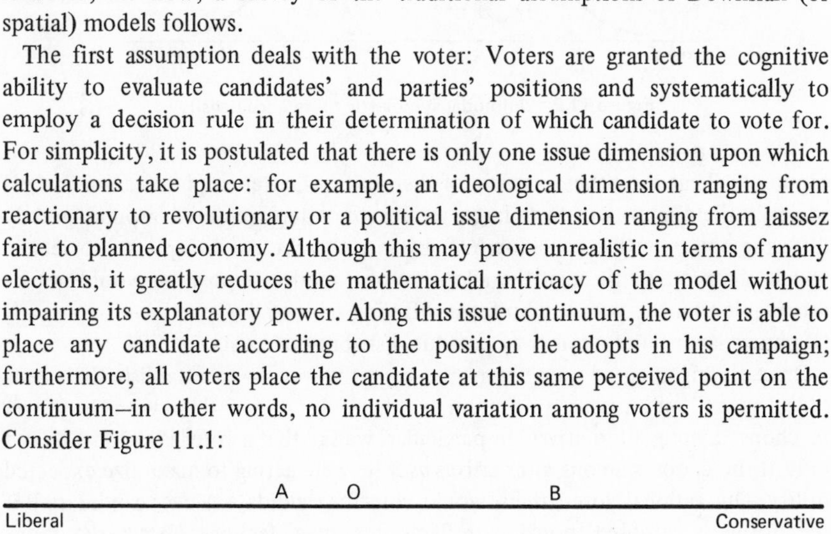

	A	O		B	
Liberal					Conservative

Figure 11.1   Issue continuum for political ideology.

In this hypothetical situation, the salient dimension is one of political ideology. All members of the society have determined that candidate 1 has placed himself at point A, while candidate 2 has placed himself at point B. The third point shown, labeled 0, represents one voter's perception of himself.

It is also assumed, then, that all the members of society can place themselves on the continuum. After each individual has determined his position, an aggregate distribution of voter preferences can be determined. Figures 11.2 and 11.3 display two distributions that have received great attention from political scientists.[6] Figure 11.2 is commonly referred to as a "bell curve" or, more technically, as a unimodel symmetric density. Substantively, the curve depicts a society in which there exists great concensus around a moderate position; most of the members of society in this example are in close proximity to a centrist position.

---

[6] Many of the new freshman-level American government textbooks discuss these patterns. See, for example, Prewitt and Verba (1974).

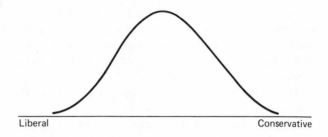

Liberal   Conservative

Figure 11.2   Unimodal symmetric preference density.

Figure 11.3, at the other extreme of distribution patterns, pictures a polarized society; there are two very large groups of voters centered around greatly differing points on the continuum. Substantively, the curve depicts a society in which compromise through the adoption of a moderate position would not be acceptable to many people who favor differing sides of the issue.

Of course, an infinite number of possible distributions exists.

Once having granted our voters the cognitive power to establish their own "ideal point" on an issue continuum, we then must endow them with the power to choose among alternatives. In particular, we say that a voter is rational if, and only if, he chooses among alternatives *as if* he were acting to maximize expected utility. Our rational voter, then, would vote for candidate A over candidate B if the former's adopted position reflects his own feelings about the issue. Obviously, a voter will endorse the candidacy of an individual who adopts his ideal point. More rigorously, in terms of distance along the continuum, the voter will support the candidate whose position is closest to his own. For example, in Figure 11.1, the voter would cast his ballot for candidate A. Having formalized the voter's decision rule, its import to political parties will be surveyed.

Second, let us consider political parties: We assume that political parties (and their candidates) seek to gain office and keep it (Downs 1957: Chap. 2). In order to achieve this objective, we further assume that political parties adopt positions

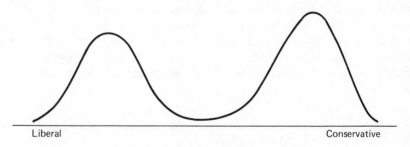

Liberal   Conservative

Figure 11.3   Bimodal preference density.

in order to maximize their vote. Admittedly, this is a great simplification of the goal structure of political parties in the United States. Goldwater and McGovern partisans also had ideological motives in supporting the candidacies of their respective leaders. But, once again, we must appeal to the mathematical simplifications inherent in this postulated structure.

The linkage between the political parties and the voters in the society is through the preference distribution. Once political actors are aware of the policy preferences of the electorate, they are able to adopt positions consistent with maximizing votes. If we enforce the further constraint that one party may only adopt positions to a fixed side of the median relative to the other party, and vice versa, the theoretical underpinnings of the model are complete. This final constraint does not seem too restrictive in terms of the American political experience; certainly, in most places outside of the South, the Republicans are viewed as the more conservative of our two major parties.

Last, we point out one result that Downs deduced from this model: the median convergence result (Downs 1957: Chap. 8). Suppose that the society is arrayed on an issue dimension in a fashion approximating the bell curve shown in Figure 11.2. The rightist party should attempt to move as far left as possible (subject only to the constraint on crossing over to the position of the leftist party): similarly, the leftist party should push as far right as possible. Indeed, should the rightist party cross the median position of the distribution (the point that is the halfway mark) and adopt a position ever so slightly to the left, the party wins a majority of the votes! The rightist party will obtain all the votes to the right of the median and, in addition, accumulate the votes of those individuals on the left whose ideal points are closer to its position. Figure 11.4 illustrates this situation. The leftist party, however, is also aware of these calculations and will attempt to squeeze past the median. Given these tendencies, Downs concludes that both parties will adopt positions at the median point of the preference distribution.

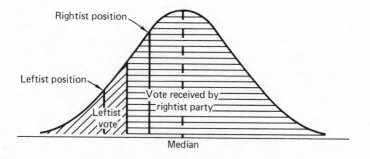

Figure 11.4 Breakdown of the vote received by two candidates.

Reflecting on this result for a moment, we can see its general validity in terms of American politics. Many observers have noted that our parties tend to be "Tweedledee and Tweedledum" with respect to their platforms. In comparison with European political parties, their American counterparts are almost indistinguishable right-of-center groups.[7] Interestingly enough, when one party has diverged from the center in its choice of a presidential candidate while the opposition has remained relatively fixed, dire consequences have followed. William Jennings Bryan, Barry Goldwater, and George McGovern were all massively rejected by the American voter in favor of their centrist opponents. In addition, some observers feel that the winning candidate did shift somewhat across the median toward his opponent, as would be predicted by the model; however, in reality, the candidates did not follow the pure vote maximizing strategy of joining their extremist opponent in the ideological wasteland.[8] Despite the naivete of the model's assumptions, the construct provides a rather penetrating insight into the general political process. With the hope of obtaining further insight into ethnic politics, we utilize the aforementioned considerations in the model that follows.

A MODEL OF ETHNIC POLITICS

As in the Downs model, we assume that there is only one issue dimension that is salient in the voter's decision. Given the nature of ethnic politics, we postulate that it is the Social Issue:

> We begin by recounting some of the events and circumstances of recent years that swept the Social Issue to the forefront of the American political scene. . . . There was, first, the crime wave. . . . Race is certainly a second key element of the Social Issue, and of course, has always been with America. But in the last decade there has been a sharp, yet apparently paradoxical change in the perceptions that white Americans have of black Americans. . . . And there was "kidlash." A fourth element of the Social Issue might be called values. [Scammon and Wattenberg, *The real majority*, 1970: 40–42. © 1970, Coward, McCann & Geoghegan, Inc.]

Consistent with the rhetoric of most ethnically divisive campaigns, we will assume that there are two ethnic groups positioned at different extremes along the continuum. In other words, the distribution pictured in Figure 11.3 will be assumed throughout this analysis with the additional caveat that each half is occupied by a different ethnic group.

---

[7] For a truly excellent and comprehensive overview of European political parties, see Epstein (1967).

[8] Fear of alienating their moderate supporters was a contributing factor in preventing convergence at an extreme position. See Hinich and Ordeshook (1969).

Although generalization is possible, we will restrict our attention to plural electorates composed of two ethnic groups. These groups may be of the same size, or a dominant majority may clearly exist. Since most of the classically divisive campaigns in the United States have centered around two groups, blacks–whites, Mexican-Americans–Whites, Irish–Italian, to name a few, this constraint does not seem overly unrealistic. Furthermore, we are mainly interested in contexts involving two candidates, each representing his own ethnic group; later, we will permit some active opposition within each subculture in order to assess the effects of a nonmonolithic voting bloc on an election.

Scammon and Wattenberg, in *The real majority*, convincingly argue that the American electorate is centrist in nature (Scammon and Wattenberg 1970: Parts 2, 4). Using both public opinion data and aggregate election results in a variety of contexts, they state:

> The strategic idea deals with the manner in which candidates for office try to make hay with both the *substance* of an election and the *structure* of the electorate. In American political life this has almost invariably manifested itself as an attempt to capture the center ground of an electoral battlefield. The reason for this tropism toward the center is simple: That is where victory lies. A classic case in point was demonstrated in New York City in the 1969 mayoralty campaign when "law-and-order" candidate Mario Procaccino proclaimed himself liberal, while "liberal" candidate John V. Lindsay reminded one and all how tough he was on law and order. It can safely be said that the only extreme that is attractive to the large majority of American voters is the extreme center. [Scammon and Wattenberg, *The real majority*, 1970: 21. © 1970, Coward, McCann & Geoghegan, Inc.]

If this is the case, then we would expect the basic preference distribution of voters to resemble a "bell curve." Turning to Downs's conclusion about convergence, we would expect to find most elections to be fairly moderating in tone and contested by almost indistinguishable candidates. Such, however, is not the case!

Elections in urban areas, for example, have become quite acrimonious with candidates proposing very different stands on the issues. The general pattern of setting one ethnic community in the city against another has become more and more the rule rather than the exception. If ethnic blocs are monolithic in their support for "their" candidate and are arrayed at different intervals along the continuum, such immoderating behavior can be predicted. More specifically, if the situation in Figure 11.5 is correct, within a given electorate, mild polarization between groups but seeming homogeneity for the entire population, then formally there is no reason to expect convergence of the candidates.

THEOREM 1: If polarization to a mild degree exists between ethnic groups and these groups vote monolithically for their own candidate, then candidates will not assume the median position of the population. Instead, in

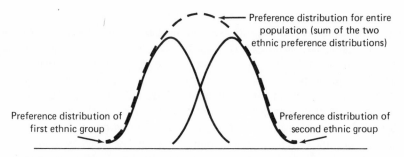

Figure 11.5 Composite preference density for hypothetical bi-ethnic society.

order to avoid challenge from within their ethnic bloc, each candidate will adopt the median preference of his own ethnic group. [The mathematical proof of this theorem as well as all other results can be found in the appendix to this chapter.]

The basic logic of Theorem 1 is obvious. Why should a candidate moderate his own stand and risk a successful challenge from within the ethnic group that provides the basis of his support? The sad fate of Arkansas Congressman Brooks Hays is an excellent example of stakes involved in alienating one's power base. Hays had been instrumental in the Eisenhower actions to avoid violence during the integration of Central High School at Little Rock. Although highly success-ful in his attempt to avoid a bloody confrontation, Hays was branded as a racial moderate—a stand on the Social Issue that was not consistent with most of his white support in the district. Elected as a conservative by white voters, his newly acquired position was not very popular, to say the least. It was so unpopular, in fact, that he was beaten by another white in the 1958 general election.[9] (The Congressman's defeat was highly unusual in that elections in the South were effectively decided in the Democratic primary; Hays had been renominated, but he lost to an arch-segregationist's write-in campaign that fall.) With no chance of gaining the votes of black residents in his district (this was prior to the Voting Rights Acts), Hays's stand on the Little Rock conflict cost him his seat.

The success of ethnic candidates, particularly blacks, has been substantially confined to areas in which their group constitutes at least a large minority. Table 11.2 lists all congressional districts in which blacks constitute at least 20% of the population and gives the race of the incumbent representative as of January, 1974. Obviously, black candidates are most successful when blacks constitute at least 40% of the district's population. Of the 435 congressional districts in this country, only 24 are at least 40% black. Interestingly, the region that

---

[9] The basic problems facing moderate southern congressmen are vividly portrayed in the autobiography of Frank E. Smith (Smith 1967).

Table 11.2
Black Population and Congressional Representation[a]

Percentage of black population in district	North incumbent		South incumbent	
	Black	White	Black	White
100 – 70	3	0	1	0
69 – 60	3	0	0	0
59 – 50	4	2	0	0
49 – 40	0	2	2	7
39 – 30	0	3	0	23
29 – 20	1	8	0	18
Total	11	15	3	48

[a]Compiled from data presented in U. S. Bureau of the Census (1973) and U. S. Congress (1973).

contains the highest percentage of blacks, the South, contains only one district with a majority black population.

Table 11.2 points up the high degree of black residential segregation in the North. Of the 297 congressional districts in this region, 271 are less than 19% black. The districts that elect black congressmen are those in the central cities: Detroit, Chicago, Baltimore, Los Angeles, St. Louis, Philadelphia, and New York City. Only Representative Dellums, whose district encompasses the Berkeley, California area, represents noncentral city dwellers.[10] Outside the central cities, blacks are just too few in number to elect black representatives on their own.

The drawing of legislative district lines in the North takes this residential segregation into account. State legislatures are generally predisposed to construct districts that make incumbents more secure. When a sizable number of blacks reside in one area, both political parties will usually agree to create an over-whelmingly black district which ultimately will elect a black legislator. Demo-crats, of course, follow this course of action to increase their own numbers in the legislature: A political fact of life is the solidarity and faithfulness of blacks to the Democratic Party (see, for example, Axelrod 1972). Republicans agree in order to remove black Democratic votes from shaky Republican districts that include both suburbs and central city; hence, a marginally Republican district becomes a safe suburban Republican district. This mutually beneficial practice, then, probably accounts for the small number of intermediate percentage black districts (that is, 30%–49% black) in the North.

A majority of the southern congressional districts that contain a nontrivial percentage of blacks do, however, fall into the intermediate range: 30 out of the

---

[10] Representative Dellums' district is only 23% black.

51 tabulated in Table 11.2. Given the overwhelming Democratic Party registration in both races in the South, blacks would have to constitute a much higher percentage of the population of the district in order to nominate a black in the primary. Only if more than one white candidate contested the primary and drained enough votes from the incumbent to throw the election to the black could the minority have a serious chance of victory; a scenario such as this has occurred in the past, but highly infrequently.[11] The overall result of the current congressional district lines retards the growth in numbers of black legislators from this region.

The obvious question to ask is whether or not the lines have been drawn in order to discriminate against blacks. The full answer to that question is elusive; concrete, unimpeachable evidence just does not exist. Besides the data problem, however, there is a reasonable counter-interpretation of the current districting scheme: population density. Contrary to the residential patterns of northern blacks, great numbers of blacks live in the rural areas of the South. Since blacks are much more evenly distributed across a state, it may be impossible to draw compact boundaries that would produce a majority black district.

Population data suggests that the black residential distribution explanation may be correct for many states in the South. North Carolina, South Carolina, Florida, Kentucky, and Virginia possess very dispersed black populations. In fact, in order to design a majority black district under the constraints enunciated by the Supreme Court an obvious gerrymander would be required. Only the most unseemly district plan, then, would produce an increase in minority representation in Congress from these states; no blacks have been elected from these districts simply because they have been unable to forge a winning coalition with segments of the white community.

States such as Mississippi and Alabama, however, seem to design their districts in such a way as to prevent the election of a black Congressman. If a fairly straight boundary were being drawn following county lines wherever feasible, which is usually the case in most states, several black majority rural counties should have been grouped together creating an absolute black majority in a district; instead, the line twists to prevent this and assigns these areas to districts with much higher white populations. For example, the third district of Mississippi stretches from the heavily black Delta country across to the white-dominated areas along the Alabama border. Figure 11.6 also shows that two other districts, the first and second, are drawn in such a way as to dilute the

[11] The victory of Parren Mitchell of Maryland's Seventh Congressional District is a case in point.

Figure 11.6 Mississippi: Map of congressional districts, counties, and selected cities (five districts). (Source: U. S. Department of Commerce, Social and Economic Statistics Administration, Bureau of the Census.)

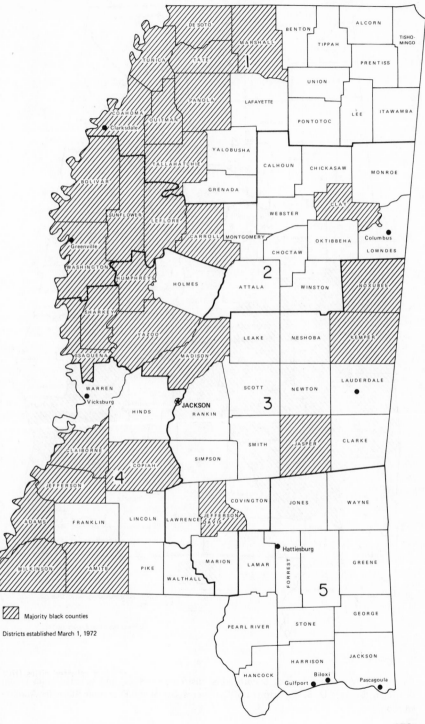

DE SOTO
MARSHALL
BENTON
ALCORN
TISHO-MINGO
TUNICA
TATE
TIPPAH
PRENTISS
1
UNION
PANOLA
LAFAYETTE
COAHOMA
QUITMAN
Clarksdale
PONTOTOC
LEE
ITAWAMBA
YALOBUSHA
TALLAHATCHIE
CALHOUN
CHICKASAW
MONROE
BOLIVAR
GRENADA
SUNFLOWER
LEFLORE
WEBSTER
CLAY
Greenville
CARROLL
MONTGOMERY
OKTIBBEHA
Columbus
LOWNDES
WASHINGTON
CHOCTAW
HUMPHREYS
HOLMES
ATTALA
WINSTON
2
NOXUBEE
SHARKEY
LEAKE
NESHOBA
KEMPER
YAZOO
ISSAQUENA
MADISON
WARREN
SCOTT
NEWTON
LAUDERDALE
Vicksburg
JACKSON
HINDS
RANKIN
3
CLAIBORNE
SMITH
JASPER
CLARKE
COPIAH
SIMPSON
JEFFERSON
4
COVINGTON
JONES
WAYNE
ADAMS
FRANKLIN
LINCOLN
LAWRENCE
JEFFERSON DAVIS
Hattiesburg
WILKINSON
AMITE
PIKE
MARION
LAMAR
FORREST
GREENE
WALTHALL
5
GEORGE
PEARL RIVER
STONE
HARRISON
JACKSON
HANCOCK
Biloxi
Gulfport
Pascagoula

Majority black counties

Districts established March 1, 1972

179

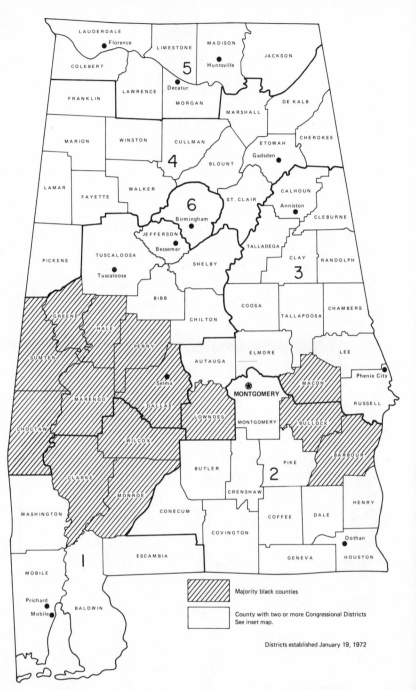

Figure 11.7 Alabama: Map of congressional districts, counties, and selected cities (seven districts). (Source: U. S. Department of Commerce, Social and Economic Statistics Administration,

180

voting power of the black majority in the Delta. Similarly, the political power of blacks in the "Black Belt" of Alabama is diminished by being divided between the second and third districts, as shown in Figure 11.7. We are not saying that shockingly obvious and technically illegal gerrymandering aimed at lessening black political power is the plan of these state legislatures; however, it appears that a much more subtle process is producing the same results.

In addition to large ethnic groups winning through the en masse support of their own nominees, ethnic candidates are also running very well in areas where they are a distinct minority. For instance, the 1974 general election found blacks winning the lieutenant governorships of California and Colorado, where they constitute 7% and 3% of the population, respectively. Both candidates ran as moderates and obtained massive white support in their election bids. Furthermore, Michigan reelected a black Secretary of State, while California elected a Japanese-American woman to the same office; again, both individuals ran well in white areas. In short, whites overlooked ethnic identification and seemed to vote on the basis of the candidates' stands.

The Social Issue was undoubtedly important in the 1974 elections: The exposure of corruption in the highest office of the land followed by the incumbent's forced resignation of that office occupied the voters' minds throughout the campaign. These events, however, tended to crosscut ethnic cleavages generally reinforced by the increased saliency of the Social Issue. The principal thrust of the campaign was not "keep the radicals in their place" but "throw the rascals out." This type of election issue did not pit one ethnic group against another, rather all groups against the perceived corrupt incumbents. Voters, particularly whites, became increasginly receptive to any candidates who adopted positions close to their own views. In other words, bloc voting began to fall apart as individuals voted rationally on the issue and sometimes supported members of other ethnic groups.

The erosion of bloc voting is not a new phenomena, but it certainly reached a peak in 1974. Evidence provided by Kramer and Levy indicates that erosion has taken place in the past, but in a rather unsystematic fashion from election to election. Although some elections show a minimal erosion of the vote away from another ethnic group's candidate, many show erosion of greater than 15%; furthermore, the erosion is basically unidirectional.[12] A common theme of these elections is the presence of a salient issue which mitigates ethnic differences and permits one of the candidates to appeal to the other group on the basis of his stand. An example would be the 1966 Massachusetts Senate race in which Republican Edward Brooke became the first black senator since Reconstruction. In that campaign, he was opposed by a white Catholic Democrat: former governor Endicott Peabody. Despite his Republican affiliation, Brooke carried a monolithic 90% of the black vote. In addition to this fairly cohesive, but small,

---

[12] In particular, see the tables in Levy and Kramer (1972: 228–241).

power base, he managed to gain the support of enough white voters because of his firm moderately liberal stand to defeat the Democrat by a healthy 61–39 margin. The next theorem explores the implications of allowing the voters of one ethnic group to support the candidate of another ethnic group if his position is more akin to their own.

> THEOREM 2: Assuming mild polarization, a candidate should move his position toward that of his opponent as long as the vote he is gaining from the opposition bloc is greater than that he is alienating within his own bloc.

Obviously, the amount of moderation, if any, will be a function of the militancy of his own ethnic bloc and the receptivity of his opponent's camp. If his own support is unswerving in its loyalty to the candidate and he has the opportunity to gain a nontrivial amount of his opponent's base, then he should converge on his opponent's position. If, on the other hand, he runs the risk of alienating a sizable portion of his base (and perhaps encouraging the candidacy of another in his ethnic group), then the individual is clearly constrained in the extent to which convergence is possible. The 1969 and 1973 campaigns of Thomas Bradley for mayor of Los Angeles are excellent illustrations of this situation.

In 1969 and 1973, Thomas Bradley, a former black police officer, opposed white conservative Mayor Samuel Yorty. In 1969, Bradley assumed a moderate stand on the Social Issue but allowed Yorty to portray him as an extreme liberal; in a sense, he gave Yorty the opportunity to set both their positions. Also, white voters in this election were not very receptive to the appeals of a black candidate. The final result was the fairly narrow victory of the incumbent. In 1973, however, Bradley did not make the same strategic errors. He assumed a forthright moderate stand on the Social Issue and took full advantage of the increased receptivity of white voters to his appeals. (During the 4 intervening years, white voters had become quite tired of the inefficiency of the Yorty administration.) The result in this rematch was the reversal of the first contest: Thomas Bradley was elected as mayor of Los Angeles. Bradley's victory was a result of his gains in the white community as well as the continuing monolithic support of the black community.

So far, our analysis has centered upon general election contests. Most of the elections that this chapter attempts to model, however, are sequential in nature: That is, a primary election is held prior to the main event. If the voting population in the primary election was identical to the voting population in the general election, no extensions to the model would be necessary. Political scientists have shown, however, that this is not the case; indeed, ideologically, the groups are quite different (Ranney 1972). Hence, the candidate is faced with the problem of selecting a position that maximizes his chances of winning both the primary and general election. We assume that he cannot change his position

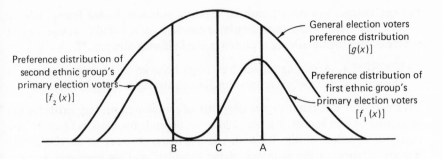

Figure 11.8   Preference densities for voters in a sequential election process.

between elections since this would impair his credibility—shades of George McGovern! Figure 11.8 illustrates this situation.

The complexity of the problem facing the candidate is apparent: A position chosen to maximize the probability of winning the primary contest may cost him the general election. Position A may allow the candidate to win the primary, but he will certainly lose to the candidate who adopts position B in the general election. The confounding influence is the sequential nature of the changed electoral process facing a candidate.

The candidate's goal in this context should be to maximize his overall probability of gaining election, where

$$\text{Probability (Election)} = \text{Probability (Nomination)}$$
$$\times \text{Probability (Election given Nomination)}.$$

We assume that these probabilities are a function of the number of votes he expects to receive given his position, his primary election opponent's position, and his general election opponent's position.[13] Consequently, the ethnic candidate who is challenged within his own group needs to consider the actions of both opponents. Referring to Figure 11.8, the candidate and his primary election opponent vie for the support of those voters represented by distribution $f_1(x)$; the candidate and his general election opponent, assuming that he has successfully won the first contest, vie for the support of voters represented by distribution $g(x)$. The first question is: Can we prescribe positions for the candidates from which there is no incentive for any unilateral change? If such positions can be found, then a measure of stability is added to the election; if such positions do not exist, then the election will be characterized by a series of

[13] The approach to sequential elections combines elements from two articles formulating very different models of the process. See Aranson and Ordeshook (1972) and Coleman (1972).

strategic changes and counterchanges in policy positions, halted finally only by election day itself. These stabilizing issue positions are referred to as equilibrium strategies, and their existence is proven in the following theorem:[14]

THEOREM 3: Assuming monolithic voting behavior of the ethnic groups in the primary election, there exist equilibrium strategies for all candidates.

We note that this result proves only that an equilibrium strategy exists for the sequential contest model. The exact location depends upon several factors: the exact specification of the function relating the probability of success in the primary election to the positions of the candidate and his opponent and the exact specification of the similar function for the general election. We know, however, that the equilibrium position lies somewhere between the median preference of the primary voters and the median preference of the general election voters, that is, in Figure 11.8, between points C and A.

Up to this point in the analysis, the stand of the candidate who is unopposed in his primary contest is assumed known and fixed. Suppose, however, that, instead of adopting the median preference of his ethnic bloc, this candidate begins to move to the center of the general election population in order to follow a concensus strategy in gaining the office. What are the implications of such a move on the candidates contesting their bloc's primary? Should rational candidates respond by shifting their position to meet this new general election threat? The answer is yes—the candidates involved in the contested primary should shift toward the center of the general election population.

THEOREM 4: If the unopposed candidate in the primary shifts toward the center of the general election population's preferences, the candidates in the contested primary should respond by shifting toward that center.

Behaviorally, this implies that the candidate who does not face a primary challenge within his own voting bloc sets the tone of the entire campaign.

An excellent illustration of the consequences of Theorem 4 is the 1969 Detroit mayoral election. Richard Austin, a moderate black, was unopposed within his own ethnic group in the primary election. Although he antagonized the more militant elements in the black community within the city, Austin attempted to adopt a position on the Social Issue consistent with the possibility of obtaining support from the liberal white community. The white community, however, found itself faced with a choice between two candidates: conservative Common Council member Mary Beck and moderate Wayne County Sheriff Roman Gribbs. Beck did not moderate her stand in the light of her black opponent's strategy; Gribbs did and won both the primary election in the white community and the

[14] The classic treatment of the concept of equilibrium strategies can be found in Luce and Raiffa (1957).

general election that followed. By a 51–49 margin, Roman Gribbs became the mayor of Detroit after one of the least embittering elections in a metropolitan area in recent times.[15]

As an aside to the last theorem, we note that uncertainty of the position of one's general election opponent violates Theorem 3 and, hence, the guaranteed existence of an equilibrium strategy is lost.[16] A situation in which such uncertainty enters the model is during simultaneous primary fights in both ethnic blocs. Under such circumstances, no policy prescriptions to any of the candidates can be made; indeed, concentrating upon winning one's primary election, rather than the election sequence, would appear to be the soundest advice possible. The 1973 Detroit mayoral race found two black and two white opponents in each community's primary election. The result was an immoderating election in which a militant black and a militant white faced each other in the final showdown. The general election vote broke along racial lines with the black candidate taking the majority; it is apparent that, between 1969 and 1973, the balance of power in Detroit has shifted from the white blue-collar neighborhoods to the black residential areas of the city. Hence, total intraethnic conflict in addition to interethnic conflict can be highly debilitating to the prospects for a campaign which will soothe already exacerbated lines of cleavage.

IMPLICATIONS AND CONCLUSIONS

This chapter has presented a rational choice model of ethnic voting behavior. Four results were derived from this simplistic model of the political environment, and relevant evidence bearing on the results was discussed. We note, in passing, that, through the application of much more advanced mathematical techniques, other conclusions can be derived from the model; however, for the purposes of this chapter, the point of diminishing marginal returns would have been reached soon. We have essentially obtained several rather interesting conclusions about the pluralistic political system in the United States through the use of straightforward mathematics.

As long as the Social Issue remains the most salient dimension in elections, ethnic candidates will remain at a distinct disadvantage in areas where their group is a minority. In order to elect an ethnic candidate, a strategy that erodes white votes must be formulated; such a strategy is impossible to implement when ethnic cleavages are the prominent consideration in the voters' minds. Only when other factors, such as the economy, break the monolithic voting

[15] *The Detroit News* and *Detroit Free Press* provided much valuable information about the election. In addition, Scammon and Wattenberg (1970: 248–251) was quite helpful.

[16] By "uncertainty," we mean that the strategy is unknown. Another usage of that term, and its implications for spatial models, can be found in Shepsle (1972).

habits of the majority group can a moderate ethnic obtain substantial white support. Failing this, the ethnic candidate is doomed to remain the loser in the election.

The South is, of course, the area in which blacks have the greatest potential for political power, but it is also one area in which the Social Issue takes on immense importance. As long as the Black Belt areas are divided between multiple majority-white districts, black candidates must appeal to white voters in order to win; such a strategy, even today, is quixotic at best in Alabama and Mississippi. This is not to say that the black voters of these states are totally irrelevant to the political process; In fact, in a multiple candidate primary or in a close two-way contest, blacks could hold the balance of power—admittedly, though, such elections are rare.[17] So, unless southern state legislatures follow the lead of their northern counterparts and design majority black districts where such boundaries are logical and natural, the prospects for further substantial gains in black political power in the South appear bleak.

The added dilemma posed by the primary system may be more readily avoidable. As was demonstrated, stability in the electoral process is greatly increased when the stance of each general election candidate is known by the opponents; when the identity of the primary victor is unclear, no equilibria need exist, and extremist candidates may be nominated. States, such as Connecticut, New York, South Dakota, Idaho, and Minnesota, have enacted laws which reduce the number of intraethnic and interethnic bloc fights within each party and encourage the nomination of moderates acceptable to both the party and the general electorate. Each state has instituted a preliminary step in the electoral process, usually a convention, which allows the members of each party to assemble and to attempt to field candidates and to adopt positions which are acceptable to all. In this way, bitter and divisive primaries may be avoided.

For example, Connecticut law provides for a "challenge primary" when a candidate defeated for nomination at the convention receives more than 20% of the delegates' votes and wishes to appeal directly to the electorate.[18] Hence, a candidate with a strong minority following may challenge the party leadership through a primary election if he finds the designated nominee unacceptable. It is a tribute to the pragmatism and accommodating qualities of the Connecticut party leaders that, during the first 15 years of the operation of the "challenge primary," 1955–1970, there were no challenges to the convention nominees.

---

[17] Senator John Sparkman of Alabama won just over 50% of the vote in the first Democratic primary of 1972 and narrowly avoided a run-off contest with a populist-type Wallace supporter. Blacks voted overwhelmingly for Sparkman in this primary and probably accounted for the margin giving him an absolute majority of the votes.

[18] For a complete discussion of the passage and effects of Connecticut's challenge primary law, see Lockard (1960).

The leadership was able to nominate candidates at least minimally pleasing to all ethnic groups in their party's coalition and to contain conflict within the bounds of the convention.

Connecticut's solution to the problems of political pluralism is, of course, only one possibility. The South, through the use of gerrymandering, has solved the problem in another fashion. The use of the convention method, however, has become more and more widespread across the North, particularly in areas dominated by the Democrats. This is not surprising: The Democratic Party, as a result of the Roosevelt Revolution of the 1930s, is composed substantially of many different ethnic groups. The party leadership must attempt to maintain the loyalty of these diverse groups or suffer a possibly devastating loss of support. The obvious solution to the loyalty problem is the recognition of this pluralism and the sharing of political power. To ignore a particular group's claims is to invite dissention within or defection from the organization; as was shown earlier, examples of unsuccessful responses to political pluralism seem as frequent as successful ones.

As rival groups in the population begin to fully exert their political power in the electoral arena, will the current power-sharing arrangements continue to be viable? It is too early to answer this question fully. If they prove inadequate to meet the challenges of plural politics, then other policies must be considered. The American political experience, unfortunately, will not provide the needed insights. Instead, the nature of politics in plural societies must be examined in more detail. Cross-cultural and cross-national regularities must be isolated, examined, and modeled; the political and social development of other plural nations must be taken into account in the shaping of American social policy. The responses and fate of foreign political institutions in plural societies will certainly provide valuable input to future models of ethnic politics in America.

But in what direction should future investigators proceed? The orientation and methods of cultural and, in particular, political anthropology may be of great use. In the past, their analyses have proven invaluable to both comparative political scientists and political theorists. Moreover, the concept of subcultural variation, of which ethnic politics is just a component, is grounded in anthropology. A theoretical perspective, such as the rational actor model of political economy, is sorely needed to organize observed behavior in the political context. The step from description to explanation is a necessary prelude to policy recommendations. The model-building process appears to be a promising and exciting area for the future interaction of anthropologists and political scientists. Without such interaction, however, we may condemn ourselves, as social scientists, to observe without understanding as ethnic conflict emerges from the political arena and manifests itself once again in far uglier forms.

APPENDIX

Proof of Theorem 1

In general, the ethnic group's median preference will not be identical to the population's median preference.

Suppose the candidate adopts the median preference of his ethnic group. The challenger has three alternatives open to him:

1. He can adopt a position to the left of the candidate; then the candidate receives the votes of half of the group (lying to the right of the median) and of those voters on the left closest to him. Hence, the candidate wins.
2. He can adopt a position to the right of the candidate; then the candidate receives the votes of half of the group (lying to the left of the median) and of those voters on the right closest to him. Hence, the candidate wins.
3. He can adopt the position of the candidate; then each receives half of the votes, and a tie ensues.

Therefore, by adopting the median position of the ethnic group, he can do no worse than tie any possible challenger. There is no reason, therefore, for him to switch to the population's mean which does not have this property.

Proof of Theorem 2

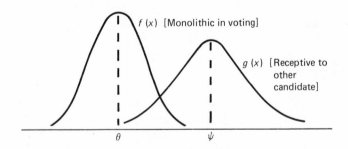

Let $f(x)$ and $g(x)$ be the preference distributions of the two ethnic groups. Let θ be the position adopted by the ethnic candidate representing $f(x)$, and ψ be the position of the one representing $g(x)$. Without loss of generality, suppose ψ is known and fixed, and consider the movement of θ. At θ the candidate may gain votes from the other bloc.

The total vote that the candidate adopting θ receives is composed of three parts: support from his own group, support from the other group, and loss from his own group through alienation.

Support from his own group is $\int^{\infty} f(x)dx$. Support from the opposition bloc is $k_2 \int^{(\theta+\psi)/2} 2g(x) \, dx$ where k_2 is a receptivity factor, $0 \leqslant k_2 \leqslant 1$. $(\theta + \psi)/2$ is the point at which voters are indifferent to both candidates.

Loss from his own group is $k_1 \int_{-\infty}^{\theta} f(x)dx$ where, k_1 is an alienation factor, $0 \leqslant k_1 \leqslant 1$.

We note in passing that, if k_1 is close to 1, then the support the candidate receives from his own bloc is very tenuous; if k_2 is close to 1, then the opposition bloc is very receptive to the candidate.

The candidate's total vote is:

$$V(\theta) = \int_{-\infty}^{\infty} f(x)dx - k_1 \int_{-\infty}^{\theta} f(x)dx + k_2 \int_{-\infty}^{(\theta+\psi)/2} g(x) \, dx.$$

As long as his vote increases, the candidate will move toward ψ. This is equivalent to the condition that $dV(\theta)/d\theta$ is positive.

$$\frac{dV(\theta)}{d\theta} = -k_1 f(\theta) + k_2 g(\frac{\theta+\psi}{2}) > 0$$

or

$$k_2 g(\frac{\theta+\psi}{2}) > k_1 f(\theta).$$

Substantively, this condition means that the candidate should move toward ψ as long as the votes he gains from the opposition are greater than the votes he alienates in his own camp *at the margin*. We note the similarity of this condition to the classical condition governing the behavior of the rational consumer in economics (see Cohen and Cyert 1965).

Proof of Theorem 3

Let $P(N)$:   the probability of nomination $\equiv g(\theta_1, \theta_0)$
$P(E|N)$:   the probability of election given nomination $\equiv f(\theta_1|\psi) = f(\theta_1)$
θ_1:   the position of the ethnic candidate
θ_0:   the position of his primary election challenger
ψ: the position of his general election opponent
$\theta_1 > \theta_0$

The proof that follows will show the existence of an equilibrium strategy by demonstrating the equivalence of this situation to a concave–convex game which we know to have such strategies (see Owen 1968).

Without specifying the exact nature of the functions, we assume the following about their behavior in the region of interest:

$\delta f/\delta\theta_1 > 0$ As θ_1 shifts toward the general election's median preference,
$\delta^2 f/\delta\theta_1{}^2 < 0$ his probability of election increases at a decreasing rate.

$\delta g/\delta\theta_1 < 0$ As θ_1 shifts toward the general election's median preference,
$\delta^2 g/\delta\theta_1{}^2 < 0$ his probability of nomination decreases at a decreasing rate.

$\delta g/\delta\theta_0 < 0$ As θ_0 shifts toward the general election's median preference,
$\delta^2 g/\delta\theta_0^2 > 0$ his opponent's probability of nomination decreases at an increasing rate.

$\delta^2 f/\delta\psi\delta\theta_1 = 0$ The rate of change in the candidate's probability of election given a change in his opponent's strategy is not dependent on the candidate's position.

We must show that $\delta^2 P(E)/\delta\theta_1^2 < 0$ and $\delta^2 P(E)/\delta\theta_0^2 > 0$.

$$P(E) = P(N)\cdot P(E|N) = g(\theta_1,\theta_0)\cdot f(\theta_1)$$

$$\frac{\delta^2 P(E)}{\delta\theta_1^2} = \frac{\delta^2 g}{\delta\theta_1^2}\cdot f + \frac{\delta^2 f}{\delta\theta_1^2}\cdot g + 2\frac{\delta f}{\delta\theta_1}\cdot\frac{\delta g}{\delta\theta_1} < 0\,\checkmark$$

$$\frac{\delta^2 P(E)}{\delta\theta_0^2} = \frac{\delta^2 g}{\delta\theta_0^2}\cdot f + \frac{\delta^2 f}{\delta\theta_0^2}\cdot g + 2\frac{\delta f}{\delta\theta_0}\cdot\frac{\delta g}{\delta\theta_0} > 0\,\checkmark$$

Hence, the equivalence is demonstrated, and the existence of an equilibrium strategy is guaranteed.

Proof of Theorem 4

We need to determine the sign of $d\overline{\theta}_1(\psi)/d\psi$.

$$P(E) = g(\theta_1,\theta_2)\cdot f(\theta_1|\psi)$$

By the results of game theory, we know that $\overline{\theta}_1$, candidate 1's equilibrium strategy, satisfies

$$\frac{\delta g}{\delta\theta_1}(\overline{\theta}_1)\cdot f(\overline{\theta}_1|\psi) + \frac{\delta f}{\delta\theta_1}(\overline{\theta}_1|\psi)\cdot g(\overline{\theta}_1) = 0 \quad (**).$$

Now, (**) is an implicit function in $\overline{\theta}_1$ and ψ. It is assumed to be continuously differentiable, $\delta P(E)/\delta\overline{\theta}_1 = 0$, and $\delta^2 P(E)/\delta\overline{\theta}_1 \neq 0$ in the interval of interest.

Then, by the Implicit Function Theorem, $\overline{\theta}_1 = k(\psi)$. Furthermore, by the Inverse Function Theorem, $d\overline{\theta}_1/d\psi = (d\psi/d\overline{\theta}_1)^{-1}$.

Taking the derivative of (**) with respect to $\overline{\theta}_1$, we obtain, after collecting and rearranging terms,

$$\frac{d\psi}{d\overline{\theta}_1} = \frac{\frac{\delta^2 g}{\delta\overline{\theta}_1{}^2}(\overline{\theta}_1)\cdot f(\overline{\theta}_1|\psi) + \frac{\delta g}{\delta\overline{\theta}_1}(\overline{\theta}_1)\cdot\frac{\delta f}{\delta\overline{\theta}_1}(\overline{\theta}_1|\psi) + \frac{\delta^2 f}{\delta\overline{\theta}_1{}^2}(\overline{\theta}_1|\psi)\cdot g(\overline{\theta}_1) + \frac{\delta f}{\delta\overline{\theta}_1}(\overline{\theta}_1|\psi)\cdot\frac{\delta g}{\delta\overline{\theta}_1}(\overline{\theta}_1)}{-\frac{\delta g}{\delta\overline{\theta}}(\overline{\theta}_1)\cdot\frac{\delta f}{\delta\psi}(\overline{\theta}_1|\psi) - \frac{\delta^2 f}{\delta\psi\delta\overline{\theta}_1}(\overline{\theta}_1|\psi)\cdot g(\overline{\theta}_1)}.$$

By inspecting the signs of each partial derivative in accordance with the assumptions made about the two functions, we find that

$$\frac{d\psi}{d\overline{\theta}_1} < 0 \quad \text{or} \quad \frac{d\overline{\theta}_1}{d\psi} < 0.$$

Hence, the equilibrium position adopted by candidate 1 shifts toward the population median as his general election opponent shifts toward that point.

ACKNOWLEDGMENTS

The author gratefully acknowledges the very helpful comments and criticisms of Susan G. Hadden, Roger H. Marz, Peter C. Ordeshook, and especially Peggy R. Sanday. Special thanks also go to Marcus Alexis, the discussant on a preliminary draft of this chapter presented at the Sugar Loaf Conference. Errors remaining in the chapter are, alas, the responsibility of the author; however, he is more than willing to share that responsibility.

REFERENCES

Aranson, Peter H., and Peter C. Ordeshook
  1972   Spatial strategies for sequential elections. In *Probability models of collection decision making*, edited by Richard G. Niemi and Herbert F. Weisberg. Columbus: Charles E. Merrill.
Axelrod, Robert
  1972   Where the votes come from: An analysis of electoral coalitions, 1952–1968. *American Political Science Review* (March): 11–20.
Broderick, Francis L.
  1969   *Reconstruction and the American Negro.* New York: Macmillan.
Cohen, K. J., and R. M. Cyert
  1965   *Theory of the firm.* Englewood Cliffs, New Jersey: Prentice-Hall.
Coleman, James
  1972   The positions of political parties in elections. In *Probability models of collective decision making*, edited by Richard G. Niemi and Herbert F. Weisberg. Columbus: Charles E. Merrill.
Downs, Anthony
  1957   *An economic theory of democracy.* New York: Harper.
Epstein, Leon D.
  1967   *Political parties in Western democracies.* New York: Praeger.
Franklin, John H.
  1961   *Reconstruction: After the Civil War.* Chicago: Univ. of Chicago Press.
Hinich, Melvin J., and Peter C. Ordeshook
  1969   Abstention and equilibrium in the electoral process. *Public Choice* (Fall): 81–106.
Hyman, Harold M. (Ed.).
  1967   *The radical Republicans and Reconstruction, 1861–1870.* Indianapolis: Bobbs-Merrill.
Jacob, Jane
  1961   *Death and life of great American cities.* New York: Random House.
Key, V. O., Jr.
  1949   *Southern politics.* New York: Vintage. Chap. 11.

Kimball, Penn
1972   *The disconnected.* New York: Columbia Univ. Press.
Levy, Mark R., and Michael S. Kramer
1972   *The ethnic factor.* New York: Simon and Schuster.
Lockard, Duane
1960   *Connecticut's challenge primary: A study in legislative politics.* New York: McGraw-Hill.
Luce, Duncan R., and Howard Raiffa
1957   *Games and decisions.* New York: Wiley. Pp. 56–71.
Novak, Michael
1971   *The rise of the unmeltable ethnics.* New York: Macmillan.
Owen, G.
1968   *Game theory.* Philadelphia: W. B. Saunders. Pp. 78–81.
Prewitt, Kenneth, and Sidney Verba
1974   *An introduction to American government.* New York: Harper.
Ranney, Austin
1972   Turnout and representation in presidential primary elections. *American Political Science Review* (March): 21–37.
Scammon, Richard, and Ben Wattenberg
1970   *The real majority.* New York: Coward, McCann, and Geoghegan.
Schlesinger, Arthur M., Jr. (Ed.)
1971   *History of American presidential elections 1789–1968.* Vol II. New York: McGraw-Hill. Pp. 1379–1490.
Shepsle, Kenneth A.
1972   The strategy of ambiguity: Uncertainty and electoral competition. *American Political Science Review* (June).
Smith, Frank E.
1967   *Congressman from Mississippi.* New York: Capricorn.
U. S. Bureau of the Census
1973   *Congressional district data book, 93rd Congress.* Washington, D. C.: U. S. Bureau of the Census.
1974   *The social and economic status of the black population in the United States.* Washington, D. C.: U. S. Government Printing Office. Pp. 119–123.
U. S. Congress
1973   *Congressional directory, 93rd Congress, First Session.* Washington, D. C.: U. S. Government Printing Office.
White, Theodore H.
1965   *The making of the president 1964.* New York: New American Library.Chap. 13.

12

The ERA:
Law, Custom, and Change

Lucy Garretson

Temple University

In 1973, after a decade of civil rights legislation, extensive opposition to an amendment to the U.S. Constitution proposing that "Equality of rights under the law shall not be denied or abridged by the United States or by any State on account of sex" would appear to be unlikely. This amendment (known as the Equal Rights Amendment or the ERA) was, in fact, quickly ratified by 30 states after its passage through Congress. However, the hope of ERA supporters that securing ratification in the required 38 states would present no serious problems has been dashed. In 1973, arguments against the passage of the amendment have been given wide coverage. Lobbying to rally antiamendment forces has been organized, and proposals have been made, in some states, to rescind the original vote for ratification. It is now apparent that securing ratification in eight more states, while blocking efforts to rescind ratification in others, will require a hard-fought campaign by ERA supporters.

Ratification of a constitutional amendment is, of course, a part of the political process. However, this chapter will not consider political strategies and tactics but instead will examine the rationale behind the arguments of both supporters and opponents of the ERA. The purpose of this analysis is to suggest why opposition to the amendment has been mobilized and has become potent, and to

193

discover what relationships may exist between this phenomenon and more general political and social trends in the United States.

An attempt will be made to formulate a cultural explanation, that is, one that includes an analysis of basic American beliefs and their relationship to the process of change in America. The two-part model presented here will make use of a model for paradigmatic culture change recently proposed by Wallace (1972) and will also incorporate a previous analysis of American beliefs concerning the nature of men's and women's roles and spheres of social existence in American society (Garretson-Selby 1972, Garretson 1973).

In order to understand the arguments pro and con, we must first look at the kinds of distinctions based on sex under existing laws that would be affected by the passage of the ERA, and we must also define the category of laws that would not be affected. Both of these categories will be briefly summarized in the following paragraphs.

We can distinguish three main categories of laws that would be nullified or would require revision should the ERA be ratified. The first set involves exemption for women from some of the obligations of citizenship that men are subject to. The most well-known and controversial is the exemption of women from compulsory military service and a corollary exemption from combat duty granted to women who choose to serve in the armed forces. This category also includes, in some states, exemptions for women from jury duty (cf. Hoyt V. Florida, cited in Brown, Emerson, Falk, and Freedman 1971: 15844). The second category of laws involves what is usually called protective legislation. Under this rubric fall statutes which limit the weight a woman may carry or load on the jobs, those which exclude women from overtime work, laws which prohibit women from certain occupations, and laws which stipulate that pregnant women must cease working at some specified period during their pregnancy. Laws that give women certain rights that men do not have comprise the third category. These would include statutes which permit alimony to be awarded an ex-wife, but not to an ex-husband. In addition to these three categories, there is a fourth set of customary procedures, which are not necessarily codified as law, that would be affected by the passage of the ERA. These include differential standards applied to women upon application for mortgage loans or credit cards. (Many of these practices have been successfully challenged in class action suits.)

In the aforementioned cases, the passage of the ERA would mean an erasure of legal distinctions based on sex, as the amendment states. For example, both men and women would be subject to a compulsory draft and would be assigned to combat duty on the basis of individual qualifications. A woman or a man who applied for a job would be judged on an individual basis of competence. Both men and women could be awarded alimony.

Exceptions to the general rule that an individual's sex should not determine his or her legal rights would include those laws that pertain to the physical characteristics of one sex or another (Brown *et al*. 1971), for example, statutes relating to wet nurses or to the regulation of sperm banks. Further, and more important, "the legal effect of the Amendment is confined to 'state action' " (Brown *et al*. 1971: 15846). Thus, like other civil rights amendments, the amendment would be applicable only in the public sector of society. It follows that there would be a privacy qualification. Both men and women would be guaranteed a right of privacy that would permit "police practices by which a search involving the removal of clothing could be performed only by a police officer of the same sex as the person ,.. (and) the separation of the sexes in public restrooms or similar public institutions" (Brown *et al*. 1971: 15846).

THE ARGUMENTS

We can summarize quickly the line of reasoning of supporters of the passage of the ERA. It is based on the argument that women, like men, are persons and should be both entitled to the rights guaranteed to men under the law and subject to the obligations of citizenship imposed on men. Special legal status implies difference and, therefore, inequality for women. "Our legal structure will continue to support and command inferior status for women so long as it permits *any* differentiation in legal treatment on the basis of sex" (Brown *et al.* 1971: 15840). Supporters argue that the amendment is necessary "to achieve the values of group equality and individual self-fulfillment." (Brown *et al.* 1971: 15840)

Objections to the amendment have been articulated most widely by Phyllis Schlafly, chief of the anti-ERA movement, who says that it will not give women anything that they have not already got or have a way of getting (Firing Line 1973: 2). She contends that the Equal Employment Opportunity Act of 1972 has already reduced discrimination on the job and will eventually wipe out discriminatory employment practices, but, she continues, "It (the ERA) will take away from women some of the most important rights and benefits and exemptions we now have" (Firing Line 1973: 2).

Included in her list of rights is the exemption of women from the compulsory draft. She is indignant at the idea that women would be subject to nonvoluntary military service that could include combat duty. Another benefit she claims is the right of women to be supported by their husbands. When challenged as to whether women really have a *legal* right to support from their husbands unless there is a separation or divorce proceeding which brings the marriage contract into court, her answer is emphatic:

No, no, no. The wife does not have to go to court to get it. All she needs to do is to go to any store and charge the bill to her husband. And in practice the wife can get whatever she chooses to spend of the husband's money. The stores give her credit because they know they can collect against him. The law gives them that right. And then it's between the store and the husband to fight about paying the bill. [Firing Line 1973: 7]

Thus, she contends that women now have important rights that the ERA would force them to give up. She opposes the amendment on the grounds that men, not women, stand to gain if it passes.

ASSUMPTIONS UNDERLYING ANTI-ERA ARGUMENTS

In order to understand the appeal Mrs. Schlafly's arguments have had for some Americans, we must look at the assumptions about the social definition of a woman and a man underlying her statements. Schlafly's argument that a wife has a right to be supported by her husband is particularly interesting here, because, for her, and probably for most Americans, it does not really need a legal basis. Americans assume that a husband goes out to work while his wife stays home. Schlafly implies, in the passage quoted earlier, that, when a wife goes out to spend money, she is not responsible for debts incurred. Furthermore, Schlafly argues that it is right, that is, normal and moral, that women be supported by men, and that a contrary case would be abnormal. The comic-strip image of the woman whose extravagant clothes-buying lands her husband in the poorhouse rests on the assumption that women are supported by men, despite the fact that about 12% of the total work force in the United States in 1970 was composed of women who were single, widowed, divorced, or separated from their husbands (Firing Line 1973: 7–8). Women in the United States do work outside the home, and many of those working women must work in order to live. Clearly, Schlafly's words apply only to relatively affluent women whose husbands are extraordinarily indulgent.

When we look at objections voiced against women serving in combat zones in wartime, we find similar anomalies and contradictions. The assumptions of the speakers and the reality are contradictory. For instance, on the Firing Line program previously cited, Buckley and Schlafly argue that women, being physically weaker than men, should be exempt from field combat because it would require them to carry heavy backpacks. To Anne Scott, an ERA supporter, Buckley remarks: "Is there something in you that wants to deny the corporate sense of male chivalry that says women ought not actually to fight wars, they ought to be spared this?" (Firing Line 1973: 2). "This" refers to fighting wars; yet neither Buckley nor Mrs. Schlafly argue that war is desirable for men, or that, given modern automatic weapons, women are incapable of killing efficiently, or even that women are "naturally" less warlike than men. The distinction between the sexes is made solely in reference to women's lesser physical strength.

This question, whether women are capable of carrying or lifting relatively heavy weights, is also tied to protective labor legislation and restrictions on work hours for women. One can point out, however, that, within the home, women carry their own children, and there are no legal restrictions on the weight of the child or the length of time the child may be carried. There are no restrictions, either legal or customary, that limit a woman's hours of housework, viz the saying "women's work is never done." Clearly, the principle of chivalry cited by Buckley does not operate within the home, but only in the outside world.

We suggest, therefore, that Buckley and Schlafly's argument can be best understood by positing an underlying assumption, namely, that they make a clear, sex-marked distinction between the "outside," the male world of work, politics and war, and the "inside," the female sphere. It seems clear, for instance, that Schlafly's insistence that women should not be and are not economically responsible is not predicated on empirical grounds but is based on her conception, shared by most Americans, of what a "woman" is, what she does, and where she does it.

I have said elsewhere (Garretson-Selby 1972, Garretson 1973) that, in order for an individual man to be defined as a socially acceptable male adult, he must hold down a job, and he must have sexual relations, which may or may not entail marriage, with women. In order for an individual woman to be defined as a socially acceptable female adult, she must marry, and she must bear and rear children. Although many, perhaps most, American women do hold down jobs at some point in their lives, their "womanhood" is not defined in terms of the job they hold, the exception being the deviant—defined as criminal—the prostitute. While men, of course, do father children and their sense of manhood may be enhanced by this proof of virility, men are not defined as socially acceptable males by virtue of parenthood. An "absent father" is not considered to be unmanly (he might be away fighting a war, for instance), but a mother who deserts or neglects her children is considered "unnatural," and unwomanly.

The "outside" male sphere is a conception very close to Schneider's (1968) "world of work," which he contrasts with what is here called the "inside," or the home. Schneider characterizes these two spheres in terms of the kinds of relations that may occur in each: Here they are considered as a marking for sex-specific activities and roles. Crossing the "inside"–"outside" line is difficult for both women and men. Women who work often leave their "womanhood" behind them in the home and are called "girls," whether they are typists or cleaning women. If they have professional training, they are "women" lawyers or "women" doctors. Men who take on "inside" jobs are similarly stigmatized. There is an overtone of suspicion about the real "manliness" of a "male" nurse or a "male" baby-sitter.

Given the rigidity of the concepts "inside" and "outside" and their clear sex marking, it seems that opposition to the ERA, at least in part, reflects an uneasiness at, or fear of, what may be coded as a hopeless muddling of cultural categories. Mary Douglas (1970, 1968) has pointed out the need shown by human beings in all cultures to create unambiguous social categories. She notes that: "Cultural intolerance of ambiguity is expressed by avoidance, by discrimination, and by pressure to conform" (1968: 199). In a similar vein, Leach (1964: 145) writes: "The thesis is that we make binary distinctions and then mediate the distinction by creating an ambiguous (and taboo loaded) intermediate category." Women doctors and male nurses are examples of such intermediate categories in American culture which mediate between the male outside world and the female inside sphere. It is argued here that the ERA is seen by its opponents as a willful attempt to blur the outlines between the "inside" and "outside" worlds, by admitting that the "outside" can not legally be defined as solely male. Uneasiness is verbalized in arguments that the ERA would mean that public toilets would not be sex-segregated (although clearly the right to privacy concept, referred to earlier would mean that one-sex public toilets could continue to be legal). It is clear that an "inside"–"outside" distinction underlies this argument, since in private homes, that is, "inside," bathrooms are *not* labeled or reserved for the exclusive use of one sex.

In actuality, the ERA, like other legal principles, would not have jurisdiction in the "inside." Law is operative primarily, if not exclusively, in the "outside." Police are notoriously reluctant to interfere in a fight between a man and his wife inside their own home: Marriage and the behavior that goes on in general in the "inside" is not subject to law unless the marriage "breaks down" or the children are "deliquent." Thus if Americans continue to believe that it is normal and right for a man to support his wife, the ERA offers no challenge to this custom. But it will present a challenge to sex-marked cultural categories: It will make official the fact that women, as well as men, operate on the "outside." It will recognize that women do work, that they do contribute to the support of husbands and children, and that some women are capable of military service, of working long hours, of carrying heavy loads, and the like. Many societies recognize differences between men and women and define male and female activities and roles as different. Thus, opposition to the ERA, on one level, may be understood, like the uneasiness expressed by some Americans to young people of different sexes wearing their hair the same length and dressing alike, as a reaction to an attack on basic assumptions about the "natural" differences and "natural" spheres of action for men and women in American culture.

However, to point out that Americans, as well as other peoples, hold sexual distinctions in the social sphere still does not explain the anomaly that successful opposition to equal rights under the law for women and men should exist. In the preceding 10 years, we have seen that, while Americans continue to make distinctions between persons on the basis of skin color, they have also supported legislation that makes discrimination on a racial basis illegal. We need further analysis to attempt to explain the appeal of anti-ERA arguments, an analysis involing an examination of the process of change in American political and social beliefs and practices in the past few years.

The model which will be used here is based on the model suggested by Wallace (1972), which he called, after Kuhn (1962), paradigmatic process in culture change. This kind of process, Wallace writes, is initiated by an innovation, which qualifies as paradigm forming if it is "an event which solves a limited problem but does so in a way which opens up a whole new line of development. It is a major 'break-through' " (Wallace 1972: 468). Furthermore, "the paradigmatic innovation has a symbolic and charismatic quality. It is often associated with the name of a culture hero (human or divine) and it can be simply represented by some visual image or phrase or manual procedure" (1972: 468). The paradigmatic innovation initiates four other stages in the paradigmatic process: paradigmatic core development, exploitation of the paradigm, the functional consequences of the paradigm, and rationalization of the paradigm. However, in the context of this chapter, we are less concerned with the working out of the process in detail than with the suggestion that, in the late 1960s there was such a paradigmatic innovation in American political and social life.

Wallace suggests that the paradigm-forming innovations which set off the processes of cultural change in the industrial revolution in Great Britain were the invention of spinning machinery and the modern engine. In the present discussion, the paradigm-forming innovation is conceived of as a new formulation of political and social belief, symbolized by the slogan "Black is beautiful." To understand why this slogan may represent an impetus to the process of paradigmatic change in American culture, we must first look at various cultural beliefs that it challenges or rejects.

The first and most obvious of these is the idea of the "melting pot." The melting pot image implies the eventual and inevitable assimilation of ethnic and racial minorities into the "mainstream," "wasp" American culture. This assimilation could be achieved by an individual. Through hard work, education, and the adoption of the Puritan ethic, "any boy can grow up to be President." Thus, obvious inequality could be rationalized. If an individual remained poor and unsuccessful, "unmelted," it was due to a lack of "real" American virtues. Humane social thinkers, however, also realized that the achievement of "The American Dream" also depended on "equality of opportunity." The civil rights agitation of the 1950s and 1960s was motivated by the assumption that individuals, regardless of race, should have an equal change at realizing the American Dream. It was believed that integration of schools, for instance, was desirable because it would give black children and white children an equal education and equal opportunity to learn, enabling them, according to their individual abilities and hard work, to conform to the prevailing cultural standards and to achieve individual success.

That disillusionment should follow on the heels of the passage of civil rights legislation is understandable. Such social science constructs as the "revolution of rising expectations" or "relative deprivation" were invoked to explain riots in the cities and renewed militant action by blacks. However, what was new and not predicted, was the assertion of conscious separateness and racial identity, the use of the word "black" by Negroes to describe themselves, the phrase "Black is Beautiful." We may hypothesize that this phrase came about as a result of the realization that racism is not simply an individual, psychological phenomenon, but that, in America, it is institutionalized and involves "the kind of naive assumption that white standards, values, and arts were the best, if not the only ones" (Bernard 1971: 37).

The rejection of white standards involves also a recognition of the sociological consequences of not being white. Thus, it was no longer sufficient progress for individual blacks to "make it," as baseball players or entertainers or even congressmen. "Black is beautiful" implies that the future of black Americans, as a group, should be of primary concern. We can analyze this development in anthropological terms, if we will, as an interjection of Durkheimian ideas into American society.

While a sociological view of society is hardly new in Western thought—one immediately thinks of Marx—in American cultural ideology, the image of the individual has dominated. Our heros have been the frontiersman, the log cabin president, the astronaut. The rejection of the inherent "rightness" of the culture of white American and the substitution of an ideal of group welfare for that of individual success constitute an important innovation in American social thinking. Development and exploitation of the paradigm symbolized by "Black is beautiful" have taken place within such widely disparate groups as the Jewish Reconstructionists, American Indians, and Italian-Americans, to name but a few. As Michael Novak writes in *The Unmeltable Ethnics* (1972: 216), "In a word, American will assimilate *individuals*. It will not assimilate groups. The new ethnic politics is a direct challenge to the WASP conception of America. It asserts that groups can structure the rules and goals and procedures of American life. It asserts that individuals, if they do not wish to, do not have to 'melt'." The aforementioned ethnic and religious movements have in common the feeling that assimilation will take away some unique prerogative or privilege; that the cultural inheritance of the group is valuable and is in danger of being inadvertantly lost or arbitrarily taken away. Most clearly, they reject the implicit assumptions of the ideology that only what is "wasp" is American.

We are now in a position to understand the appeal that anti-ERA arguments have had in 1972 and 1973. Paradoxically, the proponents of the amendment argue in terms of the individual-assimilationist model of American culture, while the opponents' success may be ascribed, in part, to the fact that they often sound more like Michael Novak than like Martin Luther King.

The legal argument in favor of the ERA stresses that "the law owes an obligation to treat females as persons, not statistical abstractions" (Brown *et al*. 1971: 15843) and that individual characteristics, not sex, should be the only basis for differential benefits or burdens imposed on different members of society. Similarly, Dr. Scott, the ERA defender on the Firing Line program quoted earlier, says: "I think what we're talking about is the human right . . . (interjection by Buckley) of individuals as individuals to be assigned or to undertake their own human responsibilities as individuals in terms of their individual merits and their individual abilities" (Firing Line 1973: 3). During the discussion of whether or not women should be drafted and should be subject to combat duty, Dr. Scott argues that women would not necessarily be given identical duties in the armed forces because "duties are awarded on an individual basis. In other words, people, according to their own individual abilities, are assigned to duty" (p. 3).

On the other hand, Mrs. Schlafly rarely uses the word "individual," but instead speaks of women as a group. For instance, in regard to the draft status of women she says: "Congress has used this power to exempt women and that's the way we like it" (p. 2). She argues that the ERA will "remove the right that the woman now has. You see, she has the legal right today to be supported by her husband and all kinds of wonderful rights" (p. 10). In other words, she feels strongly that women, as a *group*, will suffer: "The whole thing is misrepresented as a woman's rights amendment. In fact, the principal beneficiaries will be men. It will give men a great opportunity to get out from under their obligations—their obligations to be drafted and to support their families, et cetera, et cetera" (p. 10).

Both pro and con arguments embody some sexist ideas. The argument that women should be given full legal access to the male world, the world of work, of politics, of the military, of professional schools, rests on the assumption that somehow these "male" prerogatives, this "outside" world, is more valuable than the "inside" female world. It accepts the definition of "male" as superior to "female" and, therefore, demands access for women to the "male" world. On the other hand, Schlafly's arguments that women ought to be protected, supported, and exempted from unpleasant realities, such as war and alimony payments, reflect an even older assumption that women are weaker vessels who are, in the final analysis, less capable and less "adult" than men. In addition, the arguments against the ERA are, as I have stated earlier, predicated on the assumption that the "outside" male world and the "inside" female world are, and should be, different spheres and that the lines between them should be maintained. The insistence that the world of women and the world of men should continue to be mutually exclusive fits in with the development of a nonassimilation, group separateness ideology. Thus, while the notion that women are inherently weaker and inferior to men is hardly new, I contend here that the principle of protection of the rights of women as a group, voiced by the opponents of the passage of the ERA, is in line with current developments in American social and political ideology and, therefore, has an appeal that can not be conveniently dismissed as a call to overt or latent sexism.

CONCLUSIONS

We have looked at two anthropological approaches to a political phenomena, the fate of the Equal Rights Amendment. In doing so, I have departed from traditional anthropology in many respects. I am not talking here about "my village" or "my street corner." Instead, I am attempting to use anthropological constructs to talk about social and political issues in complex society. Whether or not what I have called a new paradigm in American social and political ideology—that is, the rejection of the individualistic melting pot ideology in favor of a group-oriented insistence on the maintenance of plurality and separateness—represents a truely "new" phenomenon or whether it is simply a translation, or transformation, of elements of "The American Dream" into a 1970s political and social myth remains to be seen. But I think my analysis suggests that legislation framed in cultural or social terms which are no longer pertinent, such as President Johnson's New Deal legislation of the 1960s, is doomed to failure. Policy making cannot be divorced from cultural realities, whatever they may be.

We may also suggest that the anthropological approach to complex political and social issues may be of value since it allows the analyst to view a society like modern American in the same holistic manner in which anthropologists try to view more homogeneous preliterate societies. It is, of course, literally impossible to stop being an American, if one already is one, but the exercise in objectivity can lead to a fresh look at political and social process and can allow an analysis which is not couched in the same terms as the problem it seeks to explicate. For instance, I have avoided labeling the opposition to the ERA "sexist" or "conservative." Instead, I have attempted to make sense out of anti-ERA arguments and their appeal using ideas and hypotheses about human behavior which are applicable not solely to American or Western cultures. Anthropologists have long used Western psychological and social constructs to explain behavior in non-Western societies: It is to be hoped that the application of insights gained from the study of non-Western cultures will enable us to gain a better knowledge of our own culture and of the human condition in general, so that we may contribute usefully to the formation of sane social policy.

REFERENCES

Bernard, Jessie
    1971   *Women and the public interest: An essay on policy and protest.* Chicago: Aldine-Atherton.

Brown, Barbara A., Thomas I. Emerson, Gail Falk, and Ann E. Freedman
   1971   The Equal Rights Amendment: A constitutional basis for equal rights for women. *Yale Law Journal* (April). Reprinted in the *Senate Congressional Record*, Oct 5, 1971, pp. S 15840–15869.
Douglas, Mary
   1968   Pollution. In *Reader in comparative religion*, edited by Lessa and Vogt. (3rd ed.) New York: Harper. Pp. 196–202.
Douglas, Mary
   1970   *Purity and danger.* Harmondsworth, Middlesex: Pelican Books. (Orig. 1966, London: Routledge & Kegan Paul).
Firing Line
   1973   Transcript of program taped at WETA in Wasington, D.C., March 30, originally telecast April 15th on PBS. Southern Education Communications Association.
Garretson-Selby, Lucy
   1972   The nature of American woman: A cultural account. Unpublished Ph.D. dissertation, Univ. of Texas, Austin.
Garretson, Lucy
   1973   American women in politics: Culture, structure and ideology. Paper prepared for the IXth International Congress of Anthropological and Ethnological Sciences, Chicago.
Kuhn, Thomas S.
   1962   *The structure of scientific revolution.* (2nd ed.) Chicago: Univ. of Chicago Press.
Leach, Edmund R.
   1964   Anthropological aspects of language: Animal categories and verbal abuse. In *New directions in the study of language*, edited by Eric H. Lenneberg. Cambridge, Massachusetts: M.I.T. Press. (Reprinted in Lessa and Vogt 1973: 206–220.)
Lessa, William A., and Evon Z. Vogt
   1973   *Reader in comparative religion.* (3rd ed.) New York: Harper.
Novak, Michael
   1972   *The rise of the unmeltable ethnics.* New York: Macmillan.
Schneider, David M.
   1968   *American kinship: A cultural account.* Englewood Cliffs, New Jersey: Prentice-Hall.
Wallace, Anthony F. C.
   1972   Paradigmatic processes in culture change. *American Anthropologist* 74: 467–478.

13

Economically Cooperating Units in an Urban Black Community

John R. Lombardi   Carol B. Stack

Boston University   Duke University

INTRODUCTION

This research is based on a 3-year study of a group of urbanized blacks, living principally on welfare in a small midwestern city (Stack 1974a; Lombardi 1974). A large percentage of this group was either unemployed or underemployed, and this situation, together with the housing, welfare, and social conditions, has led to the assumption of certain strategies for survival, strategies giving the group characteristics that distinguish them from the rest of the society of which they are a part and from steadily employed black families within the community.

The influence of external forces, such as unemployment, poor housing, and the welfare system—forces over which the poor have little control—tends to create continual fission and fusion of households within the black community. This pattern of household fission and fusion has typically been characterized as chaotic and disorganized. In addition, low or highly uncertain income makes economic planning, in the middle-class sense, impossible. However, we have found that as a defense against such adverse and uncertain external forces, the people of the Flats in Jackson Harbor have developed economically cooperating kin and friendship based networks. These networks function as the basis of generalized reciprocity in virtually all economic transactions, including food furniture, rent, child care, clothing. Superseding the highly fluid household composition, these networks form stable, resilient social relationships despite the hardships and uncertainty imposed by the external economy. The importance for the poor of large income and consumption sharing units has recently been reported in other studies of low-income persons in the United States. Sharing patterns among the black poor have been observed by Billingsley (1973), Ladner (1971), Rainwater (1973), and Valentine (1970). Fried and Fitzgerald (1973) have observed the importance of the resources of kin, neighbors, and friends to white working-class women without husbands or whose husbands are only sporadically available.

Sharing patterns provide the security necessary for a family to withstand fluctuations in income due to chronic underemployment and the lack of means to acquire an equity. These networks also serve as a means of regulating the distribution of goods and services within the community to ensure that no individual is significantly worse off than anyone else. Contrary to appearances, they are an expression of considerable economic forethought on the part of the members. It is our contention that these networks form a differentiated subsystem within the overall economy. This subsystem mediates the effects of the fluctuating inputs and outputs imposed by the surrounding social and economic system. In addition, it serves to regulate the distribution of goods and services.

SETTING

The Flats is the poorest section of a black community in the midwestern city of Jackson Harbor (the names are fictitious). Jackson Harbor is on a major rail line connecting several southern states with Chicago; it is on the way north for many of the black people who came to the Flats from the South in the 1930s and 1940s. The railroad remained a relatively cheap and convenient means of keeping contacts alive with relatives in the South and with friends and relatives in Chicago. Kin and friends in Chicago are important to people in the Flats, for they provide a model for an urbanized life style, contacts for the exchange of goods, and reduce the sense of isolation often felt by a repressed minority in a small city.

According to the U.S. Census, Jackson Harbor is ranked as an "urbanized area" since its population exceeds 50,000. A rather large state-run hospital is the city's major employer. Yet, only 3% of its 5000 employees are black, compared to the city's population of more than 12% black. By and large, even those 3% hold only the most menial jobs. In recent years, intensive efforts by liberal groups to increase the percentage of black employees have been totally unsuccessful. There is little industry in Jackson Harbor. An industrial company employing almost 2500 people, mostly women, recently closed down. A food processing factory with about 800 employees provides most of the industrial employment for black men. The strongly segregated craft and construction unions permit few blacks to hold jobs in their industries.

In 1968, a year of record economy in the country, unemployment among blacks in Jackson Harbor was higher than 20%. Among those working, more than 63% were service workers. In 1959, while 80% of the white families made more than $4000 per year, 60% of the black families made less. Those who found work were not significantly better off than those without work who were eligible for welfare benefits.

Jackson Harbor has been rated among the 20 most expensive cities in the United States. The income necessary for a family of four to have a "modest" standard of living has been estimated at more than $8000. In terms of average family income, the county which includes Jackson Harbor ranks in the highest 20 nationwide. Most of the white population who have chosen to live in Jackson Harbor can afford to live there; few of the blacks can.

Most of the families live in one- and two-family houses and scattered multiple dwellings. Apartment buildings are few, and there are no large housing projects. Although larger old homes in the Flats have been subdivided into tiny, inadequate apartments, the population density is much lower there than in a typical urban environment, such as Chicago. For the blacks in the Flats, however, as many such ghetto communities, crowding is severe nonetheless. Most homes in the Flats are small, wood-framed houses, bungalows, and shacks in need of repair. It is not unusual for a dilapidated four-room house to rent for $150 per month, much more than the cost of similar housing in the white community. There are too many people for the available room. Although temperatures go below 0°F in Jackson Harbor every winter, many houses have doors and windows that do not fit tightly. A common trick to seal cracks in the window casements is to fill them with water on a freezing day to provide a frigid seal until the first thaw.

Many more statistics could be added, but they would simply repeat the same depressing patterns of the situation in any "urbanized area" in the country. In all their contacts with the dominant white culture, blacks in Jackson Harbor are treated with some form of institutionalized or personalized racism.

THE STRUCTURE OF ECONOMICALLY COOPERATING UNITS

People in the Flats are continually adapting to social and economic controls imposed by the larger, industrial nation. It is important to examine the mechanisms by which the poor adapt to conditions imposed upon them by the society at large and the effects of such conditions on household structure, marital stability, and the possibility for social mobility. The conditions that have the greatest impact on the fission and fusion of households are also those conditions over which the poor have little control—employment opportunities, wages, welfare benefits, and housing.

Most of the individuals in this study were welfare recipients, as were their children and their unemployed kin and friends. Those few who were employed must be classified as underemployed due to the seasonal or part-time nature of their work and the insecurity of their jobs. Given the industrial pattern of seasonal labor and layoffs, those holding full-time jobs knew very well that, during layoffs, they would be first to go. Very few of those employed expected to hold their job for more than several months. Thus, whatever their other attributes, few employed men could be considered a reliable and stable source of household income.

It has been well documented that it is not economically advantageous for a woman to marry under such circumstances (Stack 1974b). In fact, a woman with several children may be able to maximize economic advantage by means of serial relationships. Such relationships, if they produce children, may enable a woman to extend further her network of kin through her children, thus increasing the number of people on whom she may rely (Stack 1972).

If the employment situation provides uncertain income, the welfare system provides a modicum of stable income to certain members of the community. As is well known, this too militates against the formation of stable nuclear family units. Less attention, however, has been given to another aspect of welfare regulations that affects people's ability to develop an equity. Whenever an individual acquires some money, through inheritance, savings, or winning the numbers, for example, she is immediately removed from the welfare rolls until the amount of time has passed in which the equivalent in welfare benefits would have been awarded. This makes savings, house buying, or any economic planning, encouraged for the middle classes, impossible for the poor and closes off perhaps the only other road, beside employment, to an improvement in one's economic status. The only equity or insurance a woman on welfare can acquire is through the store of good will achieved by sharing her welfare benefits and other goods and services with needy kin and friends, who in turn contribute resources and services.

The type of housing available to poor blacks and the scarcity of housing both have a severe effect on household structure. As might be expected, due to racial segregation, blacks in Jackson Harbor are forced to live in the poorest, most dilapidated sections of town. Houses are frequently condemned, and families are arbitrarily evicted because a landlord can get higher rent from another family. Removal from welfare, loss of a job, a death in the family, all may necessitate a change in residence. Most families we studied moved several times each year. Each move resulted in the rearrangement of household composition. Owing to the scarcity of housing, overcrowding was common. Many temporary arrangements became long term. Newly formed households often are successive recombinations of the same domestic networks of adults and children, quite often in the same dwellings. Households have shifting membership, but, on the average, they steadily maintain three generations of kin: males and females beyond the childbearing age, a middle generation of mothers raising their own children or children of close kin, and children. Even when people move temporarily to separate households, their social, economic, and domestic lives are so entwined with their kin that they consider themselves simultaneously a part of the residential kin groupings.

The organization of kin and family networks in the black community stands in striking contrast to family organization among both unemployed and employed white ethnics. Some preliminary research on the urban Irish in New England (Stack 1975) shows considerable economic nucleation, even among those kin still residing in extended families within Irish enclaves. Moreover, the culture of family life found among unemployed and employed families in the Flats appears to have parallels with many middle-class and professional black families. Whether black culture and these particular familial patterns derive from African forms, or from the interaction of African forms and patterns established during slavery and persisting in the face of rural and urban poverty, has not been resolved. But the continuity of family life throughout the history of black people in the United States, the continuity of cultural patterns across class lines, and the variety of cultural responses to poverty among ethnics in the cities all provide a strong argument against a culture of poverty explanation.

In the Flats, a rather stable core of kinsmen and nonkin cooperate on a daily basis and live near one another or co-reside. The basis of familial structure and economic cooperation is not the nuclear family of the middle class, but an extended cluster of kinsmen related chiefly through children but also through marriage and friendship, who align to perform domestic functions. This cluster, or domestic network, is diffused over several kin-based households, and fluctuations in individual household composition do not significantly affect cooperative arrangements.

The strength of a particular domestic network is dependent upon cooperation between adult females, between male and female kin, and between females and their childrens' fathers and fathers' kin. Close cooperation between male and female siblings who share the same household or live near one another has been underestimated by those who have isolated the female-headed household as the most significant domestic unit among the urban black poor. Likewise, a man and his kin contribute positive, valuable resources to his children, thereby enlarging the circle of people both families can count on for help.

Young women, with or without children, do not perceive any choice but to remain living at home with their mothers or other adult female relatives. Even when young women are collecting welfare for their children, they say that their resources go further when they share food and exchange goods and services daily. Young adult males tend to reside with their kin even after they have fathered children. Likewise, the jobless man, or the man working at a part-time or seasonal job, often remains living at home with his mother—or, if she is dead, with his sisters and brothers. This pattern continues long after such a man becomes a father and establishes a series of sexual partnerships with women, who are living with their own kin or friends. Households almost always have men around: male relatives, affines, and boyfriends. These men are often intermittent members of the households, boarders, or friends who come and go—men who usually eat and sometimes sleep in these households, and who contribute resources to the household.

Economic pressures among cooperating kinsmen in the black community work against the loss of either males or females—through marriage or long-term relationships—from the kin network. Female members of a network may act to break up a relationship that has become a drain on their resources. On the other hand, a man is expected to participate in his own kin network, and it is assumed that he should not dissipate his services and finances in a marital relationship. Clearly, kin regard any marriage as a risk to the woman and her children, and the loss of male or female kin as a threat to the durability of the kin network. Forms of social control against marriage emanating from the larger society are reinforced by sanctions within the Flats. Nevertheless, a woman will continue to seek aid from the man who has fathered her children, thus building up her own network's resources. She also expects something of his kin, especially his mothers and sisters. Women continually activate these lines to bring kin and friends into the network of exchange and obligation. Most often, the biological father's female relatives are also poor and also try to expand their network and increase the number of people they can depend on. All of these strategies tend to maximize and maintain long-term relationships within domestic networks.

Cooperative networks range in size: They can be as large as 50 or more individuals and include up to 7 or more households. Participants in these networks are drawn from kin and friends, but, of the two, the kin network is more enduring. An individual's kin are recognized as having some duties toward him and some claims on him. On the other hand, fictive kin relations are maintained by consensus between individuals and, in some contexts, can last a lifetime. Children very often establish close and affectionate ties with their aunts and uncles, for example, with their mother's sister's "old man" and their mother's brother's "old lady." These aunts and uncles, on the basis of their original consensual relationship, can remain in a child's personal network for a long time. Long-term ties between adults are frequently formed on the basis of the birth of a child. Women and their children's father's sisters often maintain long-term friendships, and these relationships are maintained by children and their aunts and uncles long into adulthood. Although the homes of members of a particular cooperative network in the Flats may be scattered over several miles

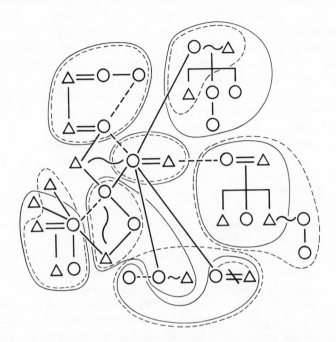

Figure 13.1   The structure and household distributions of a network containing over 50 individuals (not all children are shown). Solid bars represent consanguineal relationships; double bars tie a jural couple; a curved s-shaped line is a consensual union; a dotted line represents a long-term friendship. Initial household boundaries are shown by closed solid curves. The closed dotted curves show the household boundaries 3 months later.

and few persons in the network have cars, cab fare is spent practically every day, and sometimes twice a day, as individuals visit, trade, and help one another. The structure and household composition of a typical network is shown in Figure 13.1. The network contains over 50 individuals and initially spans 7 households. The fission and fusion of households during a 3-month period is illustrated.

THE FUNCTIONS OF RECIPROCITY

Few if any black families living on welfare for the second generation are able to accumulate enough surplus of basic necessities to be able to remove themselves from poverty or from the collective demands of kin. Without the help of kin, fluctuations in the meager flow of available goods could easily destroy a family's ability to survive. Kin and close friends who have similar economic crises know that they may share the food, dwelling, and even the few scarce luxuries of those individuals in their domestic network. Despite the relatively high cost of rent and food in urban black communities, the collective power within kin-based exchange networks keeps people from going hungry.

As low-skilled workers, the urban poor in the Flats cannot earn sufficient wages and cannot produce goods. Consequently, they cannot legitimately draw desired scarce goods into the community. Welfare benefits, which barely provide the necessities of life—a bed, rent, and food—are allocated to households of women and children and channeled into domestic networks of men, women, and children. Most of the essential and reliable resources flow from welfare mothers into kin networks.

Whether one's source of income is a welfare check or wage labor, people in the Flats borrow and trade with one another in order to maintain a flow of daily necessities. The most important form of distribution and exchange of the limited resources available to the poor in the Flats is by means of trading, or what people usually call "swapping." As people swap, the limited supply of finished material goods in the community is perpetually redistributed among networks of kinsmen and throughout the community.

The resources, possessions, and services exchanged between individuals residing in the Flats are intricately interwoven. People give various objects of exchange to others generously; new possessions, treasured items, furniture, cars, perishable goods, and services which are exchanged for child care, residence, or shared meals. Individuals enlarge their web of social relations through repetitive and seemingly habitual instances of swapping. Lily Jones, a resident in the Flats, had this to say about swapping: "That's just everyday life, swapping. You not really getting ahead of nobody, you just get better things as they go back and forth."

Cooperative domestic networks are the primary institution within which trading takes place. The trading of goods and services within domestic networks pervades the whole social—economic life of the participants. Trading in the Flats generally refers to any objects or services offered with the intent of obligating the receiving party. Mauss' (1925) classic interpretation of gift giving in primitive societies stresses the essence of obligation in gift giving, receiving, and repaying. Trading in the Flats evidences a similar obligatory nature. One who receives is expected to give and to offer goods or services, even without any request. Strong pressures of community opinion and the sanction of expulsion from the domestic trading network serve to enforce the obligation.

Ruby Banks a 25-year-old resident, analyzes her own exchange behavior and the patterened expectations and obligations with clarity.

> These days you ain't got nothing to be giving, only to your true friends, but most people trade. Trading is a part of everybody's life. When I'm over at a girl friend's house and I see something I want, I say, you gotta give me this, you don't need it no way. I act the fool with them. If they say, no, I need that, then they keep it and give me something else. Whatever I see that I want, I usually get. If a friend lets me wear something of theirs, I let them wear something of mine. I even let some of my new clothes out. If my friend has a new dress that I want, she might tell me to wait till she wears it first, and then she'll give it to me, or she might say, well take it on. That's the way I do. Lots of people done wear lots of new clothes I had.

My girlfriend Billy gave me a dress about a month ago, and last time I went over to her house she gave me sheets and towels for the kids 'cause she knew I needed them. Every time I go over there, she always gives me something. When she comes over my house, I give her whatever she asks for. We might not see each other in 2 or 3 months. If she comes over after that and I got something, I give it to her if she wants it. If I go over to her house and she got something, I take it—canned goods, food, milk, it don't make no difference.

I don't ever expect nothing back right away, but when I've given something to kin or friend whenever they think about me they'll bring something on around. Even if we don't see each other out of 2 or 3 months. Soon enough they'll come around and say, come over to my house, I got something to give you. When I get over there and they say, you want this, if I don't want it my friend will say, well find something you like and take it on. They say you shouldn't trust nobody, but that's wrong. You have to try to trust, somebody has to try to trust you, 'cause everybody need help in this world.

Last week I was sitting over at the laundry worrying that my mama didn't have nothing to eat. I took a cab over there and gave her 10 more dollars. All I had left to my name was 10 dollars to pay on my couch, get food, wash, and everything. But I ignored my problems and gave mama the money I had. Mama didn't really have nothing after she paid some bills. She was over there black and blue from not eating—stomach growling. The craziest thing was that she wouldn't touch the rent money. I gave her the last 5 dollars of my money to her. She didn't want to take no more 'cause I was helping her so much. Today she took 25 dollars out of the rent money. She paid her sister her 5 dollars and gave me 5 dollars to get the kids something to eat. I said what about my other 10 dollars, but she put me off. She paid everybody else, and I'm the one who's helping her the most. I could have most everything I needed if I didn't have to divide with my mother and her eight kids. But she's my mother, and I don't want to turn her down.

Ruby Banks' rationale shows how people intentionally obligate others in the process of swapping objects and services back and forth. A value is placed upon the goods given away, but the value is not determined by the price or market value of the object. Many goods have been acquired through previous trades. The value of the object given away is based upon its retaining power over the receiver, that is, how much and over how long a time the giver can expect returns on the gift. Two individuals rarely trade one thing in exchange for another at the same time and place. The object swapped is offered with the intent to obligate the receiver over a period of time.

The causal relationship between low economic status and trading networks is best illustrated by the example of Lydia, who at 20 had been a continuous participant in a cooperative network. When Lydia married and she and her husband both found steady employment, they moved into middle-class status in the Flats. Lydia dropped out of the domestic network, refusing to assist her sisters and friends and ceasing to participate in trading. Such behavior was condemned by Lydia's kin, but this disapproval failed to change her conduct. Lydia no longer needed the security provided by the trading system. Given her circumstances, she would be expected to give more than she would receive for an indefinite period. However, after several years Lydia and her husband separated, and she lost her job. Lydia immediately attempted to reobligate her kin by giving away many of her finest and most expensive possessions. She was establishing credit for the hard times ahead.

The expectation of future return rather than immediate exchange illustrates the insurance–savings role of trading. Goods or services are given on the understanding that the giver can receive an equivalent in return, when needed; the giver can, in effect, draw on the account.

When the resources available to a family are scarce, the fluctuations in availability can be a very important factor in determining the disposition of daily income. If these fluctuations are too large, a family could spend several days without the resources to subsist. Lombardi (1974) has shown that, in order to ensure subsistence, the average fluctuations must be kept below the amount by which the average income exceeds the subsistence minimum. If the average income cannot be increased, then means must be found to reduce the magnitude of the fluctuations in available wealth. Reciprocity is a possible means of achieving this reduction. In a more detailed demonstration, Lombardi (1974) kept daily records of income and expenditures for a typical household for a period of almost a month in order to show that, without reciprocity, fluctuations in available wealth are so severe as to leave the household without resources for several days. However with reciprocity, the impact of fluctuations is lessened, and the household is ensured a secure though meager survival.

CONCLUSIONS: THE FUNCTIONS OF POVERTY IN A COMPLEX SOCIETY

We have seen that the poor blacks living in the Flats are a part of a larger social and economic environment from which they are relatively isolated but which influences their daily lives in ways over which they have little control. Owing to unemployment, segregated housing, and educational patterns, as well as social patterns (e.g., bans on interracial marriage), blacks are not well integrated into the overall economy. Despite the hardships, they have developed economic and social mechanisms of a considerably different nature from those of the predominantly middle-class white society in which they are embedded. They have learned to survive external conditions which they perceive as highly unpredictable and arbitrary. While these external forces are totally unresponsive to their daily needs, they fluctuate so greatly as to force continual rearrangements in household composition. Irregular employment unpredictably alters an individual's ability to contribute to the household income. Although welfare provides a meager but steady income, the regulations tend to discourage two of the necessary requirements for social mobility: formation of a stable nuclear family unit and ability to develop an equity. In order to cope with all these disruptive external influences, people in the Flats have developed extended networks of economically cooperating kin and friends. These networks extend well beyond household boundaries and represent relatively stable social relationship which are maintained in the face of uncertain economic conditions and fluctuating household composition. These networks form the basis for reciprocal exchange of goods and services which enable individual members in the network to withstand the apparently arbitrary fluctuations in his or her daily economic status. Consequently, reciprocal exchanges tend to provide economic stability and a reasonable degree of economic security. While the individual cannot control the average amount of income available to him, he can, through reciprocal exchange, reduce the fluctuations and, therefore, the short-term economic hardships which would otherwise ensue.

The economic features of daily life resemble, in many ways, the features of an elementary economy. In an elementary economy, there is little surplus accumulation and minimal production of capital goods; likewise, welfare regulations discourage equity formation. In addition, there is an absence of agriculture (this is obvious, since we are discussing an urban setting), but there is continuous food-getting activities by all able-bodied members of the society. This latter does not strictly hold for our study; however, a good fraction of daily life is spent developing and maintaining the exchange networks that are necessary to obtaining a steady source of food. In an elementary economy, the relationship between production and consumption of food is immediate. People in the Flats, by and large, do not produce their own food but purchase it with the aid of food stamps at a grocery store. However, they often have no freezer and poor storage facilities. Since many do not have automobiles and have only small amounts of cash on hand, the size of each purchase tends to be relatively small. Consequently, consumption of food is relatively immediate, and frequent trips to the grocery must be made. An elementary economy is likely to have forms of generalized reciprocity, and we have seen that this is a very important economic feature of the Flats. Perhaps the major way in which their economy differs from an elementary economy is that people in the Flats are not self-sufficient with regard to foodstuffs but depend almost entirely on the external society. However, in this regard, there are still similarities, for a society with an elementary economy is subject to environmental fluctuations in food supply over which they have little control. In the Flats, it is fluctuations in monetary income and, therefore, inability to purchase food which acts as the hostile environment.

Although we have portrayed the economic life of the Flats as relatively isolated, adapting to arbitrary influences of the overall society, there are some ways in which this group, embedded in the national economy, contributes to the functioning of the larger society. As consumers of food and other goods, their influence is relatively slight, since their aggregate income is so low. However, they do act as consumers of substantial amounts of the marginal housing that the larger society has not yet seen fit to replace. In areas where urban renewal has made inroads, blacks and other poor people are merely "relocated" to other marginal areas. Often, they must pay higher rents than anyone else would be willing to pay for substandard housing until it is economically worthwhile to "renew." Consequently, poor blacks allow economic profit from deteriorating housing until other uses can be found for the land.

In addition, as a large group of chronically unemployed, they provide a pool of inexpensive and immediately available labor, which makes it easy for industry to relocate, expand, or contract quickly without the necessity of relocating labor supplies. Whenever economic exigencies require quick expansion and immediate need for unskilled labor, blacks are always available. In addition, a continual supply of unemployed individuals puts constant pressure on those who are employed to work for lower wages since they can be easily replaced. Consequently, by virtue of their poverty, the unemployed help keep wages in the industrial sector low. In addition, as has been shown by Piven and Cloward (1971), in times and areas of labor shortages, welfare benefits have been deliberately reduced, forcing more people to accept employment, while, in times of social unrest, welfare benefits have been increased. Thus, social unrest is one of the few means by which poor blacks can have any control over the factors that influence their lives. The cycle of increasing and decreasing welfare benefits has been used as a technique for regulating the poor and maintaining their utility to the larger society.

We may, therefore, view the economic features of life among poor blacks in the Flats as constituting an economic subsystem embedded in the larger society's economic system. In sharp contrast to the larger society, the embedded economy has many of the features of an elementary economy. Many of these features are necessarily adaptive to the poor who lack any influence over the arbitrary and uncertain nature of their economic environment. Consequently, they have developed stable, resilient economically cooperating networks which have the economic function of reducing the effect of external economic fluctuations on daily life. Through mechanisms of reciprocity, they regulate the distribution of resources such that no one in the network is significantly worse off then anyone else. Thus, these reciprocal exchange networks function to bring stability to a social and economic group that would otherwise be disorganized and destitute. This stable subsystem then acts as a reservoir of readily available renters and laborers which tends to stabilize fluctuations in the housing and labor markets of the larger society.

REFERENCES

Billingsley, Andrew
1973   Black family structure: Myths and realities. In *Studies in public welfare*, Paper No. 12 (Part II). Washington, D.C.: U.S. Government Printing Office.

Fried, Marc, and Ellen Fitzgerald
    1973   Family and community life in the working class. In *Studies in Public Welfare*,
            Paper No. 12 (Part II). Washington, D.C.: U.S. Government Printing Office.
Lombardi, John R.
    1974   Exchange and survival. Mimeo, Boston Univ.
Mauss, Marcel
    1925   Essai sur le don: Forme et raison de l'echange dans les societes archaiques. *Annee
            Sociologique* (n.s.) **I**: 30–186.
Piven, Frances Fox, and Richard A. Cloward
    1971   *Regulating the poor: The functions of public welfare*. New York: Vintage Books.
Rainwater, Lee
    1973   Poverty, living standards, and family well-being. In *Studies in public welfare*,
            Paper No. 12 (Part II). Washington, D.C.: U.S. Government Printing Office.
Stack, Carol B.
    1972   Black kindreds: Parenthood and personal kindreds among blacks supported by
            welfare. *Journal of Comparative Family Studies* **3**(2) (Fall): 194–206.
    1974a   *All our kin: Strategies for survival in a black community*. New York: Harper.
    1974b   Sex roles and survival strategies in an urban black community. In *Woman, culture
            and society*, edited by L. Lamphere and M. Rosaldo. Stanford, California:
            Stanford Univ. Press.
    1975   Social mobility in the 20th century city. Unpublished manuscript, Univ. of
            California, Berkeley.
Valentine, Charles
    1970   Blackston: Progress report on a community study in urban Afro-America. Mimeo,
            Washington Univ., St. Louis, Mo.

14

Policy Planning and Poverty: Notes on a Mexican Case*

Henry A. Selby

Temple University

Gary G. Hendrix

Stanford Research Institute

INTRODUCTION

Anthropologists have written much about poverty. Arguments have been waged over whether there is a black culture or a culture of poverty, whether the matrifocal family engenders black pathology (the government position) or is a consequence of poverty and, thus, pathological for black *and* white (the sociological position), or whether it is an adaptive response to employment conditions, welfare regulations, and low wages (the ecological position).

Culture, we will recall from our undergraduate days, is a patterned whole, or a set of rules for the interpretation of experience, the ideology of the human context: not so the culture of poverty. Rossi and Blum (1969) discuss the basic features of the experience of the poor and state that writers generally agree it is characterized by (*1*) intermittent unemployment, (*2*) employment at the lowest

*This research was carried out by a group of anthropologists at The University of Texas at Austin in a project entitled "Decision Making in Culture," funded by the National Science Foundation (GS-30563) and the Institute of Latin American Studies of The University of Texas. The author was principal investigator, and the other members of the research team were Jane Granskog, Gary G. Hendrix, Arthur D. Murphy, and Alex Stepick.

level of skills, (*3*) pathological family relationships, (*4*) low levels of participation in voluntary neighborhood associations, (*5*) little interest in the larger society, and (*6*) a sense of helplessness and a low sense of personal efficacy. They characterize the literature on the poor as indicating that these unfortunates share in the positive correlation between material deprivation and (*1*) family disorganization, (*2*) alienation from the larger society, (*3*) incidence of mental illness, (*4*) low competence in standard English, (*5*) higher mortality rates and bad health, (*6*) lower need achievement, (*7*) authoritarian modes of socializing children, (*8*) higher crime and delinquency rates, and (*9*) authoritarian outlooks on civil liberties and on political deviants. Similarly, Oscar Lewis, who makes passing reference to the positive aspects of the life of the poor, suggests the existence of 50-odd[1] traits characteristic of poverty, approximately 80% of which are clearly negative.

In this chapter, we adopt a different approach to the study of poverty. It is an approach emphasizing the individual's goals and their effect on certain aspects of the behavior of urban migrants and Indian villagers in Mexico whose lives, in many ways, represent conditions found among poor in the United States. The people we studied are materially deprived; their incomes range from $350 per year to a high of $1030. They are oppressed. They live in a stratified class system, and most of them are right on the bottom. They are perfectly aware of this; they know full well that, when the benefits of society are distributed, they are the last to receive, and in small measure at that. They suffer from racial discrimination: Indio in common parlance means "stupid, burrolike, unteachable." So far as a sense of relative deprivation is concerned, they feel it as much as deprived people in the United States do. They visit the city, they see television, they live in a land that exalts the democratic virtues of opportunity, and they hear daily exhortations about progress and a better life, more so than the poor here at home. An ever-increasing proportion of the young are moving away from the rural areas to the city, breaking up families, and destroying kinship networks, while, at school, teachers are making wholesale attacks upon traditional cultural values. The Mexican people we studied are not in a situation entirely different from that of the poor in our own society. A study of the strivings and strategies of the Mexican poor will yield insights about the poor everywhere.

THE MEXICAN RESEARCH

Model Building

Our approach to the study of values was rather unusual for anthropologists (although it had been foreshadowed programmatically by Joy (1967). It

[1] He claims over 70, but Eames and Goode (1972), who actually counted, could not find more than 50.

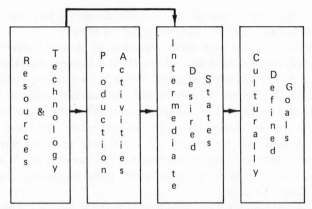

Figure 14.1 Schematic description of linear programming model of value system.

involved the adaptation of an economic production model (linear programming) to assess rationality. The goods that were to be produced were goals, and our Mexican informants were interviewed over long periods of time to find out how they thought about the goals in their lives and how they realized those goals, so that we could assess whether the individuals being interviewed were allocating their resources so as to attain their goals in an optimal fashion.

We conceived the production model in the following way (see Figure 14.1). Culturally defined goals are achieved via intermediate states and activities which are, in turn, attained through the expenditure of resources (time, labor, capital) or through the accumulation of capital and credit through productive activity (corn farming, mixed farming, wage labor, etc.). The level of technology is taken as given.

Scaling and Measurement

The task of constructing a model for a villager or urban migrant began with the discussion of his goals and the means at his or her disposal to attain these goals. For the purpose of model building, such discussions led toward the *identification* of those activities and resource expenditures permitting goal attainment. After identifying the goals, activities, resources, and their relationships in the model, equations were derived expressing these relationships mathematically. The specification of the mathematical relationships between variables in the model necessitated scaling the variables before deriving equations for the identified relationships. For example, the number of grown and working sons one has raises one's *security,* one of the village goals (see Figure 14.2), but it also raises one's productive capacity by increasing the available labor supply. Increased productivity leads to increased income, which leads to increased savings, which, in turn, affects the levels of attainment of the goals of *personal betterment, life style,* and, once again, *security.* The rates of change (in this case, "per extra son") must be ascertained by interviewing the informant.

Three types of scales were used: (*1*) culturally defined scales, (*2*) "local" scales, and (*3*) constructed scales—either a 10- or 100-point range. Cultural scales are defined by the subjects themselves. Villagers, for example, agree that there are 11 steps in the "ladder" of political and religious offices that one must climb in order to attain respect. The ethnographer, therefore, utilizes the cultural scale of 11 steps for the increments in the political ladder. But there is no such culturally defined scale for *respect,* and a 100-point scale was constructed to measure increments in respect that accrued as one ascended the 11-step ladder. Local scales are local units of measurement: pesos for income, "almudes" (a volume measure) for corn.

Questionnaire methods were considered unsuitable for the complex and difficult task of scaling. In-depth interviewing of single informants, lasting up to 200 hours in some cases, was carried out. This restricted the total sample size of villagers and urban migrants which, in 1975, was about 25, mostly urban migrants. The interview was multi-purposed. Each individual mapped his or her goals, ways of attaining them, and available resources. Each variable in the individual's map was scaled using one of the three aforementioned scales. The scaling procedure was complex, requiring many hours of interviewing, and is described briefly later.

Those variables involving attributes of people, such as leisure, were scaled by asking informants to make relative judgments about the amount of leisure a sample of people in the village have. Thus, in this case, the stimuli used to construct the scale are people, and the scale value is the amount of the variable (in this case, leisure) that the stimulus person is perceived to have. The sample of stimuli is chosen to represent the entire range of the variable. This enables one to check for consistency of relationships over the entire range, and makes possible the assessment of different rates of return at different points in the scale.

A meter stick is employed in the scaling procedure. The far left point of the line is initialized at zero, representing a stimulus point (person) who has the lowest amount of the variable being measured. Sometimes, as in the case of income, a true zero point can be established; but, for most of the values and goals being measured, this desirable metric property could not be met. The upper bound of each variable is left free to float to the point representing the most of the value the informant could imagine himself or any local person attaining. Other than zero for the low end, no numerical values are placed on the line during the scaling procedure.

The relative position of individuals on the scales is continually emphasized during the interviews, since we want the data to have interval, rather than merely ordinal, strength. We ask the informant not simply to tell us if subject A has more of a variable than subject B, but how much more. In the beginning, to ensure that the informants are able to carry out the task and that they understand the importance of relative distance in the scaling procedure, several checks are run.

First, we introduce a subject for scaling who is completely out of line with those being scaled, such as the governor of the state. Since the informant is unlikely to think that he can reasonably aspire to the levels the governor has achieved, the governor should be well above the upper bound.

Second, a "comparative distance task" is run. This is a triads or tetrads test which requires the informant to compare the magnitudes between three or four scaled subjects and to compare the distances. In the triads test, he is successively presented every scaled person in groups of three and asked to state whether the distance between A and B is greater than, equal to, or less than the distance between B and C. In the tetrad test, he is asked to compare the distances between four subjects. These comparative distance results are then compared with the scale results. In the case that there are discrepancies, we assume that the comparative distance task gives a more reliable measure, and, after explaining the discrepancies to the informant, we rescale all subjects.

Next, a check for inconsistencies in scaling is made. In the case that the informant has defined some variable as directly related to a set of independent variables, and we find that there are inconsistencies in his judgments (i.e., a subject is rated higher than another on some dependent variable when his scores on the defining variables are all lower), the inconsistency is pointed out, and an explanation is asked for. Rescaling may occur if the informant recognizes the inconsistency, but, if he insists on it, then it stands. At this stage, a further search is made for unrecognized factors that define the dependent variable in question, and, if found, rescaling occurs.

Once we are sure that we have defined the variables properly and that the scale values are as accurate as we can get them, we are ready to quantify the model by identifying the nature of the relationships between variables (linear, logarithmic, and so on) and setting up the equations.

First, one has to determine whether rates of return are constant, increasing, or decreasing over the range of the variables under consideration. In many cases, the relationships are not constant (i.e., linear). The rate of return of "cargo" to "respect," for example, is one of increasing returns. After one has passed a middle-level cargo (in the village), the rate of return, so far as the accrual of respect is concerned, increases sharply (as do the expenditures required). Decreasing returns are more typical, however, in line with the more commonly encountered decreasing marginal utility hypothesis.

Minima are set on all goal levels according to the informant's feelings as to whether life would be unbearable if he or she could not meet some given level on each goal. To ensure that an optimal solution will be attained even if the minima are not met, they are not entered into the model as constraints (which would prevent the program from going feasible and, thereby, preclude a solution); rather, the informant is penalized heavily in the objective function for not attaining those standards that are felt to be minimally necessary for a bearable life.

Specifying the Equations

Finding the right equation for the relationship between resource and activity variables is easier than for the goal variables. In the case of a linear relationship between nongoal variables, the simple regression equation is used, since the variables are not taken two at a time. If the relationship is nonlinear (i.e., increasing or decreasing returns to scale), a composite linear equation is constructed to fit the relationship. Since the contributing variables are taken two at a time, no great problems are encountered.

The goal variables, however, are much more complex, since they are defined by from three to seven predictor variables, and the predictor variables are correlated, which, given low sample sizes, lowers one's confidence in the regression coefficients as good estimators of the population values (Golderberger 1964: 192–194). Our solution was to use multiple regression equations, in the city case (where the number of cases was close to 100), and to use informant derived regression coefficients in the village case (where the number of cases was around 20). In this latter case, the informant was asked to evaluate the change in the level of the dependent variable when each of the independent variables was changed by either 10% or 20%.

A Model of a Zapotec Indian Villager's Values

We will give an example of the model based on one of our best analyzed cases, that of a Zapotec Indian villager whose name is Cristobal. Cristobal is poor, even by village standards. He became an orphan at the age of 14 and took over responsibility for his family. He has been out of the village on three occasions, twice to work and once to live with his younger brother in Mexico City. He was married at 17 and, at 37, is a grandfather. He has amassed a total capital of 3000 pesos (U.S. $240.00) after 20 years of hard work, which is invested in one quarter of a hectare of unirrigated farm land. The following is an account of the model that Cristobal operates on to get the best out of his life. The model was elicited in 140 hours of interviewing.

The Objective Function

There are five goals that Cristobal talks about when he addresses the problem of the "good life" in the village. They are: (*1*) leisure, (*2*) personal betterment, (*3*) style of life, (*4*) security, and (*5*) self-respect and the respect of others. These topics are defined well enough in his own mind, and coded well enough in his language, to enable him to talk about them easily. The objective function is a weighted linear combination of these goals, the weights being decided by Cristobal and the interviewer. He maximizes according to the following instruction:

$$\text{MAX } Z = .13X_1 + .44X_2 + .22X_3 + .18X_4 + .03X_5,$$

where

X_1 = leisure
X_2 = personal betterment
X_3 = life style
X_4 = security
X_5 = self-respect and the respect of others.

Formally, we say that these variables are defined by the activities (and states) that feed into them in the model. Each is an interval level scale that is related by equations to the other activities and states in the model. The relation of goals to activities is given in Figure 14.2 in schematic form.

Leisure

Leisure is simply defined as a logarithmic function of the time that Cristobal spends not engaged in productive agriculture. He perceives diminishing marginal returns from his investment in leisure: He realizes that he must have about 10 days off per year to recuperate from illnesses and carry out necessary social obligations, and, similarly, he realizes that, after about 60 days "off," his productivity is going to suffer, and he will, in effect, be "paying more" for his leisure. This corresponds to the villagers' feeling that there is about a 2-month period in the farming cycle when one can take it easy. Thus, the utility for leisure takes on positive value at 10 days and changes slope at 60 days, reflecting both a necessary minimum and a change on the rate of return. The function can be given as follows:

$$\text{Leisure} = .83T_1 + .42T_2,$$

where $10 \leqslant T_1 \leqslant 60$ and $T_2 > 60$.

Personal Betterment

"Personal betterment" is the most important goal to Cristobal,[2] and it is as close as he comes in his model to a purely economic concern. It refers to gains

---

[2] This is not true of all informants, as is noted later in the chapter. As often as not, villagers and town people alike stated that autonomy or independence was more important to them than getting ahead in the world materially. Autonomy and independence are coded in Cristobal's model as leisure.

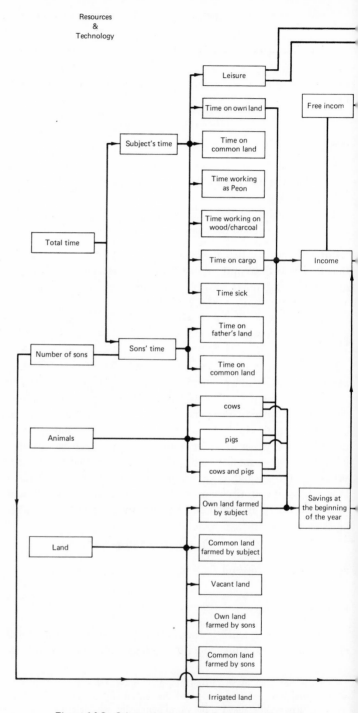

Figure 14.2 Schematic version of Cristobal's value system.

226

Production activities and desired states

Culturally defined goals vector

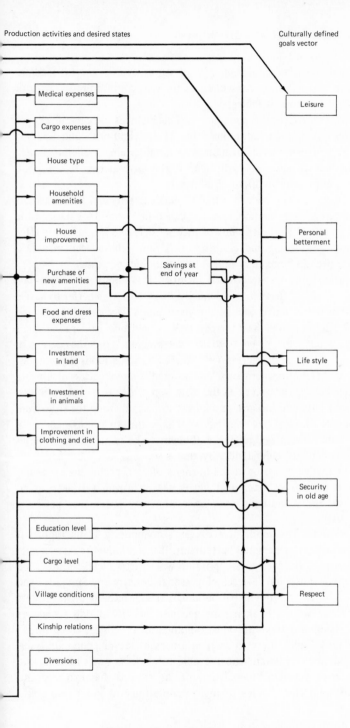

Medical expenses

Cargo expenses

House type

Household amenities

House improvement

Purchase of new amenities

Savings at end of year

Food and dress expenses

Investment in land

Investment in animals

Improvement in clothing and diet

Education level

Cargo level

Village conditions

Kinship relations

Diversions

Leisure

Personal betterment

Life style

Security in old age

Respect

Figure 14.2—*Continued*

227

made in one's material life (acquisition of capital), as well as to gains made in one's personal life that will have consequences for raising one's productivity or wealth. It is defined by seven variables:

1. *Level of savings, or capital accumulation.* This includes the capital value of all land and livestock but excludes the value of the housesite and building materials. The units that are used for monetary variables are "monetary units" which equal hundreds of pesos. As mentioned in the introduction to Cristobal, his level of savings at present[3] is 30, or 3000 pesos.

2. *Disposable income.* The second variable defining personal betterment is disposable income, or "free income," as it is called in Figure 14.2. Disposable income is locally defined as the amount of income that one has left over after the basic expenses of feeding and clothing one's family have been met. Disposable income is given in "monetary units" (i.e., hundreds of pesos).

3. *Kinship relations.* In most traditional societies, it is important to maintain close relations with one's kinsmen, and, equally important, it is better to have a large kinship group than a small one. In this particular village, which is pre-Columbian and endogamous, one has a great deal of latitude in forming one's kinship network. If one cares to be a "social entrepreneur," the rules permit it. On the other hand, being on bad terms with a large kinship group is the worst of all possible worlds. Therefore, Cristobal constructed a simple scale of kinship relations in which the highest values on the scale were for those people who had close relations with large kinship groups, and the lowest values on the scale were given to those people who had bad relations with large kinship groups.

4. *Education.* One's level of education is thought to be related to one's level of well-being. It is hard to understand why this is so, since one's literacy skills are rarely needed in the village or in the business of corn production. Presumably, education is linked with personal betterment because it is seen as an essential condition for migrating from the community to greener pastures, notably, Mexico City.

5. *Village conditions.* The modernity of one's community is an important constituent of one's level of personal betterment. If the community has a clinic, bus service, telephone, electricity, and potable water, it is clearly a desirable place to live, and it raises one's level of personal betterment. Similarly, the condition of the church, the municipal buildings, the cleanliness of the streets are important. These were all taken into account in constructing a scale of communities corresponding to points on a 10-point scale of "village conditions."

6. *Number of sons.* Children are an asset in a peasant farming community, as is well known. But male children who are able to work on one's land are the most important asset you can "own." One of the reasons that marriage and residence are such important topics to these people (and to those who study

---

[3] The present is the ethnographic present: 1972.

them) is because marriage and residence is a labor allocation game. Everyone is trying to invest sufficient money in a marriage to retain the services of the young man. Accordingly, the presence of grown and working children in a household is given a high value by Cristobal and other villagers.

7. *Health conditions.* Health conditions are important to one's personal betterment for obvious reasons: Sick people cannot work. There is not much one can do about conditions in the village, according to the way the villagers see the world. Preventive medicine is largely unknown, although there is a strong belief in the power of inoculations. Childhood diseases, in particular, cannot be prevented, even though there is a 40% chance that a child will not live to the age of five. They are constant for the community.

Personal Betterment is, therefore, defined in the following equation:

$$PB = .058 \text{ (Savings)} + .312 \text{ (Surplus free income)} - .312 \text{ (Negative income)}$$
$$+ 1.5 \text{ (Kinship relations)} + 2.5 \text{ (Education)} + 1.0 \text{ (Village conditions)}$$
$$+ 2.0 \text{ (Number of working sons)} + 1.0 \text{ (Health)}.$$

The rate of return of personal betterment is constant; that is, there is no break point where the rate of return decreases (or increases). In Cristobal's model, three variables are set as constants: education, village conditions, and health.

Life Style

A casual visitor to the village might find it hard to believe that the villagers are concerned about their style of living. To us, distinctions seem incredibly small, and everyones' lives seem monotonously similar. They themselves, however, make great distinctions between the ways that different people live, and the village is such an open place that they can keep close tabs on their neighbors.

Life style and personal betterment are linked, in the sense that they share some contributing variables, but they are not the same. One can be rich and have a grubby life style, and one can be poor and have a reasonably good style. Life style is a roster of the conditions and activities that give "movement" and "happiness" to one's life. The careful, prudent, cautious man would invest little or nothing in his style of living but would rather save every cent to buy land, cattle, and pigs. The person who wants style in his life prefers to spend money on a transistor radio or a rifle, spend some time drinking with his friends or going to the market town and shopping in the market, or, more importantly, spend some time and money looking for sexual opportunities. A person who has a rich style of life is not bored.

Life style is defined by the following six variables: (*1*) leisure, (*2*) food and dress, (*3*) village conditions, (*4*) diversions, (*5*) household amenities, and (*6*) house type.

1. *Leisure.* Leisure is defined, as before, in terms of the amount of time (in days) that one invests in nonproductive activity.

2. *Food and dress.* The diet of the village seems boring to the villagers. "There is no fruit here," they say, "we never eat meat; all we have when times are bad is tortillas and salt." And they are not exaggerating; people generally eat meat no more than once or twice a week. The diet is staple—tortillas and beans—and there is no fruit; aside from staples, everything must be bought. People who wish to relieve the boredom of the diet have to invest time in marketing (the market town is a 2½-hour walk away; bus service is maintained only one day a week).

Clothing is something that one has to care about and invest time, money, and effort into if one is to be stylish. Standard village dress is well defined: Clothing is clean and patched, but rarely shiny and new. Clothing lasts a long time in this community: A blanket which serves as an overcoat and sleeping wrap is supposed to last the wearer's lifetime and is given to the child by his godfather with that expectation. The wearing of new clothing is highly valued. It is particularly useful in the quest for sexual liaisons, both men and women are deemed to be at their most attractive when they are wearing clean, unpatched clothing.

3. *Village conditions.* Village conditions are defined in the way described in the preceding section.

4. *Diversions.* "Diversions" refers to "enjoying yourself." It requires money and the investment of time and includes drinking with one's friends, drinking with one's kinsmen at ritualized fiestas, going to market town, going to fiestas in other communities. It refers particularly to having sexual liaisons.

5. *Household amenities.* Household amenities refers to the ownership of such items as a transistor radio, a rifle, furniture in the house (i.e., a bed, tables, and chairs), up to owning a pickup truck. It should be quickly added that no one in the village under discussion owns a vehicle of any kind, but there is one in the neighboring village, and so the idea is not unknown to the villagers. There is a generalized desire to own such things as record players and television sets, now that electricity has come to the community.

6. *House type.* Housing is avowedly important to Cristobal. At the bottom of the scale (where his house is located), is the "jacalito," the house made of bamboo tied together with twine and roofed in thatch which serves as kitchen and sleeping place and accommodates neither furniture nor fiesta. In the middle of the scale is the adobe house with a separate kitchen and a porchway. In such compounds, the cooking is done away from the sleeping area, and the house is used for rituals. About 30% of the villagers have adobe houses with separate kitchens. At the top end of the scale is a kind of house that is very much admired locally. It is painted and has masonry walls, separate rooms, two stories, and steel-frame windows. It is the kind of house that represents the acme of aspiration for the villager.

The equation for life style is:

$$LS = 2.0 \text{ (Leisure)} + 3.5 \text{ (Food and dress)} + .5 \text{ (Village conditions)} + 2.0 \text{ (Diversions)} + 3.0 \text{ (Household amenities)} + 4.0 \text{ (House type)},$$

where village conditions is a constant. There are no break points in the utility function, and, therefore, constant returns are realized.[4]

Security

The fourth goal variable that Cristobal and other villagers think exercises a good deal of influence on their lives is what might be called "social security," since it entails both a feeling that one has constructed and maintained an entirely adequate kinship network within the community, and a feeling that one will not be abandoned in one's old age. Now that migration from the village to Mexico City has begun in earnest, this last problem has arisen probably for the first time in the long history of this community. So the villagers worry about the problems of growing old and not having the means to support themselves when they cannot, or do not wish to, work any longer. One of the most envied and admirable men in the village is a man who has been able to retire for the past 15 years because his sons stayed by him and have worked his lands for him. He has been able to devote his life to community service and to ritual functions, and he lives well at the same time.

Age has a complex relation to security. If one is young and has lands and sons working for one, one has a good deal of security because one can make one's household a very attractive place for one's sons to live after they are married, or, even better, one can attract one's daughters' husbands to live with one in a matrilocal contract. If one is old and has diminished savings because one has handed them over to one's children and, thereby, obligated them to remain with one, one has a good deal of security. If one is young (mid-forties), has slender resources, is barely able to seek a wife for one's son, and does not have the resources to build him his own house, then one is in jeopardy and will have difficulty inducing a son (or son-in-law) to remain with one. If one is old and has not been able to attract a child to stay with one, then one is in even greater jeopardy and has the least security of all. For a person to enjoy maximum security, he must have sufficient resources when young to contract a matrilocal

---

[4] One of the weaknesses of the present model is that, although there was much interviewing, the particular shape of the functions was not investigated as thoroughly as it should have been. The break points were not elicited directly, that is, the informants were not asked to name a figure, but indirectly through an assessment of the informant's feelings about the rate of return of the variable to his overall picture of the good life, given changes in his status quo. Obviously, these problems are not unique to our research.

marriage for his daughter, to retain the services of his son by building him a house within the family compound, and to pay the expenses of an elaborate wedding for both.

On the other hand, the value of security itself rises with age, while displaying decreasing marginal returns. People need sufficient security, but, after they attain this, they are not willing to pay much more for it.

The very complex relationship between age and security is left out of this model, since the model was run only over a 5-year period. In Cristobal's case, security was defined by two variables: (1) number of grown and working sons, and (2) level of savings. Cristobal's minimum on security is 8.0 (on a 100-point scale), and there is a cutoff point at 13.0, where the rate of return decreases by 28%. Security is given by:

$$SEC = 8.5 \text{ (Number of sons)} + 3.5 \text{ (Level of savings)}.$$

Self-Respect and the Respect of Others

Respect is an important variable in villagers' lives. If they have enough respect, they are safe from witchcraft, which is not an unimportant attribute since witchcraft is believed to be a major cause of death and serious illness. Respect of others is required in order for a person to engage in those acts of exchange that alone make community life possible. In this part of Mexico, the round of exchanges is called the *güelagüetza*: It includes help in the fields, a little corn to tide one over a period of want, small sums of money to buy at market when one is out of cash as well as large-scale benefactions, money to help pay for the wedding of one's child or for an important saint's day fiesta. Accounts are scrupulously kept (though rarely written down), and the whole village acts as a kind of insurance against disaster, since every person "of respect" is a part of the pool. Similarly, if one wants help in the fields at planting or harvest or assistance in a roof raising or house building, one can call upon those with whom one exchanges—*if* one is a person of respect.

One gains respect in a variety of ways, not all of which could be included in the model. One gains it principally by being a good kinsman, for it is in the realm of kinship that the ideals of respect are drawn up in specifics. One can also gain it through one's service to the community, through the cargo system. There is a ladder of offices in the community starting with the lowly policeman and terminating in the upper reaches of the *mayordomia* of the saints. It is a ladder of both civil and religious offices, and there are steps to the ladder. As one ascends the ladder, one gains respect, particularly in the upper reaches; but the demands on one's time and on one's finances are very severe. No office is paid; in fact, all require the expenditure of money. The office of *mayordomo* of the patron saint is in desuetude now (to no one's seeming regret), but, 15 years ago, it would have cost the average person *at least* half the value of his capital to sustain the office. Families have been known to spend up to 5 years paying off the debts that accumulated through their incumbency of the patron saint's stewardship. But the respect that accrues to one is commensurate. After passage through the highest offices, one becomes a *principal*, an elder statesman, forever freed of the burdens of taxation and municipal service and always deferred to in community affairs.

The last variable contributing to respect is education level. Although it is difficult to see what advantage one derives from a good education in the village, education is highly valued for its own sake. This is a carry-over from the traditional culture in which the "good talker" was highly esteemed; the mythagogue was admired and regarded as a teacher of the people. Respect is given by:

$$RES = 3.5 \text{ (Cargo step)} + 1.5 \text{ (Kinship)} + 1.5 \text{ (Education level)}.$$

The subjective minimum is quite low, 2.0, and the function has a break point at 5.0 where its rate of return is estimated to be halved.

Resources and Constraints

We have dealt at some length with the goals of one villager and the more immediate ways in which these goals are realized because this is the "cultural" end of the model. We can deal much more briefly with the production end of the model since, for the purposes of this chapter, we are not as interested in the intricacies of optimal corn farming schedules in temperate, semi-arid climates as we are in studying the response of economically marginal peoples to conditions of poverty. In addition, as was mentioned in the section on measurement, the problems of scaling are not nearly so difficult here as they are in the evaluation of the contribution of the states and activities to the goal categories.

Cristobal, like all the villagers, has a very limited number of ways of making a living. He has a small amount of capital (U.S. $240.00) which he has invested in unirrigable land; he has a skill—he knows how to shape wooden beams that can be sold to peole who are building houses. Some options are open to him, although not at his present low level of capital accumulation: He could become a dairy farmer, for example, though on a very small scale. (The largest herd in this dairying village is four cows.) If he raised pigs along with cows, then he could gain some profit on their sale. (There is no profit in pig raising if one has no cows providing whey for pig feed.) He shares with the other villagers a common resource: the common land. There is ample hilly, rocky, poor land surrounding the village that he can farm if he wants to. It is labor intensive: The oxen cannot be used to plough, weed, or seed; everything has to be done by hand with a hoe. The yields, however, are good, as good as on the dry farming land that he owns in the piedmont.

One last detail of Cristobal's life has to be mentioned before we examine the optimal solution for Cristobal's life. As was mentioned earlier, children are important in peasant agricultural communities. Sons who are out of their majority and who can work on one's land are particularly important economic assets. Cristobal had such a son, but, in 1971 he died of yellow fever, and Cristobal feels his loss very keenly. This keen sense of loss, which is both personal and economic, should and will turn up in the scaling of his values. He is likely to overestimate the value of his son's contribution to the "good life," if only because he feels so deprived and saddened to be without him.

Optimal Solutions

The linear programming problem is as follows: *Maximize an objective function which consists of the goals (the things the individual wants in life), subject to resource constraints.* An optimal solution will be the conditionally rational solution: It will state how Cristobal *ought* to allocate his time, capital, and labor so as best to achieve what he wants out of life. We can run the program over a number of (simulated) years and find out how he should best allocate his resources over a long period, if we assume that the equations which relate goals to activities and resources do not change, even though his status quo does. We will not be making predictions, but we will be looking more closely at the implications of Cristobal's feelings about the way his goals and activities are related.

This Year—1972

Cristobal does not need a computer to tell him that this year has been ghastly. Because of the deeply felt loss of his son and his deteriorated capital position, he feels very insecure, and, in fact, the computer records that his security level does indeed fall below the subjective minimum which Cristobal defined. His objective function takes on a negative value for that reason, and he is told that he must work as hard as is humanly possible to meet this (unsatisfactory) optimum. He is told to spend the maximum amount of time on farming in the rocky upland common and then, as soon as the growing season is over, to spend a maximum amount of time either working on wooden beams or, when he cannot obtain a permit to work in the woodland, to obtain wage labor. He is not to attend any saint's day *fiestas*, to go to town, nor purchase any luxury goods. He is to invest the absolute minimum in clothing, food, and housing. The optimal solution for this year is Hobbesian indeed: poor, nasty, and brutish, if not short.

For the next year (as is indicated in Table 14.1, for 1973), he should do much of the same. The computer tells him to switch farming strategies from corn farming to mixed dairy farming as soon as he can accumulate enough capital to buy a milk cow and a pig. He will continue farming as much of the common land

Table 14.1
Optimal Solution for Cristobal

Row number	Variable name	Year			
		1973	1974	1975	1976
1	Time spent working (in days)	312	312	210	210
2	Time spent working on common land (in days)	180	180	180	180
3	Time spent working on irrigated land (in days)	5	8	12	0
4	Time spent on cargo (in days)	0	0	0	0
5	Time spent working on wood and charcoal production (in days)	83	83	35	47
6	Time spent by son on own dry farming land (in hectares)	0	0	0	46
7	Amount of common land farmed (in hectares)	3.37	3.37	3.37	3.37
8	Amount of dry farming land owned (in hectares)	0	0	0	.575
9	Amount of irrigated land owned (in hectares)	.06	.10	.14	0
10	Income from cow—pigs (in 100's of pesos)	1.79	2.87	4.13	0
11	Income from wood and charcoal production (in 100's of pesos)	15.0	15.0	6.32	8.46
12	Total income (in 100's of pesos)	56.0	56.0	56.0	49.0
13	Savings at the beginning of the year (in 100's of pesos)	30.0	48.0	66.6	69.0
14	Savings at the end of the year (in 100's of pesos)	48.0	66.6	68.9	46.0
15	House type maintained during the year (values on 10-point scale)	0	0	0	0
16	Household amenities (values on 10-point scale)	0	0	0	0
17	Money spent on food and dress (in 100's of pesos)	36.4	36.4	36.4	36.4
18	Money spent on drinking, fiestas and diversions (in 100's of pesos)	0	0	11.0	43.9
19	Leisure time (in days)	10	10	60	60
20	Amount that he falls below the "minimum security line" (scale)	2.61	.26	0	0
	Goal variables				
21	Leisure	.5	.5	5.0	5.0
22	Personal betterment	20.9	22.2	16.4	10.0
23	Life style	5.0	5.0	25.7	60.2
24	Security in old age	7.7	7.7	8.0	13.8
25	Respect	20.0	20.0	20.0	20.0
26	Overall	13.0	15.4	15.9	21.0

as he can, making wooden beams, and hiring out his labor, until he has satisfied his minima, and then he can change his mode of living.

By 1974, his minima are satisfied (see row 20, for security), and it is interesting to see what he does. He slacks off immediately, even though his level of savings is hardly exessive at the beginning of the year (6600 pesos or U.S. $528.00) and even though he has been able to increase his capital at the rate of 50% per year (see savings, rows 13 and 14 in Table 14.1), he abruptly terminates this strategy of capital accumulation as soon as his minima are met. He is instructed to invest no money in food, clothing, and housing, to reduce his working time to 210 days per year (row 1), which raises the value of his objective function by enabling him to invest time in leisure (row 21, which notes a tenfold rise to 60 days of leisure) and time and money in enjoying himself (row 18 gives investment data). This brings about a fivefold increase in his living style (row 23) which had remained at its bare minimum since the death of his son in 1972.

In 1975, this pattern of relaxed living takes on tones of profligacy. His next oldest son comes of age, and his style of living should change drastically if he allocates his resources rationally. He is to make maximum use of his son's labors (row 6, the maximum being 46 days), and he spends an enormous amount of money on enjoying himself, which includes activities such as drinking, seducing women, going to fiestas in other communities, and spending time lounging around the market town and drinking beer with friends. It is interesting to note what he should not do. He should not spend a centavo more than the minimum on his diet and clothing, nor should he spend any money to improve his house or to purchase consumer goods, if he is to allocate his resources optimally; his investments should be made carefully so as to yield a promiscuous profligacy.

We can leave Cristobal at this point. The good times will pass in the course of a year. His minima begin to be threatened. The marginal return of enjoying himself has to change only very slightly to put him back to work again.[5] He will have new demands on his capital if he intends to keep his son with him, for, in that case, he must build his son a house, first purchasing a house plot, and that will divert his resources.

One last question remains to be answered before we conclude with a general discussion of all the models for individuals that we have constructed. How "real" are these models? Do they describe either what the locals think they ought to do, or do they come at all close to describing the way in which the locals allocate their time, capital, and labor? The answer to both questions is a provisional "yes." There most certainly are cases in which the models depart

---

[5] Sensitivity analysis indicates that a 25% reduction in the rate of return from money invested in "enjoying one's self" to "style of living" will change the optimal solution back to the hard-working profile of the first years.

Table 14.2

Informant Evaluation and Optimal Solution
(Objective Function Value)

Year	Informant-derived well-being index	Program-derived well-being index
1972	unsatisfactory life	negative value
1973	14.0	13.0
1974	15.0	15.4

from the observed behavior, but, in some of these cases, the informants realize that the model is "right" in the sense that they are acting suboptimally. For example, the villagers do not adopt dairying and mixed farming with the alacrity that the model suggests they ought to. A detailed economic analysis by Granskog (1974) has shown that the linear programming models are right economically and wrong culturally. When she questioned the villagers closely on their economic strategies, they pointed out that, although the expected value of income from mixed farming was greater, they felt more secure if they had a year's supply of corn at hand, and they felt that they would rather make every effort to achieve sufficiency in corn, even though this violated the principle of profit maximization which they endorse in general. So, in this respect, our claim would be that, even where the model is wrong, that is, inadequate descriptively, it may be right in that the locals realize, and are content with, a suboptimizing strategy.

In any simulation, there is the problem of the fit of the simulated model to the behavior of the system. The one measure that seems to give face validity to these results is the very close relationship between where the informants think they ought to be, that is, what they regard, within reason, as the best they could achieve, and where the program locates them. Table 14.2 gives Cristobal's feelings about where he could be, along with the optimal solution, and they are extremely close.[6]

In a model for a comparatively affluent urban migrant that was developed in the same project and reported in Stepick and Hendrix (1973: 40), measures were available on 12 behavioral variables comparing the observed distribution of time and money with the program-derived optimal value, and, with one exception— row 8—the fit is impressive, as can be seen in Table 14.3.

Our preliminary analysis indicates that we can state, with a certain amount of

---

[6] The reader may recall that the number refers to a level of overall achievement of a person known to the informant. We are not suggesting that our informants can directly interpret or yield assessments in terms of real numbers.

Table 14.3

Observed and Optimal Values for Twelve Variables in City Model

Row number	Activity	Observed value	Optimal value	Percentage difference
1	Time spent working (in days)	242	232	4.1
2	Time spent on community service (in days)	52	56	7.6
3	Time spent with mistress in second household (in days)	39	40	2.0
4	Time spent enjoying oneself	20	22	10.0
5	Money spent on health care	U.S. $100	U.S. $80.00	20.0
6	Money spent on diet and clothing	U.S. $728	U.S. $588.00	19.2
7	Money spent on enjoying oneself	U.S. $108.00	U.S. $109.00	.9
8	Money spent on consumer goods	U.S. $120.00	U.S. $224.00	100.0
9	Money spent on children's schooling	U.S. $84.00	U.S. $85.50	1.0
10	Amount of money retained in cash	0	0	—
11	Amount of money spent maintaining second household	U.S. $291.20	U.S. $289.60	.05

confidence, that the informants tend to act rationally (if we include the full range of culturally defined goals in the objective function).

The Model's Implications for Public Policy

By way of conclusion, we shall discuss briefly four themes from this research that have seemed important to us and to public policy formation.

Goal Priorities Are Not Obvious

One of the simplest and most obvious lessons is that goal priorities of the poor are not immediately obvious. The literature on poverty would lead one to believe that the most important preoccupation of the poor is the pursuit of economic security. Our research shows that this is only partially true. Of highest importance to the Indian villager and city migrant, as often as not, is what they call "liberty," which can be interpreted as a desire for independence, autonomy, freedom from outside interference—in a word, a feeling of control over their own lives.

Sometimes the villagers we interviewed put it in hedonistic terms. They justified their remaining in the economically backward village by saying, "If I do not want to go to work, then I do not go to work, and no one can tell me I have to" or "Sometimes I feel like going drinking with my friends, and, although my wife gives me hell for it, I am able to do it here, where I would not be able to in the city." In the city, one construction worker whom we studied extensively was worried about his economic security and about the education of his child in secondary school, but he still used a major part of his resources to maintain a second wife and a second family of small children, saying, "A man has to have liberty to pursue his manliness" and "If you are not independent, then you are a caged man and do not have any sense of freedom at all."

When we plotted the optimal solutions for our informants, answering the question of how they best could arrange their lives, given their conscious goals and their means of satisfying those goals, the "city solution," in essence, said, "Take all the liberty you can, until it starts to cut severely into your productive effort." The average optimal work week for the city dweller was 4½ days, when he could work 6 or 7 days. In the village, the optimal work week was about the same, unless the villager was failing to meet minimum levels of noneconomic values of self-respect and social security, in which case he had to work twice as much to provide an economic substitute for these nonmaterial goals.

Rates of Return Are Variable and Nonlinear

Not only is it important to find out what a person's goals are, it is also necessary to examine carefully the utility payoff of each goal. Minimum standards are crucial. If important minima are not satisfied, then distortions appear in the activity mix until the minima are met. In the village model, the two more influential minima are in the areas of "social security" and "self-respect and the respect of others." If a person is deficient in both, he is placed in a double bind because the demands are contradictory. To gain his minimum level of security, he must either increase the number of working children, difficult to do by fiat, or increase his savings, which requires an increase in his working time and a concomitant decrease in family- and community-oriented activities. Contrariwise, to achieve a minimum of self-esteem and respect from others, he has to devote himself to the collective good by serving in time- and money-consuming municipal offices. If he sponsors a religious festival (costing thousands of pesos), his savings will deteriorate accordingly; if he devotes time to kinship relations, he must do so at the expense of available work hours. In short, he can only extricate himself from his predicament by working at a superhuman pace—by rising every day at three in the morning to cultivate an extraordinary amount of common land, in the hope of raising sufficient resources so that he has free time and money to attend to his other needs.

The distortion this breeds in his activity profile can be seen in the change occurring as soon as he meets his minima. His work pace slackens immediately, and he develops his social life to a marked degree. The possible analytical distortion is the facile conclusion that he is working for his economic well-being, which not only is not true but renders his activity pattern uninterpretable.

Students of traditional Mesoamerican life have often wondered about the supposed irrationality of villagers who "squander" thousands of pesos in elaborate marriage ceremonies or in the sponsorship of fiestas. These marriage sponsorships may seem costly and spendthrift in our eyes, but, in their eyes, it is critical in anchoring the child and the child's spouse to their side, thereby providing a measure of security that alone allows the pursuit of other (including material) goals. Sponsoring a fiesta generates sufficient respect for the pursuit of an enjoyable lifestyle as well.

Decreasing marginal utility has a conventional place in microecnomic theory and need not be discussed here. It should be noted, however, that threshold effects in our data, representing changes in rates of return, are built into the model. We noted, for example, an upper bound on the accumulation of material wealth for our richest urban migrant. This upper limit appeared when his income increased to 20% above current levels. In interviewing this subject, it was clear that the marginal utility of more income sank to zero because it would propel him into a different world and a different style of life—that of urban lower middle class. The situation reminded us of conversations Selby had had with petty officers in the Navy who refused warrant officer status, despite the desirability of increased pay and prestige, on the grounds it would entail an entirely different style of life—the wardroom style.

Similarly, we noted that the decreasing marginal utility of the value of self-respect and the esteem of others, in the village case, made the filling of high office quite difficult. Those suitable for high posts had already satisfied their goals, and they evaluated the return as too small to justify the trade-off in time and money. The possible connection between this (formally rational) attitude and the oft-noted marginal participation of the urban poor in the institutions of the larger society suggests a further line of reasoning. If a person accepting a position of high office cannot justify doing so in terms of its symbolic rewards (i.e., "respect"), then, presumably, his motives are other than those defining the office. Monetary gain is one such possible motive, since the decreasing marginal return of income for poor people is not as marked as it might be for individuals better off economically. Therefore, a poor person takes the post to increase, not respect, but his level of economic well-being. Whether here at home or in an

Indian village, "being on the take" becomes an expected behavior, a means of rationalizing apparently irrational behavior.

Paths Are Complex and Overdetermined

A third point sometimes overlooked in social research is that the paths (or, more correctly, "edges") are overdetermined; a goal may be satisfied in more than one way. This, of course, means that different activity mixes can be constructed, depending on ecological relations (in our case, village versus city) and personality (taste preference for activities), among other possible factors. It also means that the generative model we construct of goal satisfaction will not predict, except in a probabilistic way, what any individual will do.

One of the goals both villager and city migrant wish to meet is a style of life. It can be obtained by eating well (including in one's diet a quantity of store-bought items, particularly meat), by dressing well (not wearing patched, secondhand clothes and dressing one's children in new fatigues for school), by spending time and money in constructing and furbishing one's dwelling, by improving one's education, by improving the conditions of one's community, by improving the quality of one's kinship relations, and by having available time and money in order to enjoy oneself: drinking, socializing, exploring the world through books and magazines (if one is literate), traveling, visiting the market town, the big city, or relatives in other parts of the country, or just "watching the Fords go by," as we used to say. Likewise, some of these activities will help satisfy goals other than life style. Increased time in drinking and visiting relatives will raise one's level of respect and security. Eating better will increase one's level of health, and so on. The goals are related to the activities in cross-cutting, complex ways.

One of the results of our research has been the focusing of our attention on the conditions under which villagers and urban migrants alike would improve their diet, their dress, and their housing. We find it almost impossible to get them to change. They repeatedly assure us that these items are important to their overall well-being and that they will strive to raise their style of life (as we define it), but they follow their true desires, as represented by the model, by putting these activities in the bottom rank of their priorities. At the risk of sounding mystical, it is as though they unconsciously take externalities into account when they plan for action but are oblivious of them when they talk about their goals and activities.

Were one to wish to intervene in their lives and change their patterns of diet, dress, and housing, clearly one would receive conscious support from them, on the one hand, but one would have to subsidize their activities heavily in order to induce them to carry through the necessary programs. If one used one's "common sense," or took their "ideological" statements at face value, one would be nonplussed by their inconsistency in wanting these improvements and being unwilling to bring them about.

Dynamic Shifts and Discontinuities Occur

In running the model over time and carrying out sensitivity analyses, we have come to be impressed by another aspect of the subjects' behavior—the way major shifts take place in activity mixes. When we run the model over time, we are not making predictions about the subject's future behavior or his behavior under changed circumstances. We are asking about the implications of his currently held value system, given his status quo at the time of the interview, and these operations are a means of interpreting and understanding the models. Two results of this analysis have already been mentioned: the urban migrant's resistance to entry into the lower middle class and the down-playing of the importance of food, dress, and diet in decisions about how best to improve life style.

Another result can be taken from the model of the villager we know best and will serve to illustrate, once again, the rationality underlying supposedly bizarre behavior. Cristobal's case is illustrative. Cristobal lost a 16-year-old working son last year from yellow fever. He sorely misses him, and this is reflected in the interviews and the scaling results. In running his model over time, we find that his next oldest son comes of age in 4 years, in the sense that he will be finished with school and able to help his father with the work. The result is dramatic. Cristobal's optimal solution shows that what he "ought" to do, given his present ideas and a working son to help him, is go on a binge. As was noted, his economic position deteriorates; in fact, his overall income drops 13% from $448 (U.S.) a year to $392. He changes his farming strategies entirely, taking advantage of his son's labor input to move from small scale animal husbandry to labor intensive dry corn farming, and he spends the whopping sum of $7 a week (U.S.) on his libertine life. His savings drop 33% from $552 to $368.

A closer examination of the results of running the model over time shows that Cristobal's binge is a temporary reaction to a changed set of circumstances. During the period when he was working alone, he slowly accumulated resources in order first to meet his minimum security levels and then his minimum level of respect and esteem. Thereafter, his holding of land and livestock slowly improved as he settled down to an equilibrium solution he could live with. With the advent of his son's majority, this equilibrium is distorted completely, and he appears to be destroying himself. (Villagers have been known to do this, falling in love with the dissipated life and eating up their resources, as they say locally, in whoring and drinking.) By the end of the year, however, a reaction sets in, and feedback processes are activated to terminate this temporary strategy. Cristobal will have to rebuild his economic base because, if he does not, the son will not be able gainfully to use his time in working for the father, the father will not be able to arrange a decent marriage for the son, the son will leave, and Cristobal will be back to square one. His security has sunk close to the minimum level by the end of his year's dissipation, and his level of respect is close to the margin as well. The model is very sensitive to these minima and will put him "back to work" very quickly when the thresholds are reached.

The point of this discussion is to illustrate that what might be viewed as self-destruction behavior may not be. A change in an individual's life circumstances (such as the loss of a son) may cause a dramatic perturbation in behavior without altering one's goals in the slightest.

These are some of the lessons we have learned from the analysis and research on the villagers and urban migrants of Oaxaca. We feel we have but scratched the surface; much remains to be done by way of analysis, experimental work, the construction of new model forms, interviewing, and so on. But if our work has shown that it is both possible and necessary to construct pictures of people's lives that include some of the nonmaterial, psychological, social, and cultural constraints upon their behavior, then we will be pleased.

CONCLUSION

Our analysis points out the error of defining poverty as a kind of pathology. We have gone further, as well, by showing not only that poor people are coping with their environment and their material deprivation in non-middle-class ways, but the ways in which they are adapting and how they have constructed a value system within which they are entirely consistent, even when it generates behavior seemingly inconsistent, bizarre, or even self-destructive. We hope we have shown by examples how important it is to be aware of Shaw's admonition that doing good for others is a risky business if the others in question do not share the same tastes. We also hope that we have not romanticized the life of these poor villagers and urban migrants, because, if we have, we not only would be unfaithful to their experience, but we would be denying them their own insight into poverty: It is better to be rich than poor.

And lastly, at the risk of sounding banal, we hope we have shown in our research something of which we are all aware: Life is complex, and understanding how people operate in a cultural milieu requires more than superficial examination of their stated priorities, more than a commonsense understanding of their problems; it requires an attitude toward their lives corresponding more closely to the way we view our own.

ACKNOWLEDGMENTS

We gratefully acknowledge the support of NSF, as well as the material and moral encouragement of Bill Glade, the Director of the Institute of Latin American Studies.

REFERENCES

Eames, Edwin, and Judith Goode
1972   *Urban poverty in a cross-cultural context.* New York: Free Press.
Golderberger, A. S.
1964   *Econometric theory.* New York: Wiley.
Granskog, Jane
1974   Agricultural efficiency in a Zapotec Indian village. Unpublished doctoral dissertation, University of Texas, Austin, Texas.
Howry, Jeffrey, and Gilbert Hendren
1970   Optimize or satisfice? Adaptation in two band-level societies. Manuscript, Harvard Univ.
Joy, Leonard
1967   An economic homologue of Barth's presentation of economic spheres in Darfur. In *A.S.A. Monographs 6: Themes in economic anthropology*, edited by Raymond Firth. London: Tavistock Publications. Pp. 175–189.
Rossi, Peter, and Zahava D. Blum
1969   Class, status and poverty. In *On understanding poverty*, edited by Daniel P. Moynihan. New York: Basic Books.
Stepick, Alexander, and Gary G. Hendrix
1973   Predicting behavior from values. University of California at Irvine, *Working Papers in Behavioral Science* No. 43. Irvine, California.

The Issues of Language

III

The Issues of Language

15

The Language Debate: Education in First or Second Language?

Patricia Lee Engle

Instituto de Nutrición de Centro América y Panamá

INTRODUCTION

For the past 50 years, the proper treatment of children whose home language differs from the language of the school has been an educationl, sociological, psychological, and, in many respects, a political issue. The debate centers around two straightforward questions: (1) Will a child learn to read more rapidly in his second language if he is first taught to read in his primary language? (2) Will the child achieve greater general knowledge of other subject matter areas in his second language if he is taught these subjects first in his native language?

In some minds, the debate is settled. In a historical UNESCO conference, resulting in the monograph, *The use of vernacular languages in education* (1953), the assembled experts established as *axiomatic* that the best medium for teaching is the mother tongue of the pupil. Similar views have been voiced more recently: for instance, from Saville and Troike (1971: 50), "An axiom of bilingual education is that the best medium for teaching is the mother tongue of the student." Such statements are made about reading as well. Weber (1970) believes that there is some evidence that this approach (teaching reading first in the native language) has long-term benefits. Saville and Troike (1971) feel that

247

"the basic skills of reading transfer readily from one language to another" (p. 50). Advocates of the other side, however, are not silent. Pozas and Pozas (1956), working in Mexico, felt that reading, writing, and learning a foreign language were inextricably related processes; therefore, a child should be taught to read as he is learning a new language, using a "direct method." However, Bull (1955), in his review of the UNESCO monograph, commented on the difficulty of establishing appropriate learning materials in many vernaculars. He accused the UNESCO group of placing the psychological and pedagogical needs of the child above political realities, in which linguistic unity is a necessary and significant goal to be achieved through education. Venezky (1970), in reviewing the literature on this question, stated, "One would conclude that the native literacy approach, although possessing obvious cultural advantages over the standard language approach, has yet to be proven scholastically superior" (p. 338).

The question, then, is as yet open to debate. The primary purpose of this chapter is to survey some of the relevant literature in order to evaluate the evidence bearing on the issue of what language to use in teaching minority children in a bilingual culture. The problem has worldwide significance. The pioneering research has been in countries such as the Philippines and South Africa. Only recently has choice of language medium in schools become an issue in the United States. This review will summarize some of the critical international literature.

A REVIEW OF THE MAJOR ISSUES

In the areas to be discussed, both the relationship between the national language group and the minority language group and the status of the minority language vary according to the political situation. For instance, in the highlands of Mexico and Guatemala, Indians descended from the Maya, who speak primarily oral Mayan languages, are taught in Spanish in the national schools. Their relationship to the major culture is that of an isolated, impoverished minority. In terms of language status, each of the Mayan languages is primarily oral and is spoken by only a fraction of the Indian population. None of the languages are used internationally. On the other hand, Canada's French-speaking minority are (presumably) economically and socially equivalent to the English speakers, and their language has a long and lustrous written tradition. Spanish speakers in the United States fall between those two groups; they are an impoverished minority, in large part, but speak an internationally recognized language.

In this chapter, the term vernacular refers to a language spoken by a subgroup and is not the dominant language of the country (UNESCO 1953). The vernacular is the child's first language and the predominant language spoken in the child's home. The second language, usually the national language, is the one in which the child is to develop competence. In most cases, the implicit or explicit goal of governing agencies is to teach the language of the majority in the most efficient way, not to preserve the language and culture of the minority. However, some systems of education also value the preservation of the subgroup's culture and language for its own sake.

The two primary modes of instructing children of a nondominant language group who are expected to learn the language of the dominant group can be labeled the "Native language approach" and the "Direct method approach." Each of these approaches is summarized in Table 15.1.

A survey of the literature advocating each approach yielded a number of supporting arguments. Although they neither exhaust the various positions nor reflect unanimous agreement, a summary of these arguments is presented to

Table 15.1

Schooling components	Native language approach	Direct method
I. Reading	Introduce reading in first language until child achieves good reading level, then introduce reading in the second language.	Introduce second language orally; begin reading instruction in second language only when the spoken language has been learned reasonably well.
II. Introduction of other subjects	The native language is used as a medium of instruction for other subjects; gradually the second language is introduced as medium of instruction.	Second language is used as a medium of instruction for other content areas.
III. Teaching of unused language	The second language is first introduced as an oral subject in structured and ordered form.	No equivalent: First language is not taught as a subject.
IV. Teacher characteristics	Teacher is a bilingual native speaker (probably from the ethnic group of the students).	Teacher is a fluent speaker of second language and may or may not be from community.
V. Program goals	The approach suggests that the vernacular will be used in written form in other contexts; thus, a program goal is to make students literate in both the first and second languages.	Program goal is to make students literate in second language, to become part of the larger society. Little interest is shown in first-language literacy.

highlight some of the main contrasts between the two instruction modes (see Table 15.2).

To summarize, the foci of the disagreements are:

1. the transfer of reading skill from one language to another;
2. the appropriate stage in the child's development for introducing reading and the second language;
3. the effects of pride in culture and language on reading and educational learning;
4. the relative rates of learning educationally related skills when presented in the vernacular or when presented in second language;
5. the best instructional methods for teaching a second language;
6. the characteristics of teachers and teacher training programs that lead to success in teaching under the two systems;
7. differences in learning styles in home and school learning;
8. the presence and possible effects of negative stereotyping of students by teachers;
9. long-term goals for the students.

One final problem must be kept in mind. Whenever a program in an oral vernacular is recommended, the development of dictionaries, materials, and equipment must be undertaken, and the relative cost of this effort cannot be ignored.

Table 15.2

Arguments for native language approach	Arguments for direct method approach
I. Reading	*I. Reading*
A. Once the child has learned to read, transferring this skill to a new language is easy (Saville and Troike 1971; Gudschinsky 1970).	A. The child becomes confused by first learning to read in the vernacular, then having to transfer to another language; the direct method is simpler (Bull 1955; Pozas and Pozas, 1956).
B. It is easier to learn to read an orthography that has a regular phoneme—grapheme relationship (as do most of the vernacular languages which linguists have recorded) (McQuown 1941; Columbia 1926).	B. (no equivalent) Depending on the languages, the first and the second might also have regular orthography.

Continued

Table 15.2 (*continued*)

Arguments for native language approach	Arguments for direct method approach
I. *Reading*	I. *Reading*
C. The child can begin reading when he is ready; his readiness period is not wasted.	C. The child should learn the second language as soon as possible, since the older he is, the harder it will be for him to learn a second language (Venezky 1970).
D. What he is reading makes sense and is, therefore, easier to read (Modiano 1973).	D. Reading will make sense to the child since he should be taught the second language orally first (Tireman 1948).
E. He may recognize letters more easily because the language is familiar (Piaget and Inhelder 1969; Weinreich 1967).	E. (no equivalent)
F. He has increased respect for his language and culture because it is being taught in school (Weinreich 1967).	F. Teaching literacy in the dominant second language will give the person tools for admission to the dominant culture and will aid in his economic development (Bull 1955; Ramos *et al.* 1967; Heath 1972).
G. Increased self-pride makes it easier for child to learn to read (no real evidence).	G. (no equivalent)
H. (no equivalent)	H. The time and expense necessary to create good materials in every native language makes the other approach prohibitive
II. *Medium of instruction of other subjects*	II. *Medium of instruction of other subjects*
A. Because the child can understand what is being said, he will be more likely to succeed and, therefore, develop a sense of being successful in school; he may not feel as isolated as when the language is strange (Ramos, Aguilar, and Sibayan 1967; Lavallee 1973).	A. Child will learn the second language as children first learn a language—informally, from hearing it spoken.

Continued

Table 15.2 (*continued*)

Arguments for native language approach	Arguments for direct method approach
II. Medium of instruction of other subjects	*II. Medium of instruction of other subjects*
B. Child learns how to learn in his own language (Holm 1973).	B. (no equivalent)
C. Again, the prestige of the local language is enhanced by making it a language of instruction.	C. (no equivalent)
D. As the child learns the concepts in two languages, he becomes more flexible, better able to handle the concepts (e.g., Giles 1971).	D. Some subjects, such as math, are better handled with only one language, as they are very difficult to switch from language to language (Saville and Troike 1971).
E. Any language can be used to express any concept (UNESCO 1953).	E. Most vernaculars do not have the technical terms necessary for advanced learning. Thus, either the language can be adapted or the second language could be learned instead (Pozas and Pozas 1956; Bull 1955; Ramos *et al.* 1967).
F. The child is given opportunities for self-expression in his own language, which he would not be able to have in a second language for at least several years.	F. The child will learn more rapidly and will be competent sooner if he is given all instruction in the second language.
G. (no equivalent)	G. Good materials in the vernacular are often difficult to find or develop.
III. Introduction of second language as a subject	*III. Introduction of first language as a subject*
A. Second language can be introduced systematically (e.g., according to rules of language acquisition). Thus, the child is more likely to understand than if language were simply presented randomly, as is the case when the second language is used as the medium of instruction (Saville and Troike 1971).	A. Child learns language like a young child would; therefore, the first language need not be systematically taught (no evidence).

Continued

Table 15.2 (*continued*)

Arguments for native language approach	Arguments for direct method approach
IV. Teacher Characteristics (presuming that the teacher is from the same community or group as the children)	*IV. Teacher Characteristics (presuming that the teacher is from dominant cultural group rather than from that of the children)*
A. The teacher can better relate to the community (Modiano 1973).	A. Teacher may be better-trained than the native teacher (Ramos *et al.* 1967).
B. The children and teacher can communicate from the initial days onward (Modiano 1973).	B. Teacher may have a good mastery of the second language, which the native teacher may not have.
C. The teacher may understand the learning styles of the children, and how they are different from those needed in the school setting (although he may not do anything about it) (Philips 1970; John 1972).	C. (no equivalent)
D. Teacher may be seen as more trustworthy (Modiano 1973).	D. (no equivalent)
E. Teacher may not have negative stereotypes about the children and their language (Gumperz and Hernandez—Chavez 1972).	E. (no equivalent)
F. Children can see the occupation of teacher as one for which they might qualify by their schooling and, thus, have higher life expectations (no evidence).	F. (no equivalent)
V. Program goals	*V. Program goals*
A. The students are taught in order to help them integrate, both psychologically and economically, into the dominant culture. (The same result is given by both approaches for different reasons).	A. The students are taught in order to help them integrate, both psychologically and economically, into the dominant culture (Pozas and Pozas 1956).

Continued

Table 15.2 (*continued*)

Arguments for native language approach	Arguments for direct method approach
V. Program goals	*V. Program goals*
B. An individual has a right to maintain his native language (Comas 1956).	B. (no equivalent)
C. Literacy in the native language will be developed as well as literacy in the second language.	C. (no equivalent)

EMPIRICAL COMPARISONS OF THE TWO APPROACHES

Searching through many documents and files and personal contacts unearthed 25 relevant studies, carried out in countries ranging from South Africa to the United States. Of these 25 studies 7 are truly experimental in that variables were controlled, a comparison group was selected, and data were gathered systematically. Of these 7, 4 are noteworthy in their thoroughness, and these will be discussed in detail.

Iloilo I and Rizal (Ramos *et al.* 1967)

The Phillippine studies referred to by these place names represent two carefully designed studies executed between 1948 and 1967. In some respects, the results conflict with each other, and one can begin to understand some of the factors only by examining the differences between the two and integrating the findings. The language situation in the Philippines is complex; there are many vernacular languages; Tagalog (or Pilipino) is the national language, and the government would like to encourage English in the elementary schools as an additional national language.

The original Iloilo experiment was conducted in an area of the Philippines that speaks Hiligaynon as its mother tongue. The Iloilo I study was designed to analyze the effects of initial instruction in the vernacular on the eventual learning of the curriculum in English.

The study was statistically well-designed. The experimental group received instruction in the vernacular for grades 1 and 2, and in English for grades 3 through 6. The shift from the vernacular to English was abrupt. The controls were given all instruction in English from grades 1 through 6. Instructional materials were identical throughout, with the exception that the first and second grade experimental materials were translated from English into Hiligaynon. Assessment of abilities and achievement occurred before grade 1 and after each grade through grade 6. Assessment in grades 1 and 2 was in the vernacular for the experimental group, and in English for the controls. All of the assessment was in English for the third through sixth grades. Tests of reading, arithmetic problems, understanding social studies, and learning language skills were given at each grade.

The sample included 14 elementary schools, equated for SES, teacher quality, the principal's qualifications, and supervisors. Experimental teachers were generally of higher SES than controls. Children were further equated on the Philippines Mental Ability Test, chronological age, and school attendance. At the beginning of the project, the sample included 1164 controls and 758 experimental children. When the experimentals were matched with controls, the sample size decreased to 188 experimentals and 189 controls. Unfortunately, the attrition rate was very high; by the end of sixth grade, only 28% of the sample remained. Reports of the actual numbers differ. The report of the sixth grade evaluation indicates that 232 experimentals and 301 controls remained in the study. Of these, 82 were matched.

The methods employed for second language teaching were different from the standard methods. The new method was based on language patterning and drills, emphasizing both structure and sound relationships. Teachers were given training in teaching in Hiligaynon and in teaching English as a second language.

At the end of the first year of the study, the experimental children were significantly higher on reading (in the language of instruction) and social studies. The differences in arithmetic were not significant. At the end of the fourth year (2 years of instruction in English for the experimental group, 4 years for the control), a nonsignificant superiority in the control group was found for reading and arithmetic, and a significant superiority was demonstrated for language. The experimental group had a slight superiority in social studies.

The confusion with which the project is reported and quoted is exemplified in a comment by Venezky (1970) in reviewing the study. He reports that an independent investigation of the fourth-year results by the Director of Public Schools showed significantly superior performance of the controls on all tests, including social studies. Venezky includes no reference. He alludes to the "overenthusiasm" of the program's director for the native language approach as a confounding factor, and this observation of enthusiasm is echoed in the report by Ramos *et al.* (1967). Although one cannot discard a study because the director believes in it, one can suggest that the Hawthorne effect may be operating in a situation in which one group is seen as more exciting and more significant than the other. The investigators did not seem aware of this problem.

In the sixth-year evaluation (with the reduced sample size), the experimentals were superior to the controls in social studies achievement tests and slightly higher in arithmetic and reading tests. The controls scored slightly higher in language.

A personality inventory was given at the end of grades 4, 5, and 6. Children in the experimental groups reported themselves significantly higher on one of the four or five dimensions of that test, although the dimension varied from year to year.

The results of this study were widely accepted in the Philippines; all children were then given instruction in their vernacular for the first 2 years of school, and in English for the remainder. We might feel that such an adoption of policy is premature, particularly when the sample was so small, and when only one model had been attempted. Other variations, such as introducing the second language in the first grade as a language of instruction, were not mentioned.

The study suffers from a number of problems typical of many such studies. The tests were inadequately validated in English and then simply translated into the vernacular. Variables were not independent; a new method of instruction was confounded with the basic hypothesis (differences in language). No control for the Hawthorne effect was made; the children could well have been achieving because they felt special. The two curricula in first and second grades were unequal in that the English materials were published and polished, whereas the Hiligaynon lessons were on "rough dittos, often unclear." The teacher's level of knowledge of English was recognized as extremely low. The high drop-out rate suggests that the final sample was extremely select in terms of the factors such as economic level that permit a child to stay in school.

Even though this study is not an ideal comparison of the Direct method and Native language approaches, it does indicate that experimental children in this situation were not hampered in achievement if they began reading and instruction in their own language in subject matter areas. If, that is, they were able to stay in school for 6 years.

The Rizal study was designed to gather information as to the most appropriate time to introduce reading in English and English as a medium of instruction, questions that had not been answered by Iloilo I. Five groups were defined according to the grade level of the children at introduction of English for reading and as a medium of instruction (see Table 15.3).

Once again, schools were systematically selected, equated on significant variables, and carefully matched. Teachers received instruction in the teaching of

Table 15.3
Design of Rizal Study

Grade in which English is first used as a medium of instruction	Grade in which English reading begins	
	First	Second
First	Group 1	
Third	Group 2	Group 4
Fifth	Group 3	Group 5

(1973) assessed the relative effects of the native teachers (*promotores*) and the state and federal teachers, who were primarily from the dominant culture, on the community in which the school was located. *Promotores* are usually sixth-grade graduates from an Indian community who receive training. She used five measures of the effect of teachers on the community: the number of teacher-sponsored projects (this is one of the roles the teacher is supposed to fulfill), the percentage of adult literacy, the percentage of children in school, the percentage of girls in school, and the percentage of females whom the teachers indicated knew enough Spanish to be tested. Chi-square analyses on each variable between the two kinds of schools were significant, favoring INI schools. Indians also unanimously preferred Indian teachers. Thus, it appears clear that either the ethnicity of the teachers or the vernacular in the schools, has some effect on the rest of the community, and that this effect is greater than the effect of the *mestizo* (non-Indian) teacher on the community.

Is the difference between the schools a function of the language method or the cultural sensitivity the Indian teacher brings to the work that a *mestizo* teacher lacks? Two Indians in her sample teach in the direct approach schools. The children learned more from the two Indians than from the *mestizos*, but less than was learned by children in INI schools. A study of this question is needed.

Uganda Study

Lagefoged, Glick, and Criper (1971) report a different method of assessing the effects of the language of instruction and beginning reading on the achievement of elementary school pupils. The method of identifying the language of instruction was retrospective self-reporting; students about to graduate from the Primary VII grade were asked a number of questions about their educational and home backgrounds. Specifically, they were asked whether or not they began first grade in the national language (English), when they first began to learn English as a language or a subject, and what was their sex, home background, aspirations, mobility, age, and location with respect to city or country. Teachers were also given questionnaires about their training, credentials, years of teaching experience, years of teaching in the current school (a measure of teacher mobility), and number of special courses in English. Finally, all students were administered reading tests in the vernacular and in English.

In all, 1560 pupils were tested from 58 schools. The major analytic method was cross-tabulations using extreme groups. The highest and lowest groups were compared.

Individuals' characteristics apparently did not have an effect on the reading scores. Early introduction of English, sex, home background, aspirations, mobility, and age were not significant variables. Home background was significant when all children were included in the cross-tabs (children of professionals scored higher). The only other significant variable was location. Children who lived in the city scored much higher than children in the rural areas.

The lack of a relationship between initial instruction in English and scores on the English reading test in Primary VII appears to contradict the finding of the Rizal experiment that the more years of schooling in English, the greater knowledge of the English language. We do not know, however, the *total* number of years of instruction in English that the children received; that data would offer a clearer comparison. We only know the language of the first year. Furthermore, the number of subjects on which the statistic is based is small. In the cross-tabs procedure, the lowest 203 and the highest 203 students were selected for further analysis. In this case, less than 10% of the children had received instruction in English in the first grade. Of that 10%, about half are low scorers, and half are high scorers. Despite these disclaimers, and without further information, the data suggests that initial primary instruction in English is not significantly related to achievement 7 years later on a language test.

In order to look at differences between teachers, sums of scores on the test for each of the 58 schools were computed. Using these criteria, the six highest schools and the six lowest schools were selected. Almost every teacher variable differed between high and low schools. In the high schools, there were more "Grade III" (highest credential) teachers, more years of teaching experience in a single school, and more teachers who had taken a special course in teaching English. When these factors, plus others mentioned previously but not found to be significant, were regressed on total score for each school, 83% of the variance was accounted for. Thus, the teacher variables have a highly significant effect on student achievement. The factors are confounded, however, in that the better schools are likely to be in the city, and the location of the school was a significant factor in predicting test scores. The authors report that none of the rural schools use English as a medium in first grade; therefore, the effect of city versus country is confounded in the previous analysis as well. However, these data clearly point to the significance of teacher quality for pupil success. The study is noteworthy in that teacher quality is considered, whereas other studies give only passing attention to the capabilities of the teacher as a variable in school success.

The final study to be reported in detail suggests that a direct method approach may be superior.

St. Lambert Experiment

The St. Lambert home–school language switch experiment (Lambert and Tucker 1972) differs radically from the previous studies reported. First, it is not a comparison of the two models, but a demonstration of the value of the direct approach. The experimental group was introduced to reading and instruction in a second language; all schooling for the first 2 years was in a second language. In other studies, such as Modiano (1973) and Ramos *et al*. (1967), this has been the control condition. The control groups, in this case, are monolingual speakers of each language, who receive instruction in the second language only as a separate subject from second grade on. The study is directed toward determining whether reading and content matter learned in the second language will transfer to the first language without systematic instruction, whether children will learn the second language as well as children who are native speakers of that language, and, finally, whether children will be in any way, either cognitively or emotionally, handicapped by the experience.

The second difference between this project and those previously reported is the nature of the populations. The children in this project were speakers of the dominant language (English) and were learning the nondominant language (French) in Montreal. In all other studies, the subjects have been members of minority groups who were to learn the language of the majority (or the nationally recognized language, as in the Philippines). Lambert, Just, and Segalowitz (1970) recognize that the situation may differ radically from those previously reported because of these sociolinguistic factors. Third, the parental input differed. The parents were middle class and active in schooling their children; for example, they were the deciding force in many phases of the experiment. The parents conceived the project and supported it through 6 years. Their motivations were primarily integrationist; they wanted their children taught French in order to facilitate social contacts with French-speaking society (Lambert and Tucker 1972). Again, this strong parental role differs considerably from the absence of comments about parents in the previous studies. Fourth, both languages involved here have international stature and literary traditions. The study is reported because it is among the most thoroughly conceived and conducted, and the results provide provocative insights into other work.

In Lambert's program in St. Lambert School, children from English-speaking homes were introduced to French in kindergarten. The teacher spoke only French to them in kindergarten and grade one. In the upper grades, 60% of the instruction was in French, and 40% was in English, covering English language arts. The language of the school as a whole was English; the children spoke English to their peers outside of the classroom. The French classes were always taught by a native French speaker, either from Canada or from Europe, and the English language arts were taught by an English speaker.

Two experimental groups were used; the pilot class ($n = 26$) began in one year, and the follow-up class began in kindergarten the following year. The second group functioned as a replication of the pilot group. The control classes were monolingual English-speaking or French-speaking classes. All were from (presumably) similar socioeconomic situations and home background. Systematic interviews in the homes of all of the parents suggest that, indeed, they were to a large degree matched. The Hawthorne effect, as we have noted, is frequently a significant confounding factor. Aware of such a problem, Lambert *et al.* attempted to select classes as controls that were also considered special in some way. The French control class was engaged in an experimental mathematics curriculum. One of the two English control classes was taken from a school that had a reputation for excellent second-language teaching. The second English control group was in the same school as the experimental groups. It is unlikely that the latter class felt particularly special. However, his attempt to equate for this factor is unique in the present review of the literature.

In general, this study is of much higher quality than studies reviewed earlier. Besides equating groups and using achievement tests in English and French, and using verbal and nonverbal intelligence tests, the evaluation included a measure of listening comprehension, story telling (language production), phoneme discrimination, creativity, and attitude toward the program and toward self (the last two were not administered every year).

In sum, the results indicated that the experimental children were generally at the same level of achievement and intelligence as the control groups in the appropriate language. The children in the pilot group were tested through grade four. At that grade, they were identical with English controls on achievement and intelligence; they were slightly lower than English controls on one measure of story telling and comprehension of adult language. In French, again, their achievement test scores were in the fiftieth percentile of the Montreal norms. The children were also lower than the French controls on their story retelling ability in French. In other words, their achievement is apparently unhampered by learning in a weaker language for 4 years, but they still do not have nativelike facility with the language.

In other investigations, Lambert found that a person's attitude toward the particular ethnolinguistic group whose language he is learning has a substantial effect on language learning (Lambert 1967). Lambert has also reported negative stereotypes of one Canadian group for the other (1967). Therefore, he assessed the attitudes that the children held toward English Canadians, French Canadians, French from France, and themselves. The latter was designed to assess negative self-concepts that might have developed through the language learning process. The results indicated that the children, in general, had high conceptions of themselves, and that they identified fairly completely with the English Canadian set of values. Their attitudinal responses to the categories of English Canadians, French Canadians, and French from France were not striking, nor entirely consistent, but there was a trend to rate English Canadians highest, then French from France, and French Canadians lowest. In a questionnaire given to fourth and fifth graders, however, the children rated themselves as both English and French Canadian. Thus, they may be acquiring some qualities of biculturalism. Regardless of their responses to the comparisons of ethnolinguistic groups, the children reported much satisfaction with the program and a desire to learn more French. The English controls, on the other hand, who had been receiving *less* French in a FFL (French as a foreign language) program, generally were less satisfied and would have preferred less French. Thus, one would have to conclude that the program did have significant and positive (from Lambert's perspective) effects on the attitudes of the children.

This study is highly significant and provocative in that it presents strong positive effects of a direct method approach to teaching a second language. All of the characteristics commonly found in the direct method approach are present: The second language is first introduced orally; reading is introduced in the second language; the second language is the medium of instruction; and the teacher and students differ in ethnic and linguistic background.

Can these results be generalized to minorities in the United States? In interpreting these results, Campbell (1970) immediately recommended this method for English instruction of Spanish-speaking children in the United States. Lambert himself raises the puzzling question of when and how the Canadian children learned to read in English, since all of their reading instruction was in French (1970). He suggests two hypotheses: First, the children learned to read without school stimulation and had essentially picked it up on their own or at home; second, the skills had indeed transferred from one language to the other, and, even further, learning the concept in one language had stimulated learning it in the other. He favors the second explanation. The difference between the two arguments is critical; only if the second is true is there any substantial value in the transfer argument. The test of the difference obviously lies in using the same techniques with children who are not likely to be given reading instruction in the home, such as poor Mexican-American children. Lambert is, at the moment, planning such research. If he still finds that reading is learned in the second language, a clearer case for transfer could be made.

These four studies have highlighted the methodological problems involved in large-scale field research necessary to answer the two questions posed at the beginning of this chapter. No direct comparison of the two methods was found; The Iloilo studies showed the effects of teacher training; the Uganda report suggested that teacher quality was more significant than the early introduction of English; the Modiano study clearly favored the native language approach over poor instruction (not the direct method as described); and the Lambert study demonstrated the possibility of a successful direct method approach. No study could clearly eliminate the importance of teacher preparation and skill; in fact, it appeared to be a consistent factor in three of the studies (Iloilo, Uganda, and Modiano). No study has as yet conclusively answered the questions that were initially posed.

Summary

The studies reported do not indicate a clear direction. What generalizations can be made? First, teaching second language literacy without oral language training is not likely to succeed. Second, bilingual programs do not, apparently, retard children's language development in their native language. Third, the effectiveness of the program may increase with the number of years that it is in operation. Initial disadvantages and slower rates of progress appear to be necessary for all bilingual children, no matter which approach is used. Fourth, the training of the teacher apparently has some effect in various situations. The ethnicity of the teacher probably has an effect, but it has never been adequately tested. Fifth, a program may be effective if it involves oral language taught in the very early years. Again, that direction is not clear. Sixth, the success of a bilingual program is related to a vast complex web of factors that differs in each situation: how much language is used in the home, the relationship between the languages in the larger society, the values placed on each language, and so on. Seventh, the Hawthorne effect can alter results, and is too often not taken into consideration. Finally, some studies have observed a transfer from one language to another in the absence of any teaching in the second language, and this effect seems stronger among middle-class children.

In the first section, nine issues were identified as sources of debate between proponents of the two positions. Some are psychological; they refer to the actual processes of learning, the transfer of specific reading skills, and the most appropriate developmental period to begin teaching reading. Teacher quality and instructional methods are also critically important. We have seen that these issues are of considerable importance in the preceding studies. These can be addressed by well-designed studies controlling for the myriad of other factors that can influence the results, such as teacher ethnicity and instructional materials.

A second group of issues concerns the social factors in learning, such as the role of pride in the culture and language in second language learning, the effects of differences in the child's style of learning and the school style, and the effect of the ethnicity of the teacher on learning. In other contexts, much has been said about teacher negative stereotyping of students, and this factor may well have an impact. Finally, the eventual political goals for the students must be considered. These social factors will be discussed in more detail.

Role of Pride in the Culture and Language in Learning to Read and in Learning a Second Language

Lambert (1967) has provided a convincing demonstration of the hypothesis that learning a second language depends on the desire to become part of an ethnolinguistic group. His findings seem to hold in several cultures: Canada, the United States, and the Philippines (Gardner and Lambert 1972). He has also demonstrated a slight tendency for children in contact with a less-respected group to increase their respect for that group (Lambert and Tucker 1972). However, the argument of the native literacy approach appears to be that teaching a child in his own language will give him a greater sense of respect for himself and his language (e.g., Saville and Troike 1971), which will, in turn, enhance his learning capabilities. Although this argument seems sound, no empirical test could be found. When a language is threatened, language loyalty may become stronger (Weinreich 1967), which would impede the learning of a second language. On the other hand, as the need to defend a mother tongue decreases, the child may be more open to learning a second language.

A second aspect of this issue is the psychological effects of second language learning on a child both as he first enters a foreign language speaking environment, and after he becomes reasonably fluent in that language. Sociolinguists and psycholinguists agree that language is far more than a set of speech sounds; rather, it is a complex network of social patterns that indicate membership in a group, manners of speaking and behaving, and, perhaps, attitudes toward other groups. Thus, learning a second language well may have substantial and long-range personality effects.

A final issue is the child's experience of success and failure as he enters schools. Again, although no studies were found that systematically examined this factor, it seems reasonable that a child who can understand nothing that is going on will have less of a sense of success than a child who does. However, one could argue that a carefully sequenced oral language course, introducing the second language at a rate and manner that the child can understand, would also decrease his feeling of failure. A teacher who does not speak the child's language and has no tools for teaching oral language and no knowledge of how to do it is bound to present the child with feelings of failure. In addition, success may not be indicated in the same way in different cultures. For instance, Modiano (1973) reports that children prefer a class in which they have to work hard, even though that work appears to be painful. Another example is in the American-Indian culture, where success does not involve competition (Cazden and John 1969).

Role of Learning Styles in Academic Learning

Recently, there has been considerably evidence that American-Indian children's learning styles are diametrically opposed to the styles that the Anglicized school represents (Philips 1970; John 1972; Cazden and John 1969). Modiano (1973) also discusses the learning styles that are typical of Indian children in Chiapas. Little work has been done on the sociolinguistic styles in classrooms (Cazden and John 1969), although it is recognized as crucially important.

Possible Effects of Negative Stereotyping by Teachers

Although the significant effects of stereotyping by teachers on children's performance, reported in Rosenthal and Jacobson's study (1968), have been questioned, there is much other evidence supporting the idea that teachers' expectations of students have a significant effect on learning (Cicourel 1972). Language accents may influence teachers (Williams 1969; Gumperz and Hernandez–Chavez 1972). One striking example of the effects of stereotyping is reported by Walker (1969). Cherokees were 90% literate in their own language in the nineteenth century; they are now practically illiterate. The decline is attributed to lack of materials and to the alien (American) teachers who felt that Cherokee was a dying language, that the children should be assimilated, and that they were culturally impoverished. In that situation, teacher stereotyping appears to have had a radical effect on language learning.

The Eventual Political Goals for the Students

Although national goals for the students, in political terms, were not frequently discussed in the studies presented, these goals apparently have an overriding effect on the kinds of studies attempted and the results noted. For instance, a country that desires rapid acculturation and assimilation will see no value in learning to read in the native language, whereas a country with a more tolerant attitude toward the right of individuals to be different and toward different cultures may perceive that literacy in the vernacular is a reasonable goal.

SUMMARY AND CONCLUSIONS

In the beginning of this chapter, two questions were posed: (1) Will a child learn to read more rapidly in a second language if he is first taught to read in his primary language? (2) Will the child achieve greater general knowledge of other subject matter areas in his second language if he is taught these subjects first in his native language? The characteristics of two of the approaches generally taken, the direct method and the native language approach, were described, and a summary of the issues supporting each was given. The studies summarized varied in every conceivable way, and most provided no substantial evidence as to which approach is better. However, there have been significant and important studies that relate to many of the implicit assumptions and variables in each method. These studies serve to indicate what variables must be controlled for in assessing the effectiveness of the two methods. A more careful research strategy is obviously necessary; one more study simply varying either the time of introduction of the second language or the time of introduction of reading cannot lead to general conclusions about the best methods for introducing reading and subject matter in a second language. This chapter has outlined the variety of issues that must be considered or controlled for in designing a study. As language planners in a number of countries and in the United States are being forced to make decisions on language policy with insufficient information, continued research is essential. Because of the vast number of variables involved, the worldwide nature of the problem, and its immense social, economic, and political significance, close cooperation between researchers in developing comparable studies in differing locations is essential.

ACKNOWLEDGMENTS

I would like to extend my appreciation to the large number of people who took the time and effort to communicate with me on this project. These include Dr. Nancey Modiano, Catholic University; Dr. Nancy Gonzales, Boston University; Dr. Courtney Cazden, Harvard University; Dr. Vera John, University of New Mexico; Dr. Carol Feldman, University of Chicago; Dr. Norman McQuown, University of Chicago; Dr. Rudolph Troike, Center for Applied Linguistics; Dr. Sirarpi Ohannessian, Center for Applied Linguistics; Dr. Maria Brisk, Center for Applied Linguistics; Mr. George Sanchez, Center for Applied Linguistics; Dr. John Gumperz, University of California, Berkeley; Dr. Edward Hernandez, Stanford University; Dr. Susan Ervin–Tripp, University of California, Berkeley; Mr. Wayne Holm, Rock Point Community School, Minyfarm, Arizona; James Kari, University of New Mexico; and the following people from the Ford Foundation, New York: Margorie Martus, Robert Myers, Siobhan Oppenheimer–Nicolay, K. N. Rao, and Melvin J. Fox. Finally, I would like to express my deep appreciation to those people who served as the instigators of this project: Dr. Howard Freeman, Dr. John Netherton of the Ford Foundation in Mexico, and Dr. Robert E. Klein of the Institute of Nutrition of Central American and Panama. This review of the literature was originally prepared for the Ford Foundation Office of Mexico, Central America, and the Caribbean.

REFERENCES

(Asterisks indicate supplementary reading suggestions.)

*Anderson, T. H., and M. Boyer
  1970   *Bilingual schooling in the United States*. Austin, Texas: Southwest Educational Development Laboratory.
*Arnold, R. D.
  1968   Retention in reading of disadvantaged Mexican-American children during the summer months. Paper presented at International Reading Association Conference, Boston, Massachusetts, April.
*Arsenian, B.
  1945   Bilingualism in the post-war world. *Psychological Bulletin* **68**: 145–190.

*Bordie, J. G.
  1970   Language tests and linguistically different learners: The sad state of the art. *Elementary English* **47**: 814–828.
*Bruck, M., W. E. Lambert, and G. R. Tucker
  1973   Cognitive and attitudinal consequences of bilingual schooling: The St. Lambert Project through grade 6. Mimeo.
*Bruck, M., G. R. Tucker, and J. Jakimik
  1973   Are French immersion programs suitable for working class children? A follow-up investigation. Mimeo.
Bull, W. A.
  1955   The use of vernacular languages in fundamental education. *International Journal of American Linguistics* **21**: 288–294. (Reprinted in *Language in Culture and society*, edited by D. Hymes. New York: Harper, 1964. Pp. 527–533.)
Campbell, R. N.
  1970   English curricula for non-English speakers. In *Twenty-first annual roundtable: Bilingualism and language contact*, edited by J. E. Alatis. Washington, D.C.: Georgetown Univ. Press.
Carroll, J. B.
  1968   The psychology of language testing. In *Language testing symposium*, edited by A. Davis. London: Oxford Univ. Press.
Cazden, C. B., and V. P. John
  1969   Learning in American Indian children. In *Styles of learning among American Indians: An outline for research*, edited by S. Ohannessian. Washington, D.C.: Center for Applied Linguistics.
Cicourel, A. V.
  1972   Language socialization and use in testing and classroom settings. Final report to Ford Foundation, February.
*Cole, M., J. Gay, J. A. Glick, and D. W. Sharp
  1971   *The cultural context of learning and thinking.* New York: Basic Books.
Columbia University Teachers College, The International Institute of Teachers Colleges
  1926   *A survey of the public educational system in Puerto Rico.* Columbia Univ. Teachers College, New York Bureau of Publications.
Comas, J.
  1956   La lengua vernacula y el bilingüismo en la educación. *America Indigena* **16**: 93–109.
*Darcy, N. T.
  1963   Bilingualism and the measurement of intelligence: Review of a decade of research. *Journal of Genetic Psychology* **103**: 259–282.
*Ervin–Tripp, S.
  1970   Structure and process in language acquisition. In *Twenty-first annual roundtable: Bilingualism and language contact*, edited by J. E. Alatis. Washington, D.C.: Georgetown Univ. Press.
*Feldman, C., and M. Shen
  n.d.   Some language related cognitive advantages of bilingual five year olds. Mimeo, Univ. of Chicago.
*Fife, R. T., and H. T. Manuel
  1951   *The teaching of English in Puerto Rico.* San Juan, Puerto Rico: Department of Education Press.
*Fishman, J. A., V. C. Nahirny, J. E. Hofman, and R. G. Hayden
  1966   *Language loyalty in the United States.* The Hague: Mouton.

*Gastrodo la Fuente, A.
1961   La alfabetizacion en lenguas y los promotores culturales. *A William Cameron Townsend.* Mexico, D. F.: Instituto Linguistico de Verano.

*Gaarder, A. B.
1970   The first seventy-six bilingual education projects. In *Twenty-first annual round-table: Bilingualism and language contact,* edited by J. E. Alatis, Washington D.C.:

*Gaarder, A. B.
1967   Organization of the bilingual school. *Journal of Social Issues* **23**: 110–120.

Gardner, R.C., and W. E. Lambert
1972   *Attitudes and motivation in a second language learning.* Rowley, Massachusetts: Newbury House.

*Giles, W. H.
1969   Mathematics in bilingualism: A pragmatic approach. *ISA Bulletin* **55**: 19–26.
1971   Cultural contrasts in English–French bilingual instruction in the early grades. Paper presented at Conference on Child Language, Chicago.

*Giroux, M., and D. Ellis
1968   Apprenticeship in bilingualism in Welland's Public Elementary Schools. Report at the 10th Annual Conference of Ontario Educational Research Council, Toronto, Canada.

Gudschinsky, S. C.
1970   Psycholonguistics and reading: Diagnostic observation. In *Reading difficulties: Diagnosis, correction and remediation,* edited by W. K. Durr. Newark, Delaware: International Reading Association.
1971   Literacy in the mother tongue and second language learning. Paper presented at Conference on Child Language, Chicago, November 22–24.

Gumperz, John J., and Eduardo Hernandez–Chavez
1972   Bilingualism, bidialectism and classroom interaction. In *Functions of language in the classroom,* edited by C. B. Cazden, V. P. John, and D. Hymes. New York: Teachers College Press.

*Halle, M.
1972   On a parallel between conventions of versification and orthography; and on literacy among the Cherokee. In *Language by eye and ear,* edited by J. F. Kavanaugh, and I. G. Mattingly. Cambridge, Massachusetts: M.I.T. Press.

Hasselmo, N.
1967   How can we measure the effects which one language may have on the other in the speech of bilinguals? In *Description and measurement of bilingualism: An international seminar,* edited by L. G. Kelly. Toronto: Univ. of Toronto Press.

Heath, S. B.
1972   *Telling tongues; Language policy in Mexico, colony to nation.* New York: Teachers College Press, Columbia Univ.

*Herbert, C. H.
1971   Initial reading in Spanish for bilinguals. Paper presented at Conference on Child Language, Chicago.

Holm, W.
1973   Bilagaana Bizaard: E^S_F L in a Navajo bilingual setting. In *Bilingualism in the Southwest,* edited by P. R. Turner. Tucson, Arizona: Univ. of Arizona Press.

*Horn, T. D., and R. D. Arnold
1967   Capsule description of San Antonio language-bilingual research project. Mimeo, Univ. of Texas, Austin.

John, V. P.
  1972   Sociolinguistic perspectives and education. In *Sociolinguistics: Current trends and prospects*, edited by R. W. Shuy. 23rd Annual Roundtable, Monograph series on languages and linguistics, No. 25. Washington, D.C.: Georgetown Univ. Press.

*Kelly, L. G.
  1967   *Description and measurement of bilingualism: An international seminar.* Toronto: Univ. of Toronto Press.

Keith, M. T.
  1970   Sustained primary program for bilingual children. In *Reading goals for the disadvantaged*, edited by J. Allen. Newark, N.J.: Newark International Reading Association.

*Kolers, P. A.
  1969   Bilingualism and information-processing. *Scientific American* **218**: 78–86.

*Knear, S.
  1971   Development of prereading skills in a second language or dialect. Paper presented at Conference on Child Language, Chicago.

*Kreusler, A.
  1961   Bilingualism in Soviet non-Russian schools. *Elementary School Journal* **62**: 94–99.

Ladefoged, P., R. Glick, and C. Criper
  1971   *Language in Ethiopia, Kenya, Tanzania, Uganda, and Zambia.* Nairobi: Oxford Univ. Press.

*Lado, R.
  1964   *Language testing.* New York: McGraw Hill.

Lambert, W. E.
  1967   Social psychology of bilingualism. *Journal of Social Issues* **23**: 91–109.

Lambert, W. E., M. Just, and N. Segalowitz
  1970   Some cognitive consequences of following the curricula of the early school grades in a foreign language. In *Twenty-first annual roundtable: Bilingualism and language contact*, edited by J. E. Alatis. Washington, D.C.: Georgetown Univ. Press.

Lambert, W. E., and G. R. Tucker
  1972   *Bilingual education of children: The St. Lambert Experiment.* Rowley, Massachusetts: Newbury House.

Lavallee, M.
  1973   Piagetian stages and the acquisition of a second language (French). Progress report on a doctoral dissertation, March.

*Leopold, W. F.
  1939– Speech development of a bilingual child: A linguistic record. 4 vol. Evanston,
  1947   Illinois: Northwestern Univ. Press.

*Macnamara, J.
  1966   *Bilingualism in primary education.* Edinburgh: Edinburgh Univ. Press.
  1967a The bilingual's linguistic performance—a psychological overview.*Journal of Social Issues* **23**: 58–77.
  1967b The effects of instruction in a weaker language. *Journal of Social Issues* **23**: 121–135.

*Malherbe, E. G.
  1946   *The bilingual school: A study of bilingualism in South Africa.* London: Longmans Green.

McQuown, N. A.
  1941   Linguistics contributes to native education. *International Science* **1**: 2–6.

Modiano, N.
 1968   Bilingual education for children of linguistic minorities. *American Indigena* 28: 405–414.
 1973   *Indian education in the Chiapas Highlands.* New York: Holt.
Natalicio, D. S., and F. Williams
 1972   Oral language assessment. Paper presented at the American Educational Research Association, Chicago.
Philips, S. U.
 1970   Acquisition of rules for appropriate specch usage. In *Twenty-first annual roundtable: Bilingualism and language contact*, edited by J. E. Alatis. Washington D.C.: Georgetown Univ. Press.
Piaget, J., and B. Inhelder
 1969   *The psychology of the child.* New York: Basic Books.
Pozas, I. H., and R. Pozas
 1956   Del monolingüismo indigena al bilingüismo en lengua nacional: Una experiencia educativa del centro coordinador indigenista del Papaloapan. Oaxaca, Mexico.
*Pozzi-Escot, I.
 1972   Report on the research carried out by the linguistics development plan of the National University of San Marcos. Paper presented at Seminar on Bilingual Education, Lima, Perú, January.
Ramos, M., J. V. Aguilar, and B. F. Sibayan
 1967   *The determination and implementation of language policy.* Philippine Center for Language Study Monograph Series No. 2. Quezon City, Philippines: Alemar/ Phoenix.
*Richardson, M. W.
 1968   Two patterns of bilingual education in Dade Country, Florida. In *Foreign language learning: Research and development, an assessment*, edited by Thomas E. Bird. Menesha, Wisconsin: George Banta.
*Ronjat, J.
 1913   *Le developement du language observe chez un enfant bilingue.* Paris: Champion.
Rosenthal, R., and L. Jacobson
 1968   *Pygmalion in the classroom.* New York: Holt.
Saville, M. R., and R. C. Troike
 1971   *A handbook of bilingual education.* Washington, D.C.: Teachers of English to Speakers of other Languages.
*Schrager, T.
 1971   "Ain't" did not hurt no one. Unpublished research paper, Harvard Graduate School of Education.
*Serduchenko, G. P.
 1962   The eradication of illiteracy and the creation of new written languages in the USSR. *International Journal of Adult and Youth Education* 14: 23–29.
*Spolsky, B.
 1970   Navajo language maintenance: Six-year-olds in 1969. *Language Sciences* 13 (December): 19–24.
Stern, H. H. *(Ed.)*
 1963   *Foreign languages in primary education: The teaching of foreign or second languages to younger children.* Report on an international meeting of experts, April, 1962, International Stuides in Education. Hamburg: UNESCO Institute of Education.

*Arana de Swadesh, E.
  1971　Los programas educativos para las zonas indigenas. Paper dated March 23.
*Taylor, T. H.
  1969　*1968–69 (Year Five) Findings: A comparative study of the effects of oral–aural language training on gains in English language for fourth and fifth grade disadvantaged Mexican American children.* Austin: Univ. of Texas.
Tireman, L. S.
  1948　*Teaching Spanish-speaking children.* Albuquerque: Univ. of New Mexico Press.
*Tucker, G. R.
  1970　An alternate days approach to bilingual education. In *Twenty-first annual roundtable: Bilingualism and language contact*, edited by J. E. Alatis. Washington, D.C.: Georgetown Univ. Press.
*Tucker, G. R., W. E. Lambert, and A. d'Anglejan
  1973　Are French immersion programs suitable for working class children? A pilot investigation. *Language Sciences* **25**: 19–26.
UNESCO
  1953　*The use of vernacular languages in education.* Monograph on fundamental education, No. 8. Paris: UNESCO.
Venezky, R. L.
  1970　Nonstandard language and reading. *Elementary English* **47**: 334–345.
Walker, W.
  1969　Notes on native writing systems and the design of native literacy programs. *Anthropological Linguistics* **11**: 148–165.
Weber, R. M.
  1970　*Linguistics and reading.* Washington, D.C.: ERIC Clearinghouse in Linguistics.
Weinreich, U.
  1967　*Languages in contact.* The Hague: Mouton.
Williams, F.
  1969　Psychological correlates of speech characteristics: On sounding "disadvantaged." Mimeo. Institute for Research on Poverty, Univ. of Wisconsin, March.

16

Language, Communication, and Public Negotiation*

John J. Gumperz

University of California, Berkeley

Modern postindustrial society increasingly requires public participation in the decision-making processes that affect the quality of life. The last few decades have seen the growth of citizen-originated interest groups which have as their main purpose the monitoring of public policy. Such groups are demanding, and are beginning to achieve, far-reaching changes in areas such as public health, law, education, labor negotiations. Partly as a result of their initiative, policy-making agencies themselves are cooperating more and more with citizens advisory groups.

School systems attempt to give parents' groups some voice in curriculum and budgetary planning. City planning efforts, such as the recent model city programs, work largely through lay committees. Labor union negotiations are becoming increasingly complex and involve more rank and file members. Even as a consumer of services, it is necessary to learn and practice the rhetoric of public communication in order to obtain adequate benefits from health and welfare programs or other service agencies. To make oneself heard, it is no longer enough to gain the ear of a single individual or a small group of policymakers. Formal

*Work on this paper was supported by National Science Foundation Grant No. NSF GS-30546.

negotiations have begun to play a major role in society. The ability to communicate and negotiate in open meetings, the opening up of channels of communication, is an important factor in maintaining the quality and continuity of urban life.

Along with these changes in communication patterns in modern societies, and perhaps because of them, we have become aware of the essential ethnic diversity of modern societies. While the phenomenon of ethnic mixture in large urban centers, defined by Furnivall as "plural societies," is well-known, the major distinguishing characteristics of plural societies, the relative social isolation of groups, no longer prevails. That is, in recent years, large cities have become places where ethnic groups live and work together under conditions that make it harder to maintain specific patterns of cultural difference. The work conditions in modern industrial settings call for a standardization of life styles as a prerequisite of job opportunities. Thus, complex modern societies can no longer provide social groups with their own ecological niche. Even where living patterns are distinctive and cultural values differ, in an economy in which service industries prevail and different social groups interact intensively at work, intergroup relationships become a part of the fabric of life. They are an important factor to be taken into account in public policy decisions.

To the extent that cultural differences affect the ability to communicate, there is a need for direct studies of communication difficulties, to isolate the sources of culturally based confusion, before a change in other social factors can be expected. Recent anthropological work on communication processes has begun to show that what is involved in cultural confusion and misunderstandings of communication is much more than the gross factors of racial or ethnic stereotypes and prejudices. Mere differences in values or attitudes are not the only causes. A large proportion of misunderstandings are traceable to subtle processes of inference which underlie all communication and which are affected by cultural differences.

Some preliminary insights into the nature of the factors involved in these inferential processes are found in studies of cross-cultural communication of the last decades. The work of such anthropologists as Hall (1966) and Birdwhistell (1970) has shown that different assumptions about spatial relations and conversational posture, different interpretations of gestures and voices qualities, can radically change the interpretation of those attitudes that shape the speaker's evaluation of an interactional exchange. While cross-cultural misunderstandings are annoying in brief, relatively impersonal meetings among strangers, their effect becomes more serious in prolonged contacts, such as occur in negotiations, where so much depends on the mutual trust and good will of all participants. Here attitudes conveyed through signaling cues, which are hardly noticed in the course of the interaction and which do not appear when proceedings are published in written transcripts, can have an important effect on the outcome.

The importance of such barriers to communication is being increasingly recognized in the area of law. It was the subject of a recent report published by the American Association of Law Schools (Carl 1973). In a clinic, American law professors and law students and their foreign colleagues are taught how to overcome the problems inherent in communicating with culturally different peoples involved in common legal problems. The report lists the following major features of the communication:

1. Semantic barriers arising from the use of specialists' words which a speaker thinks he understands because he knows their everyday common meaning. Some common examples are words like *complaint, action, cause,* and the like. Although speakers may be aware that both technical and lay meanings exist, they lack familiarity with the possible uses of alternate meanings (see also Gumperz 1974a). They are unable to tell whether a word is used in its technical or in its lay sense. As a result, they may misjudge the nature of the verbal activity.

2. The voice quality with which a message is spoken. It has long been noted that certain melodic patterns may denote sincerity, irony, or hostility (Adams 1957). The signs involved here are culturally specific. They are independent of the overt linguistic form of any message. Even though a speaker may speak English, his way of signaling these affective, metalinguistic meanings may be that of his own culture. Yet, failure to follow the commonly accepted English signaling norms for affect will decrease the individual's effectiveness in committee meetings and public gatherings.

3. Other factors are spatial relations of the type studied in recent work on dinesics (Scheflin 1972), that is, notions as to what is the proper distance between participants in business meetings: when to move closer, when to keep a distance, conventions concerning body contact, and the like. All these vary with culture.

The functioning of all these subconsciously signaled, culturally determined aspects of the form of verbal exchanges and of the gestures accompanying them has so far been discussed primarily in relation to contacts among members of geographically distinct groups. Some writers on the subject suggest that similar areas of difference may also affect contacts among subcultures within the city. But intrasocietal differences have hardly begun to be studied systematically. Studies of interethnic contact within single societies have seen ethnic diversity as realized only in terms of semantically insignificant surface speech differences. Causes have been sought in the overt content of what is said and done and not in styles of communication as such. It was thought that, if a population speaks the same language, it can be assumed that it also shares commonality of experience and common ways of signaling social meanings.

There have been, however, several recent studies in urban communication during the last few years which show that this is not the case. Perhaps the most instructive, in this respect, is the research of Erickson (Chapter 9 of this volume). Erickson filmed and tape-recorded a series of student–counselor advising sessions in which ethnic backgrounds of both counselors and students varied. Interaction in such sessions is usually seen as expressively neutral or instrumental, directed toward the goal of helping the student in planning course work or discovering academic strengths and weaknesses. Counselors can hardly be said to be prejudiced, as defined by the usual attitude measures. Yet Erickson's highly detailed and subtle indices showed significant, if complex, relationships between the amount of useful information that the student obtained and the ethnicity of participants.

The interviews were analyzed at three levels or channels of communication: (*a*) nonverbal signals, such as gaze direction, proxemic distance, kinesic rhythm or timing of body motion and gestures; (*b*) paralinguistic signals–voice, pitch, and rhythm; (*c*) implicit semantic content of messages. A series of indices were constructed which served to isolate instances of interactional asymmetry or "uncomfortable moments" in the interview. Identification of such passages was found to be highly reliable when checked both across coders and against the evaluations of original participants who were shown the films.

The results reveal a direct relationship between these *indices of asymmetry* and the amount of *usable information* that the student derived from the interview. The lower the asymmetry was, the greater was the amount of practical information obtained. Asymmetry, in turn, was related (*a*) to similarity of ethnic background of participants and (*b*) to ability to find some common base of experience on which to build the interaction.

What seems to happen is that, at the beginning of each conversation, there is an introductory phase when interpersonal relationships are negotiated and participants probe for common experiences or some evidence of shared perception. If this maneuver is successful, the subsequent interaction is more likely to take the form of an interrelated series of moves in which speakers cooperate to produce a well-coordinated sequence of exchanges. The ability to establish a common rhythm is a function, among factors, of similarity in ethnic background. Thus, in spite of the socially neutral nature of the interviews, it seems that Poles, for example, communicate most efficiently with other Poles, less easily with Italians, even less easily with Jews, and least easily with Puerto Ricans and blacks. It is important to note that, while participants can learn to identify moments of uncomfortableness when viewing their own tapes, their interpretations of what happened and why often differ greatly. Furthermore, black counselors seem somewhat less affected by ethnically different advisees than their white counterparts. Perhaps the communication difficulties they experience in their own everyday lives make them more tolerant of ethnically based differences in communication styles.

While Erickson has dealt mainly with nonverbal signs and speech rhythm, our own analyses of classroom interaction and of adult gatherings in situations of ethnic diversity, in which rhythm is analyzed along with differences in dialect, suggest that speech style can lead to similar communication failures (Gumperz 1969; L. Lewis 1970). Yet, while the pervasivness and persistence of social dialect distinctions in modern urban centers has been documented in a number of recent sociolinguistic studies (Labov 1973), most studies thus far concentrate on correlations between linguistic variables and conventional indicators of social class, race, and ethnicity (see Sanday, Chapter 6 of this volume). The communicative effect of such differences is only now beginning to be examined, and research, so far, concentrates only on misunderstanding of facts. In a preliminary analysis of doctor—patient interviews in a medical clinic, Shuy (1973) points to a number of cases of misunderstandings due to (*a*) patients' lack of knowledge of medical language, (*b*) the doctors failure to understand patients' dialects. Although Shuy shows that dialect differences can materially affect the diagnostic process, the instances he cites are extremes, and his implicit definition of misunderstanding as "failure to comprehend the literal meaning of words and sentences" is a narrow one.

Work by ethnographers of communication, such as Kernan (1969) and Kochman (1972), suggests that there are additional, covert, more subtle and, perhaps, more general symbolic effects of dialect differences. A recent Berkeley dissertation (Piestrup 1973) builds on such ethnographic studies in reexamining the effect of dialect deviance on childrens' reading scores in English. The findings, based on tape recordings of more than 20 classroom sessions, show that there is a third factor—"teaching style"—which mediates the relationship between dialect deviance and reaching achievement. With teachers whose teaching is responsive to student initiative and who are tolerant of different communication styles, dialect deviance does not affect reading. With rigid unresponsive teachers, there is a negative effect. Dialect differences in the classroom seem to affect teachers expectation and, hence, as Rist (1970) has shown, teachers evaluation of student achievement.

Piestrup's notion of responsiveness in teaching style is similar to Erickson's notion of ability to find a common topic. Both studies suggest that successful communication is, in large part, a function of *shared presuppositions* governing the actor's interpretation of what he sees or hears. The following examples from our conversational data suggest how such presuppositions may be conveyed and how misreading of signaling cues can result in misunderstanding.

From a class in language arts for low-income, inner-city, sixth-grade black children taught by a black college student:

(1)   Student: [reading from an autobiographical essay]
                 This lady, didn't have no sense.
      Teacher: Do you know another way of saying that?
      Student: Sure, She didn't have any sense. *But not*
                 this lady; she didn't have no sense.

The teacher, intent on teaching grammar, interprets the student's use of the "substandard" double negation as a grammatical mistake. Only by the second repetition of the deviant phrase does the student succeed in conveying the idea that the switch into black English was meaningful in itself. The use of the double negative along with the term *sense* in the italicized phrase serve as a metasignal to suggest that the word *sense* is to be interpreted in terms of the more restricted meaning it often carries among blacks—'feeling and concern for what is proper among blacks'—rather than, as in the general meaning 'knowledge or understanding of any situation.' The teacher in this case was aware of the signaling potential of code switch. Because of the teaching situation, she merely failed at first to react to what the child apparently intended to convey. However, others unacquainted with this culturally specific communication style might have noticed only the deviant grammar and attributed it to lack of knowledge.

From a tape-recorded tutorial session: A second-grade child is tutoring a first grader in reading. The student's attention has wandered and he is about to start reading again.

(2) Student: Page thirty three. Where's thirty three?
     Tutor: Thirty three.
     Student: Thirty three, is this thirty three?
     Tutor: Thirty Three.
     Student: T h i r t y   t h r e e.

The phrase *thirty three* here occurs seven times with different meanings signaled largely through intonation. Another way of putting the different meanings into words would be:

(3) Student: We were on page thirty three. Where is it?
     Tutor: This is it.
     Student: O.K. is this it?
     Tutor: That's what I said.
     Student: I'm reading it now: thirty three.

The first grader is relying in intonation to convey meanings which, according to adult speech norms, are usually conveyed through words. Similar differences between adult and child communication styles occur throughout our texts. We have found a number of instances in which teachers, unaware of the potential communicative significance of the child's intonation and stress, decode the children's behavior as playing or not cooperating rather than attempting to read. Repeated differences in interpretations of this kind can, over time, have a serious effect on the classroom atmosphere and on the child's motivation to learn.

A further example comes from an oral report by a graduate student in educational psychology, who served as an interviewer in a survey. He was sent to interview a black housewife in a low-income neighborhood. The contact had been made over the phone by someone in the office. The student arrives, rings the bell, and is met by the husband, who opens the door, smiles, and steps toward him saying:

(4)   Husband: So y're gonna check out ma ol lady, hah?
       Interviewer: Ah, no. I only came to get some
                      information. They called from the office.
       [Husband;   dropping his smile, disappears without a
                      word and calls his wife.]

The student reports that the interview that followed was stiff and quite unsatisfactory. Being black himself, he knew that he had "blown it" by failing to recognize the significance of the husband's speech style in this particular case. The style is that of a verbal game, used to "check out" strangers, to see whether or not they can respond with the appropriate idiom. Intent on doing well in what he saw as a formal interview, the interviewer failed to notice the husband's stylistic cues. Reflecting on the incident, he himself states that, to show that he was onto the husband's game, he should have replied with a black dialect phrase like *yea, I'ma git some info* ('I'm going to get some information') to prove his familiarity with local verbal etiquette and culture. Instead, his standard English reply was taken by the husband as an indication that the interviewer was not one of them and, perhaps, not to be trusted.

In all these cases and in others we have examined (see Gumperz 1974b for more details), certain aspects of voice quality, pronunciation, or of the use of dialect or technical terms act as metaphoric cues to signal message function and affect the interpretation of meaning. Along with the speech rhythm and non-verbal signs studied by Erickson, these form a class of metalinguistic signs (Bateson 1970), or contextualization cues (Gumperz and Gumperz 1976), which indicate how a speaker wishes his words to be interpreted. By means of such contextualization cues and through the culturally determined inferences they suggest, the speaker may differentiate between literal or humorous, technical or colloquial meanings or indicate whether he means to inform or to instruct, to argue or to agree.

Our studies during the last few years have shown that these cues vary with age and with communicative experience. Their appropriate use is acquired as part of the socialization process, and their learning is subject to the same principles as the learning of grammatical and lexical rules.

There is reason to believe that choice of communication strategy at the level of contextualization cues may be an important cause of differences in interpretation of what, on the surface, seems like the same messages in public negotiations. Unlike casual meetings in the street, these events are governed by strict procedural rules. They constitute instances of enforced contact in which all participants know, or are assumed to know, the broad outlines of the formal rules and the parameters of the occasion. Members would not be selected as representatives by their peers unless they were seen to have rhetorical skills and to be famliar with procedures. Yet, despite, or perhaps because of, the shared agreements on goals and on the overt forms of behavior, hidden cultural specifics play an important part in the encounters. A single word or phrase may trigger unexpected shifts in the mood of the meeting or may unexpectedly set back an agreement that already seemed within reach.

It has always been a well-known fact in management studies (Sofer 1970) that more information than is made explicitly available, much of it at the level of personal judgment, shapes the outcomes of organizational encounters. A recent British study highlights this point (Silverman and Jones 1974). Analyses so far, however, have focused almost entirely on information content and information flow. The form of the verbal and nonverbal exchanges has not been examined, nor have negotiations been studied within the context of intracultural communications.

As was pointed out earlier, such negotiations are of increasing importance in modern public life. If it can be demonstrated through case studies that breakdowns or impasses are often simply a function of miscommunication, of failure to appreciate the significance of certain verbal cues rather than of uncooperative attitudes, it should be possible to work out practical ways of improving interethnic communication. What is needed is a better understanding of the functioning of linguistic contextualization cues and of their bases in speakers' background. It can be assumed that, if participants in meetings or professional negotiations can be made aware of these phenomena, they can learn to avoid their effects and, thus, increase their ability to deal with more substantive issues.

Recent theoretical studies in philosophy of language and ethnography of communication suggest a theoretical basis for new empirical approaches to these issues. In contrast to earlier semantic analyses which were concerned almost entirely with lexicon and with the relation of words to things, philosophers of language, following Wittgenstein and Austin, now concentrate on speaking as an activity and on the effect that utterances produce (Grice 1971; Searle 1971). A basic distinction is made among (a) the propositional content of an utterance, that is, the lexical information it carries; (b) the illocutionary force, that is, what it reveals about what the speaker intends to achieve with his utterance; and (c) the perlocutionary effect, the impact that a message has on the listener. While ultimate effects are never entirely predictable, both propositional content and illocutionary force are communicated, and interpretation processes subject to semantic analysis.

Examination of a number of common utterance types reveals some striking differences between propositional content and illocutionary force. For example, sentences with the syntactic form of questions, such as *May I have a match, Can you open the door?* are generally interpreted as requests. *What's happening* is a common greeting. Statements like *Your car is blocking my driveway* may count as directives. In order to account for such discrepancies, it has been suggested that the hearers interpretation of what a speaker means in any one utterance is the result of a process of inference in which the propositional content of messages is reinterpreted in the light of certain context-bound presuppositions (Searle 1971). To some extent, such presuppositions are a function of physical settings and of such factors as participants' personal knowledge about each others' background, the history of previous transactions and of topics discussed. Presuppositions, however, also depend on social expectations concerning the nature of the verbal activity enacted (for example, conversation, discussion, argument, formal negotiation, verbal game) and concerning the social relationship or the mutual rights and duties among participants that this activity implies. If a speaker, as part of a conversation, says *This room is quite cold*, a hearer who feels obliged to make the speaker comfortable may interpret the remark as a request to close the window or turn up the heat. If the same utterance is said as part of an argument, or in the course of joking or banter, the same interpretation does not follow.

Although a great deal of work is now being done on the linguistic analysis of processes that underlie the interpretation of such indirect speech acts, and it is generally agreed that context is crucial to understanding, analysis, for the most part, deals with single sentences or two or three sentence sequences. What is meant by context and how context enters into the interpretation process has not been systematically discussed. It has, furthermore, been assumed that contextual assumptions are shared and that their interpretation presents no problem.

Work with everyday verbal interaction sequences, such as those illustrated in our examples, indicates that these assumptions are not justified. Setting, discourse topic, and background knowledge of participants constrain the type of verbal activity that can be enacted, but *they do not uniquely determine it*. No set of extra linguistic social rules can account for subtle changes in mood, mode, and quality of talk, as have been described in Ervin Goffman's recent *Frame Analysis* (1975). To account for the shifts in focus within any one setting, we must assume that judgments of what activity is enacted are *semantic judgments* which are signaled, in large part, through verbal cues. We hypothesize that, at the start of any one verbal encounter, a speaker, building on his background knowledge, makes a semantic judgment about what activities can normally be enacted. Once talk begins, this judgment is then either confirmed and sharpened or altered by assessing discourse topic, nonverbal cues, as well as contextualization cues of the type discussed in connection with our examples. At the verbal level, then, a speaker's co-occurrence judgments about the relationship between topic and contextualization cues play an important part in signaling the contextual and social presuppositions in terms of which component messages are to be interpreted.

The following example recorded during a helicopter trip will illustrate the point. As the craft begins to descend, the stewardess picks up the microphone and says:

(5)   S: We have now landed at San Francisco where the local
           time is 10:15. We would like to thank you for
           flying SFO Airlines and wish you a pleasant trip.
           [The stewardess then continues over the P.A. system,
           with only a slight pause] Isn't it quiet
           around here? Not a thing moving.

The first passage is spoken in staccato rhythm, even stress and contoured intonation. Both topic and prosody identify it as an announcement. In the next passage, rhythm, intonation and stress shift to suggest conversation. The shift caused the audience to look around and provoked comments like *I wonder what's happening*. Others replied by saying that some ground personnel were on strike. Note that the distinction between announcing and conversing represents more than a difference in label, there is also a shift in illocutionary force. The announcement has the force of a representative (Searle 1974), and the intent is to conform to a legal requirement. If a passenger had responded to the stewardess's *We thank you . . .* with *You're welcome*, his remark would have been interpreted as impertinent or, perhaps, a bad joke. The second passage, also a representative from the point of view of speech act theory, affects the hearer as a conversational statement intended to provoke a verbal response, which it does. Its force is clearly different.

A similar shift in verbal activity is signaled in the last sentence of example 2. This sentence is spoken with unusually slow rhythm. Throughout the tape, this same rhythm is used in reading and is maintained even when the student knows and can easily decipher the words in question. It is this shift in rhythm that suggests our gloss, 'I am reading thirty three.'

Apart from their role in signaling verbal activities, contextualization cues have other semantic functions. They can also topicalize a phrase within a sentence that forms part of what is otherwise seen as a unitary verbal exchange. This is the case in example 1, which consists of an exchange in which the dialect phrase *she ain't got no sense* is embedded in a standard English passage. Here, the use of forms ordinarily associated with in-group black activities metaphorically suggests that the word *sense* is to be interpreted in its black meaning (see Blom and Gumperz 1972 for a more detailed discussion).

As our discussion suggests, contextualization cues can take a number of linguistic forms depending on the linguistic repertoire (Gumperz 1971) of the participants. Apart from shifts in stress, intonation, and rhythm, choice of pronunciation, choice of words or syntactic structure, choice of dialect or language in bilingual situations, the use of stereotyped openers or sequencing strategies (Schegloff 1972) may all have similar contextualization functions. Although all such cues can carry meaning, whatever meanings are conveyed are conveyed in the course of the speech activity. Unlike words that can be discussed out of context, the meanings of contextualization cues are implicit and cannot be talked about directly. Their signaling value depends on the participants' tacit awareness of their meaningfulness. When all participants understand and notice the relevant cues, there is no problem. However, when a listener does not notice a cue or is unaware of its function, interpretations may differ and misunderstanding may occur. Note that, when this happens and when a difference in interpretation is brought to participants' attention, it is talked about in attitudinal terms. A speaker is said to be unfriendly, impertinent, rude, uncooperative, or failing to understand—it is not ordinarily noticed that he may have failed to perceive a shift in rhythm or a change in pronunciation. Miscommunication of this type, in other words, is seen as a social faux pas and leads to misjudgments of the speaker's intent; it is not likely to be identified as a mere linguistic error.

Some aspects of linguistic contextualization cues are universal and seem to hold for all types of talk, regardless of speech community. For instance, slowing down of sentence rhythm and careful enunciation always suggest an increase in formality. A raise in pitch and increase in stress signal new information or excitement (Chafe 1972). Loudness means emphasis, and so on. The nature of such universals is discussed in detail in a recent paper by Brown and Levinson (1974). The cues involved here, however, are gradual or scalar; they do not take the form of discrete sequents. What is involved is a change from normal in one or another direction. But while semantic directionality is, in large part, universal, the situated interpretation of the meaning of any one such shift in context is always a matter of social convention. There are conventional notions about what count as normal and what count as marked kinds of rhythm, intonation, and loudness. By signaling a speech activity, a speaker also signals the social presuppositions in terms of which his/her message is to be interpreted. Conventionalized notions of normality also differ within what, on other grounds, counts as a single speech community. When this is the case, as when the teacher fails to appreciate the semantic import of children's systematic use of intonational and rhythmic cues, miscommunication can occur.

Furthermore, there are other contextualization cues which have completely conventionalized meanings. The husband's opener *So y're gonna check our ma ol lady*, when said with the right stress and intonation, is one of a set of idiomatic openers for verbal game used in some black groups. The communicative uses of code switching are similarly conventionalized and rely on speakers' knowledge of the values associated with the codes in question, as are the often highly complex linguistic constraints that govern the use of code switching strategies (Gumperz 1975). Since the conventions governing the interpretation of contextualization cues are not overtly verbalized, they must be learned indirectly through regular and direct association with their users. Understanding of contextualization cues is, therefore, in large part, a matter of shared background, of similar past communicative experience and values; where communicative backgrounds differ, as in modern ethnically diverse urbanized societies, these differences will also be associated with difference in contextualization cues. Because these cues function indirectly, empirical analysis is a major problem in the study of intracultural communication.

New types of discovery methods are needed to identify differences in the perception of cues. The method we have begun to work out relies on the isolation of illustrative passages from natural conversation just long enough to form a proper context. These are both transcribed, literally, and described to form a written and tape-recorded record which can then serve as a basis for eliciting judgments from speakers about what cues they respond to in arriving at particular interpretations.

During the last few months, we have isolated a number of typical instances of interpretation differences and have experimented with eliciting strategies capable of making explicit the unverbalized perceptions and presuppositions that underlie speakers' interpretations. Here are some examples.

(6)   Conversation between husband (A) (middle-class American) and wife (B) (middle-class British).

Transcription	*Description*
A: Do you know where today's paper is?	A, using question form, asks for location of newspaper.
B: I'll get it for you.	B does not reply to question but offers to get the paper. *I'll* is marked by stress and slightly raised pitch. Suggesting annoyance?
A: That's O.K. Just tell me where it is. I'll get it.	A retorts that he is asking for information, not making a request. Stress on *I'll*.
B: No *I'll* get it.	B reiterates offer, with *I'll* now marked by very emphatic stress, suggesting increasing annoyance

(7)   Conversation between mother (A) and 11-year-old son (B).

Transcription	*Description*
A: Where are your shoes?	A uses unmarked question form to ask for location of shoes.

B: In the closet.

B replies in unmarked statement form giving the location.

A: I want you to put them on *right now.*

A retorts with a request. The *right now,* said with stress and raised pitch, suggest annoyance and imply that B should have put on his shoes after the first question.

(8)   Conversation between an undergradate employed as a research assistant (A), who is busy writing at his desk, and a faculty member, his supervisor (B), who is passing by at some distance. The two are on first-name terms.

Transcription	*Description (partial)*
A: Hey, John, come and help me with this. I'm putting it all down.	A calls out, requesting B to step over and assist him.
B: What is it?	B retorts, asking the reason for the request.
A: I'm almost done. I just need to fix it up a little.	A markedly fails to identify what is wanted and reports on the details of what is being done.
B: What do you want me to do?	
A: I'm writing down everything just the way you said.	
B: I don't have time right now.	

(9)   Telephone conversation between a faculty member (A) and a student research assistant (B).

Transcription	*Description*
The telephone rings.	
A: Hello.	A responds to ring with unmarked conventional response.
B: How's the family?	B retorts with a conventional question about A's family. The retort is a marked absence of a greeting (e.g., Hi, John) or identification (this is X).
A: Fine.	A retorts with conventional answer, implying that he recognized B's voice.
B: I'll get back to you next month about that thing.	
A: That's O.K. I can wait.	
B: I'm finished with that paper. It's being typed.	
A: Come to the office and we'll talk about it.	

Taken by themselves these passages reflect quite ordinary everyday exchanges. Similar incidents have long been analyzed by small group researchers, students of psychiatric case records, sociologists, and others. Component passages have been examined for what they reveal about participants' psychological characteristics and their role relationships with others. In making such analyses, however, analysts tend to assume that evaluation of the verbal evidence itself presents no problem, that it is simply a matter of testing for conformity to generally accepted rules of etiquette and enunciation.

In order to show that such assumptions are unjustified, these and similar recorded examples were played to listeners of different communicative and ethnic backgrounds. Elicitation strategies such as the following were used to determine differences in marking and contextualization cues:

1. The incident was first played in its entirety, then played again sentence by sentence.
2. The respondent was asked a series of probing questions, each of which builds on the preceding response:
   a. What is A trying to achieve by talking in that way?
      What impression does he make?
   b. What is it about the way he says it that makes you think he is trying to . . . ?
   c. Could he also be trying to . . . ?
   d. How should he have said it if he wanted to . . . ?
   e. How did B interpret what A said?
   f. How can you tell that B misunderstood?
   g. How should B have replied to show that he did understand?

The initial questioning concentrates on subjective evaluations of content and quality. Subsequent questions attempt to induce judges to relate their evaluations to the surface form of what is said. We are looking for comments such as the speaker "raised his/her voice," "his/her tone dropped," "is being too loud," "used. . . ." Given such comments, the passages in question can then be given detailed transcriptions to identify the relevant phonetic or prosodic cues.

Whenever a judge identifies some special expression or mode of talking, a range of alternative expressions, which lead to different interpretations, is also elicited. All answers are evaluated for their relevance to the present context. If necessary, the passage in question is played over several times. Furthermore, elicitation concentrates on exchanges consisting of speaker A's remarks and B's responses, not on a single utterance. Our main goal is to investigate the relationships between listeners' interpretations and identifiable features of message form and content, *not to get at "true" or "real" meanings.*

Examination of examples 6–9 in these terms reveals a number of differences in interpretation. Some judges identify the first utterance in example 6 as a request for information, others as a request for action; others again suggest that it is ambiguous. Some interpret the mother's remark in example 7 as an order to put on shoes; others feel it could be a request. In example 8, a number of judges note A's failure to state clearly what he is doing and what he wants B to help him with. These same judges also note B's failure to say hello in the telephone conversation of example 9 and suggest that this omission seems rude. Others, however, instead of mentioning A's vagueness in example 8, claim that B's insistence on asking what is wanted is out of place. A common comment was: "Why didn't B say that he doesn't have any time in the first place?"

At first glance, these evaluations seem to reflect individual interpretations of what are essentially inherent ambiguities or differences in degree. Although some trends begin to emerge, it would be premature to claim that they relate to cultural background. But when we examine choice of alternative expressions and sequencing strategies, more systematic relationships begin to emerge.

Judges who identify the husband's opener in example 6 as a request suggest that the wife's annoyance is justified since, if he did not want her to get the paper, he would not have used that expression. He would have said, *I wonder where the paper is*? These same judges also claim that the child's answer to the mother's order in example 7 is impertinent, and that this justified the mother's annoyance. What the child should have done to justify himself, they say, is to answer indirectness with indirectness and reply with something like *Why, is it raining*?

Those individuals who identify the openers in examples 6 and 7 recognize their use as meaningful strategies. Patterns become clearer with example 9, where everyone notes the callers failure (*a*) to identify himself and (*b*) to open with a greeting such as "Hi." Since the participants know each other and can be presumed to recognize each other's voice, self-identification is not necessary, but the lack of a greeting is significant. Some judges merely state that this seems odd, or perhaps rude. Others, however, recognize it as part of a meaningful strategy, an indirect way of suggesting that the speaker wants something. Frequently, they illustrate their comments with anecdotes from their own experience, citing similar verbal strategies. These same judges point to the speaker's failure to state what he wants in example 8 as a similar instance of indirectness. The strategy underlying both examples seems to be something like this: Do not verbalize explicitly what the conversation is about, rely on the listener's background knowledge. If he is a friend, he will guess what is wanted and will cooperate, and, if he enters into this type of interaction at all, he can be presumed to understand.

The marked failure to say something that is normally expected can be seen as a conventionalized contextualization cue. It is meaningful in the same sense that the use of the idiomatic opener in example 4 and the switch to black English in example 1 are meaningful. Whenever a particular subgroup of listeners (*a*) identifies such conventionalized meaningful contextualization cues and (*b*) agrees on their meaning and on appropriate sequencing strategies, while other subgroups do not see these cues as meaningful, we have fairly good evidence that the difference in interpretation also reflects significant differences in communicative background. It can be shown that the use of such conventionalized cues, being both covert and highly context bound, is not always easy to learn. They are learned primarily in the course of informal peer group interaction under conditions allowing for maximum feedback, and this suggests some commonality of family or ethnic background (for more detail, see Gumperz and Gumperz 1976). In fact, judges who see meaningful indirectness in examples 8 and 9 are either black or are familiar with black rhetoric. We might tentatively identify the relevant strategies as reflecting black rhetorical style.

The interpretations of examples 6 and 7 represent differences in degree or quality, rather than in conventionalization. The signaling cues here bear similarity to degrees of pitch height or loudness. We might visualize the distinction in terms of the following scale involving different degrees of requestness.

1. Get me the paper.
2. Can you get me the paper?
3. Do you know where the paper is?
4. I wonder where the paper is?

Here the semantic distinction between requests and questions takes the form of what Ross (1974) calls a "squish." Subgroups of speakers differ on where to draw the line between a question and a request. The evidence of relation to differences in cultural background is somewhat weaker than in the case of conventionalization, but it does seem significant that the mother and wife in examples 6 and 7 are English and that other English judges tend to favor the request interpretation, while Americans tend toward the question interpretation.

More data are needed, based on larger and more varied samples of interaction. It should be pointed out, however, that, by relating perception and interpretation of contextualization cues to cultural background, we are not attempting to predict usage or to relate the incidence of linguistic variables to other characteristics. The goal is to identify strategies of interpretation that are potentially available to speakers of certain backgrounds and to alert people to the ways in which culture can affect interpretation of seemingly unambiguous messages.

Once such strategies are identified, it becomes possible to test our understanding of their meaning and distribution by constructing more systematic tests to be used with larger samples of judges. These tests take the form of alternate verbalizations of similar socially realistic episodes, built on naturally occurring examples which are recorded by good mimics who are familiar with the relevant strategies. These can be submitted to ethnically and occupationally stratified samples, and results are subject to statistical analysis of the usual kind.

The following key sentence, extracted from a test that we are constructing to deal with communication problems of students from India who are used to Indian styles of English, may serve as an example:

A: You may run all the way to the post office, but I'm
   sure it will be closed by the time you get there.

Question: Which of the following two statements is closest to what the speaker really meant?

   a. It doesn't matter whether or not I give you permission to go to the post office. Even if I do and if you run, you won't make it before closing time.
   b. It is possible that you could run to the post office, but it will be closed by the time you get there.

The linguistic issue here hinges on the meaning of the modal "may." Speakers of American English use "may" to mean either "permission" or "possibility." Speakers of Indian English in India use it only to indicate permission. Our results with this type of question show that recently arrived speakers of Indian English unanimously choose interpretation (a); speakers of American English choose interpretation (b). Indian students who have lived in the United States for some time will be aware of interpretation (b) if they have lived in typically American settings and have formed close friendships with Americans. Those who have lived surrounded by other Indian friends are less likely to be aware of interpretation (b). Understanding of communicative strategies is, thus, less a matter of length of residence than of communicative experience.

CONCLUSION

Misunderstandings caused by such interpretation differences reflect phenomena that are typically sociolinguistic, in the sense that their interpretative weight is much greater than their purely linguistic import. Whenever they occur, they have the effect of retrospectively changing the character of what has gone before, of reshaping the entire course of an interaction (Garfinkel 1964; Sacks 1972). A mistake in one such feature would lead the listener to think, "I thought we were on the same wavelength, but we are obviously not." Although, once cues are discovered, their linguistic nature is quite apparent, discrepant practices may persist despite years of intergroup contact. Often, speakers may be aware of vague difficulties in communication or of their inability to involve others in serious talk, yet rarely do they see, nor does conventional grammatical analysis suggest, that such difficulties may have linguistic causes.

The examples we presented to illustrate the effect of cultural background on conversational inference are, for the most part, drawn from everyday talk. As we have pointed out, such talk differs from public negotiations, which are governed by explicit rules of procedure. There is a set agenda and a distinct rhetoric that governs discourse style as well as the allocation of rights to speak. Interaction is seen as instrumental and goal directed, and only topics that can be related to these goals are admissable. Participants, moreover, tend to be practiced discussants, selected for their command of procedural rules and their effectiveness in public settings.

Yet sociologists concerned with rules of interaction have frequently pointed out that, even in very formal settings, rules are managed and interpretive conventions negotiated in the course of interaction itself. They cannot be regarded simply as given. Recordings of typical negotiating sessions show that formal rules apply only to a portion of ordinary sessions. As involvement grows and discussion heats up, formality is relaxed, and verbal strategies and con textualization cues from ordinary conversation creep in. Moreover, when previously isolated minority groups begin to take part in public negotiations, their command of the conventions of public rhetoric is often less than thorough, and the chance of miscommunication increases. Note that, while the use of informal conversational strategies in negotiation is in practice quite frequently, deviant usages are judged by the same standards as those used in negotiations. If anything, therefore, miscommunication is even more serious in these settings than in informal talk.

Thus, there is a great deal of scope for empirical studies of the type illustrated here. Although such studies cannot hope to resolve actual differences in goals, ideology, and basic interests, they can alert participants to the range of possible misunderstandings and to the differing meanings that can be assigned to seemingly trivial speech cues. Thus, they may teach us to distinguish real conflicts of opinion from mere differences in rhetorical conventions.

ACKNOWLEDGMENTS

I am grateful to Jenny C. Gumperz for her help in clarifying many of the basic concepts in this paper. Maurice Bloch, Claudia Mitchell Kernan, Eugene Hammel, and Erving Goffman made helpful comments on our earlier draft.

REFERENCES

Adams, J. G.
1957   Culture and conflict in an American village. *American Anthropologist* **59**: 225ff.
Bateson, G.
1970   *Towards an ecology of mind.* New York: Ballantine Books.
Birdwhistell, R. L.
1970   *Kinesics and context.* Philadelphia: Univ. of Pennsylvania Press.
Blom, Jan-Petter, and J. J. Gumperz
1972   Social meaning in linguistic structures: Code-switching in Norway. In *Directions in Sociolinguistics*, edited by J. J. Gumperz and D. Hymes. New York: Holt.

Blurton Jones N. (Editor)
  1967   *Ethological studies of children*. Cambridge: Cambridge Univ. Press.
Brown, Penelope, and Stephen Levinson
  1974   Universals in language usage: Politeness phenomena. Unpublished manuscript.
Carl, B. M.
  1973   *Clinic in transnational legal communication*. Washington, D.C.: Association of
          American Law Schools.
Chafe, Wallace
  1972   Discourse structure and human knowledge. In *Language comprehension and the*
          acquisition of knowledge, edited by R. O. Freedle and J. B. Carroll. New York:
          Winston.
Garfinkel, Harold
  1967   *Studies in ethnomethodology*. Englewood Cliffs, N.J.: Prentice-Hall.
Goffman, Irving
  1975   *Frame analysis*. New York: Harper.
Grice, H. P.
  1971   Utterers meaning sentence meaning and word meaning. In *The philosophy of*
          language, edited by John R. Searle. Oxford: Oxford Univ. Press.
Gumperz, John J.
  1969   Verbal strategies in multilingual communication. In J. Alatis (ed.), *Georgetown*
          University Monograph Series on Languages and Linguistics No. 23. Georgetown.
  1971   *Language in social groups*. Stanford, California: Stanford Univ. Press.
  1974a   Linguistic anthropology in society. *American Anthropologist* **76** (December):
          285–798.
  1974b   The sociolinguistics of interpersonal communication. Working Papers, Centro
          Internasionale di Semiotica e di Linguistica, Urbino, Italy.
  1975   Code switching in conversation. Unpublished manuscript.
Gumperz, John J., and Jenny C. Gumperz
  1976   *Language, speech and social action*. New York: Academic Press. (in preparation).
Gumperz, J. J., and E. Herasimchuk
  1972   Conversational analysis of social meaning. In *Sociolinguistics: Current trends and*
          prospects, edited by Roger Shuy. Georgetown Univ. Monographs in Languages
          and Linguistics. Georgetown: Georgetown Univ. Press.
Gumperz, J. J., *et al.*
  1973   *Report of the natural conversation work group*. Mysore, India: Central Institute
          of Indian Languages. (in press)
Hall, E. T.
  1966   *The hidden dimension*. New York: Doubleday.
Kernan, C.
  1969   *Language behavior in a black urban community*. Monograph II. Berkeley:
          Language-Behavior Research Laboratory, University of California.
Kochman, T.
  1972   *Rippin and Runnin*. Urbana: Univ. of Illinois Press.
Labov, W.
  1973   *Language in the inner city*. Philadelphia: Univ. Pennsylvania Press.
Lewis, L.
  1970   Culture and social interaction in the classroom: An ethnographic report. Working
          Paper No. 38, Language-Behavior Research Laboratory, University, of California,
          Berkeley.

Piestrup, A. M.
  1973   *Black dialect interference and accommodation of reading instruction in first grade.* Monograph IV. Berkeley: Language-Behavior Research Laboratory, Univ. of California.
Rist, R. C.
  1970   Student social class and teacher expectations. *Harvard Educational Review* 39: 411–415.
Ross, John R.
  1974   A fake NP squish. In *New ways of analysing variation in English*, edited by C. J. Bailey. Washington, D.C.: Georgetown Univ., School of Languages and Linguistics.
Sacks, Harvey
  1972   On some puns with some intinuations. In *Sociolinguistics: Current trends and prospects*, edited by Roger Shuy. Washington, D.C.: Georgetown Univ., School of Languages and Linguistics.
Schegloff, E.
  1972   Sequencing in conversational openings. In *Directions in Sociolinguistics*, edited by John Gumperz and Dell Hymes. New York: Holt.
Searle, John R.
  1971   What is a speech act. In *The philosophy of language,* edited by John R. Searle. Oxford: Oxford Univ. Press.
  1974   A taxonomy of illocutionary acts. In *Minnesota studies in the philosophy of language*, edited by K. Gunderson. Minneapolis: Univ. of Minnesota Press. (in press)
  1975   Indirect speech acts. In *Syntax and semantics:* Vol. 3. Speech acts, edited by P. Cole and J. Morgan. New York: Academic Press, pp. 59–82.
Scheflen, A. E.
  1972   *Body language and the social order.* Englewood Cliffs, N.J.: Prentice-Hall.
Shuy, R.
  1973   Problems of communication in the cross-cultural medical interview. Paper presented to the American Sociological Association, August. Mimeo.
Silverman, D., and J. Jones
  1974   Getting in: The managed accomplished of correct selection outcomes. In *Man and organization: The search for explanation and social relevance*, edited by J. Child. London: Allen and Unwin.
Sofer, C.
  1970   *Men in mid-career: A study of British managers and technical specialists.* Cambridge: Cambridge Univ. Press.

17

National Policy Programming: A Prototype Model from Language Planning*

Lilyan A. Brudner
University of Pittsburgh

Douglas R. White
University of Pittsburgh

Anthony S. Walters
Cornell University

INTRODUCTION AND HISTORICAL BACKGROUND

This chapter presents a linear programming formulation of a prototype model with national policy planning variables. A linear programming formulation provides an explicit statement of the inputs and expected outcomes of a planning problem, given specific weightings, to a diverse range of variables. Such a model is constructed to assist modern government planners in becoming more receptive to public needs and interests. A wide range of factors can serve as variables in a particular planning problem. In the present case, optimization analysis is used to bridge the gap between the subjective evaluation of social costs and benefits and the relatively objective financial and practical constraints of the administrative sector of policy planning (Walters, Mangold, and Haran 1973).

*Research reported in this chapter was carried out under the auspices of the Committee on Irish Language Attitudes Research, consisting of scientists appointed by the Minister for Finance, Republic of Ireland. Lilyan A. Brudner was project Director, and Douglas R. White, Deputy Director and Research Methodologist. Although Brudner and White authored preliminary drafts of the interim and main drafts for the committee (1974, 1975), any interpretations of the research results in this chapter are solely the responsibility of the authors and not the committee.

Case study material from language planning research in Ireland is used to construct the prototype model. The model is constructed to conceptualize general features of planning formulation where maintenance of a language is a major objective. Since the founding of the Irish state in the 1920s, the maintenance and extension of the Irish language has been a goal of official policy. English began to replace Irish as the major spoken language of Ireland around the seventeenth century. During the nineteenth century, the remaining monolingual Irish-speaking population largely gave way to bilingualism in English and Irish.

Currently, although Irish is the first national language in Ireland it is not as widely spoken, in the Republic, as English. The number of native speakers of Irish is relatively small and may be declining. Home bilingualism is characteristic of only a small percentage of the population. In order to maintain the Irish language, the government of the Republic of Ireland has instituted a wide range of policies that are designed to support the use of Irish in public administration, in education, in the Irish-speaking bilingual communities in the west of Ireland (the *Gaeltacht*), and in many areas of Irish life. The major problem has been that of replacing speakers each generation through programs of language teaching in the schools. A system of support for Irish has traditionally involved making Irish a required school and examination subject and also providing financial incentives to motivate language use and maintenance.

Survey research undertaken by the Committee on Irish Language Attitudes Research (1975) indicates that, while a majority of the public support the objectives of maintaining the Irish language, there is less support for its replacement of English as a national goal. The general public also reports that language policies have not been as effective as they might have been: The government is seen by different segments of the population as doing too much, too little, or doing the wrong thing in language support policies. Strategy, tactics, and cost of language maintenance programs are public issues of debate, and, in these areas, we find that apparent majority concensus breaks down, as different subgroups within the population have markedly different orientations, interests, and demands. A major factor in determining public opinion is that past policies have not tended to augment speaker replacement as effectively as many members of the population had expected.

The outlines of government policy were laid down with the founding of the Republic. Government policies over time have been altered, often on a piecemeal basis. The planning situation itself has generated controversy. The following patterns of planning problems emerge from previous studies. These may be more widely generalizable to modern government planning problems:

1. Goals are determined by a few individuals who have little objective data available to them on public demands, requirements, and interests. Judgments on policy objectives are also made by a few individuals, and it is assumed that the

population is homogeneous in attributes and interests for planning purposes. Planning considerations do not take into account the characteristics and demands of a highly diverse population. Information on population characteristics and attitudes toward the Irish language and language policies was gathered from research undertaken during the period 1972–1974 to supplement available information on population demands and needs.

2. The quantity of resources required for the attainment of goals is frequently not established: Some language support resources are underutilized, others are poorly exploited, and still other resources may be overestimated. More information on population needs can improve consideration of future allocation of resources.

3. The social and economic costs of a policy to a diverse community are reckoned informally on the basis of political judgments of the policy decision makers. Insensitivity to social, as well as financial, costs may have a negative influence on public support of general policy objectives. In Ireland, certain policies within the program of policy developments were seen as having unduly high social and financial costs to particular classes of constituents. A critical evaluation of the contribution of such policies could lead to reformulation of policy planning for a specific segment of a population.

4. The conditions of a country are assumed to be stable, even when the country has undergone rapid social change: Financial inducements, for example, that led to policy support early in this century may be inadequate inducements today, when the standard of living has vastly improved for a majority of the population.

5. No method is provided for determining which goals require monitoring. Without an explicit model of objectives and constraints, a program of policy supports may be poorly coordinated or implemented. In Ireland, for example, although the goal was to revive Irish as a spoken language, in the school system, emphasis was placed on reading and writing, rather than on learning Irish as a living spoken language. The monitoring of performance on written examinations was emphasized, and, in the past, schools were oriented toward teaching Irish as a school subject.

These examples, drawn from the history of the Irish language planning problem, indicate that a majority of support for major policy objectives does not guarantee that an optimal solution to a planning problem can be determined: Policy failure potential increases when objectives and constraints are not rigorously explored.

Intuitive judgment can identify only the gross constraints and objectives in a planning situation. In order to satisfy policy demands of a complex heterogeneous constituency, planners may need to balance universal benefits and incremental benefits: universal benefits being "those producing greatest benefits for the largest number of people" and incremental benefits "those giving highest priority to those who have the least of a value" (Gans 1968: 91). In order to balance benefits in a complex planning situation, a planner may need to develop a highly complex model of weights and priorities across multiple values to respond to the demands and requirements of diverse population aggregates. At the same time, in allocating benefits, planners need to keep in mind financial costs and consideration of multiple goals.

When language maintenance is a primary goal for language planning, it may be necessary to weigh subgroup interests against constraints on the production of speakers. The planning problem becomes increasingly complex when time is an additional factor in the problem. As Gans (1968: 89) notes, a policy may satisfy the values of those who supply it, but "may not appeal to any need or demand among intended users." Policies that are oriented toward values, but which do not take demand and supply into account, result over time in a situation in which they fail to attact, satisfy, and maintain the support of constituents.

A linear programming formulation of a model is designed to make explicit that knowledge of a situation which is taken into account by the planner, and how a particular rank ordering of weights and priorities influences an outcome. In Ireland, many constraints on the planning problem are directly related to the problem of language maintenance and the replacement of speakers through the educational system. For this reason, the prototype model takes into account the programs that favor language transmission in the schools and assigns probabilities and weights to different speaker production tracks.

Three problems in particular require consideration in a language maintenance situation. These have been identified by Labov (1963, 1964, 1966a, b, c):

1. Labov has defined the transition problem as one in which time horizon data on a population at two or more points in time, or at two or more generations, are required. In studies of language maintenance or change, data are required on language characteristics of a population to determine how change at one point in time evolves from change at an earlier stage. Thus, language maintenance models account for differential speaker production tracks, and also for time as a factor in speaker production and maintenance rates.

2. Labov has defined the embedding problem as the study of the sociolinguistic matrices that convary with language selection: Different sectors of a population have diverse probabilities for attaining a specific level of ability and for language use and policy support. In order to plan for language maintenance, the diverse patterns of language ability and use are made correspondent with population characteristics, such as age, sex, occupation, region, or ethnic affiliation. The present model is simplified to present a general set of constraints for language maintenance planning, and many population characteristics have not been build into the prototype model. The model,

however, can be expanded to incorporate a larger set of constraints which map out in greater detail the variables associated with the embedding problem.

3. Labov has defined the evaluation problem as involving the subjective goal orientation correlates or determinants of language behavior and support. In a separate paper on dimensions of language assessment, Brudner and White (1976) explored the findings of extensive survey research on evaluation at the national level, and attitudes were shown to be multi-dimensional and amenable to factor analysis. Data on the evaluation problem in Ireland have also been simplified in the prototype model to allow for a more parsimonious formulation of the objectives and of the constraints placed on the planner, given minimal assumptions about values, goals, and population diversity.

AN OPTIMIZATION MODEL: THE CASE STUDY

Objective Function

To deal with a goal-oriented system as an optimization problem requires having an objective function, some value that is optimized, subject to constraints. The goals, in the reference terms of the Minister for Finance of the Republic of Ireland (Committee on Language Attitudes Research Regarding Irish 1974), indicated the "aims of restoring Irish as a general means of communication." It remains ambiguous, however, as to whether this restoration is to be interpreted as "in addition to" or "instead of" English.

The survey research of the national population indicated that 70–80% of the populace supported the bilingual situation, the maintenance or furthering of Irish in addition to English, while only a small minority favored the monolingual situation, restoration of Irish instead of English or of English instead of Irish.

Since the terms of reference of the Minister for Finance specifically asked for an investigation of "current attitudes towards efforts to restore Irish" and public support for "policy developments which seemed to offer a greater chance of achieving the aim of restoring Irish" (Committee on Language Attitudes Research Regarding Irish 1974), any attempt to construct an optimization model for policy assessment must begin with the assumption that the goal of furthering or maintaining Irish refers to Irish in a bilingual situation, and not to the replacement of English by Irish.

The goal or policy objective, then, relates to the production of *bilingual* Irish–English speakers, and not to the production of monolingual speakers. We can regard the production of Irish–English bilinguals as the outcome of one of three processes:

1. Home bilingualism: Both Irish and English are learned in the home.
2. School bilingualism: Irish is learned in the school as a second language (although it may be the primary language of instruction).

3. Adult bilingualism: Irish is learned as an adult, after leaving school, in a formal education setting.

We should note, as well, that many home bilinguals, particularly in the Gaeltacht or native Irish-speaking areas, attend schools in which Irish is the primary language of instruction, but it is assumed that both Irish and English are learned in the home (thus, these are considered home rather than school bilinguals, in spite of schooling in Irish).

If the objective function is set to maximize the production of bilingual speakers, subject to constraints on demand for attendance at schools with different Irish language programs (varying from all Irish to no Irish), and also subject to constraints of cost, we have a first approximation of an optimization problem that represents the policy planning situation in the context of different evaluations of outcomes in the population.

The problem in defining the objective function, however, is to define some function that describes the *value* of producing additional bilinguals relative to demand and cost constraints. Three additional factors help to define the objective function. First, the percentage of home bilingualism in the total population—families in which Irish and English are learned in the home—is very low (approximately 6% of the population). Second, since schooling is compulsory to the age of 14, the schools have the greatest gross potential for achieving bilingual skills. Third, adult acquisition of bilingual skills is insubstantial. If schools are the institutional medium for the diffusion of language skills to the greatest percentage of the population, one must beware of defining an objective function that simply maximizes the number of persons able to speak Irish irrespective of age, since the skill learned in school can easily be lost if there is no usage or retention of Irish after leaving school. The objective function should, thus, assign a greater *value* to an adult speaker than to a child in school and also assign a higher value to a preschool home bilingual child than to a school-age bilingual child.

The goal expressed by the objective function can be reformulated as "the production of adult bilinguals who will tend to retain their ability to speak Irish." We can assign values to persons with bilingual skills in different age cohorts according to (*1*) the intrinsic value associated with different levels of adult bilingual skills and (*2*) the average adult skill level retained by persons in younger age cohorts having different language abilities. Thus, for example, a native bilingual child will have a higher likelihood for bilingual skills as an adult, and these bilingual skills will have a higher value than lesser skills.

An example of the assignment of values to persons with six different levels of ability to speak Irish for different age cohorts is shown in Figure 17.1. In this figure, for example, it is assumed that the value of bilingual skills reaches its maximum at age 50 (and remains constant thereafter), that the average native

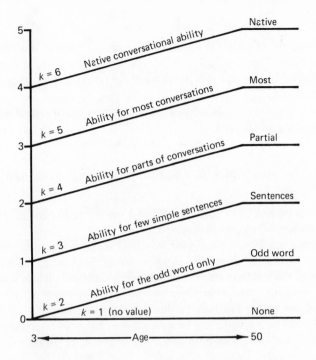

Figure 17.1 Example of assignment of values to persons with six different levels of ability to speak Irish.

bilingual child of age 3 will still have "most conversations" ability as an adult, the average child with "most conversations" ability will retain "partial conversational" ability as an adult, and so forth. In short, the value of bilingual skills increases with age (up to a point) and is greater for higher levels of ability within the same age cohort. These assignments of value, denoted by the coefficients A_{ik}, can be adjusted to reflect either the objective factors of language retention or the subjective factors of speaker skill and age evaluation by the population.

These values can be used to assign a *total value* to an age-specific distribution of language skills in the population. On the assumption that greater value is assigned to nonschool bilinguals, the total value of having 25% of the population "able to speak Irish," if these are primarily younger school-age cohorts, is less than a distribution in which 25% of the adult population is "able to speak Irish."

An objective function in which the value of bilingual speakers is weighted for age-specific levels of ability can, thus, be expressed as follows:

$$\text{Max} \sum_{p=1}^{n} \sum_{i=1}^{I} \sum_{k=1}^{K} A_{ik} \, x_{ik}^{p} + B_{ik} \, y_{ik}^{p} \tag{1}$$

where

x_{ik}^p = the number of people in school of age i, having language proficiency k in period p.

y_{ik}^p = the number of people not in school of age i, having language proficiency k in period p.

A_{ik} = the value (weight) associated with a person in school of age i and language proficiency k.

and

B_{ik} = the value associated with a person not in school of age i and language proficiency k.

The objective function, therefore, says that we are trying to maximize the total value (to the country) of the bilingual speakers.

The programs available to a person in school differ very much from those available to a person not in school, although we will later assign them the same names and will differentiate only by whether or not the person is in school. The weights A_{ik} and B_{ik} were determined by the survey research of the national population. These will be discussed further in the next section.

Note that i can be a specific age or an age cohort but must be the same length as the period p, and i and k are both true at the beginning of period p.

Constraints

The constraint set defining the model is as follows. Symbols will be explained as they appear.

$$\sum_{h=1}^{H} \sum_{j=1}^{J-1} u_{i-1,j,h,k} x_{i-1,h}^{p-1} - d_{i-1,k}^{p-1} - m_{i-1}^{p-1} = x_{ik}^p \qquad (2)$$

for $i = 2, \ldots, I; p = 1, \ldots, n; k = 1, \ldots, K$. Here $u_{i,j,h,k}$ is the (h,k) element of a matrix of transition probabilities of movement from language proficiency h to language proficiency k in any given period. There is one matrix for each age (i) and language program (j) combination. This, summed over h and j, gives all the students who move to proficiency k and are of age i at the start of period p. Next $d_{i,k}$ is the factor signifying people who drop out of the school system at age i, with language proficiency k, at the beginning of period p. This factor includes people who drop out of the educational system by finishing it (i.e., graduation).

Finally, m_i^p = the death or emigration rate for age i. This variable includes migration, since anyone emigrating will leave the system.

Thus, this constraint says that the number of students at the beginning of time period p of age i and language proficiency k will be the fraction of students who move to proficiency k after having been of proficiency h and age $i-1$ in period $p-1$, minus those who leave the school system, minus those who die or move out of the country (i.e., leave the system completely).

The reason j is only summed to $J-1$ is because J stands for no program and that is not a possibility for students. In the next constraint, dealing with those not in school, "no language program" is a possibility.

$$\sum_{h=1}^{H} \sum_{j=1}^{J} v_{i-1,j,h,k} \, y_{i-1,h}^{p-1} + d_{i-1,k}^{p-1} - m_{i-1}^{p-1} = y_{ik}^{p} \tag{3}$$

for $i = 2, \ldots, I; p = 1, \ldots, n; k = 1, \ldots, K$. Here, $v_{i,j,h,k}$ is again the (h,k) element of a transition matrix.

This constraint states that the number of persons not in school of age i and language proficiency k at the start of period p will be the fraction of people who move into that age group and proficiency level plus those who leave the school system minus those who leave the system altogether.

$$\sum_{h=1}^{H} \sum_{j=1}^{J-1} u_{i-1,j,h,k} \, x_{i-1,h}^{p-1} = x_{i,k}^{p} \tag{4}$$

for $i = 1; k = 1, \ldots, K; p = 1, \ldots, n$.

This is the birth rate for the country of concern. It is also possible to include, in this equation, a term to define those who immigrate into the country. In that case, i would be $1, \ldots, n$ for this new term, and $i = 0$ for the birth term. This equation feeds new students to Eq. (2).

It should be noted here that the matrices U and V take into account the proportion of people moving to and from each proficiency level via each language program. The attainment level of each program or the proportion attaining given levels can be parameterized by modifying the elements of U and V. Both matrices allow for loss as well as gain in language proficiency.

$$\left(\sum_{k=1}^{K} f_{ij} x_{i,k}^{p} \right) c_{ij} \leqslant C_{ij}^{p} \tag{5}$$

for $i = 2, \ldots, I; p = 1, \ldots, n, j = 1, \ldots, J-1$. Here, $f_{i,j} x_{i,k}^{p}$ is the fraction of students of age i, in program j at period p; c_{ij} is the cost per student for each age and program; and C_{ij}^{p} is the budget for age i, program j, in period p.

This constraint simply sets a budget for training students of age i in program j, across all proficiency levels.

$$\left(\sum_{k=1}^{K} g_{ij} y_{ik}^{p} \right) e_{ij} \leqslant E_{ij}^{p} \tag{6}$$

for $i = 2, \ldots, I$; $p = 1, \ldots, n$; $j = 1, \ldots, J - 1$. Here, $g_{ij} y_{ik}^p$ is the fraction of persons not in school of age i taking part in program j in period p; e_{ij} is the cost per participant by age and program; and E_{ij}^p is the budget allowed for nonschool program j and age group i in period p.

As in Eq. (5), this constraint sets the budget for nonschool programs. Again, j only goes to $J - 1$, since J indicates no program.

$$\sum_{k=1}^{K} f_{ij} x_{ik}^p \leq T_{ij} r_{ij} \tag{7}$$

for $i = 1, \ldots, n$, and $j = 1, \ldots, J - 1$, where T_{ij} are the number of teachers for age i and program j, and r_{ij} is the student–teacher ratio for age i and program j.

This constraint says that there must be enough teachers (from training colleges) to teach the students in each program. This constraint, and the one that follows, have strong implications for the money that must be directed into the country's training colleges in order to produce the necessary number of teachers for the programs in question.

$$\sum_{k=1}^{K} g_{ij} y_{ik}^p \leq T_{ij}' r_{ij}' \tag{8}$$

for $i, \ldots, n$, and $j, \ldots, J - 1$. T' and r' are teachers (or other personnel and ratios for adult programs.

This constraint is the same as Eq. (7) but applies to persons not in school.

Effects of different teaching methods and experiments involving the effects on attainment of different types of capital investment or resource investment (e.g., teachers) would have to be investigated before being entered into the model. Having once solved the linear programming formulation presented earlier, the attainment variable could be reintroduced and solved for by methods of parametrization.

The advantage of this model is that earlier research has provided precise and quantitative estimates of the average language retention rates for adults, the average school attainment rates for different programs, and the basic sociodemographic variables, by carefully checking the national survey results against census figures. The data provide a base line model with quantitative parameters that can be further elaborated by additional research. Policy planners can add the necessary data on public demands, budgetary constraints, capacity constraints, resource constraints, and so on.

The model is also extremely useful both for language research and policy planning in that it is "staged" through time, as different age distributions of speakers are generated over time. By utilizing data on previous periods from the census and other sources on the sociodemographic, educational, and other variables, the model can be used to simulate the past trajectory of language development and also to forecast future trajectories. Past policy decisions can be checked for whether they were optimal or suboptimal given the constraints at that time. The effects of possible policy alterations can be simulated, optimal allocations on policy variables can be identified, and their consequences for future language development can be forecast. These methods can be extended to plan optimal policy trajectories that are periodically reassessed.

A PROTOTYPE MODEL

The model is staged in 5-year intervals, with corresponding division of the age cohorts into 5-year periods. Thus, for the subscript i, or age cohorts we have

$i =$	1	for	0–4 years
	2		5–9
	3		10–14
	4		15–19
	5		20–24
	6		25–29
	7		30–34
	8		35–39
	9		40–44
	10		45–49
	11		50–54
	12		55–59
	13		60–64
	14		65 +

Of course, parallel to these age cohorts are educational levels; thus:

$i =$	2	primary school (5–9)
	3	junior cycle postprimary (10–14)
	4	senior cycle postprimary (15–19)
	5	University (20–24)

Within the primary and postprimary educational levels, four types of Irish language school programs are recognized:

$j =$	1	no Irish
	2	Irish as a subject only
	3	some courses through Irish
	4	all Irish curriculum

Thus, an ij school program, in which $i = 2$ and $j = 4$, corresponds to an all-Irish primary school program, and so forth, for 16 general types of school programs.

Six types of language ability levels are recognized by the use of the subscripts h and k:

h or $k =$	1	no Irish
	2	the odd word
	3	few simple sentences

4   partial conversational ability
5   most conversations ability
6   native speaker ability

Thus, variables that are subscripted as $(ihjk)$ have $4 \times 6 \times 4 \times 6$ or 576 permutations. In practice, these are regarded as h by k (36-cell) transition matrices for each of 16 types of school programs.

In addition to the school program variables, we also have the language program variables for people not in school, also with the subscript j, as, for example:

for adult, $j = 1$ beginner Irish television programs
2   intermediate Irish television programs
3   advanced Irish television programs
4   adult Irish language courses
5   no program

For each of the "nonschool" age cohorts, say, the 10 codes for age 20 onward ($i =$ 5–14), we have a total of 40 im permutations, and $40 \times 36 = 1440$ $ihmk$ permutations. The total number of A value coefficients is 84; the same holds true for $x_{ih}, d_{ih}, y_{ih}, e_{ih}$.

With the parameters defined, it is evident that the total model consists of 196 variables and 1434 constraints. Given this number of variables it becomes obvious why an optimization code is a suitable and, perhaps, the only feasible means of formulating a solution for this complex problem. Linear programming optimization codes, for example, are capable of solving problems of this magnitude by using existing computer programs.

Given these data, then (much of which are already available), this linear programming model can be used to solve for optimal allocation of resources to achieve policy objectives subject to the constraints set forth earlier.

Other constraints can also be introduced, in future models, to reflect factors in language planning and changes in the values assigned to specific age–proficiency weights. By surveying the population, the departments involved in language planning may wish to change the objective function weights (A and B) to reflect changes in the attitudes of people in the country.

Additional resource constraints, as well as technical constraints, will also be incorporated in future models. A major part of any optimization analysis involves determination of a relevant constraint set that adequately bounds the problem. The prototype model presented in this chapter gives a strictly minimal constraint set, in order to simplify the presentation of the basic model.

POSTOPTIMALITY ANALYSIS

Discussion

Following the solution of this optimization model of language planning, postoptimality analysis can be used to determine the effects on the objective function of the loosening or tightening of any of the constraints. We can determine, for example, the sensitivity of the objective function to the budget by changing the budget by an incremental amount of money and observing the corresponding change in the objective function. In thinking about the increments in the value of the objective function, the value coefficients have been designed in such a way that the units of the objective function can be translated into "fluent adult speaker" equivalents.

Postoptimality analysis can determine the "shadow prices" of producing fluent adult bilinguals. This indicates how much it is worth (in fluent adult speaker equivalents) to raise the budget by one unit, or how much the speaker output equivalents of the objective function would increase in response to an increment in the public demand for language programs.

Goal Programming and Differential Objectives

This analysis has relied extensively on the model for optimization analysis of problems in social development developed by Walters (1969) and further elaborated upon in Charnes, Kirby, and Walters (1970). In addition, the approach of "goal programming," in terms of that model as well as this one, "is particularly applicable . . . since it enables us to make essential evaluations of marginal trade-offs between possible courses of action and the opportunity costs of the various goals which are considered as constraints" (1970: B165). The postoptimization sensitivity analysis allows for a direct examination of the "trade-offs" in other parts of the system that such goals affect.

The concept of differential goals—multiple goals introduced as constraints—can be utilized in the planning context to introduce some of the differences in goal or value orientations within different sectors of the population. One such area of differential goals mentioned in the introductory section of this chapter involves various sectors of the population that have different criteria for evaluating policy outcomes. There, it was suggested that such differences could be introduced into the planner's model by simultaneously taking into account all of these differential goals. This can be done easily if these differential goals are noncontradictory and specific to identifiable aspects of the process being modeled.

The use of optimization models, therefore, need not reflect a single-mindedness of value orientations toward societal allocations or outcomes of policy decisions, but can take into account the multiplicity of goal orientations, values, and constraints that actually exists in any national population.

ACKNOWLEDGMENTS

The authors would like to thank Sara B. Nerlove for her helpful criticisms and suggestions during the preparation of this chapter. For the execution of the research, we appreciate the extensive support and many invaluable suggestions from members of the Committee on Irish Language Attitudes Research and especially the management subcommittee which established research proprieties. Citations to members of the research team and consultants are given in the research reports of the committee (1974, 1975): To all of these people we are immensely grateful for the successful completion of the project.

REFERENCES

Brudner, L. A. and D. R. White
  1976   Dimensions of language assessment. In *Social factors in language contact*, edited by W. F. Mackey and J. Orenstein. Quebec, Canada: Laval Univ. Press. Forthcoming.
Charnes, A., M. J. L. Kirby, and A. S. Walters
  1970   Horizon models for social development. *Management Science* 17: B165–177.
Committee on Irish Language Attitudes Research
  1974   *Interim Report for the Minister for Finance.* Dublin Ireland: Private Circulation.
  1975   *Report.* Dublin, Ireland: The Stationery Office.
Gans, H. J.
  1968   *People and plans.: Essays on urban problems and strategies.* New York: Basic Books.
Labov, W.
  1963   The social motivation of sound changes. *Word* 19: 273–309.
  1964   Phonological Correlates of Social Stratification. *American Anthropologist* 66: 164–176.
  1966a   On the effects of social mobility on linguistic behavior. *Sociological Inquiry* 26: 186–203.
  1966b   Hypercorrection by the lower middle class as a factor in linguistic change. In *Sociolinguistics*, edited by W. Bright. The Hague: Mouton. Pp. 84–101.
  1966c   *The social stratification of English in New York City.* Washington, D.C.: Center for Applied Linguistics.
Walters, A. S.
  1969   Contemporary computational techniques in linear programming with applications to new models in social development, Unpublished doctoral dissertation, Univ. of Texas.
Waters, A. S., J. Mangold, and E. G. P. Haran
  1973   A comprehensive model for long range academic strategies. SUPA offprint, Carnegie-Mellon Univ.

IV

Government and Policy

18

Behavioral Simulation as a Tool for the Analysis of Policy Problems*

Otto A. Davis

Carnegie–Mellon University

Margaret A. Frederking

State University of New York at Buffalo

INTRODUCTION

The major goal of behavioral simulation is to determine the process by which individuals, groups, or organizations solve problems or make decisions. Because of the emphasis on process, the entire effort is sometimes called process modeling. As a technique for modeling the behavior of individuals, organizations, or even systems, simulation permits (*1*) analysis of different stages of decision making and problem solving and their interaction, (*2*) examination of decision criteria and priorities including the conditions under which these may or may not be operable, and (*3*) identification of relative weights or rankings

*Thanks and appreciation are due to the Ford Foundation for a public policy grant to the School of Urban and Public Affairs of Carnegie–Mellon University which made this research possible. Part of the work was also indirectly supported by the Ford Foundation via the Brookings Institution, whose project on the regulation of economic activity served as a source of support for the Workshop on the Regulatory Process at Carnegie–Mellon University. Finally, one of the authors is indebted to the Center for Advanced Study in the Behavioral Sciences, and especially its POSTS program, for a year of relief from traditional duties which helped to make possible the culmination of this and other work. Finally, only the authors and not the sponsoring institutions are responsible for any errors, omissions, views, opinions, and such contained herein.

associated with decision variables. Few, if any, of the other methodologies of scientific investigation allow one to study the details of the process of decision making and problem solving while simultaneously attending to all three of the aforementioned points.

The flow chart is generally the major tool employed to determine the appropriate process. It is a powerful organizational device which allows the researcher to break his task into components. These subunits, though functionally inter-related, may be worked on sequentially. The flow chart forces the researcher to be specific and to attend to detail. It is also important because it is generally the intermediate step between the observation of the process and the final reduction of that process to a computer program.

The computer plays several roles in behavioral simulations. On the one hand, those intellectual methodologies associated with it are, in general, the critical ingredients in the analysis. On the other hand, it basically makes the entire exercise possible by reducing the burden of calculation. Finally, it is usually the critical element in the attempt to address the question of the validity of the simulation. After having reduced the problem solving or decision-making process to a computer program, the researcher usually feeds into the computer those conditions, parameters, and characterizations of events that were the inputs into the real process. In this way, the researcher is able to determine whether the machine will make the same decision or choose the same solution as did the person or persons being simulated.

Behavioral simulation is only beginning to be used for the purpose of analyzing public policy problems. The traditional objective of such a simulation was simply to replicate the process of problem solving or decision making and, thus, to contribute to a better understanding of the behavior under consideration. As we shall see, behavioral simulation has potential beyond the mere understanding of how existing decision processes function.

Within the past several years, there has been an increasing awareness that the understanding of existing decision processes is important in and of itself and that the traditional formal tools of policy analysis, such as benefit—cost analysis, do not properly address this issue. Several quantitative methodologies have been applied, over the past few years, to the study of various types of governmental decision making. In a series of papers, Davis, Dempster, and Wildavsky (1966a, 1971, 1974) report estimates of a simultaneous equations model of both the executive and congressional sides of the federal appropriations process. Jackson (1971, 1974) uses regression analysis to study the forces that appear to influence the voting behavior of the members of the Senate of the United States. Joskow (1972) also uses regression to study how the regulatory authorities set rates for electric power in New York. McFadden (1968) uses conditional logit analysis to study the revealed preferences of a governmental bureaucracy. Wainer, Gruvaeus, and Zill (1973a) use three-mode factor analysis to determine the systematic influences upon voting in the U.S. Senate and a different statistical analysis (Tukey's Jackknife) (1973b) to predict Senate votes, particularly the rejection of the nomination of G. Harrold Carswell as an Associate Justice of the United States Supreme Court. Davis and Jackson (1974) use a combination of regression and logit analysis to study the Senate defeat of the Family Assistance Plan.

The methodologies used in all of the aforementioned studies contribute to our understanding of governmental decision making. However, none of these studies pays much attention to issues associated with process and procedure. Of the scientific methodologies that seem suited to the study of governmental decision making, only behavioral simulation forces the researcher to pay close attention to this set of issues.

In this chapter we review three examples of the use of behavioral simulation in the study of governmental decision making and present a case study of the process by which the Federal Communications Commission issues broadcast licenses. By presenting these examples and this case study, we hope to illustrate just how behavioral simulation can be used to analyze public policy issues.

SIMULATION OF THE BUDGETARY PROCESS

Budgetary processes have been the focus of two of the most impressive of the behavioral simulations, and budgeting is an excellent subject for such studies. First, it is repetitive in the sense that there is usually an annual cycle of budget making. Second, budgeting is often viewed and recognized as being complicated and complex. Especially in such a situation, one should find the decision makers simplifying their task and operating by some rules of thumb. Finally, the repetitive nature of the exercise and the public availability of budgets implies that the activity can be checked and the simulation tested.

John P. Crecine (1967, 1969) and Donald Gerwin (1969) produced the interesting budget simulations. Crecine's topic was the budgetary processes of the cities of Cleveland, Detroit, and Pittsburgh. Gerwin concentrated upon a single entity—the school district of the city of Pittsburgh. For our present purpose, however, the two are sufficiently similar; therefore, for the remainder of this discussion, we shall concentrate solely on Crecine's simulation.

Basically, Crecine views the budgetary process as being composed of three interrelated parts. The mayor begins the process with some initial calculations. With a preliminary expenditure estimate, he asks whether a wage increase is desired. If one is desired, he adjusts his budget estimate to include the proposed increase. Then he asks whether or not estimated revenues are sufficient to cover the expenditures. If not, he has to seek additional revenue; otherwise, he simply continues the process of getting his initial estimates and sends out his budget letter. Armed with his budget letter, the departments make up their requests, which are then submitted to the mayor. The mayor's budget office takes the requests and goes through some routines to produce a proposed budget, generally required to be balanced, which is then submitted to council for action. The major parts of Crecine's model consist of the rules by which departments make up their requests, the procedures utilized by the mayor and his budget office in considering the requests and adjusting them to produce a proposed budget, and the procedures and rules of thumb followed by the city councils in producing the appropriations.

Crecine's models fit well, and his simulation produces results that are not substantially different from those produced by the actual budgetary processes within the three cities. Hence, he concludes that his simulation is a success.

In their original studies, Crecine and Gerwin were interested in using simulation as a descriptive device, not as a basis for policy analysis or even as a managerial tool. Obviously, the first step is to study the existing process. One can go further and use behavioral simulation to improve the decision process and to ask why past decisions were made. One can examine the process in an attempt to discover which rules of thumb or other guides to behavior were crucial. A simulation also simplifies the process of change, in the sense that it requires that the existing process be laid out explicitly. Hence, one might suggest new rules or changes of the old ones and test for the effects of such alterations. Thus, one can see whether or not the suggested alteration would have made a difference and judge whether or not such a difference would be an improvement.

Crecine's simulation of local budgetary processes is now being used as a tool in the evaluation of our new policy of revenue sharing. Researchers allow the simulation to reproduce recent history under two sets of assumptions—(*1*) that revenue sharing monies are available and (*2*) that such monies are not available. Then, one observes the programmed simulation's prediction of how outcomes and allocations might have differed from what actually occurred.

A BEHAVIORAL SIMULATION OF CHANGES IN A ZONING ORDINANCE

The executive and legislative process by which a zoning ordinance can be changed is another example of a process that was successfully simulated by Davis and Rueter (1972). Since cities are inherently dynamic, whether growing or decaying, zoning ordinances cannot be written once and for all. What appears appropriate for one time often is not suitable for another. The process of changing a zoning map is essentially responsive. Typically, a developer (or someone else) will want either to erect structures or to put existing ones to new uses which are not permitted by the current ordinance. Hence, they will want to change it.

The simulation begins with the initial petition or council bill to change the ordinance. The basic idea of the simulation is that there are a number of problems that must be dealt with before proposed changes in the map can be approved. These include special map patterns which are viewed as being undesirable; consistency with previous zoning actions; consistency with area developments and plans; physical development, problems with public facilities, such as roads, parking, water, schools, recreation, and so forth; and the prevailing public opinion. In addition, the city council will be concerned with the revenue considerations of proposals. The essence of the simulation consists in specifying the procedures and behavioral rules associated with analysis of these problems and programming them for the computer.

The program was written in such a way that the information for each of the cases, which took place in Pittsburgh between 1963 and 1965, could be read into the computer to produce a decision on each case for the city planning commission and, where appropriate, for the city council. In this way, the computer's decisions could be compared with those made by both the city planning commission and the city council, and this comparison could constitute one of the tests of the simulation procedure. The simulation correctly "predicted" the decision of the city planning commission 96.8% of the time, and the computer decided as the council did 94.2% of the time. On the basis of this and other evidence, the authors judged the simulation to be a success.

INTRODUCTION TO THE SIMULATION OF THE GRANTING OF BROADCAST LICENSES

In the remainder of this chapter, we report in somewhat greater detail on a behavioral simulation of the process by which the Federal Communications Commission (FCC) grants broadcast licenses. Presumably, these licenses are supposed to be granted on the basis of some notion of the public interest. In those instances in which there is only one applicant for a frequency, there is not a substantial problem for the FCC, since the public interest is operationally defined to mean that the license simply is granted if certain minimal qualifications are satisfied. However, if there is more than one applicant for the same frequency, the FCC has to determine who appropriately should be awarded the license.

In an effort to make explicit the basic criteria for the selection of a licensee in such "comparative" cases, the Commission produced its Policy Statement on Comparative Broadcast Hearings (Federal Communications Commission 1965). The policy statement identifies the objectives as being: (1) "best practicable service to the public" and (2) "a maximum diffusion of control of the media of mass communications." The specific comparative criteria for the accomplishment of these objectives are diversification of control of the media of mass communications, integration of ownership and management, proposed programming service, past broadcast record, efficient use of frequency, and character.

The policy statement does not detail how these criteria are to be measured, nor does it make explicit the relative weights to be given these criteria. Both of these issues must be addressed for the decision process to be simulated, and the latter may be one of the more important outputs of such a study.

In addition to these issues, critics of the FCC have long argued that the decisions are not made according to the stated criteria. For example, Nicholas Johnson (1967), a former commissioner, commented that "this crazy quilt design for disposing of broadcast properties is unworthy of a sophisticated administrative process." Behavioral simulation is a tool that should be capable of casting considerable light upon the question of whether or not decisions are made in accordance with specified criteria.

A SKETCH OF THE BEHAVIORAL SIMULATION

The details of the administrative process for noncomparative cases are somewhat similar to those of its comparative counterpart and only differ in obvious ways. Hence, our attention will be devoted exclusively to the comparative process; this aspect is the most relevant for policy analysis.

The process begins with the Broadcast Bureau, which receives the initial applications. If that bureau concludes that each of the competing applications meets the minimum qualifications, then the bureau chief designates the group of applications to receive a hearing on the standard comparative issue: "To determine which of the proposals would on a comparative basis, best (better) serve the public interest" (35 Fed Reg. 16064). In the event that the mutually exclusive applicants are requesting facilities in different communities, the chief may designate a 307(b) issue and its associated contingent comparative issue: "To determine in light of Section 307(b) of the Communications Act of 1934, as amended, which of the proposals would better provide a fair, efficient, and equitable distribution of radio (television) service" and "to determine, if it is concluded that a choice between applications should not be based solely on Section 307(b) considerations, which of the proposals would best (better) serve the public interest on a comparative basis." Should there be other issues involved, the chief forwards the applications to the Commission with recommendations. Hearing issues are specified with participant rights to petition the Review Board for change, deletion, or enlargement.

Following the hearing of evidence and the filing of proposed findings, the hearing examiner must evaluate the arguments for and against each applicant. That applicant judged best (better) is assigned a preference generally described by "substantial," "strong," "moderate," "clear," or "slight." Demerits may also be assigned. An initial decision is issued; applicants may seek review from the Review Board and the Commission.

Though the policy statement provides no mathematical formulas, it qualitatively expresses the Commission's preferences on certain policy-related issues and, therefore, provides a good starting point for modeling the comparative decision process. Further sources of information are past decisions and decision makers themselves. These resources have been used in the effort to ascertain decision rules and decision variables.

The computer program processes one case at a time, assigns appropriate credits and demerits, and notes features of the applicants' proposals to generate a vector of "scores." An additional feature of the program forms linear combinations of the scores generating a single value for each applicant. The various issues that form the basis for the computer program follow.

Diversification. The diversification portion of the program operates on a demerit system. The size of the demerit varies with type of interest and with location of the interest with respect to the community to be served. The program weights demerits by the stockholder's percentage ownership in the interest. Figure 18.1 indicates in more detail how diversification demerits are computed.

An omission deserves note. With respect to interests in broadcast stations or CATV franchises, there is no consideration of area covered or size of audience.

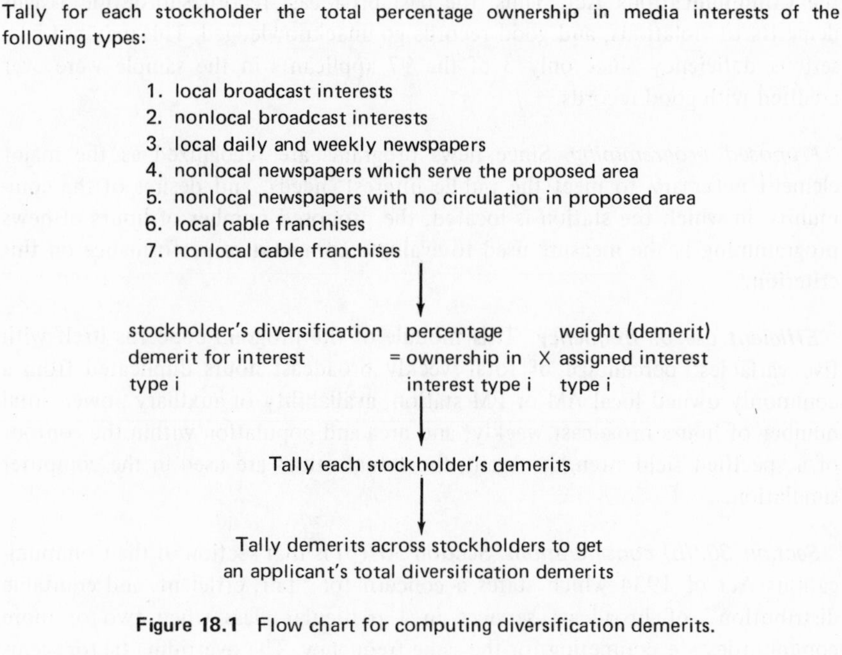

Tally for each stockholder the total percentage ownership in media interests of the following types:

1. local broadcast interests
2. nonlocal broadcast interests
3. local daily and weekly newspapers
4. nonlocal newspapers which serve the proposed area
5. nonlocal newspapers with no circulation in proposed area
6. local cable franchises
7. nonlocal cable franchises

↓

stockholder's diversification	percentage	weight (demerit)
demerit for interest	= ownership in	X assigned interest
type i	interest type i	type i

↓

Tally each stockholder's demerits

↓

Tally demerits across stockholders to get
an applicant's total diversification demerits

Figure 18.1 Flow chart for computing diversification demerits.

This information is generally not included with other data concerning the stockholder's interests, except when the station owned is in or near the proposed principal community.

Integration of ownership and management. Although the Commission attempted to be explicit in its discussion of credits on this criterion, the wide potential range of combinations of local residency, civic participation, broadcast experience, duties with respect to station operation, time to be spent at the station, and percentage ownership makes interpretation difficult. How are engineers and technicians rated as opposed to station managers or news directors? How much credit should be given the owner who will manage construction and operation for 6 months and then serve as a consultant?

An applicant's integration score is obtained by summing the weighted credits for each stockholder's integration characteristics. The weights are the stockholders' (or partners') percentage ownerships in the applicant entity. Figure 18.2 provides more detail concerning organization of the integration subroutine.

Past broadcast record. According to the policy statement, only unusually good or poor past broadcast records are to be considered. There appears to be no readily available and agreed upon measure of "unusually good" broadcasting, but unusually poor service may be identified by violation of FCC regulations or the Communications Act. Thus, the past broadcast record subroutine assigns demerits to violations, and good records go unacknowledged. This may not be a serious deficiency since only 3 of the 97 applicants in the sample were ever credited with good records.

Proposed programming. Since news programs are recognized as the major element necessary to meet the public interest, needs, and desires of the community in which the station is located, the proposed number of hours of news programming is the measure used to evaluate comparative performance on this criterion.

Efficient use of frequency. This module of the program concerns itself with five variables: percentage of total weekly broadcast hours duplicated from a commonly owned local AM or FM station, availability of auxiliary power, total number of hours broadcast weekly, and area and population within the contour of a specified field strength. Again, the actual values are used in the computer simulation.

Section 307(b) considerations. Section 307(b) is that section of the Communications Act of 1934 which states a concern for "fair, efficient, and equitable distribution" of broadcast services in a particular class when two or more communities are competing for the same frequency. The overriding factor seems

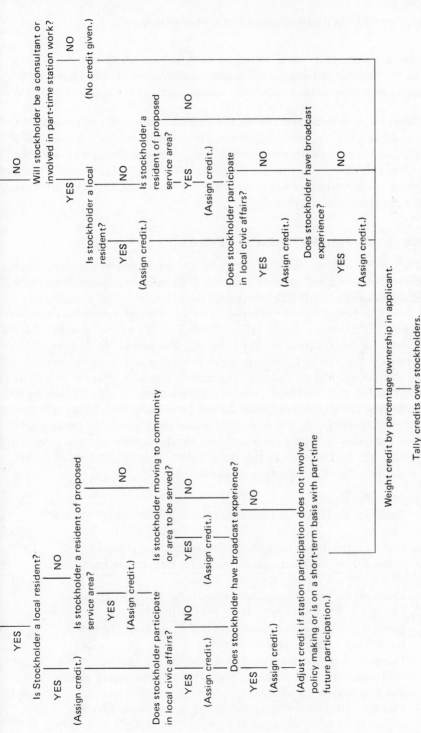

Figure 18.2 Flow chart for computing credits for integration of ownership and management.

317

to be the number of local broadcast outlets, particularly if there is some disparity between services for the communities involved. The reciprocal of the number of stations is the comparative measure used in the computer simulation.

Comparative renewals. Two of the cases examined are contested renewals that were decided on the basis of criteria similar to those for evaluating new applicants. Such cases are characterized in the computer program by a dummy variable with value 1 for renewals, 0 otherwise. The weight that is applied to this dummy variable may then be interpreted as the relative value the FCC attributes to an ongoing broadcast concern.

SIMULATION PARAMETERS AND WEIGHTS

The credits and demerits used to compute integration and diversification scores, as indicated in Figures 18.1 and 18.2, are called parameters. One of the distinguishing characteristics of behavioral simulation is the fact that the process of validation begins with the selection of an initial set of parameters (and also weights for the process of aggregation). There is no generally accepted hard and fast rule for the selection of this initial set. The analyst simply uses all the information that can be found as well as his own intuition. Then the parameters (and also the weights) are varied in a systematic manner so that the outputs of the simulation—the "decisions" which the computer makes and other associated information—can be compared with the real decisions for the relevant collection of cases. Presumably, the not necessarily unique set of parameters (and weights) whose associated outputs correspond most closely to what was really decided constitute the best estimate of the "true" values. Only the final set of integration and diversification parameters are listed:

Integration Parameters
1. Credit for the owner who will hold a full-time policy position at the station.   .60
2. Credit for the wholly integrated owner for his local residence.   .05
3. Credit for the wholly integrated owner for his participation in civic affairs.   .10
4. Credit for the wholly integrated owner for his broadcast experience.   .25
5. Credit for the owner who is to hold a full-time policy-making position and who does not now live in the community to be served but will move there if awarded the CP.   .02
6. Fraction of the credits described in 1–5 for the owner who is to hold a full-time policy-making position for a given period of time and then serve as consultant.   .50
7. Fraction of the credits described in 2–5 for the owner who will act as consultant to the managers of the broadcast facility.   .25

Diversification Parameters

1. Demerit for each local broadcast (cable) facility which the applicant owns.   1.00
2. Demerit for each nonlocal broadcast (cable) facility which the applicant owns.   .40
3. Demerit for each local daily newspaper which the applicant owns.   1.00
4. Demerit for each applicant-owned nonlocal newspaper which circulates in the community to be served.   .50
5. Demerit for each applicant-owned local weekly newspaper.   .50
6. Demerit for each applicant-owned nonlocal newspaper.   .25

After integration and diversification scores have been computed, they are linearly combined with other features of the license application according to the entries in the weight vector. The values of the weights used are arbitrary, but, again, their relative size is based on inferences from the policy statement and past decisions. The entries in the weight vector are elements that apply to the diversification score, the integration score, the availability of auxiliary power, the percentage of broadcast hours duplicated from another facility, hours of broadcasting per week, number of persons in the service area, square miles served, hours of news broadcast per week, possible Section 307(b) issues, past broadcast record, and whether the application is a renewal (see Table 18.3).

SIMULATION PERFORMANCE: PREFERENCES AND DECISIONS

We present the results involving the final set of integration and diversification parameters run on an initial sample of 26 cases and a validation sample of 12 cases. Since the second sample substantiated earlier findings, all results are reported together. The initial cases are numbered between 1 and 52; the validation cases range from 53 to 74.

For those cases in which the integration criterion was a decisive factor, Table 18.1 shows preferences assigned by the FCC and differences between the preferred applicant and his competitors on simulation generated integration scores. The applicant (not all are listed) whose number appears in the second column received an integration preference according to the superscript vector, where 4 indicates a significant preference, 3 a moderate preference, 2 a slight preference, and 1 explicit note of no preference. The position of the preference superscript in the vector indicates who made the decision: (*1*) hearing examiner, (*2*) Review Board, or (*3*) Commission. The letter superscripts following the applicant number refer to footnotes to the table where information about final decisions in each case is provided. Score difference entries are the preferred applicant's (as indicated in the second column of the corresponding row) simulated integration score minus the score of the competing applicant in whose column the entry appears. Negative differences indicate that another applicant

Table 18.1
Integration Preferences and Simulation Results

Case number	Preferences[a]	Score differences[b] (applicant number)				
		1	2	3	4	5
1	1^{4c}		.668			
4	$1^{4,2,4d}$		.939			
5	2^{3d}	.483				
6	2^2	.294		−.547	$.453^h$	
	$3^{4,4c}$	.841	.547	1.000^h		
14	$1^{4,4c}$		.172			
15	$1^{1,1ce}$		.142			
18	3^{4f}	−.194	−.325			
	$2^{,3}$	.125		.325		
	$1^{,3c}$		−.125	.194		
22	$2^{4,3g}$	.300				
27	2^{2c}	−.047		.288	$.173^h$	
35	$1^{3,1c}$		.277	$.725^h$		
37	$1^{4,4c}$		.583			
38	1^{1c}		.063			
45	4^2	−.359	−.201	.039		−.218
	2^2	−.158		.240	.201	−.017
	1^{4c}		.158	.398	.359	.141
46	3^{3c}	−.086	.256			
47	2^{3c}	$.580^h$		.594		
48	3^{4c}	$-.690^h$	.060			
49	2^{4c}	−.473				
51	3^{2c}	$.000^h$	.000			
52	3^{3c}	.255	.255			
54	$1^{3,2i}$		$.331^h$	.021		
55	$2^{3,3c}$	.508				
60	$2^{3,1c}$	.088				
64	$1^{3,2,3d}$		.143			
65	2^{2c}	.169				
66	$2^{3,4c}$	.555				
68	1^{4i}		$.271^h$	.300	$.309^h$	
69	$2^{4,2i}$	.206				
72	$1^{4,4c}$		.625			
74	$3^{2,2c}$	.065	.166			

[a]The applicant whose number appears received an integration preference according to the superscript vector: 4 indicates a significant preference, 3 a moderate preference, 2 a slight preference, and 1 explicit note of no preference. The position of the preference superscript in the vector indicates who made the decision: (1) hearing examiner, (2) Review Board, or (3) commission. That is, in Case 4, Applicant 1 was given a significant integration preference by the hearing examiner, a slight preference by the Review Board, and a strong preference by the commission.

scored higher (better) than the preferred applicant, an expected occurrence when different degrees of preference are assigned to two or more applicants. On Case 6, for example, 2^2 indicates that Applicant 2 received a slight integration preference from the hearing examiner. The score differences show that Applicant 2 scored better than two competing applicants but worse than a third: .294 better than Applicant 1, .453 better than Applicant 4, and .547 worse than Applicant 3. Both the hearing examiner and Review Board gave significant preferences to Applicant 3 in Case 6, as shown by $3^{4,4}$ in the next row. Applicant 3's positive score differences indicate that it outscored its competitors on the integration criterion. The fact that the third applicant was actually awarded the construction permit is shown by the reference to footnote c in column 2. It is helpful to note that the applicant with fully integrated stockholders will earn a maximum score of 1.0.

On the basis of integration alone, the simulation appears to produce results that are usually in agreement with the final decisions of the FCC. Hence, this portion of the simulation argues that the FCC does take integration seriously, as is stated in their policy statement.

On the other hand, one of the major points of interest in a behavioral simulation is those instances in which the stated preferences of the real decision makers differ most markedly from those computed in the simulation. We turn now to several of these "deviant" cases.

Case 18. We have no explanation for the hearing examiner's finding. The Review Board, however, also disagreed with the initial decision. Although the

Table 18.1 (*continued*)

[b]Entries under "Score differences" are the preferred applicant's simulated integration score minus the score of the applicant in whose column the entry appears. Negative differences indicate that another applicant scored higher than the preferred applicant, an expected occurrence if several degrees of preference are assigned.

[c]This applicant was granted a construction permit by the FCC.

[d]For these cases, the other applicant was favored by the Review Board. In subsequent decisions, the applicant shown received the permit.

[e]Applicant 1, after receiving two favorable decisions, requested dismissal of its application. Applicant 2, therefore, got the construction permit.

[f]This preference was applied to the integration subcategory "factor of familiarity by reason of outstanding participation in civic affairs." Note that the Review Board did not support this preference or the hearing examiner's award of the permit to Applicant 1.

[g]The hearing examiner and Review Board split their decisions. The applicants subsequently merged.

[h]These applicants were dismissed before issuance of the hearing examiner's initial decision.

[i]The hearing examiner chose the applicant shown. The other applicant received the Review Board's vote and, therefore, got the construction permit.

Review Board ranked Applicant 2 above Applicant 1 on this criterion, it acknowledged that they were close.

Case 45. Applicant 5 does not get a preference because of a confusing description of job assignments. The examiner is concerned about "time consuming business interests," a general lack of broadcast experience, and the fact that two of the manager–stockholders are septuagenarians.

Case 46. Applicant 1 proposes integration at the expense of integrated station management in a nearby city. The examiner, therefore, gives a preference to the other applicant. Our simulation does not take such trade-offs into account.

Case 49. Applicant 2 is applying for renewal of its television license. The Commission seems to have put much effort into defending this renewal—a subject of controversy within the FCC. Part of the disparity in our integration scores for the two applicants may be due to Applicant 2's vague integration proposal—despite the fact that the station has been broadcasting at least 5 years.

Case 51. Here we are puzzled. Case information states that Applicant 3 will offer "key employees" ownership opportunities and that it is *"contemplated"* that stockholders will participate on a full-time basis. Does this proposal merit even a slight preference?

For cases in which diversification preferences were assigned, Table 18.2 examines diversification demerit differences. The applicant whose number appears under "preferences" received a diversification preference according to the superscript vector, where 4 indicates a significant preference, 3 a moderate preference, 2 a slight preference, 1 explicit note of no preference, −2 a slight demerit, and −4 a substantial demerit. The position of the preference superscript in the vector indicates who made the decision: (*1*) hearing examiner, (*2*) Review Board, or (*3*) Commission. That is, in Case 4, Applicant 1 received a moderate diversification preference from the hearing examiner and no preference from the Commission. The lack of a middle entry here indicates no statement of preference by the Review Board for Applicant 1. The Review Board gave a moderate preference to Applicant 2 in that case. The letter superscripts following the applicant numbers refer to the table footnotes which contain information about decisions in the cases.

The entries in the three large sections of Table 18.2 are the differences between the diversification demerits of the applicant in whose column they appear and the demerits of the preferred applicant. The first of these sections contains total diversification demerit differences, which are then separated into local and nonlocal demerit differences. Local demerits are adjusted for local competing media, according to the formula $\Sigma_i \, d_{ij}/D_i$, where i indexes types of media interests—television, radio, daily and weekly newspapers—d_{ij} is Applicant j's demerits for category i, and D_i the number of local competing media of type i.

Here, where lower scores are preferable, a negative difference indicates that the preferred applicant scored worse (higher) than the competitor. Such apparent

Table 18.2
Diversification Preferences and Simulation Results

Case number	Preferences[a]	Total diversification demerit differences[b] (applicant number)					Adjusted local demerit differences[c] (applicant number)					Nonlocal demerit differences[d] (applicant number)				
		1	2	3	4	5	1	2	3	4	5	1	2	3	4	5
2	1[3e]		.850					.225					.400			
4	1[3,,1f]		.850					−1.000					1.850			
	2,3,1	−.850					1.000					−1.850				
	2,2g	.000					.000					.000				
5	1[1,1e]		4.048					−.053					5.048			
14	1[3,3eh]		.372					.000					.372			
15	1[4,3e]		.333	.174				.333	.000				.000	.174		
18	3[4,3i]	−.174	.159				.000	.333				−.174	−.174			
	1[3,4j]		1.000					.125					.000			
22	2[2e]	.196	1.000	.267[k]	1.148[k]		.000	.125	.000	.000[k]		.196	.000	.267[k]	1.148[k]	
27	1[3,3e]		1.000	.050[k]				.000	.012[k]				.000	.000[k]		
35	1[4e]		.051	.800	.080			.000	.000	.000			.051	.800	.080	
45	5[4]	.000	.051	.800	.080	.000	.000	.000	.000	.000	.000	.000	.081	.800	.080	.000

Continued

323

Table 18.2 (continued)

Case number	Preferences[a]	Total diversification demerit differences[b]					Adjusted local demerit differences[c]					Nonlocal demerit differences[d]				
		1	2	3	4	5	1	2	3	4	5	1	2	3	4	5
46	2^{-4}	-.051	-.749	.749	.029	-.051	.000	.000	.000	.000	.000	-.051	-.749	.749	.029	-0.51
47	3^{-2}	-.800	-.029	.720	-.720	-.800	.000	.000	.000	.000	.000	-.800	-.029	.720	-.720	-.800
48	4^{-2}	-.080				-.080	.000				.000	-.080				-.080
51	3^{3e}	.897	-.292[l]	-.550			.498	-.500[l]	-.750			.399	-.168[l]	.200		
	2^{1e}	-1.000[k]					-1.000[k]					.000[k]				
52	3^{3e}	.400[k]	1.333				.000[k]	.083				.400[k]	.333			
54	3^{4e}	-3.020[k]	-1.020				.000[k]	1.200				-3.020[k]	-3.020			
55	3^{3e}	.200	.100				.000	.000				.200	.100			
	$3^{,4m}$	.144	1.000[k]				.000	1.000[k]				.144	.000[k]			
59	$2^{3,3e}$	1.240					.500					.240				
	$1^{3,3e}$		.000					.000					.000			
60	2^{3e}	.380					.000					.380				
64	$2^{4,4,3f}$	1.041					.000					1.041				
65	2^{2c}	.974					.000					.974				
68	1^{4i}		.282[k]	2.750	1.270[k]			-.032[k]	.001	-.016[k]			.472[k]	2.000	.920[k]	
69	$1^{3,4m}$		3.600					.000					3.600			
72	$1^{2,2}$		1.500					1.000					.000			

[a] The applicant whose number appears received a diversification preference according to the superscript vector, where 4 indicates a significant preference, 3 a moderate preference, 2 a slight preference, 1 explicit note of no preference, −2 a slight demerit, and −4 a substantial demerit. The position of the preference superscript in the vector indicates who made the decision: (1) hearing examiner, (2) Review Board, or (3) Commission. That is, in Case 4, Applicant 1 received a moderate diversification preference from the hearing examiner and no preference from the Commission. The Review Board gave a moderate preference to Applicant 2 in that case.

[b] These entries represent the differences between the diversification demerits of the applicant in whose column they appear and the demerits of the preferred applicant. The simulation generates these demerits by applying diversification weights in the appropriate parameter set to applicant characteristics.

[c] Local diversification demerits are adjusted for competing media according to the formula $\Sigma_i\, d_{ij}/D_i$, where i indexes types of media interests—television, radio, daily and weekly newspapers—d_{ij} is Applicant j's demerits for category i, and D_i the number of local competing media of type i. Differences are as explained in Footnote b.

[d] Entries in column j represent the differences between Applicant j and the preferred applicant for the nonlocal media interest component of the total diversification demerit.

[e] This indicates that this applicant was granted a construction permit by the FCC.

[f] Applicant 2 received the Review Board's vote, but Applicant 1 was chosen by the hearing examiner and Commission.

[g] Applicant 2 received the Review Board's vote, but Applicant 1 was the final winner.

[h] Applicant 2 eventually received the permit, as Applicant 1 had to withdraw after favorable decisions from the hearing examiner and Review Board.

[i] The applicant shown received the hearing examiner's grant but was not the final winner.

[j] The hearing examiner and Review Board split their decisions; the applicants merged.

[k] These applicants were dismissed before issuance of the hearing examiner's initial decision.

[l] Applicant 2 was disqualified in the proceeding.

[m] The applicant lost the hearing examiner's decision but was chosen by the Review Board and received the construction permit.

inconsistencies may often be explained by examination of differences in the separated local and nonlocal categories. For example, in Case 4, Applicant 1 had fewer total diversification demerits than Applicant 2, by .850. Applicant 2 had no local but several nonlocal interests. This fact is revealed by the positive score under local demerit differences and the negative entry under nonlocal differences.

If the entries in Table 18.2 are examined closely, one must conclude that the simulation performs well in regard to diversification. The differences in the scores that were generated by the computer simulation generally are both in the same direction and often are toward the order of magnitude of the preference rankings assigned by the real decision makers. Of course, the simulation is not capable of distinguishing the differences in judgment, when these exist, between the levels of decision making in the FCC, since only one preference is calculated (although, in some instances, the difference between local and nonlocal demerits is rather interesting). The level of agreement between the simulation and the actual decision participants is high.

In this instance, too, it is instructive to examine some of the "deviant" cases, in which the simulation and the real decision makers are not in full agreement.

Case 5. This decision is between two local broadcast owners. Applicant 2's station is a daytime-only facility, while Applicant 1 provides nighttime service as well. This disparity was acknowledged by the hearing examiner but not deemed even "slight." The simulation does not account for differing limitations in operating hours.

Case 14. Applicant 1 owns both local and nonlocal broadcast interests, and Applicant 2 owns a large number of nonlocal interests. We expect that the FCC chose not to distinguish between the two as they are both poor on diversification grounds.

Case 45. As the simulation does not take into account the media interests of close relatives, Applicant 2's diversification score does not show grounds for a substantial demerit. Re-evaluation giving one stockholder demerits for his father's nearby AM station increases the diversification score for Applicant 2. A special consideration here is the fact that the signal of the new station would be carried by the CATV station in the city where the stockholder and his father have journal and standard broadcast station interests.

Case 47. Applicant 2 owns 100% of a local AM station. Applicant 3 owns 25% of a local cable system and interests in other nonlocal systems. That the two are considered equal suggests, perhaps, that television or cable interests should be weighted more highly than radio interests.

Case 59. The zero difference between the applicants' scores results from the fact that Applicant 1, the preferred applicant, owns a local CATV system and Applicant 2 owns the only local radio outlet, a daytime-only AM station. In this case, the FCC's preferences seem to include both diversification and efficiency considerations. Granting the FM permit to Applicant 2 would mean that the only two radio stations in the community would be in the same hands with much duplicated programming. Although Applicant 1's receipt of the permit implies that a local CATV system and the FM station will be commonly owned, this situation may have seemed preferable in view of the small size of the cable system and the alternate applicant's proposed duplication.

Table 18.3 contains results generated by summing the products of weights with integration scores, diversification demerits, and variables representing other comparative criteria. The simulation chooses as winner the applicant with the highest total score. For each run or combination of weights, the number of correct predictions is shown. For instance, in Run 1, nonzero weights were assigned to the dummy indicator for availability of an auxiliary power source and to variables measuring percentage of broadcast hours duplicated from another station, the area served with a signal of a given field strength, and the total number of hours to be broadcast weekly. Given these characteristics of the applicants, the simulation correctly decided 22 out of 38 cases with the numbers of the cases incorrectly decided indicated in Footnote d of Table 18.3 and information on selection for cases in which two or more FCC decisions varied given in Footnotes e and f. In all runs other than Run 1, integration scores and diversification demerits are assigned nonzero weights. After including these measures, the simulation performs better: From 31 to 33 of the 38 cases are decided in agreement with FCC decisions (or according to at least one FCC decision where choices varied at different levels of hearing). For Run 2, diversification, integration, the Section 307(b) measure, area served, and the renewal indicator are assigned nonzero weights. The simulation decided 33 cases correctly, missing only Cases 3, 46, 47, 51, and 53 as shown in Footnote g of Table 18.3.

Comparison of Run 1 with other runs in Table 18.3 indicates the significance of diversification and integration: All runs with diversification and integration did better than those with just efficiency variables. In general, diversification, integration, the Section 307(b) issue, area served within the contour of a given field strength, and the renewal dummy are important criteria if the arguments presented here are correct.

Cases in which the Section 307(b) issue is significant are numbers 21, 24, 46, and 53. Cases 21 and 24 can always be made correct by sufficiently increasing the Section 307(b) parameter as a function of the values of the other weights. Cases 46 and 53 are, however, universally missed. In Case 46, Applicant 2 would have received a Section 307(b) preference but was found to be financially and legally unqualified. By eliminating Applicant 2, we always correctly choose Applicant 3. In Case 53, the applicant chosen by the simulation and preferred by the simulation on Section 307(b) grounds was found unqualified on the basis of financial and suburban community issues.

Table 18.3
Simulation Performance

Run	Diversification	Integration	Weights — Auxiliary power	Weights — Percentage duplication	Weights — Section 307(b)[b]	Weights — Area served	Weights — Hours broadcast	Weights — Renewal[c]	Number of Cases correctly decided[a]
1			1				1		22[d,e,f]
2	-2	1		-1	6	1		1	33[g]
3	-2	1		-1	6	1		1	32[h,e]
4	-2	1	1		6	1		1	31[i]
5	-2	1			6	1	1	2	33[g]
6	-3	1			9	1		3	33[g]
7	-2	5			15	1		3	33[j]
8	-5	2			15	1		3	33[g]
9	-2	4			12	1		3	31[k]

[a] Footnotes show cases missed by number.

[b] Cases 9, 21, 24, 46, 53, 54, 66, and 74 involve a Section 307(b) issue.

[c] Cases 28 and 49 are contested renewals.

[d] Cases missed: 2, 3, 6, 15, 18, 24, 27, 35, 46, 47, 51, 52, 53, 65, 66, and 74.

[e] Applicant 1 scored highest in Case 5. The hearing examiner decided in favor of Applicant 1 in three decisions. The Review Board, however, decided once in favor of Applicant 2.

[f] Applicant 2 scored highest in Case 22. The hearing examiner ruled in favor of Applicant 2, the Review Board in favor of Applicant 1. The parties subsequently merged.

[g] Cases missed: 3, 46, 47, 51, and 53.

[h] Cases missed: 3, 24, 46, 47, 51, and 53.

[i] Cases missed: 3, 18, 35, 46, 51, and 53.

[j] Cases missed: 46, 48, 51, 53, and 60.

[k] Cases missed: 3, 24, 46, 47, 49, 51, and 53.

Cases 28 and 49 are contested renewals. They, too, can always be made correct by adjusting the size of the renewal parameter to reflect the absolute value of the other weights. It is interesting to note that without these weights, Cases 28 and 49 would always be wrong. For Case 28, the hearing examiner decided in favor of the challenging applicant, as does our simulation. Even with a renewal weight, as shown in Table 18.3, the new applicant in Case 28 wins. The renewal weight would have to range from approximately 9 to 48 (as a function of the values of the other weights) to duplicate the Commission's decision for the renewal applicant: Our simulation sympathizes with the dissenting opinions.

Runs 2–5 indicate that little is gained by adding such variables as total broadcast hours, percentage of broadcast hours duplicated, or presence of auxiliary power sources. Similar results for amount of news broadcast and population served are not presented. Two possible interpretations follow from these findings. Either these aspects of an application really are not important, given integration and diversification characteristics, or they are so basic as to act as preselectors. That is, if an applicant proposes many fewer broadcast hours or many more hours to be duplicated from another station, he may feel disadvantaged and wish to withdraw. Failure to find the news variable a helpful predictor may suggest either that hours of news broadcast is not a good surrogate for programming quality or that FCC decision makers do not examine programming proposals.

Results including a weight for past broadcast record have been omitted. The simulation actually performs better if violations of FCC regulations count positively rather than negatively. This result appears to occur because the existence of a poor broadcast record at least implies meaningful broadcast experience of some description. Furthermore, it appears that the FCC regards minor rule violations (violations on only a few occasions or of only one rule) lightly as opposed to other issues.

CONCLUDING REMARKS ON THE FCC SIMULATION

The results obtained from a simulation of FCC decisions involving 97 applicants competing for 38 broadcast licenses seem to suggest a limited degree of consistency in FCC decision making. Though the objective decision process discussed herein can successfully predict over 86% of FCC decisions, 10 of the 38 cases considered involved multiple decisions in which more than one applicant was selected at different stages of the hearing. Thus, the issue of consistency is probably more complicated legally than it need be, given the predictive power of the simulation.

The issue of consistency and predictability may be even more important when viewed in light of some results which cannot be discussed in detail here. Collecting a sample of comparative cases—those instances in which the FCC had to choose between two or more applicants for a frequency—produced another sample of cases in which the FCC made its decisions by default. In these instances, more than one applicant filed initially for some given frequency, but all but one applicant withdrew before an initial decision could be issued. Hence, these cases are no longer comparative, in the sense that, by FCC policy, the remaining applicant is awarded the permit (license) if it is basically qualified. Empirically, this phenomenon of changing from comparative to noncomparative status appears to be significant. A special effort was required to collect a sample of only comparative cases. Among the 97 applicants in the 38 comparative cases, there were 20 dropouts. Also, we have data on 48 applicants involved in 16 cases which switched from comparative to noncomparative.

If one believes that our behavioral simulation is an accurate expression of policy for the awarding of broadcast licenses, it makes some sense to utilize the weights and other instruments that were derived on the basis of the sample of comparative cases to infer, for the other cases, whether those who dropped out might have had some chance of obtaining the licenses. The answer is overwhelmingly positive. According to the weights and values inherent in this simulation, in most cases that became noncomparative because of drop-outs, the final licensee was not the preferred applicant. On the basis of this evidence, one is tempted to conclude that the very process of making awards tends to frustrate the expressed and implied policies of the FCC.

What causes these withdrawals? There probably is no single answer. In some instances, private deals involving pay-offs may be a reason. Under existing law, such deals may not be illegal and may even be encouraged on certain occasions. In other cases, the answer appears to be the uncertainty associated with the FCC's decision process; uncertainty as to outcome, in part, but largely uncertainty as to the length of time required before a decision is resolved and station construction initiated. The average time span from the date of the last application to the initial decision is 27 months for the 38 cases in our main sample. This figure, of course, does not include the time that may be required for appeals. In addition to the costs of the uncertainty, there are the more tangible costs of the legal and engineering counsel that must be retained. Thus, the nature of the decision process itself appears often to have a perverse influence on the outcome.

Two suggestions are obvious here. First, there would be minimal expense in utilizing a behavioral simulation such as this one to inform applicants initially of the outcome predicted by the computer if there are no withdrawals. In and of itself, this information might encourage those favored by existing policies not to withdraw before a decision can be made. Alternatively, it might encourage them to ask for more if a private deal is proposed and, thus, indirectly help to discourage such deals. Clearly, under this suggestion, the output or prediction of the behavioral simulation would only be a forecast, and the actual decision-making process would be left intact. The only effect upon policy would be to help encourage favored applicants to await a decision.

A second possibility might be to utilize the behavioral simulation as an integral part of the decision-making process itself. The prediction of the computer simulation might be made available to all participants and actually used as a basis for any subsequent litigation. Thus, all attention could be given to possible overriding of the simulation's decision. This procedure might reduce work loads and help to speed the process. The end result might be reduced time and monetary costs of decision making.

CONCLUDING REMARKS ON BEHAVIORAL SIMULATION

The examples discussed herein earlier should provide ample evidence of the potential usefulness of behavioral simulation as a tool for the analysis of policy problems. Its major advantage is its almost unique emphasis upon process. While such an emphasis is not important for all policy problems, it clearly is critical for some. One can predict that it will become an increasingly popular tool as its advantages become more widely known.

REFERENCES

Crecine, John P.
   1967   A computer simulation model of muncipal budgeting. *Management Science* 13: 786–815.
   1969   *Governmental problem-solving: A computer simulation of municipal budgeting.* Chicago: Rand McNally.
Davis, Otto A., M. A. H. Dempster, and Aaron Wildavsky
   1966a   A theory of the budgetary process. *American Political Science Review* LX: 529–547.
   1966b   On the process of budgeting: An empirical study of congressional appropriation. *Papers in Non-Market Decision Making* 1: 63–132.
   1971   On the process of budgeting II: An empirical study of congressional appropriation. In *Studies in budgeting*, edited by R. F. Byrne, A. Charnes, W. W. Cooper, O. A. Davis, and Dorothy Gilford. Amsterdam: North Holland. Chapter 9.
   1974   Towards a predictive theory of government expenditure: U.S. domestic appropriations. *British Journal of Political Science* 4: 419–52.
Davis, Otto A., and John E. Jackson
   1974   Senate defeat of the Family Assistance Plan. *Public Policy* XXII: 245–273.
Davis, Otto A., and Frederick H. Rueter
   1972   A simulation of municipal zoning decisions. *Management Science* 19: 39–77.
Federal Communications Commission
   1965   Policy Statement on Comparative Broadcast Hearings. 1FCC2d0393–0400.
Gerwin, Donald
   1969   *Budgeting public funds: The decision process in an urban school district.* Madison: Univ. of Wisconsin Press.

Jackson, John E.
  1971   Statistical models of senate roll call voting. *American Political Science Review* **65**: 451–70.
Johnson, Nicholas
  1967   Dissenting Statement in Farragut Television Corporation et al. 8 FCC 2d 0291.
Joskow, Paul L.
  1972   The determination of the allowed rate of return in a regulatory hearing. *Bell Journal of Economics and Management Science* **3**: 632–44.
McFadden, Daniel
  1968   The revealed preferences of a government bureaucracy. Technical Report No. 17, Project for the evaluation and optimization of economic growth, Institute of International Studies, Univ. of California, Berkeley.
Wainer, Howard, Gunnar Gruvaeus, and Nicholas Zill II
  1973a   Senatorial decision making: I. The determination of structure. *Behavioral Science* **18**: 7–19.
  1973b   Senatorial decision making: II. Prediction. *Behavioral Science* **18**: 20–26.

19

Social Indicators: A Focus for the Social Sciences

Roxann A. Van Dusen and Robert Parke

Social Science Research Council

SOCIAL INDICATORS: A FOCUS ON MEASUREMENT

In a recent paper on the development of social indicators research since the mid-1960s, Otis Dudley Duncan focused on levels of research activities and levels of application of research findings. Within the first category, Duncan identified three distinct activities: (1) *social bookkeeping*—that is, systematic data gathering; (2) *social accounting*—the development of meaningful classification frameworks for the data; and (3) *social science*—the development of theories, models, and measures that utilize and give meaning to these data. Duncan listed three applications or uses of such research—social forecasting, social reporting, and social advising: (1) *Social forecasting*, needless to say, is heavily dependent on the models that social science has evolved to understand social processes; (2) *social reporting* communicates and interprets the results of studies using social indicators to trace social trends (in the past *and* into the future); and (3) *social advising* involves the application of knowledge and understanding of these trends to problems of public policy (Duncan 1974a).

There is a sense in which these six activities are interrelated hierarchically, for the success of research activities—data collection, codification, and analysis—

333

depends, in part, on their relevance for research applications—forecasting, reporting, and policy advising. For example, the national reports on social trends, which have now appeared in a number of countries, depend on the quality of the data available, as well as the interpretive skill and insight of their authors; their promise lies, ultimately, in their ability to inform administrators, researchers, and the public in general of the basic nature of social conditions and social trends (Federal Republic of Germany 1973; France 1973; Great Britain 1970–1973; Japan 1973; United States 1973). In another sense, the relationship between research and its applications may be reversed: better models of social processes may help us refine our data requirements, and greater emphasis on social reporting may put a premium on improving our data collection activities.

Given the interdependency of these social indicators activities, it is no wonder that a major dilemma in social indicators research is that of determining where to begin. Some approach the field deductively, evolving a set of social concerns— a conceptual framework of sorts into which the data may be fit. The search for appropriate statistics is the second step (O.E.C.D. 1973). Others have taken a more inductive approach. Working with the data available, they seek to understand and, ultimately, to model the processes of social change (Ivanovic and Fanchette 1973; McGranahan, Richard–Proust, Savani, and Subramanian 1972).

We would not argue, nor do we believe, that any starting point is as good as any other. But the real dilemma is not whether to start with data or with theory; rather, the problem is rooted in a system which, in recent years, has tended to demand that we begin at the very last step: social advising. The reason for this policy orientation in social indicators research may be traced to the climate of the times in which it developed. Social indicators become the focus of attention of social scientists, commentators and policymakers in the mid-1960s, when public interest was centered on rapid and widespread social change: the civil rights movement, antiwar and student resistance activities, and urban riots. Furthermore, the 1960s were a time when the public, the decision makers and the academicians all agreed that something could and should be done about these trends. Interests in social indicators developed from the belief that the basis for improved social policy lies in improved measurement of social conditions and trends and increased understanding of the causes and consequences of social change.

The social indicators movement represents an interdisciplinary attempt at the scientific measurement of social change. We have defined social indicators as "statistical time series that measure changes in significant aspects of social change," noting that they express "something about the composition, structure or functioning of . . . society, and express it in quantitative terms that can be compared with similar measures in the past or future" (Social Science Research Council 1973a: 1). Within this broad defintion, there are many issues or debates that may be delineated: whether indicators are or should be neutral or normative, descriptive or analytical, aggregated or discrete, objective or subjective, based on data about individuals or about organizations, problem oriented or descriptive of the dynamics of systems, and so on (Zapf 1972).

These issues reflect the diversity of disciplinary and professional affiliations of the participants in social indicators research, as well as the heterogeneity in the substantive focus of research, methodology, geographic scale of study, and perceived purpose and audience of the research. Because of this diversity, research attention tends to get dispersed. We proceed to application activities— forecasting, reporting, and advising—on the assumption that the data are already available, or that they can be obtained easily. So often is this not the case, that many have identified the primary target of social indicators research, at the present time, as "social bookkeeping"—the improvement of our time series data base. In the following section, we will examine several aspects of this task.

Official Statistical Data

In February 1974, the U.S. government published its first chartbook of statistics selected and organized to describe social conditions and social trends in the United States. Entitled *Social Indicators 1973*, the volume is organized around eight major social areas: health, public safety, education, employment, income, housing, leisure and recreation, and population (United States 1973). *Social Indicators 1973* joins a rapidly expanding literature of national compendia that are designed to present periodic reports on the state of society and the nature of social trends. In 1973, Great Britain published its fourth issue of *Social Trends* (Great Britain 1973), Japan issues its *Whitepaper on national life* (Japan 1973), and Germany and France both published their first such document (Federal Republic of Germany 1973; France 1973). Similar volumes from Norway and Canada appeared in 1974 (Norway 1974; Canada 1974), and, somewhat later, there will be publications stimulated by the OECD Social Indicators Programme (O.E.C.D. 1973).

Most of the material presented in these national reports comes from well-established official census and administrative data-collection programs. However, these national reports have also taken advantage of private survey data to broaden the scope of their presentation (see discussion in Duncan 1974a). The United States' *Social Indicators 1973*, for instance, made use of a variety of private data, including the Gallup Poll for surveys on fear of crime and confidence in ability to obtain health care, the National Opinion Research Center's measure of criminal victimization, the Institute for Social Research's surveys of job satisfaction and time budgets, and the A.C. Nielson Company's surveys of television viewing habits.

Official census and administrative data have provided the basis for much work in developing social indicators, not so much because they offer ideal measures of the composition, structure, and functioning of society, but because they offer comparable and repeated measures over a fairly long period of time. The efforts that are expended in improving official data—both their collection and their analysis—and in supplementing them with private research findings will continue to be an important part of the expanding data base for social indicators.

In addition to continuing efforts to improve the quality of official statistics, there has been growing interest in launching new programs that will yield more meaningful information on contemporary social concerns. Two such programs— one in crime, the other in education—deserve mention.

Figures on reported crime for the United States have been, and will continue to be, provided from official police statistics released through the FBI's Uniform Crime Reports. Many crimes, however, are not reported to the police, the percentage of unreported crime varies widely for different types of crime, and police recording procedures are not always "uniform," despite the FBI's attempts to make them so. As a result, the National Crime Survey is being conducted by the Bureau of the Census on behalf of the Law Enforcement Assistance Administration (LEAA) of the U.S. Department of Justice. Begun in July 1972, this program of nationwide crime victimization surveys—using questions such as "During the last 12 months, did anyone beat you up, attack you or hit you with something, such as a rock or bottle?" (U.S. Department of Justice 1975: 143)—is designed regularly to provide statistical data on the incidence of common crime, its costs, the characteristics of victims, and the characteristics of criminal events. Since the survey questionnaires were designed so that crimes recorded could be classified in accordance with the categories used in the Uniform Crime Reports, the National Crime Survey will provide estimates of the amount of crime that goes unreported. It will also provide an assessment of citizen reasons for failing to report crimes to the police.

In another area, learning, a federally sponsored data collection activity has been launched. For years, we had abundant administrative data on education, but no clear idea of what children were actually learning. The "National Assessment of Educational Progress" (NAEP) has been designed as a period national survey of the knowledge, skills, and attitudes of young Americans in 10 subject areas. Each year, a series of written and performance exercises in 2 subject areas are administered to in-school probability samples of 9-, 13-, and 17-year-olds, to household probability samples of young adults of ages 26–35, and to 17-year-old early graduates or drop-outs. Approximately 80,000 to 100,000 young people participate each year. The program has been in operation for nearly 4 years, and first assessment reports have already been published in the areas of science, citizenship, and writing.

In both these cases, the new government surveys resulted from the realization that previous indices (on crime and education) were not telling us what we wanted to know about social conditions. The official police statistics not only underestimated the incidence of various crimes; they gave no indication of the degree and types of victimization suffered by different age, sex, racial, and socioeconomic groups. As for education, we have known for a long time that such statistics as school attendance, teacher–pupil ratios, and school years completed do not measure how much children are learning in school. The NAEP should help us greatly on this important question.

It is not surprising that both these massive data collection programs have been undertaken under the auspices of federal government agencies. The problem with developing time series of this sort is that they require greater administrative continuity, financial investment, and time commitment than private research can usually offer. There are instances of long-term private research studies of social change, notable among them Firth's study of Tikopia (1959), but they only serve to reinforce the point. The techniques used in collecting and analysing the data are so (necessarily) idiosyncratic that statements about social trends must be carefully hedged. Furthermore, since researchers cannot count on being able to return to a study area or project after two or three decades, other strategies and data sources are required.

Replication Studies and the Exploitation of Survey Archives

One strategy for the development of time series on basic social trends is through what Duncan has called the replication of baseline studies (Duncan 1969). This strategy rests on the premise that there exist, in social science, a number of important studies that deserve to be repeated and that are sufficiently well documented to permit contemporary investigators to duplicate the measurement methods of the original study. Duncan's own work in recent years has exemplified this approach. For example, in 1971, at his instigation, the Detroit Area Study re-asked a number of questions originally asked in the 1950s. The results provide data on changes in the Detroit area in a number of fields, including the division of responsibility within families, changing racial attitudes both of whites and of blacks, changes in the religious participation of the population, and changes in the general level of optimism about the society (Duncan, Schuman, and Duncan 1973).

Replication is the strategy of the General Social Survey, an NSF-funded project of the University of Chicago's National Opinion Research Center. Annual surveys are being conducted, in which the questions are selected from questionnaires used in surveys extending back to the early 1950s. The survey results—covering such topics as political preference, religious preference, job satisfaction, fear of crime, and attitudes toward civil liberties and race relations—are being made available on punchcards at nominal cost in order to insure the widest possible participation in the analysis of the trends they describe.

Another notable example of the replication strategy is Featherman and Hauser's current replication of the 1962 Survey of Occupational Changes in a Generation. This work, using survey resources of the Census Bureau, will provide comprehensive trend data on the degree of inequality of opportunity in the United States and the changing importance of ethnicity, family background, education, and other factors in occupation advancement (Featherman and Hauser 1975).

Another closely related strategy for developing time series data is through exploitation of the wealth of material that has been accumulated in survey data archives. There exist today extensive archives of past surveys, the potential usefulness of which for comparative and longitudinal studies is well recognized. For instance, the survey archives of the Inter-University Consortium for Political Research, located at the University of Michigan, have long been used for the analysis of trends in political participation and attitudes. Other aspects of social change will be opened to analysis as a result of a project to access and analyze National Opinion Research Center surveys covering the past quarter century. NORC'S Director, James Davis, proposes to obtain historical and current measures of key sociological variables based on public opinion items as well as "hard" data on population characteristics; to analyze the data separately for different birth cohorts; and to employ the more powerful techniques now available for use in the analysis of multiway contingency tables to locate trends, constancies, and tendencies toward convergence or polarization in a population. Conceptually, he expects to organize the data in terms of a model representing the life cycle of the individual.

The largest archive of public opinion survey data is the Roper Public Opinion Research Center. In 1972, its holdings included the response data from more than 10,000 surveys done in 68 countries since 1936, and the Roper Center annually acquires between 400 and 500 additional data sets. However, access to the wealth of material at the Roper Center has been limited by the lack of adequate cataloguing and the considerable expense involved in identifying, retrieving, and cleaning much of the data. As an effort to enhance the research community's ability to undertake longitudinal studies, the Social Science Research Council's Center for Social Indicators has monitored a pilot project for the dissemination of survey trend data in the Roper Center's archives. The product of this project is an index to all questions asked more than once in the 4000 American national surveys in the Roper Center archives. This, and associated activities, are expected to increase substantially our resources for the analysis of social change.

An Impediment

Our focus has been on the development of time series, and on efforts to encourage the development of a broad range of indicators of social change through expansion of the research community's ability to explore time series data. However, there is a major hurdle to encouraging and promoting the use of survey archives for replication and longitudinal studies—one that is neither methodological, theoretical, nor even a result of the lack of sufficient data. It is normative: The conviction shared by most social scientists that "new" research is superior to "old" repeated studies is expressed in the assumption that only the uninspired, or the unendowed, would undertake a replication study. Along with this conviction has gone the carving of disciplines into small proprietary units: "my group," "my survey," "my index," "my village." At best, information is shared with students, but even they are rarely encouraged to replicate the original study. Take, for instance, the Human Relations Area Files. Legitimate criticisms have been raised about both the quality of the data and the classification system employed by the HRAF, and there have been numerous attempts to improve that archive, including the Standard Ethnographic Survey and the present project to incorporate the HRAF into the larger Yale library system. However, much of this dissatisfaction reflects the old preference for new, personalized research. This preference for "new, innovative" surveys, by the research community and by funding agencies as well, provides an arid environment for social indicators research.

SOCIAL INDICATORS AND THE SOCIAL SCIENCES

The search for reliable data, for meaningful measures, and for serviceable models of social change has made social indicators a genuinely interdisciplinary endeavor, and it is instructive to outline the contributions of the various social science disciplines to the development of the social indicators enterprise. Perhaps the strongest legacy in the social indicators movement is that of economics. Indeed, the "social" in "social indicators" is often treated as a residual category denoting that which is "noneconomic." This definition of social indicators as parallel to economic indicators has been influential in shaping research priorities for the social indicators community. As Duncan wryly notes (Duncan 1974b):

> They have time series statistics; therefore, we should have time series statistics. They have "economic accounts"; hence we must invent "social accounts." Their data aggregate nicely into global magnitudes (like GNP) or synthesize neatly into composite indexes (Consumer Price Index); we should strive for measurements that offer similar possibilities for aggregation. They make forecasts that are widely publicized; we should work harder at forecasting. There is an "Economic Report"; so we must have a "Social Report." They have their Council of Economic Advisers; we shall have a Council of Social Advisers.

As social indicators research has developed, however, the "movement" has, in a sense, outgrown the classic debate between economics and the other social sciences. Because so much of the data that are readily available and amenable to analysis of changes over time are vital statistics, censuses, and official surveys, sociologists and demographers represent a large proportion of the social indicators community. Because the "behavioral" movement in political science in the 1950s and 1960s put a premium on collecting and archiving reliable data for comparative studies (Truman 1973), the social indicators community has been able to draw upon political data archives for such material as Arthur S. Bank's cross-polity time series study (Banks 1971), Charles Taylor and Michael Hudson's *World handbook of political and social indicators* (Taylor and Hudson 1972), and Ted Robert Gurr's work on cross-national models of political conflict and development (Gurr 1970). The cliometricians, and those involved in "social scientific history," through their interests in working with large aggregates of empirical data, in borrowing theoretical concepts and models from other disciplines, and in generalizing through systematic comparisons, have created a wealth of material that both extends existing data series back in time and creates innovative data sets for previous eras against which general social science propositions may be tested (Landes and Tilly 1971). Pointing to the inadequacy of "objective" measures of well-being as indicators of individual life satisfactions, psychologists, among others, have developed the notion of subjective or perceptual measures of life quality. There has been considerable research not only on the relation among satisfactions (i.e., the relation of satisfaction with one's work to satisfaction with one's family life [Andrews and Withey 1974]), but also on the relationship between "objective" and "subjective" situations (Strumpel, forthcoming; Thurow 1974). Finally, interest in modeling and monitoring social change in small (subnational) areas has brought together the talents of geographers (Smith 1973), rural sociologists (Sismondo 1973), and statisticians (Bixhorn and Mindlin 1972) in an attempt to develop indicators of community-level change.

Despite the heterogeneity of disciplinary affiliations within the social indicators community, there has been, until very recently, a certain parochialism reflected in the almost exclusive reliance on household surveys, official censuses, and other administrative and vital statistics data. Other approaches are now being considered: Psychologists employ controlled experimental situations; anthropologists rely on careful behavior observation techniques and in-depth interviews with expert informants; and political scientists and historians have evolved elaborate procedures for working with a variety of written records, including newspapers, correspondence, biographies, and the like. These techniques have not yet been fully exploited by the social indicators community, and they represent promising new directions for social indicators research.

Social Indicators: A Role for Anthropology

There are three areas of concern in the current development of social indicators in which the experiences and analytical techniques of anthropologists can be of particular help. One of these is the development of models of social systems and subsystems and, ultimately, models of social change. Much work is needed on theoretical constructs of social processes, especially if we are to structure the vasts amounts of data now becoming available on social trends. Work in this area includes simple models of social and demographic processes (Stone 1971), path-analytical models of occupational mobility (Blau and Duncan 1967), the application of econometric analytical techniques to social and demographic time series for the United States (Mason and Hodge 1973), and models of national social and economic development (Hamblin, Jacobsen, and Miller 1973).

Progress to date on models of change has been fitful and suggests that, perhaps, we need models of social structure before we can develop models of changes therein. As Barth contends: "to formulate hypotheses about change we must be able to specify the connection, the processes that maintain a social form" (Barth 1967: 665). Can Barth's approach to social change be operationalized through, for instance, the economist's notion of changing marginal propensities? Does the view of social structure as network(s) of social relations offer us a more accessible (or more elegant) model of social process than, for instance, the sociologist's focus on institutions? Operationalizing and testing theories of social change will be an important focus of future social indicators research. The benefits of such work will contribute not only to a better understanding of social trends, but also to a refinement of social science concepts and methodological techniques.

A second area of activity in social indicators development involves the meaning of social change for the individual. In addition to work on indexes of "real" or "objective" changes, there is considerable interest in subjective measures of well-being (Campbell and Converse 1972). The research problem is to develop and refine measures of subjective well-being and relate them to measures of changes in the objective environment. The experience of anthropologists in distinguishing between the informant's perception of a particular situation or fact, the interviewer's perception, and the researcher's reconstruction (or, perhaps more honestly, hunch) of the informant's perception is relevant here. There is growing recognition, within the social indicators community, that we are dealing with several different "realities."

In addition to models of social change and measures of subjective perceptions, there is a third area of social indicators development in which the experience of anthropologists may be helpful. Most social indicators are based on national data, but there is growing interest in local community indicators and comparative urban and regional studies (Social Science Research Council 1973b). Interest in social trends at other than the national level has raised several problems, the most basic of which is obtaining information. The costs of cross-sectional surveys are often prohibitive for local community studies; however, information which *is* available—aggregate national information—is not always amenable to community-level analysis. Recognition of these data problems has led to a search for techniques other than surveys for collection of community level data. What *are* the best ways to collect information about a city? Where do you look for information about changes in economic activity of a community over time? How else can we view a region other than as a collection of municipalities ranked by size? Do, for instance, the types of network studies undertaken by Mitchell lend themselves to replication (Mitchell 1969)? Would replication of network studies yield meaningful measures of social change? Anthropologists can use their insights and experiences from small area research in answering these questions of analysis of community-level social change.

Social Policy Research and Action: The Role of Social Indicators

In examining the role of the social scientist in policy making, Biderman argued recently that the academician's tendency toward generalization and abstraction has limited the social utility of his knowledge (Biderman 1970: 224):

> By virtue of his aim of maximizing generality, his [the acadamician's] influence is often such as to remove such pragmatic specificity as makes knowledge useful at the lowest levels ("information") or at intermediate bureaucratic levels ("intelligence").

Biderman urges a reorientation of the social sciences toward the collection and organization of data with which to confront questions of societal policy ("policy knowledge") and by means of which to communicate information about society to the public in general ("enlightment"). As he noted (Biderman 1970: 224): "In a democratic social order, the latter two—policy knowledge and public enlightenment—are closely related. Policy cannot be too far removed from what broadly held conceptions will sustain."

The social indicators movement represents the kind of approach to academic participation in policy making to which Biderman referred. It calls for academic participation at a much more basic level than that of the individual expert as consultant, research center as social laboratory, of social sciences forums (journals, meetings, lectures, and the like) as informed, if informal, panels for evaluation and review of existing or proposed policy. It is founded in the belief, recently articulated by Sheldon and Parke (1975), that "comprehension of what the main features of the society are, how they interrelate, and how these features and their relationship change is . . . the chief purpose of work on social indicators."

REFERENCES

Andrews, F. M., and S. B. Withey
   1974   Developing measures of perceived life quality. *Social Indicators Research* 1 (May):
           1–26.

Banks, Arthur S.
1971   *Cross-polity time series.* Cambridge, Massachusetts: M.I.T. Press.
Barth, Frederick
1967   On the study of social change. *American Anthropologist* **69**: 661–669.
Biderman, Albert D.
1970   Information, intelligence, enlightened public policy: Functions and organization of societal feedback. *Policy Sciences* **1**: 217–230.
Bixhorn, Herbert, and Albert Mindlin
1972   Composite social indicators for small areas. Washington, D.C.: Government of the District of Columbia, Executive Office, Office of Planning and Management Systems Groups.
Blau, P. M., and O. D. Duncan
1967   *The American occupational structure.* New York: Wiley.
Campbell, Angus, and Philip E. Converse (Eds.)
1972   *The human meaning of social change.* New York: Russell Sage Foundation.
Canada. Statistics Canada
1974   *Perspective Canada.* Ottawa: Information Canada.
Duncan, Otis Dudley
1969   *Toward social reporting: Next steps.* Paper No. 2 in Social Science Frontiers Series. New York: Russell Sage Foundation.
1974a   Developing social indicators. *Proceedings of the National Academy of Sciences* **71**(12) (Dec): 5096–5102.
1974b   *Social indicators, 1973*: Report on a conference. New York: Social Science Research Council.
Duncan, Otis Dudley, Howard Schuman, and Beverly Duncan
1973   *Social change in a metropolitan community.* New York: Russell Sage Foundation.
Featherman, David L., and Robert M. Hauser
1975   Design for a replicate study of social mobility in the United States. In *Social Indicators Models*, edited by Kenneth C. Land and Seymour Spilerman. New York: Russell Sage Foundation.
Federal Republic of Germany
1973   *Gesellschaftliche Daten 1973.* Bonn: Presse-und Informationsamt der Bundsregierung.
Firth, Raymond
1959   *Social change in Tikopia.* New York: Macmillan.
France. Institut National de la Statistique et des Etudes Economique (INSEE)
1973   *Données Sociale.* (1st ed.) Paris: Imprimerie National.
Great Britain. Central Statistical Office
1970–   *Social trends*, Nos. 1–4. London: HMSO.
Gurr, Ted Robert
1970   *Why men rebel.* Princeton, New Jersey: Princeton Univ. Press.
Hamblin, Robert L., R. Brooke Jacobsen, and Jerry L. L. Miller
1973   *A mathematical theory of social change.* New York: Wiley.
Ivanovic, B., and S. Fanchette
1973   Grouping and ranking of thirty countries of subsaharan Africa. Paris: UNESCO.
Japan. Economic Planning Agency
1973   *Whitepaper on national life 1973: The life and its quality in Japan.* Tokyo: Overseas Data Service.
Landes, David S., and Charles Tilly (Eds.)
1971   *History as social science.* Englewood Cliffs, New Jersey: Prentice-Hall.

McGranahan, D. V., C. Richard–Proust, N. V. Sovani, and M. Subramanian
1972   *Contents and measurement of socio-economic development: A staff study of UNRISD*. New York: Praeger.
Mason, W. M., and R. W. Hodge
1973   *A proposal to use the tapes from the March current population surveys to study the changing socioeconomic location of Blacks and women in the United States*. Unpublished manuscript.
Mitchell, J. C.
1969   *Social networks in urban situations: Analyses of personal relationships in Central African Towns*. Manchester: Manchester Univ. Press.
Norway. Statistisk Sentralbyrå
1974   *Socialt Utsyn*. Oslo.
O.E.C.D. Social Indicator Programme
1973   *Vol 1: List of social concerns common to most OECD countries*. Paris: OECD.
Sheldon, Eleanor B., and Robert Parke
1975   Social indicators. *Science* 188(4189) (16 May): 693–699.
Sismondo, Sergio
1973   *Application of structural indicators for the measurement of development: Selected findings for rural communities in Kent County*. Richibucto, New Brunswick: New Brunswick NewStart.
Smith, David M.
1973   *The geography of social well-being in the United States: An introduction to territorial social indicators*. New York: McGraw-Hill.
Social Science Research Council. Center for Coordination of Research on Social Indicators
1973a   *Social Indicators Newsletter* 1 March.
1973b   *Social Indicators Newsletter* 3 December.
Stone, Richard
1971   *Demographic accounting and model-building*. Paris: OECD.
Strumpel, Burkhard
forthcoming
        Economic well-being in a system of social indicators.
Sweden. Statistiska Centralybrån
forthcoming
        Social Utveckling. Stockholm.
Taylor, Charles L., and Michael C. Hudson
1972   *World handbook of political and social indicators*. (2nd ed.) New Haven, Connecticut: Yale Univ. Press.
Thurow, Lester C.
1974   Equity concepts and the world of work. Bureau of Social Science Research Working Group on Quality of Employment Indicators. Washington, April 1974.
Truman, David B.
1973   The Committee on Political Behavior, 1949–1963: An introduction. *Committee on Political Behavior 1949–1963, Committee on Governmental and Legal Processes 1964–1972: A report of the activities of the committees*. New York: Social Science Research Council.
United States Department of Justice. Law Enforcement Assistance Administration. National Criminal Justice Information and Statistics Service.
1975   *Criminal victimization surveys in the nation's five largest cities*. Report no. SD-NCP-C-3.

United States. Executive Office of the President. Office of Management and Budget
1973   *Social Indicators, 1973*. Washington, D.C.: U.S. Government Printing Office.
Zapf, Wolfgang
1972   Social indicators: Prospects of social accounting systems. *Social Sciences Information* 11(3/4): 243–277.

Author Index

Subject Index

A

Achievement, *see* Educational achievement
Achievement tests, 53, 78, 80–88, 257, 258, 262
Africans, 41–45, 47–48
Afro-Americans, 75. *See also* Blacks, Negroes
  as viewed by Anglo-Americans, 45–47
A.I.D., 16
American Anthropological Association, ii, 3–5
"American Dream," 85, 199, 202
American electorate, 175
American English language, 289
American Indian Studies, 60
American Indians, 5, 6, 11, 20, 41, 44, 45, 53, 60, 63, 78, 81–83, 86, 87, 91, 200, 265. *See also* Children, Students
  English assessments of, 40–41, 44, 45
American Revolution, 46, 47, 49

Anglo-Americans, 41, 45, 50, 53, 85, 87, 100. *See also* Children, Students, Whites
  norms and values of, 60, 69
  views on Afro-Americans, 45–48
Anglo-conformity model, vi, 54, 60
Anthropologists, i, ii, iv–vii, xi, xii, 3–14, 18–23, 27, 29–33, 50, 220
  economic, 148
  physical, vii
Anthropology
  academic, vii
    development of the discipline, 3–4, 20, 29–30
    funds for research, v, 4
  applied, iii, 6
    ethical problems of, 20, 21
  linguistic, *see* sociolinguistics
  training in
    "emics," 18
    for effective roles in public policy, 29–33
    funding of, 4